A2 Geography

Ann Bowen

John Pallister

Heinemann Educational Publishers
Halley Court, Jordan Hill, Oxford, OX2 8EJ
Part of Harcourt Education
Heinemann is the registered trademark of Harcourt Education Limited

First published 2001

10-digit ISBN: 0 435352 82 2
13-digit ISBN: 978 0 435352 82 0

08 07 06
10 9 8 7 6 5

Designed and typeset by The Wooden Ark, Leeds
Printed and bound in Spain by Edelvives

Acknowledgements
The authors and publishers would like to thank the following for permission to reproduce copyright material.

Maps and extracts
T=top M=middle B=bottom
p.21 Emily Moore / The Guardian; **p.25** B The Met Office; **p.39**, **40** Maps reproduced from Ordnance Survey mapping with the permission of the Controller of Her Majesty's Stationary Office, © Crown copyright, License no. 10000230; **p.42** Philips Modern Atlas / George Philip Ltd; **p.52** John Sweeney / The Observer; **p.53** Maps reproduced from Ordnance Survey mapping with the permission of the Controller of Her Majesty's Stationary Office, © Crown copyright, License no. 10000230; **p.57** David Ward and Geoffrey Gibbs / The Guardian; **p.62** T Paul Brown / The Guardian; **p.62** B Stephen Moss / The Guardian; **p.64** Scarborough Borough Council; **p.65** The Press Association; **p.91** M Seismograph reading / The Guardian; **p.92** T Tim Radford / The Guardian; **p.92** B The Guardian; **p.95** T As adapted from The Sunday Telegraph 19th July 1998; **p.96** Chris Morris / The Guardian; **p.97** The Financial Times; **p.103** Roy Collard, Physical Geography of Landscape / Unwin Hyman; **p.105** Maps reproduced from Ordnance Survey mapping with the permission of the Controller of Her Majesty's Stationary Office, © Crown copyright, License no. 10000230; **p.107** B Collard and Hilton, Process and Pattern in Physical Geography / Unwin Hyman 1979; **p.113** T The New Scientist; **p.114** The Daily News; **p.114** USA Today; **p.115** Patrick Wintour and Michael White / The Guardian; **p.115** David Austin; **p.126** Paul Simon / The Guardian; **p.138**, **140** Maps reproduced from Ordnance Survey mapping with the permission of the Controller of Her Majesty's Stationary Office, © Crown copyright, License no. 10000230; **p.166** Time Magazine; **p.167** The Financial Times; **p.170** Maps reproduced from Ordnance Survey mapping with the permission of the Controller of Her Majesty's Stationary Office, © Crown copyright, License no. 10000230; **p.171** Discovery Guides Ltd.; **p. 175** The Financial Times; **p.176** John Vidal / The Guardian; **p.184** Time Magazine; **p.189** The Financial Times; **p.193** Stockholm Environment Institute 1997; **p195** US Army; **p.203**, **p.204**, **p.214**, **p.217** The Financial Times; **p.210** Maps reproduced from Ordnance Survey mapping with the permission of the Controller of Her Majesty's Stationary Office, © Crown copyright, License no. 10000230; **p.224** Growth of out of town retail parks, GeoActive Series 7 Spring Issue, Unit 138 / Stanley Thornes 1996; **p.228** B Sue Warn and Chris Warn, The North / Cambridge Regional Geography CUP 1986 / **p.231**, **232** 1996 Inter-censal survey / City of Newcastle Upon Tyne; **p.232** Maps reproduced from Ordnance Survey mapping with the permission of the Controller of Her Majesty's Stationary Office, © Crown copyright, License no. 10000230; **p.234** Telegraph Group Ltd 1998; **p.235**, **237**, **238** G. Nagle, Changing Settlements / Nelson Thornes 1998; **p.241** R. Potter, Urbanisation in the Third World / OUP 1992; **p.243** Madras: Managing Change in a Developing Country, GeoActive Series 6 Summer Issue, Unit 124 / Stanley Thornes 1995; **p.244**, **245** Cairo: Urban Problems and Solutions, GeoActive Series 8 Spring Issue, Unit 156 / Stanley Thornes 1997; **p.248** Ann Bowen and John Pallister, Understanding GCSE Geography / Heinemann Educational Publishers 1999; **p.251** The Environment Agency 2000; **p.260** T G. Nagle, Changing Settlements / Nelson Thornes 1998; **p.261** Maps reproduced from Ordnance Survey mapping with the permission of the Controller of Her Majesty's Stationary Office, © Crown copyright, License no. 10000230; **p.277** Maps reproduced from Ordnance Survey mapping with the permission of the Controller of Her Majesty's Stationary Office, © Crown copyright, License no. 10000230; **p. 278**, **289**, **290**, **292** The Financial Times, 18th April 2001; **p.281** British Airways; **p.296** The Tourist Board of Costa Rica.

Websites
Links to appropriate websites are given throughout the book. Although these were up to date at the time of writing, it is essential for teachers to preview these sites before using them with students. This will ensure that the web address (URL) is still accurate and the content is suitable for your needs. We suggest that you bookmark useful sites and consider enabling students to access them through the school internet. We are bringing this to your attention as we are aware of legitimate sites being appropriated illegally by people wanting to distribute unsuitable or offensive material. We strongly advise you to purchase suitable screening software so that students are protected from unsuitable sites and their material. If you do find that the links given no longer work, or the content is unsuitable please let us know. Details of changes will be posted on our website.

Contents

Websites
On pages where you are asked to go to www.heinemann.co.uk/hotlinks to complete a task or down load information, please insert the code **2822S** at the website.

Acknowledgements

Photographs
Cover photograph by Stone

p.5 (Fig 1.1 a) John Pallister; **p.5** (Fig 1.1b) John Pallister; **p.5** (Fig 1.1c) John Pallister; **p.5** (Fig 1.1d) John Pallister; **p.7** (Fig 1.2a) John Pallister; **p.7** (Fig 1.2b) John Pallister; **p.8** (Fig 1.5a) John Pallister; **p.8** (Fig 1.5b) John Pallister; **p.14** John Pallister; **p.18** John Pallister; **p.19** John Pallister; **p.20** (Fig 2.2) John Pallister; **p.20** (Fig 2.3) John Pallister; **p.21** John Pallister; **p.22** John Pallister; **p.24** John Pallister; **p.25** Apex Photo Agency; **p.29** (Fig 2.17) John Pallister; **p.29** (Fig 2.18) John Pallister; **p.31** (Fig 2.21a) Geophotos/Tony Waltham; **p.31** (Fig 2.21b) John Pallister; **p.31** (Fig 2.22) John Pallister; **p.32** John Pallister; **p.33** (Fig 2.24) John Pallister; **p.33** (Fig 2.25) John Pallister; **p.34** John Pallister; **p.35** (Fig 2.27a) John Pallister; **p.35** (Fig 2.27b) John Pallister; **p.36** Richard Hudson; **p.37** John Pallister; **p.38** John Pallister; **p.40** (Fig 2.34) John Pallister; **p.40** (Fig 2.35) John Pallister; **p.41** (Fig 2.36) John Pallister; **p.41** (Fig 2.37) John Pallister; **p.41** (Fig 2.38) John Pallister; **p.43** John Pallister; **p.44** John Pallister; **p.45** John Pallister; **p.46** Richard Hudson; **p.47** (Fig 2.46, 2.47a) John Pallister; **p.47** (Fig 2.47b) John Pallister; **p.48** John Pallister; **p.50** (Fig 2.54a) John Blakeston; **p.50** (Fig 2.54b) "Author picture used in People, Places and Themes (Credited to John Pallister)"; **p.51** John Pallister; **p.52** Patrick Gowen/ North Sea Action Group; **p.56** (Fig 2.63) London Aerial photo Library; **p.56** (Fig 2.64) Katz Pictures/Richard Smith; **p.57** North Wales Police; **p.58** (Fig 2.67a) John Pallister; **p.58** (Fig 2.67b) John Pallister; **p.58** (Fig 2.68) John Pallister; **p.59** Still Pictures/Don Hinrichson; **p.60** John Pallister; **p.61** (Fig 2.71a) John Pallister; **p.61** (Fig 2.71b) John Pallister; **p.61** (Fig 2.71c) John Pallister; **p.63** Cardiff Harbour Authority; **p.65** (Fig 2.76a) PA Photos; **p.65** (Fig 2.76b) PA Photos; **p.66** Ecoscene; **p.69** John Pallister; **p.73** Rex Features; **p.74** Popperfoto/Reuters; **p.78** John Pallister; **p.80** John Pallister; **p.83** John Pallister; **p.84** (Fig 3.33) John Pallister; **p.84** (Fig 3.34) USGS/J G Moore; **p.86** John Pallister; **p.87** John Pallister; **p.88** Geophotos/Tony Waltham; **p.89** John Pallister; **p.94** USGS/J G Moore; **p.100** John Pallister; **p.101** John Pallister; **p.102** John Pallister; **p.103** John Pallister; **p.104** John Pallister; **p.106** John Pallister; **p.109** (Fig 3.75) Popperfoto/UPI; **p.109** (Fig 3.76) Photolibrary Wales; **p.110** John Pallister; **p.111** (Fig 3.79) John Pallister; **p.111** (Fig 3.80) John Pallister; **p.112** John Pallister; **p.116** (Fig 3.90) John Pallister; **p.116** (Fig 3.92) Still Picture/DERA; **p.117** (fig 3.93) John Pallister; **p.117** (Fig 3.94) John Pallister; **p.119** John Pallister; **p.121** John Pallister; **p.122** (Fig 4.5a) John Pallister; **p.122** (Fig 4.5b) John Pallister; **p.126** (Fig 4.12a) John Pallister; **p.126** (Fig 4.12b) John Pallister; **p.127** John Pallister; **p.129** John Pallister; **p.130** John Pallister; **p.131** Richard Hudson; **p.132** John Pallister; **p.133** (Fig 4.22) John Pallister; **p.133** (Fig 4.23) John Pallister; **p.135** (Fig 4.26) John Pallister; **p.135** (Fig 4.27) John Pallister; **p.138** Richard Hudson; **p.139** (Fig 4.32) John Pallister; **p.139** (Fig 4.33) John Pallister; **p.143** (Fig 4.38a) John Pallister; **p.143** (Fig 4.38b) John Pallister; **p.143** (Fig 4.39) John Pallister; **p.144** John Pallister; **p.147** Geophotos/Tony Waltham; **p.148** (Fig 4.46) John Pallister; **p.148** (Fig 4.47a) John Pallister; **p.148** (Fig 4.47b) John Pallister; **p.150** (Fig 4.49) John Pallister; **p.150** (Fig 4.50) Richard Hudson; **p.152** Geophotos/Tony Waltham; **p.154** (Fig 4.56a) John Pallister; **p.154** (Fig 4.56b) John Pallister; **p.155** John Pallister; **p.157** John Pallister; Corbis/Staffa in Widstrand; **p.160** Science Photo Library/Pekka Parvienen; **p.161** (Fig 4.63) John Pallister; **p.161** (Fig 4.64) John Pallister; **p.162** (Fig 4.65) John Pallister; **p.162** (Fig 4.66) John Pallister; **p.162** (Fig 4.67) John Pallister; **p.163** (Fig 4.68a, b, c) John Pallister; **p.164** John Pallister; **p.168** John Pallister; **p.169** (Fig 4.76) John Pallister; **p.169** (Fig 4.77) John Pallister; **p.173** John Pallister; **p.174** Science Photo Library/Earth Satellite Corporation; **p.180** (Fig 5.13a) Panos Pictures/Sean Sprague; **p.180** (Fig 5.13b) Still Pictures/Mark Edwards; **p.180** (Fig 5.14) John Pallister; **p.182** John Pallister; **p.183** (Fig 5.18) John Pallister; **p.183** (Fig 5.19) John Pallister; **p.187** Science Photo Library/Richard Folwell; **p.188** John Pallister; **p.189** (Fig 5.29) John Pallister; **p.189** (Fig 5.30) The Environmental Picture Library/Irene R. Lengui; **p.192** Woodfall Wild Images/Paul Kay; **p.194** John Pallister; **p.196** John Pallister; **p.198** Still Pictures/Ron Giling; **p.201** Panos Pictures/Libov Taylor; **p.204** Corbis/Nik Wheeler; **p.205** Still Pictures/Luiz C Marigo; **p.206** John Pallister; **p.207** (Fig 5.63) John Pallister; **p.207** (Fig 5.64) John Pallister; **p.208** (Fig 5.65) John Pallister; **p.208** (Fig 5.66) John Pallister; **p.209** (Fig 5.68) John Pallister; **p.209** (Fig 5.70) Robert Harding/Mike Newton; **p.212** John Pallister; **p.215** Still Pictures/Hartmut Schwarzbach; **p.219** Ann Bowen; **p.220** (Fig 6.2) Ann Bowen; **p.220** (Fig 6.3) Ann Bowen; **p.222** (Fig 6.4) Ann Bowen; **p.222** (Fig 6.5) Spectrum Colour Library; **p.227** (Fig 6.10) Ann Bowen; **p.227** (6.11) Ann Bowen; **p.228** Ann Bowen; **p.229** Ann Bowen; **p.230** (Fig 6.15) Ann Bowen; **p.230** (Fig 6.16) Ann Bowen; **p.232** (Fig 6.18b) Ann Bowen; **p.232** (Fig 6.19c) Ann Bowen; **p.235** Ann Bowen; **p.236** Jefferson Air Photography; **p.237** Hulton Getty; **p.238** (Fig 6.28) Moss Side & Hulme Partnership; **p.238** (Fig 6.29a) The Museum of Science & Industry in Manchester; **p.238** (Fig 6.29c) Manchester Arndale Centre; **p.240** Panos Pictures/Maria Luiza Carvalho; **p.242** Panos Pictures/Peter Barker; **p.243** Still Pictures/Mark Edwards; **p.245** Still Pictures/Martin Wright; **p.246** Corbis/Yann Arthus-Bertrand; **p.247** Still Pictures/John Maier; **p.249** Still Pictures/Julio Etchart; **p.253** Robert Harding; **p.254** Science Photo Library/Simon Fraser/Northumbrian Environmental Management Ltd; **p.265** John Pallister; **p.267** (Fig 7.4) John Pallister; **p.267** (Fig 7.5, 7.6) John Pallister; **p.269** (Fig 7.8a) John Pallister; **p.269** (Fig 7.8b) John Pallister; **p.269** (Fig 7.9a) John Pallister; **p.269** (Fig 7.9b) John Pallister; **p.271** (Fig 7.12) John Pallister; **p.271** (Fig 7.13) John Pallister; **p.272** (Fig 7.14) John Pallister; **p.272** (Fig 7.15) John Pallister; **p.273** John Pallister; **p.276** John Pallister; **p.279** (Fig 7.25a) John Pallister; **p.279** (Fig 7.25b) John Pallister; **p.285** (Fig 7.34) John Pallister; **p.285** (Fig 7.35) John Pallister; **p.287** (Fig 7.38) John Pallister; **p.287** (Fig 7.39) John Pallister; **p.287** (Fig 7.40) John Pallister; **p.288** John Pallister; **p.291** John Pallister; **p.295** John Pallister; **p.297** BBC Natural History/Doug Wechsler; **p.298** (Fig 7.56a) John Pallister; **p.298** (Fig 7.56b) John Pallister; **p.298** (Fig 7.56c) John Pallister; **p.298** (Fig 7.56d) John Pallister; **p.299** (Fig 7.58) John Pallister; **p.299** (Fig 7.59) John Pallister; **p.300** John Pallister; **p.304** (Fig 7.67a) John Pallister; **p.304** (Fig 7.67b) John Pallister.

The publishers have made every effort to trace the copyright holders, but if they have inadvertently overlooked any, they will be pleased to make the necessary arrangements at the first opportunity.

Chapter 1 Geography and geographical skills

Figure 1.1 What is the common geographical link between these photographs?
Can you give a definition of Geography? Geography is widely used as a heading in quizzes and game shows. In this context it is usually used to refer to places, which is a useful starting point. However, giving an actual definition of Geography as an academic discipline is more difficult. Before going any further, write down as precise and full a definition of Geography as you can.

a The Iguacu Falls, Brazil
b Summer storms in Steamboat Springs, Colorado
c Cattle ranching in Costa Rica
d Redevelopment around docks in Buenos Aires, Argentina

What is Geography?

One definition of Geography is 'the study of the physical and human features of the Earth's surface and of the inter-relationships between them'. There are others, but whatever definition is used it must include reference to the surface of the Earth in order to make it geographical. Put another way, Geography is a spatial subject; geographers investigate, describe, explain and analyse patterns and processes on or near the Earth's surface. One simple rule is this – if the subject under study can be mapped, it is spatial and therefore geographical.

Spatial associations

Geographers study spatial associations between features of the Earth's surface. For example, there is a very clear and strong association between climate on the one hand and vegetation, soils and landscape features on the other. As a result major global natural environments, such as tundra, hot desert and tropical rainforest, can be recognized. There are also spatial inter-actions between climate, vegetation and soils. Each of these three elements in the system affects the others. This is basic to the concept of ecosystems (Figure 1.3), although relationships do not have to be equal in both directions. Climate is the main determining factor for the type of natural vegetation cover present, although the climate of a place is also affected by the amount of water returned into the atmosphere by transpiration. Climate at the global scale is the major influence on soil type. It affects the speed and type of weathering of the parent rock, and determines the direction of water movement in the ground (depending upon whether or not precipitation exceeds evapo-transpiration). At the local scale the relative importance of relief, drainage and parent rock on soil formation increases. Vegetation is the other major global influence upon soil type. It exerts the greatest effect upon the characteristics of the organic layer at the top of the A horizon in soil profiles.

Non-spatial studies

Examples

- *Fieldwork study of rocks to ascertain characteristics such as hardness, mineral composition and fossils present*
- *Biological study of how plants and animals grow and reproduce*
- *Consumer household surveys of amount spent on different types of goods and services*
- *Social surveys of ways in which people spend their leisure time (such as how long people watch TV or how many take part in various sporting activities)*
- *Observations of facilities offered in sports and leisure centres or of attractions in theme parks.*

All of these are essentially non-geographical studies because they are non-spatial. There is no focus in these studies upon variations at or near the Earth's surface. Most belong to other disciplines, notably geology, biology and sociology.

Spatial studies

Examples

- *How different rock characteristics affect landscapes and landforms*
- *The relationships between vegetation cover and climate in different areas*
- *Where people shop and buy services and the relative amount spent in different types of location*
- *Variations in socio-economic characteristics between people living in different residential areas of a city*
- *How the size of the sphere of influence of an attraction varies according to facilities offered.*

All of these are clearly geographical because there is a focus upon the Earth's surface. They refer either to one area or to two or more areas for comparisons between them. The key words which provide the spatial links are 'landscapes', 'landforms', 'areas', 'where', 'location' and 'sphere of influence'.

From these spatial associations and interactions the concept of zonal world regions has been conceived. Major types of climate, vegetation and soils coincide and can be recognized on world maps in zones across the Earth's surface (Figure 1.4). The trend in their distribution is from west to east. They are aligned roughly parallel to lines of latitude. Latitude and insolation are major controls on the global pattern of temperature making climate the dominant factor within these associations of climate, vegetation and soils.

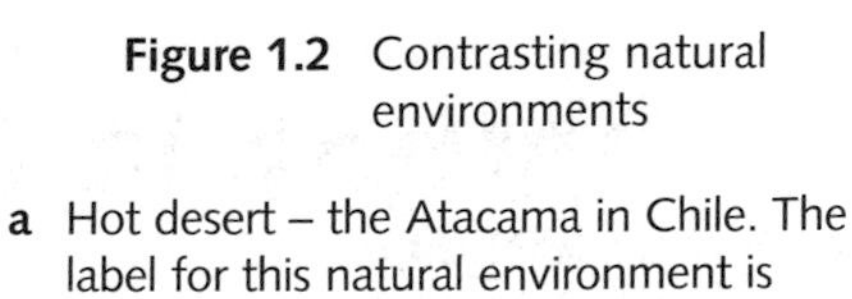

Figure 1.2 Contrasting natural environments

a Hot desert – the Atacama in Chile. The label for this natural environment is based upon climate. The definition for a desert is an area with under 250mm annual precipitation.

b Tropical rainforest – in Malaysia. This natural environment is labelled according to natural vegetation. The main factor is its climate, which is hot and wet all year.

Physical and human factors

The spatial associations between physical and human factors, and between different human factors, are much more varied and complex. Global summaries such as the zonal concept in Figure 1.4 are less easy to make and less satisfactory. Some natural environments, notably hot desert and tundra regions, are too hostile for continuous permanent settlement. The small pockets of settlement that exist within them are

Climate
Animals
Vegetation
Soils

Figure 1.3 The concept of ecosystems. The inter-relationships shown between the different elements are not of equal strength in both directions.

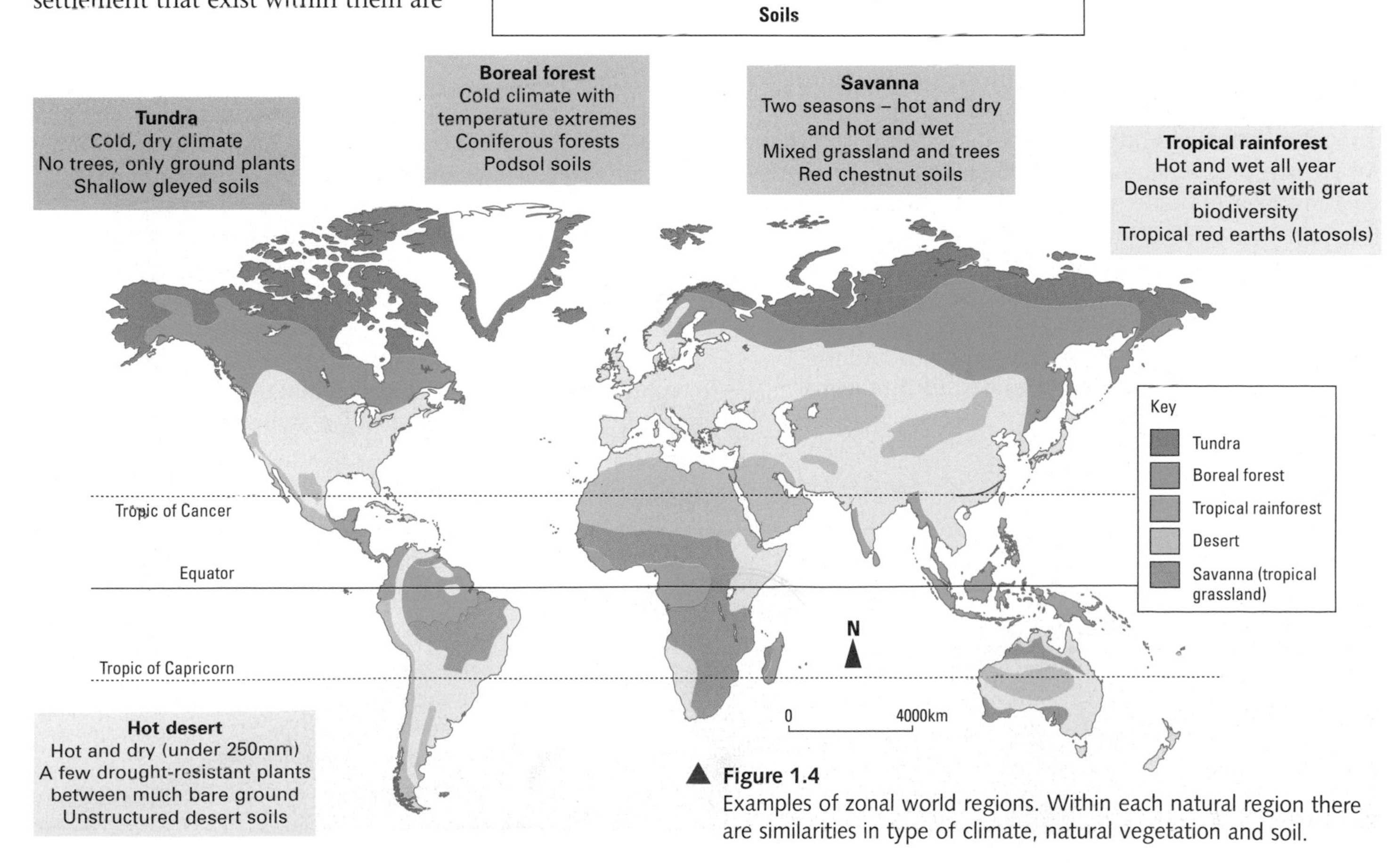

Figure 1.4
Examples of zonal world regions. Within each natural region there are similarities in type of climate, natural vegetation and soil.

directly related to economic opportunity, frequently a mineral source, and are surrounded by vast areas of emptiness. However, some of the world's highest densities of population have existed for thousands of years in the Nile valley in Egypt, where the green of the irrigated and cultivated land is in stark contrast to the barren desert all around (Figure 1.5).

Figure 1.5 Types of desert settlement

a Aerial view of one small isolated settlement in northern Chile, based on mining, in a region virtually without surface streams

b Part of the almost continuous green strip of cultivation along the banks of the Nile in Egypt

Patterns and spatial change

Emphasis upon the spatial factor means that geographers have a strong interest in examining patterns and the distribution of phenomena over the Earth's surface. They use these as a starting point from which to suggest reasons for the variations observed. Both physical and human landscapes change over time. Some changes are rapid, such as with mass movements and volcanic eruptions. Others happen within a relatively short time span, such as building new roads and housing estates. Many changes take place quite slowly, although the total amount of change can be very significant in the long term. Included within this category are physical processes such as rock weathering, human processes such as migration from rural to urban areas and movement within urban areas leading to the segregation of residential zones according to residents' socio-economic characteristics, and environmental changes resulting from global warming and other types of pollution. Whatever its speed, spatial change is ever present. Often it is easier to observe spatial change in human landscapes. The pace of change appears to be greatest of all in large urban areas. Many CBDs, inner cities and rural–urban fringes are in such a constant state of flux that they can be described as dynamic regions. The same dynamism can be seen in some regions designated for growth that are naturally attractive to a wide range and great number of modern economic activities. At the same time regions out-of-favour economically are undergoing unplanned decline. Inherently, rural areas are less subject to change, but pressures for change can be great both on commercial farms and in villages, close to urban areas, that are undergoing the process of suburbanization. Overall it can be claimed with some justification that Geography is a dynamic subject.

How is 'A' level Geography different from GCSE and AS Geography? Clearly the depth of study is greater. More content is covered in each topic. Topics that are re-visited, such as population and settlement, are explored more fully. There are opportunities for studying places in fuller detail in order to illustrate and exemplify general geographical patterns and themes. Another important difference is greater breadth of study. For convenience of study and assessment, topics continue to be studied and examined separately, but you are expected to consider and understand inter-relationships between different topics. This broadens the scope of the work at A2. You will be required to demonstrate breadth in writing answers to essay questions which are designated as synoptic (page 12).

Questions

1 Refer to Figure 1.1.
   - **a** Outline the geographical setting shown on each photograph.
   - **b** What inter-relationships might be investigated by a geographer in each of the four areas?

2 For each of two natural global environments:
   - **a** outline the main features of its climate, natural vegetation and soil type
   - **b** explain the associations and interactions between climate, vegetation and soil.

3
   - **a** Investigate and identify changes occurring in your local area or region which illustrate the assertion that Geography is a dynamic subject.
   - **b** Explain why the pressures for change are greater in some areas than others. Answer either with reference to a place named in part **a** or in more general terms.

The content of Geography

The study of Geography has long been subdivided into two branches – physical and human.

Physical geography

It includes three main study areas:

Geomorphology – the study of landforms and of the processes responsible for them ('geo' means Earth and 'morphology' refers to shape, in this case the shape of the land surface)

Climatology – the study of the characteristics and distribution of the world's types of climate and of the atmospheric processes responsible for them

Biogeography – the study of vegetation and soils and of the processes responsible for them.

Climatology and biogeography were included within AS. The three topic areas used in A2, coastal, tectonic and glaciation, are rooted within geomorphology, although they cannot be studied fully without references from time to time to climate, vegetation and soils.

Human geography

The content of human geography does not lend itself as neatly to sub-division. Despite this, some separate study areas can be recognized. (The list below is not exhaustive.)

Economic – the study of activities which create employment and generate income, including their distribution and the processes responsible for them

Political – the study of the influence of governments upon people, processes and activities and the ways in which they change both spatially (from country to country or from region to region within a country) and temporally (from time to time)

Population – the study of demographic characteristics such as fertility, mortality, change and structure and their spatial and temporal variations

Urban settlement – the study of towns and cities, including functions, morphology, growth and change.

Two topic areas included in AS, population and settlement, re-appear in A2, but the emphasis is different. Population pressure and resources is the focus for AS and challenges and issues in managing cities is the theme for A2. The third human topic is recreation and tourism, which belongs to the general heading of economic activity; however, it contributed little to the study of economic activity at AS level.

Regional geography

Throughout AS and A2 the specification (or syllabus) adopts the thematic approach to geographical study. Therefore, study of specific places is undertaken by case studies. An alternative approach would have been to apply geographical ideas and techniques to named areas of study. This is regional geography. A region is an area of the Earth's surface in which one or more common characteristics can be recognized, which distinguish that region from the other areas around it. Within the UK, the broadest sub-division is into just two regions, a 'poor' North and a 'rich' South (Figure 1.6).

However, there is as much debate about the validity of this division as there is about where the North actually begins. For statistical purposes the government and other agencies use the standard regions of the UK (Figure 1.7).

▲ **Figure 1.6** The division of the UK into two regions; is it myth or reality?

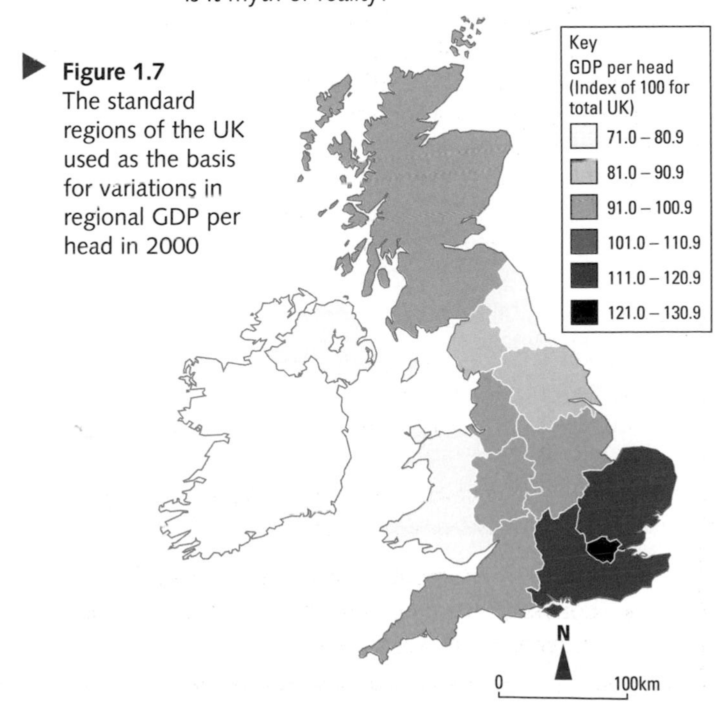

▶ **Figure 1.7** The standard regions of the UK used as the basis for variations in regional GDP per head in 2000

Each of these regions is suitable for a separate regional study because regions such as Greater London, the South West, North East England and Northern Ireland have had individual histories of economic activity, and of growth and decline. Social, and in some cases physical, differences between them exist as well. Therefore a variety of geographical factors can be used to illustrate the distinctiveness of each of the UK's regions, some of which are based as much on historical legacy as present day reality (Figure 1.8). Current physical, economic, social and political themes of the geography of the UK can be studied in each of these regions in order to assess their relative importance and overall effects. By examining the full range of factors, the total geography of the region is being considered. The distinctive pattern of geographical activities, and how these have changed over time, can be explored and explained at the regional level. Using a regional basis for studying separate elements in order to build up the total geographical picture for an area is a synthesis.

Figure 1.8 A mental map of North East England, historically based

Questions

1 a Define physical geography.
  b Why is it essential for all geographers, even those specializing in human branches of the subject such as urban geography, to study some physical geography?

2 a Where in the world do physical factors continue to dominate the area's geography?
  b Why is the extent of such areas smaller than it has ever been?

3 Identify a local geographical issue in the town or region where you live.
  a Outline the geographical nature of the issue.
  b State the views of different groups of people to the issue.
  c Make an assessment of the costs and benefits of any proposed changes upon the natural environment.

4 For one region within the UK (local or otherwise),
  a identify the distinctive characteristics which distinguish it from other regions
  b explain how and why these characteristics are changing.

Geographical methods of study

The geographical approach to study at Advanced Level

- *Study physical and human processes*
- *Examine the interactions between them*
- *Look for outcomes over space and time*
- *Illustrate these through a study of places and environments*

In having the surface of the Earth as the geographer's area of study one of the problems is that there are virtually no limits to the number and complexity of the inter-relationships between natural and human phenomena. This is why some techniques of classification are required. A classification is an attempt to place like phenomena into similar groups so that it is easier to:

- make comparisons
- draw conclusions
- identify anomalies.

Use of places

One method of classification is to divide up the Earth's surface into smaller areas and to study the geography of each one separately. This is the regional approach. However, because the content of A2 is arranged in themes, case studies are used instead in which general geographical themes and ideas are exemplified by references to real places. However, all places are unique; therefore studies of places also reveal differences from the general pattern, which can be analysed and explained. Displaying case study knowledge is one of the most effective way of adding depth to examination answers, especially in those requiring extended prose and in essays.

Case studies
Study technique

- *Choose an area which is a good example for the study theme*
- *State its location (often with the support of a sketch map)*
- *Identify and state its main geographical characteristics*
- *Examine and explain any changes that are occurring*
- *Highlight the ways in which it is unique*
- *Comment on how it is useful to the geographical theme under study*

Use of geographical factors

Another form of classification is to identify factors. A factor is anything that influences an outcome, either entirely or in part. The simplest classification is into physical and human. Physical (natural/environmental) factors, include relief and drainage, climate, soils and vegetation. The human factors referred to most are economic, social and political. Although some examination questions demand that you write about the effects of just one named factor, it is more usual for you to have to refer to a range of factors in an answer, typically going across the physical–human divide. A few factors can be either physical or human depending on use. Environmental is one of them. Used without qualification, it should refer to the natural environment, which gives it the same meaning as physical or natural. However, when used in a human context, for example in environmental quality surveys conducted in urban areas, it should be qualified by 'human', although in practice this is not always the case.

One mnemonic (memory aid) for factors is to think of SHEEP.

S – Social: related to the characteristics of people or society.

H – Historical: past events, whether physical or human, which help to explain the present.

E – Economic: activities such as employment, output and trade which can be given a monetary value

E – Environmental: the surroundings for what is being studied, usually natural, although it can be human in urban areas

P – Political: decisions and actions from governments and other organizations such as the EU and UN.

Natural factors may be under-represented, in which case the P can be used to refer to physical instead of political. Alternatively, environmental can be maintained and used to mean physical factor. These five provide the broad headings for factors. They can be broken down further according to need. Physical or natural environmental factors can be split up into relief, drainage, vegetation and soil. On occasions, one more precise factor needs to be used. Demographic, with its focus upon population characteristics such as fertility, mortality, structure and migration, is an example of a narrower social factor. Cultural is another widely used social factor; its focus is upon human behaviour, which includes customs, religion and language. Technology is an economic factor of increasing importance especially in relation to the rise of 'high-tech' activities.

▲ **Figure 1.9** Sheep grazing, unaware of their potential usefulness to students of Geography!

Factors (as used in examination questions)

The word is widely used, but not always well dealt with by candidates in examinations.

Question - 'Identify and comment upon the factors which lead to ....'

For 'identify':

- *think of the SHEEP factors*
- *decide which apply*
- *organize them into physical and human*
- *use this order or the order of importance for the question set.*

For 'comment upon':

- *write about each factor in the context of the question set*
- *suggest which are stronger than the others and why.*

Question - 'Evaluate the relative importance of the factors responsible for ......'

- *Do as above but it is even more critical that separate factors are identified*
- *Make a separate comment at the end of the answer about the relative strength of the different factors*
- *Finish by mentioning and emphasizing the role of the one (or two) factors considered to be most important.*

Synoptic questions and answers

The essay questions in the A2 examination are designated synoptic. This means that in answering you are required to make connections between the different aspects of Geography studied over the two year AS and A2 course. This reflects the fact, already mentioned, that it is difficult to study in Geography one topic or theme in isolation from another. The examination specification (syllabus) is laid out by topic area. However, it is generally unsatisfactory, and often impossible, to make a detailed study of one topic without drawing upon some knowledge and understanding taken from another. Take the study of coasts (A2 Topic 1) as an example. Weathering and mass movement (A2 Topic 2) affect rates of cliff erosion and coastal retreat; marine erosion may be the principal factor for cliff retreat, but it is not the only one. Rivers (AS Topic 1), by depositing their loads in estuaries and deltas, are the main source of sediment input into the coast system. Elements of weather (AS Topic 2) are powerful influences upon the size and strength of breaking waves and extreme climatic events can cause storm surges capable of great damage in the coastal strip. Climatic change (AS Topic 2) and associated rising sea levels are causing physical alterations in the coast zone and changing management needs and methods. A study of plant successions, by which vegetation colonizes coastal environments such as sand dunes and mud flats, is included in Energy and Life (AS Topic 3). On top of these physical considerations there are additionally the varied attitudes and interests of people, who sometimes work with and sometimes against nature in the coast zone. In the chapters which follow, the main places where clear inter-relationships between different topics exist, in relation to both AS and A2, have been highlighted.

When writing answers to synoptic essay questions, keep a sense of perspective because most of the content in the answer should be taken from the topic area for which the question is set. However, to gain a mark within the highest band of assessment, you are expected to include broader geographical references as well. This is done by placing your answer within as wide a geographical context as possible. Do not be afraid to explore wider relationships, particularly towards the end of the answer, when comment related back to the question theme becomes of greater importance. However, do not do this at the expense of not covering the subject content for the topic area being examined.

Synoptic

What does it mean?

- *Knowledge is shown for a range of geographical subject matter*
- *Understanding is shown across different geographical topic areas*
- *Connections between some of the different topic areas in AS and A2 are made*
- *The views of people on a variety of geographical issues are appreciated*
- *A broader perspective and overview of the geographical subject content are shown.*

Geographical skills at Advanced Level

Geography students are expected to show proficiency in a wide variety of skills. Important geographical skills such as mapping, statistical processing and presenting data in graphs and diagrams continue the process of classification and help with the task of finding order within the complex patterns observed on the Earth's surface.

The recommended procedure for interpreting maps, graphs and diagrams is summarized below. The approach is equally valid for:

- interpreting stimulus materials included in examination questions
- analysing the results of data collected for the coursework component.

How to interpret maps, graphs and diagrams:

***1** Describe the general pattern*

This is based upon a first impression of what can be seen. It is what you observe before looking more closely and starting to notice features which do not match the general pattern.

***2** Illustrate the general pattern by examples of places and values*

Use only those which support the general pattern. Try to select places or values that are most significant. Often the extremes are used, or else the range within which the majority of recorded values lie. When describing patterns from a map, values should be supported by spatial references to places, regions or areas.

***3** Identify anomalies to the general pattern*

Describe clearly in what way these are exceptions to the general pattern. State what makes them stand out from most of the others by quoting differences in size and/or location.

Fieldwork

The most obvious use of investigative skills is in the coursework enquiry. This involves fieldwork.

How to undertake a fieldwork investigation and write up the results:

Topic and aim(s)
The first need in defining a geographical topic is to ensure that it is spatial. Are the results capable of being mapped? This is the key question that needs to be asked. The overall aim must be stated precisely and crisply. Aims written out as a question or hypothesis have a higher chance of leading to a successful outcome than those written down as general statements.

Summary of the investigative method for coursework

- *Define (as precisely as possible) the topic and its aim(s)*
- *Devise a plan of investigation*
- *Gather relevant data*
- *Process and present the data collected*
- *Write a report by compiling and organizing the data*
- *Conclude by making an overall assessment in line with aim(s)*

Plan of investigation
Keep the aim in mind when planning the data collection. Ensure that sufficient data is collected to enable a thorough investigation of the aim to be undertaken. Data collection and information gathering are the foundations of any investigation.

▲ **Figure 1.10**
The Leaning Tower of Pisa. Observe what happened with suspect foundations. Without adequate data collection your investigative study is vulnerable to a similar fate.

Gathering data
Think about where the data will be collected and why you are going to collect it. Collecting data can be very time consuming, therefore it is essential that all you are going to gather will further the aim of the investigation. Think about how and when the data will be collected; choose methods, times and places carefully in an attempt to maximize the quality and value of the information to be collected. Give careful thought to questions used in questionnaires. Yes/No answers are useless (except for ascertaining the suitability of the person for interview). Show an awareness of the suitability of the methods used and possible alternatives.

Processing and presenting data
Use a variety of methods to represent the data collected. Do not allow yourself to become stuck in tram lines and use (or over-use) only one or two methods of presentation. Insert maps, graphs, tables, sketches and photographs as close as possible to the point in the text to which they refer. Give everything a title and annotate as many of the presentations as possible, even graphs and diagrams, in order to highlight what they show that is relevant to the investigation. Comment upon the usefulness of the methods used.

Writing the report
Keep checking that what you are writing matches the aim(s) of the work. (The clearer your aim(s), the easier this is to do.) From time to time add short summaries to highlight how the aim(s) is (are) being met. Try to use the higher order writing skills that are shown in Figure 1.11. Do not spend too much time on description, much of which can be done by annotation of maps, graphs etc.

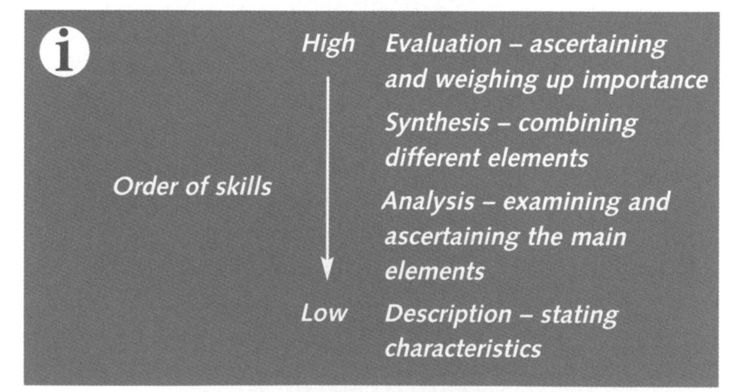

▲ **Figure 1.11** Hierarchy of writing skills

Concluding
Make an overall summary for the aim(s). Assess the extent to which they have been met on the evidence of the data collected. Place the final result in its broader geographical context (either for the topic area or for the region, or for both). Discuss the reliability of the data used.

Observation

Another skill that permeates every aspect of Geography is observation. Geography is a visual subject. Observation has a direct role in fieldwork. The significant features of the multitude of patterns observed at the surface need to be summarized and recorded for future use. This can be done in several ways – by taking photographs, drawing field sketches, making measurements and recording values for defined criteria as in an environmental quality survey. In all other geographical work about places that cannot be visited photographs give a visual record of the Earth's appearance at or near the surface. Even when not directly engaged in geographical study, the true geographer is observing and storing images to be processed later and related to geographical patterns identified elsewhere.

▲ **Figure 1.12**
The only practical way to complete some types of fieldwork, particularly those involving measurement, is in a group or with the help of others. How the data is used and written up must be individual. This is very important at 'A' level.

Use of the Internet

Availability of up-to-date information is less of a problem than it has ever been, with the Internet. Gathering information is easiest when you have a reference from a newspaper, TV channel or organization to a particular web site. Otherwise you need to use a search engine (Figure 1.13), which slows down the process. It has also been known to increase levels of frustration as finding pathways through the mass of available information is not always easy. A wealth of geographical information is out there, but finding and filtering it successfully demands high skill levels. All Internet users need to bear in mind that the material may be unreliable or come from biased sources. Therefore you are advised to check sources and comment on the extent to which you can have confidence in the data obtained.

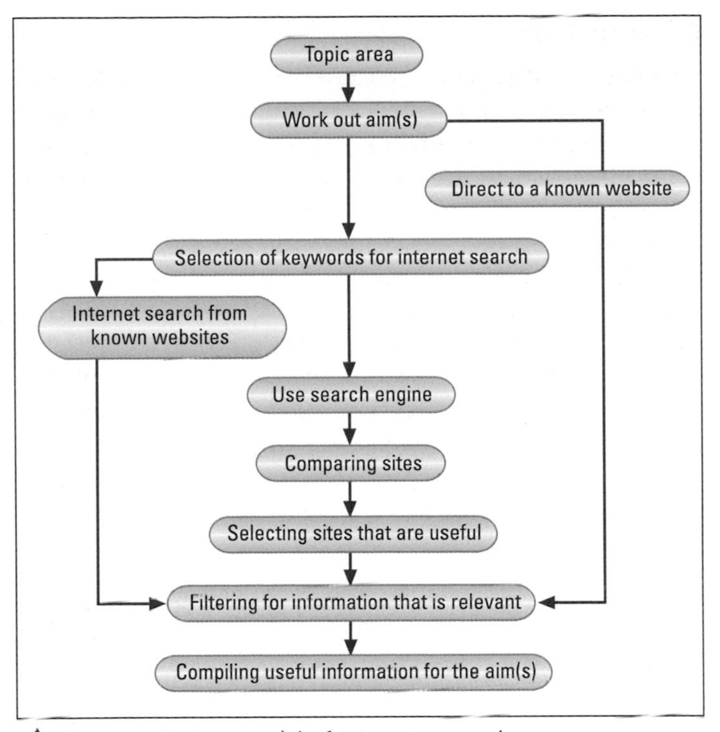

▲ **Figure 1.13** One model of Internet research

Examination technique

Advanced level examination questions are of two basic types, essays and structured questions. All examination questions, however, have one thing in common: each contains a command word (or words). It is vital for examination success that they are recognized and acted upon. This is crucial because command words determine the form of the mark scheme used by examiners to assess answers. Fortunately there are only a limited number of command words in regular use. The command words commented upon in Figure 1.14 are arranged as far as possible in order of increasing complexity. Those in the top half of the table tend to be used more frequently, but not exclusively, in structured questions. Likewise those in the bottom half of the table are more likely to be used in essay questions. Greater content in longer essay answers invites appraisal to an extent that is not possible in short answers to highly structured questions. However, command words are not the only determinant of level of difficulty and question complexity. Topic area and content examined are also significant and can dominate in some questions.

Essay questions

Read, plan and write are the three stages of good essay writing.

Read the question carefully and more than once. A quick flick of the eyes through the title can lead to a wrong interpretation of the question, perhaps more along the lines of what you would prefer the question to be. Identify the command word (or words) first. Then concentrate upon trying to understand the main theme

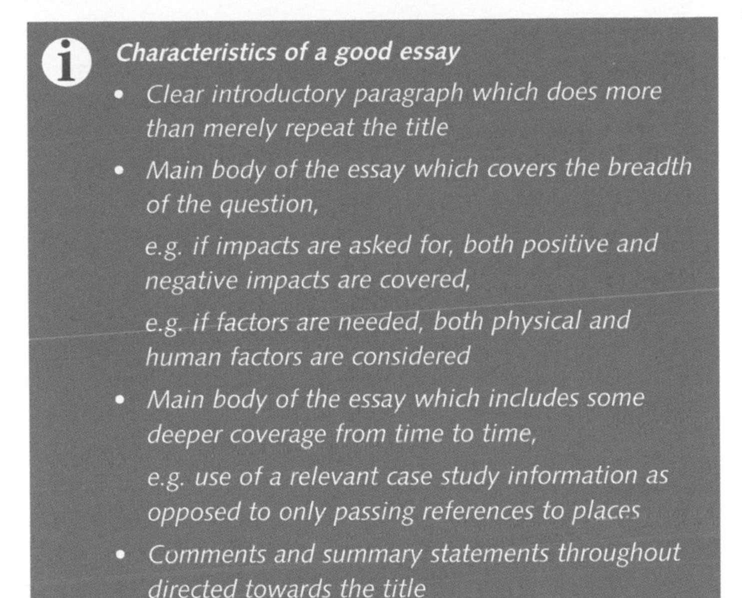
Characteristics of a good essay

- *Clear introductory paragraph which does more than merely repeat the title*
- *Main body of the essay which covers the breadth of the question,*

  e.g. if impacts are asked for, both positive and negative impacts are covered,

  e.g. if factors are needed, both physical and human factors are considered
- *Main body of the essay which includes some deeper coverage from time to time,*

  e.g. use of a relevant case study information as opposed to only passing references to places
- *Comments and summary statements throughout directed towards the title*
- *Final conclusion which summarizes the answer to the question set*

of the question. Some questions are tied to named areas of the world. It is clearly fatal, and a total waste of energy, time and ink, if a question about LEDCs is answered in relation to MEDCs. Many examination candidates underline parts of the question. In general this is good policy, provided that only the most significant elements are highlighted in this way. It works best when the command word is distinguished from the theme, which in turn is shown to be separate from any specified area of study. Some candidates underline virtually every word in the question, in a uniform manner, which is of little value. Targeting the significant is essential.

Plan a little before starting to write. Some examination candidates use the plan for writing down in summary form the content to be used in the main essay. This is almost like a practice run which can end up resembling a mini-essay. In extreme cases examination plans have been known to be longer than the final essay, when candidates later changed their minds about including all of the information. For the majority of candidates, plans of this kind are a waste of good examination time, time which could have been put to better use by starting to write the answer with at least some potential for picking up marks. The more valuable type of plan is one laid out in the form of punchy bullet points, listing headings or factors considered useful for the answer. Indeed if the word 'factors' is included in the question, given the problems (already referred to) that this often causes, it should be regarded as obligatory that headings for the relevant factors are noted down before beginning to write the essay. They can be written down just as they come to mind, in any order. Then just before you start to write the essay, think about the best order and put numbers or letters by their side. Also list any areas or case studies likely to be useful as a source of supporting information. Scratchings such as these over six or seven lines, written down in two or three minutes, are on most occasions more valuable than any written plan covering half a page or more. There is no point creating a plan with lots of information and then repeating it all in the essay.

Start writing relatively quickly to satisfy the desire to begin answering as soon as possible. The introductory paragraph is important in several ways but there is no fixed way to begin an essay. The introductory paragraph can be used to set the scene before starting the more direct answer to the question in the second paragraph. For example, key terms used in the title can be defined. This is an approach used by many. Or the question theme can be elaborated upon and placed in its broader geographical setting. If well done, both approaches demonstrate your geographical understanding and ease you into answering the question, as well as into the essay writing process. Danger looms only if you drift too far away from the question set and do not change direction in the second paragraph. Alternatively if you are confident about the answer, you can give an indication of your proposed route through the answer by outlining the main lines of argument you intend to follow. Or you can identify and briefly comment upon the factors that are important before discussing each one more fully.

The main body of an essay comprises geographical information, hopefully all relevant. Depth can be achieved by the use of case study materials as support for key points. Look at the title from time to time while writing, just to check that you are still answering the question set. Add comments or short summary statements at the end of long paragraphs or sections, which are directed towards the title or the sub-theme under examination. These summaries are separate from the overall conclusion in the final paragraph. Command words included in part E of Figure 1.14 demand that you write a meaningful final conclusion, in which the relative importance of the different factors or of the various elements covered are assessed and commented on. If the essay is designated as synoptic, you will be expected to take a broader geographical perspective. Even if the essay is not designated as such, it is still a good idea to widen the final discussion by comparing your results with those found elsewhere, or by commenting upon recent changes, or by speculating about what might happen in the future. All are ways of displaying greater geographical understanding and they improve the chances of rounding off an essay on a high note.

Information box

Importance of maps and diagrams in exam answers

Use:

- *in physical geography – because a labelled diagram of a landform can save many words*
- *in case studies – because a map is best for showing locations and patterns, such as the zones into which an urban area can be sub-divided.*

Annotated sketch maps and diagrams, drawn with reasonable accuracy, confirm knowledge and understanding and can greatly enhance the worth of any answer. Using labels that are relevant to question needs is more important than perfect accuracy.

Do not use:

- *if they add nothing more and merely duplicate what you have already written*
- *if your knowledge is sketchy and accuracy will be questionable*
- *if you have much to write and too little time in which to do it*
- *you add them as an after-thought so that they are placed out of position.*

Structured questions

Responses need to be quick, brief and precise.

Answers must be geared to the number of marks for the question and not to filling the number of lines left for the answer. Too many examination candidates believe that, once all the lines that the examination board has left for the answer have been filled, a full answer must already have been given. Sufficient lines for a full mark answer will have been left, but only provided that the candidate:

- begins to answer the question straight away without repetition of part or all of the title
- includes only information and comment relevant to the question.

If not, extra writing paper should be used until the number of points made match or exceed the number of marks available. Some questions are open ended and could well have been used in other examinations as titles for part-essays worth ten or fifteen marks. However, when only four or five marks are attached to the question, there is no time to build up a long and considered response. Instead relevant points should be stated from the first word without any attempt at scene setting. The most frequent weakness observed in candidates' answers to structured questions in Advanced level examinations is their limited coverage. For questions with four or five marks attached to them, only one or two points are made, in a relatively long winded manner which soon fills all the lines. The candidate is unable to claw back from other questions the shortfall in marks that has resulted.

▼ **Figure 1.14** Command words regularly used in Advanced level questions

	Command word(s)	Meaning	Comment
A	Describe	Say what something is like State characteristics Make points Quote factual details	Used for stating what maps, graphs, photographs etc. show. Quote useful values or other evidence observed in support.
B	Examine	Describe what you know and understand about	Use of all three is mainly confined to structured questions, in which the amount expected is suggested by the number of marks. They can form the first part of an essay question.
	Outline	Give brief details	
	Identify	Select certain distinguishing features	
C	Contrast	Differences between two or more things	It may be used for description or explanation, or both; this depends upon the other wording.
	Compare	Places more emphasis on the similarities between things	
	Similarities and differences		Clearer commands as to what is expected than compare and contrast, but having the same meaning.
	Comment on	Consider more broadly or begin to suggest reasons	When used in a structured question worth a limited number of marks.
D	Justify	Support a choice that has been made or give evidence to support a viewpoint, statement or conclusion.	Used in structured questions when one selection has to be made from a range of options.
	Explain	Give reasons for processes occurring or for a situation that exists.	
	Account for	Give reasons why something exists or occurs.	
E	Analyse	Write about the essential points. Break it down and examine each point in a critical manner.	
	Comment on	Develop the discussion of the subject matter, expressing your own opinion, if need be supporting it with reasons.	When used in essays.
	Discuss	State the arguments, investigate them and debate them by giving reasons for and against the viewpoint.	
	Evaluate	An opinion needs to be expressed based upon evidence presented in the answer.	Both require a judgement to be made.
	To what extent?	Weigh up or interpret the statement or issue. Consider each aspect, commenting on relative strengths and weaknesses.	

Stimulus materials are a feature of some structured questions. In the earlier part of this chapter on geographical skills some detailed advice was given for approaching examination questions directly based upon source materials (page 13). The three key procedures are repeated below (Information box). Never lift raw data from a source without using it or indicating its significance. Unless there is a very good reason to the contrary, always use continuous prose rather than bullet points or lists. Familiarize yourself with the demands of those command words most frequently used in structured questions in parts A to D of Figure 1.14. Do not emulate the performance of the candidate whose answer, to what should have been an easy 'A' level question, was worth zero marks (Figure 1.15). The candidate clearly had some knowledge of CBDs, but can you find anything in the answer which is descriptive (rather than explanatory) and clearly derived from the photograph? How can the answer be changed to make it worth the four marks? Answering your own question is not a well known route to examination success, no matter what you think of the examiner's ability to set questions.

Form of answer for a question based on a photograph, map, graph or diagram.

1 Describe the general pattern.

2 Illustrate the general pattern by examples of places and values.

3 Identify anomalies to the general pattern.

Question

Describe the characteristics typical of a CBD, which can be seen on the photograph showing the southern part of Manhattan in New York. (4 marks)

Answer

CBDs are busy places with lots of roads, where all the roads and railways meet. The roads are full of cars. Commuters travel in large numbers to work in the shops and offices. These are located close together. Shops need to be in the CBD to get large numbers of pedestrians so that they can make a profit. Many offices locate in the CBD for prestige reasons. Because land values are high, many companies build upwards rather than outwards. One of the typical characteristics of the CBD is that few people live there so that they are deserted at night.

▼ **Figure 1.15** How to achieve zero for one of the easiest of structured Advanced level questions.

Questions

1. Give an answer to the question in Figure 1.15 which would be worth four marks in an examination.
2. Describe what Figure 1.7 shows by using the advice for answering given in the information box on this page.
3. Give a brief definition, with the help of an example (where appropriate), to show that you understand the meaning and use in Geography of the following terms:

spatial	spatial association	zonal region
inter-relationship	region	synoptic study.

Chapter 2 Coast processes and problems

Figure 2.1 Beachy Head west of Eastbourne where the chalk scarp of the South Downs reaches the sea. In January 1999 hundreds of thousands of tonnes of chalk cliff behind Beachy Head lighthouse crashed into the sea, almost connecting the lighthouse to the land. The cliffs in the foreground suffered further collapse in the winter of 2001. Coastal erosion is a natural process but some believe that the rate of erosion is increasing.

The coast and marine energy

The coastal zone is a restricted environment. Wave action is concentrated within narrow limits, confined to the zone between the highest point reached by storm tides and the lowest limit of the area exposed during low spring tides. Freak events, such as storm surges associated with cyclones and tsunamis (tidal waves) from earthquakes, can temporarily extend the height and width of the zone of wave action. Indirectly the action of the sea has an effect above the highest point reached by tides because undercutting of the cliffs leads to the collapse of cliff faces well out of reach of direct wave attack. Onshore winds may carry beach material inland, forming sand dunes, but only for a limited distance. Where rivers meet the sea in broad shallow estuaries, sea water penetrates several kilometres inland up the channel during high tides. Although tidal effects are largely confined to river channels, more extensive areas of salty marsh land and mud flats occur in lowland areas on the sides of major river estuaries such as the Thames and Tees.

▲ **Figure 2.2** Part of the tidal stretch of the River Stour in east Kent. Tidal rivers and estuaries are at their most unattractive when their muddy banks are exposed at low tide.

▲ **Figure 2.3** Cliffs are unstable landforms. Walking along the bottom of an active cliff can never be without risk.

It may be restricted in extent but the coastal zone is a dynamic environment undergoing constant, and some would argue increased, change. Waves are the powerful agents of change as they break ceaselessly in the inter-tidal zone. The ebb and flow of the tide never stops. Waves break against active cliffs for a period before and after high tide, twice a day, every day of the year. Waves wash over the beach as the tides come and go, redistributing sand and shingle and reshaping its profile. At the same time waves are adding to or removing beach materials. They are also transferring sediments along the coast (coastal drift). Another important reason why breaking waves are great forces for change is that they are releasing energy gained from well beyond the restricted coastal zone. Waves, driven by winds and currents, gather energy from long journeys across the world's oceans. Many of those that break against the west coasts of Britain release energy generated by thousands of kilometres of travel across the open Atlantic Ocean.

Most people perceive the coastline of the British Isles as a permanent feature. It is shown as a solid line on all maps. Annual holiday makers and day trippers to Britain's coastal resorts may expect some of the human features to change between visits, but not the beach and sea front behind it. Yet those who have any understanding of the purpose of groynes recognize that beaches in some of the UK's major coastal resorts only exist as a result of human intervention. They are part of a deliberate attempt to impede the continuous natural drift of sediment along the coast. Figure 2.4 shows lines of groynes without which active cliff erosion would have continued further east from Beachy Head. Eastbourne would have been without a beach; without its beach the town's position as one of the UK's leading seaside resorts would be unsustainable. The signs of recent wave attack can be observed in the foreground of Figure 2.4 where the profiles of these active cliffs are more vertical than those of the inactive cliffs in the background, which are under the protection of the beach and sea wall. Coastal defences lull people into a false sense of security and stability. In reality the position of the coastline is constantly changing. In places land is being lost to wave erosion. Along other parts of the coast land is being gained by deposition. Between the two, waves are transporting and re-transporting eroded materials and beach sediments by longshore drift. People living along coastlines where land is being lost are understandably some of the unhappiest and most worried people in the country. In the long term there is probably little that anyone can do to stop the erosion. What is being observed around the coasts of the British Isles today is no more than a continuation of what has been happening for thousands of years.

▲ **Figure 2.4** Looking along the Channel coast from Beachy Head in the direction of Eastbourne

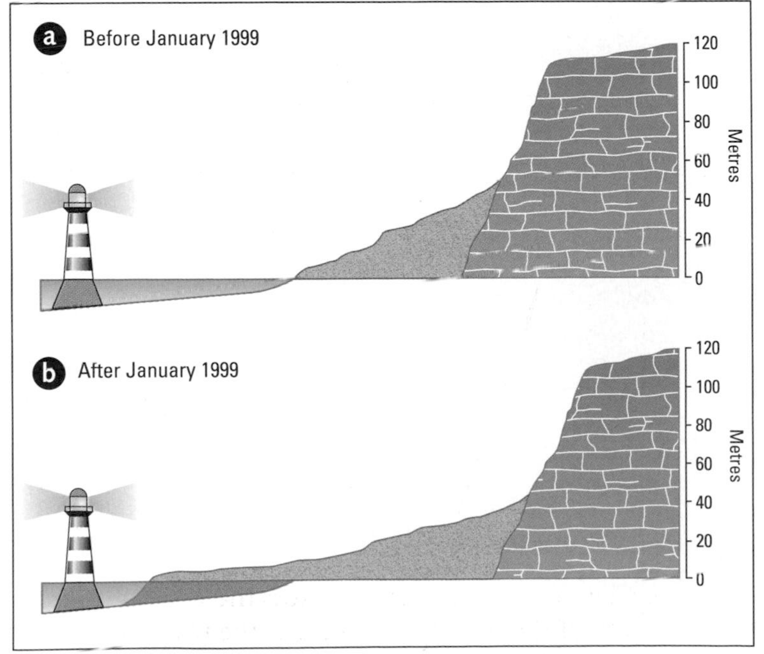

▲ **Figure 2.5a** Coastal profiles at Beachy Head before and after January 1999

Beachy Head cliff collapse January 1999

How serious was the collapse at Beachy Head?

This was the largest single loss of coastline in living memory. A 15m by 60m section of the chalk cliff crashed into the sea – that adds up to hundreds of thousands of tonnes of chalk.

What caused the collapse?

Experts think that the weather played the most important part, but rough seas, rising sea levels and the fact that Britain is naturally tilting were also important.

The South of England had been very dry for thirty months until 1998, when eight of the twelve months had above average rainfall. This meant the chalk cliffs at Beachy Head first dried out and became brittle, and then, when the rainy period started, became waterlogged and soggy. Cold weather at the beginning of January meant the water in the rock froze. When water freezes it expands, and this forced the cliff to crumble.

Waves also played a large part in eroding the cliff. Erosion (from the Latin word erosio meaning 'gnaw') is when rocks are slowly worn away by the action of water, ice and wind. It is usually a slow process, but over the past few weeks the waves have been rough and strong on the south coast.

Sea levels seem to be rising. Over the next 50 years sea levels are expected to rise over 20cm. The countries of the world are constantly (very, very slowly) on the move. Britain is tilting, with Scotland rising and the south of England sinking.

Are other parts of the coastline at risk from collapse?

Yes. The most vulnerable are stretches of the east and south coast. Holderness in Yorkshire, Lyme Regis in Dorset and part of the cliffs on the Isle of Wight are among those at greatest risk.

▲ **Figure 2.5b** Extract from *The Guardian*, 19 January 1999

Only a few thousand years ago the outline of the British Isles looked radically different from what it does today. Britain was joined to Europe until rising sea levels, which began at the end of the Pleistocene ice age, formed the Straits of Dover between five and six thousand years ago. It flooded large areas of lowland that used to form the extension of eastern England into what is now the North Sea. Mouths of rivers in eastern England were drowned and widened into shallow ria estuaries. Lowlands were inundated to create large inlets of the sea, such as the Wash, around which the reclaimed Fenland lies at, or slightly below, the present day sea level. Only two thousand years ago in Roman times the coast of Holderness was several kilometres further east. At least twenty villages and towns are known to have been lost to the sea within the last three hundred years along this part of the Yorkshire coast (Figure 2.6). Modern settlements which have replaced lost old settlements, such as Bridlington, Withernsea and Kilnsea, only survive because of coastal protection works.

Along the west coasts of the British Isles rising sea levels produced different results. A much smaller area of land was flooded but the coastline has become more broken. Both reflect greater average height of the land and more rugged relief. River estuaries were drowned to form either deep branching ria estuaries, extending several kilometres inland, which are characteristic landscape features in south-west England and Ireland, or deeper and straighter fiords, as in some of the Scottish sea lochs. Within Europe the effects of persistent rises in sea level over the last one thousand years of recent settlement have been most dramatic for the Dutch (pages 66–67). Forty per cent of the land area of the Netherlands (the name itself means 'low-lying lands') lies below present day sea levels. If it had not been for sea defences the country would be only about half of its current size and without its most productive land.

Changes in relative levels of land and sea are still occurring. Ever since the retreat of the ice sheets, the northern and western parts of the British Isles have been rising. The land has been springing back up to compensate for the removal of the weight and pressure from the great ice masses on top of it. The clearest visual evidence of this uplift is the flat shelf of land which fringes the coasts of Scotland, in many places about eight to ten metres above present mean sea level. Known as the raised beach, in many places it offers the only level land for settlement, farming, lines of communication and, of course being Scotland, golf courses (Figure 2.7). The process responsible for this uplifting of the land is isostatic readjustment (see the Information box). The rising of the north and west of the British Isles is affecting the south and east, which is being tilted downwards making it even more vulnerable to present and future rises in sea level. The general sinking of south-east England is part of a natural process, even if locally it is made worse by the unintentional actions of people. For example in the London Basin where the removal of water from aquifers in the chalk, and the concentrated weight of buildings, people (and wealth) are depressing the soft clay rocks below.

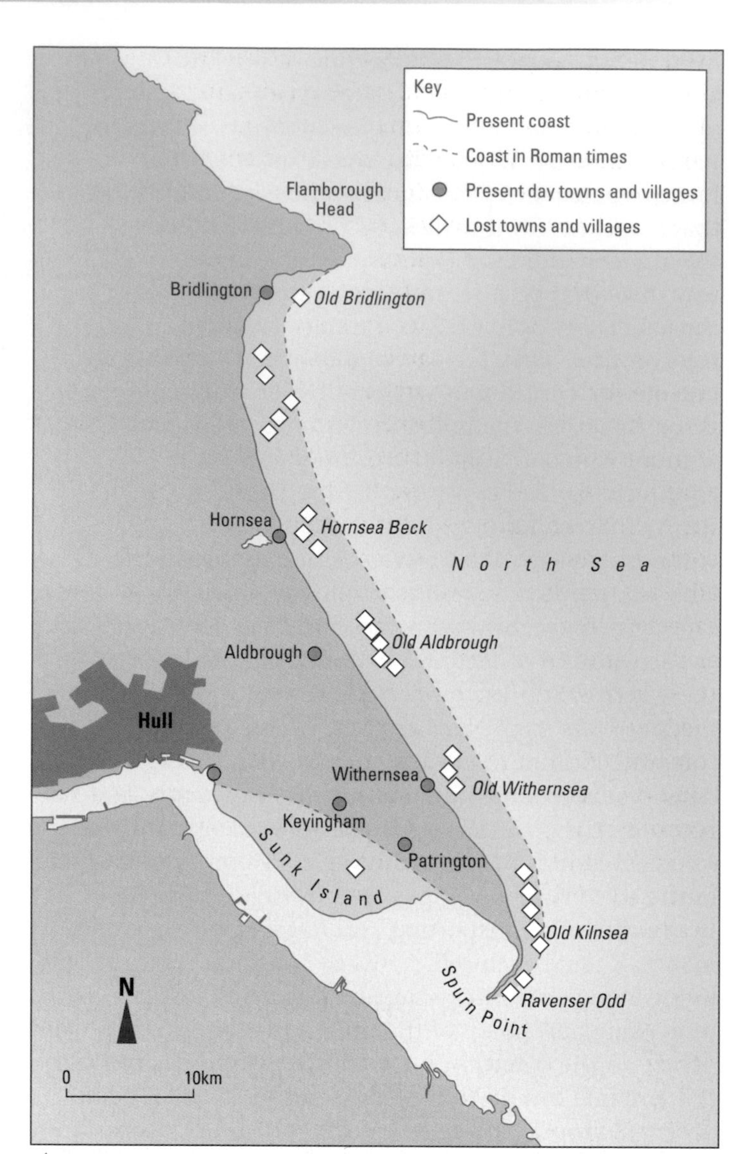

▲ **Figure 2.6** The retreating coastline of Holderness

▲ **Figure 2.7**
The raised beach at Brora in north-east Scotland forms a platform of level land about eight metres higher than the present sandy beach. Most of it is grass covered and used for an 18-hole links golf course.

Even though arguments may remain over the causes of global warming, in particular the relative roles of physical processes and human actions, mean temperatures are rising with inevitable consequences for low-lying coastal areas. More of the world's fresh water that is locked up in ice will melt and find its way into the sea, and sea levels will continue their rise in the same way that they have done almost without interruption for the last ten thousand years. It has been estimated that sea levels could rise by some 90m if it became warm enough for the total Antarctic ice sheet to melt, but this is much too distant a prospect for anyone to contemplate at present. Even without this, sea levels will rise simply as a result of the thermal expansion of warmer water. Until the current warming trend is reversed, perhaps by cooling related to the onset of another major ice advance, the map of the coastline of the British Isles, and especially that of the east coast, will continue to change as the sea water advances. The increased frequency and severity of stormy weather in the British Isles, which is predicted to accompany global warming, and which some believe is already happening, will speed up rates of coastal erosion, especially along the east coast which is composed of geologically young sedimentary rocks. These are much less resistant to erosion than the old hard rocks which outcrop in northern and western Britain (Figure 2.8).

Eustatic and Isostatic changes in sea levels

Relative levels of land and sea are continually changing.

***Eustatic** refers to those changes in relative levels caused by changes in the mass or volume of water.*

- *Mass changes according to the relative amount of water stored on the land, such as in glaciers, other surface stores and underground.*
- *Volume changes with the temperature of the water; as ocean water warms up, it undergoes thermal expansion and its volume increases.*

***Isostatic** refers to those changes in relative levels caused by movements of the land. An example is the land rising after having been depressed by the weight of ice during the Pleistocene.*

- *Where ice sheets accumulate, land surfaces are depressed by their weight.*
- *As the ice sheets gradually melt, pressure is eased and the land gradually rises again.*
- *The land readjusts with time, although the rising back is gradual and is still occurring after the Pleistocene.*
- *In the British Isles the ice sheet was thickest in northern Scotland and it is here that the evidence for the rising of the land is greatest.*
- *The isostatic recovery of the land is happening despite rising sea levels.*

▼ **Figure 2.8** Some of the basic differences between highland and lowland Britain

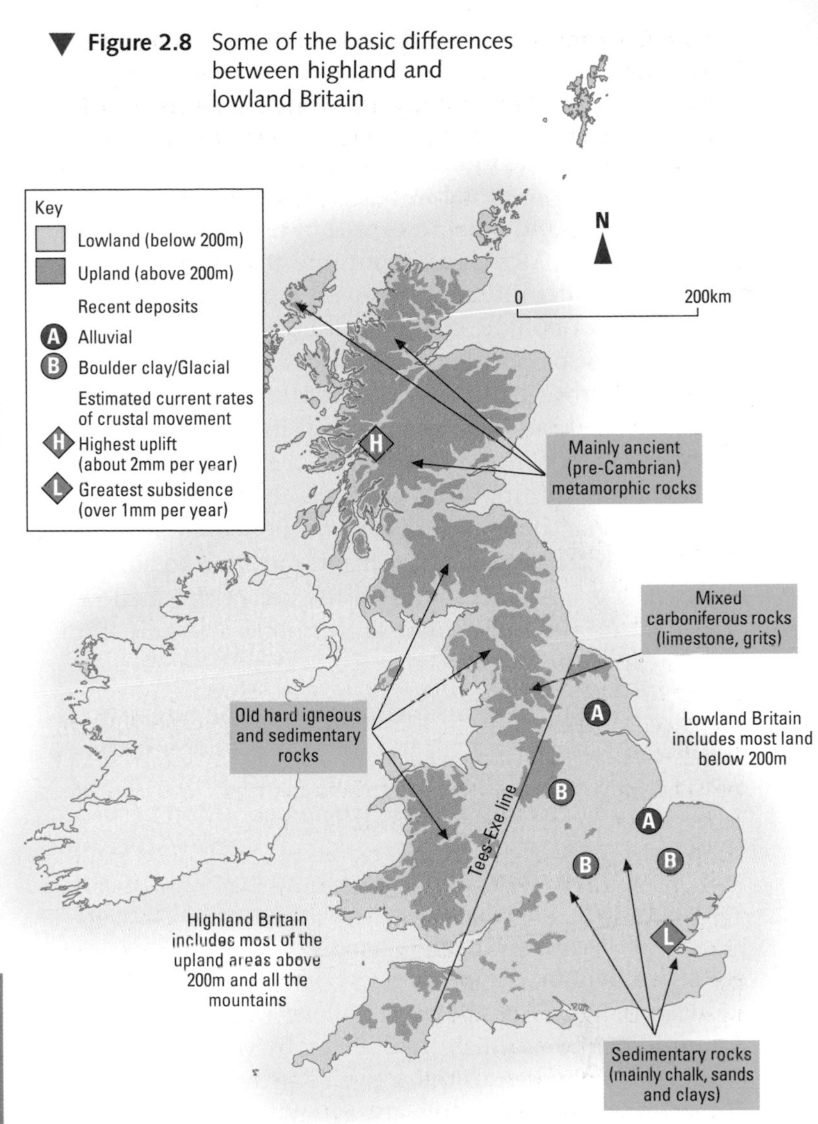

Questions

1 a Study Figure 2.1. Draw a labelled sketch to describe the coastal scenery at Beachy Head.

b Analyse the changes over time at Beachy Head.

c Outline and give reasons for the spatial changes in coastal scenery between Beachy Head and Eastbourne.

2 **Investigation**

For one other stretch of coastline in the British Isles (either local, or one regularly visited, or one for which information is available on the net), identify and comment upon the changes that have recently occurred.

3 a Summarize the main physical differences between north-west and south-east Britain.

b Outline some of the effects of these differences upon coastal scenery.

4 'The coastal zone is a restricted but dynamic environment'. Explain this statement.

The coast as a system

The coast is an open system. The inputs which provide energy to drive the system are waves, winds, tides and currents. From time to time the energy input is boosted by storm surges and tidal waves. A small proportion of the sediment is provided from within the system by wave erosion of cliffs. Most is an input into the system from outside, the chief source being rivers which are transporters of boulders, sand and silt from land to sea. Weathering also contributes; cliff faces above the high water mark are affected and any loose materials broken off either fall or are carried within reach of the waves by different types of mass movement. Locally other sources are significant as inputs; for example, there are offshore deposits of glacial debris and river-borne sediments in the North Sea, which waves pick up and move on to adjacent coasts. The glacial drift found on the bed of the shallow North Sea off the north coast of Norfolk is a residue from the retreat of the Scandinavian ice sheets.

Longshore drift is responsible for most of the interactions within the system through transfers of sediment. Loose materials are relocated from sections of coastline dominated by erosion to those where deposition occurs to form constructive landforms such as beaches, spits and bars. Winds can carry sand inland as an output from the coastal system. Deposited coastal sediments that remain in position for a considerable length of time are colonized by seral communities as part of a plant succession. Soil is created which allows more stable plant communities to establish themselves, by which time the area is also taken out of the active coast system, until and unless change occurs within the system to allow active wave action to begin again.

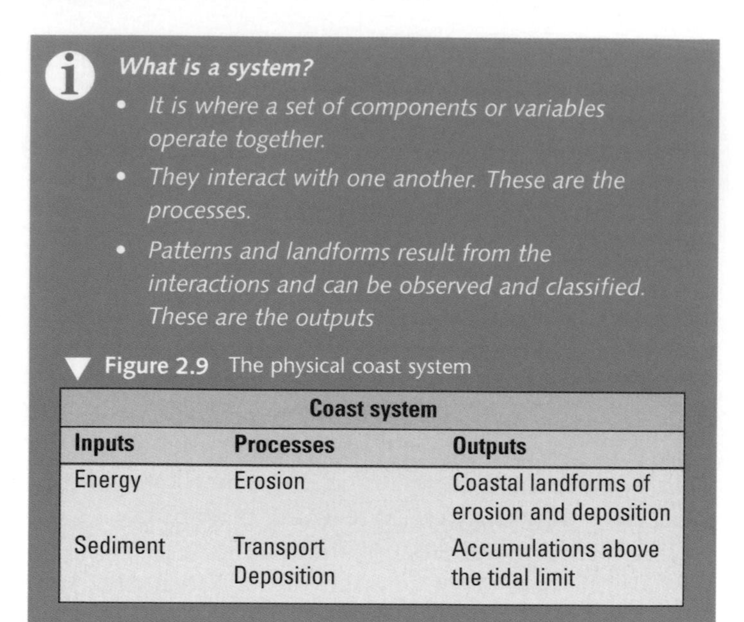

What is a system?

- *It is where a set of components or variables operate together.*
- *They interact with one another. These are the processes.*
- *Patterns and landforms result from the interactions and can be observed and classified. These are the outputs*

Figure 2.9 The physical coast system

Coast system		
Inputs	**Processes**	**Outputs**
Energy	Erosion	Coastal landforms of erosion and deposition
Sediment	Transport Deposition	Accumulations above the tidal limit

Waves

Waves are of crucial importance to understanding how the coastal system works. In the open ocean wind rippling the water surface can lead to growth into recognizable waves. Without currents this shows itself as a non-moving swell. The circular motion of waves at the surface is copied below in a series of circles which become smaller with increasing depth. All of this changes as the waves are driven by winds and currents into shallow coastal waters (Figure 2.10). Shallow water interferes with the circular movements below the surface, which are slowed down by the friction of the sea bed. The result is that the length of the wave shortens and the front of the wave steepens. The speed of flow of water at the top of the wave begins to exceed that of the rest of the wave below so that it topples over and the wave breaks. The jet of water from the breaking crest of the wave moves forward with twice the speed of the wave as a whole and creates the swash.

Figure 2.10 Waves

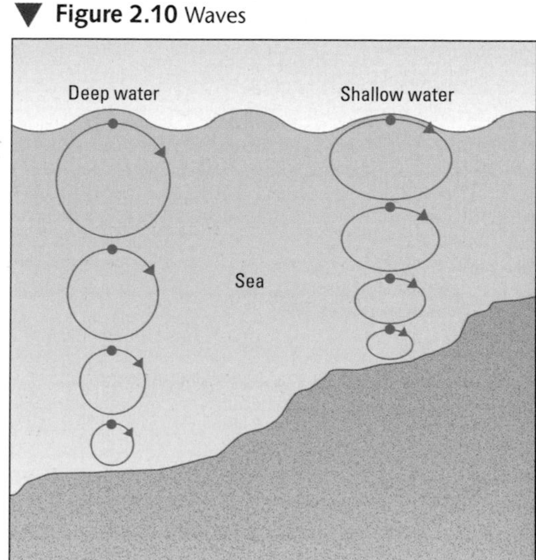

a How waves change as they approach the shoreline

b Waves in Filey Bay during quiet weather. The effects of increasingly shallow water near the beach is shown in the appearance of the waves. The lines of surface swell visible across the outer bay become breaking waves nearer to the shore line. On this occasion the waves are breaking gently and can be described as constructive breakers.

A common classification for waves is into destructive (plunging breakers) and constructive (spilling breakers), although not all waves are as easy to distinguish as this simple classification suggests. The differences between the two types of wave are summarized in Figure 2.11. All the energy accumulated by movement is released when the wave breaks. Since destructive waves are high and short, there is a sudden impact of water upon whatever the breaking wave hits. These waves are sufficiently high for the water motion to be almost circular so that the great force of water is directed downwards when they break. This gives a strong backwash, which increases the likelihood of loose material being clawed back down the beach into the sea. The rapid sequence of breaking waves under storm conditions means that the new swash is running into the backwash from the next breaker, reducing further any chance of sediment deposition. In contrast, the more elliptical shape of water movement in a constructive wave means that the forward movement of the breaking wave is more pronounced than its downward force. By breaking forwards a strong swash is pushed up the beach, while the energy of the backwash is reduced as water seeps into the sand and shingle. Not all the load is carried back into the sea. This promotes deposition. As a simple summary, very large waves erode and very small waves deposit.

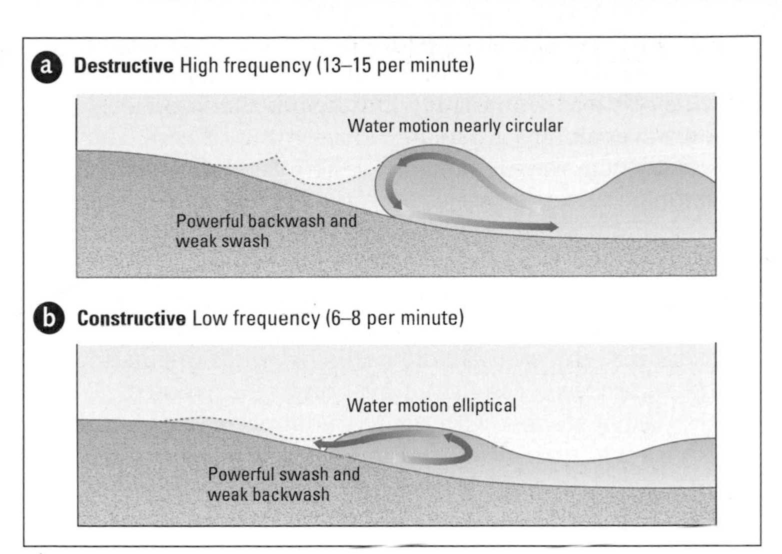

▲ **Figure 2.11** Destructive and constructive waves

Fetch, wind direction and wind strength are the main factors determining the height and energy of breaking waves. Fetch is the distance of uninterrupted water surface over which the wind has blown to form the waves. Stated in another way, it is the distance available to the wind for the generation of waves. The longer the length of open water over which the winds travel, the longer the fetch and the greater the amount of energy released when waves break in the coastal zone. The maximum fetch in the British Isles is for westerly winds blowing onshore on the west coast after an Atlantic crossing. Their fetch is longer than that which can be reached by northerly and north-easterly winds in more enclosed seas such as the North Sea. The westerly winds are also the prevailing winds, the winds that blow with the greatest frequency in the latitude of the British Isles. Where the fetch is very large, as along the west coasts, the factors which control the height of the breaking waves are the strength of the wind and the length of time it has been blowing at that strength. Strong winds are one of the characteristics of the British climate, because it lies in the zone dominated by low pressure and frontal depressions within the general world circulation. There is a high incidence of storm and gale force winds all down the western side of the British Isles. Storm waves generated by strong winds travel fast and follow in rapid succession, which contribute to their highly destructive nature.

▲ **Figure 2.12a**
December 2000. Riding the storm. A train is hit on Dawlish sea front in Devon as a high tide combined with winds, which reached over 120kph in parts of Britain.

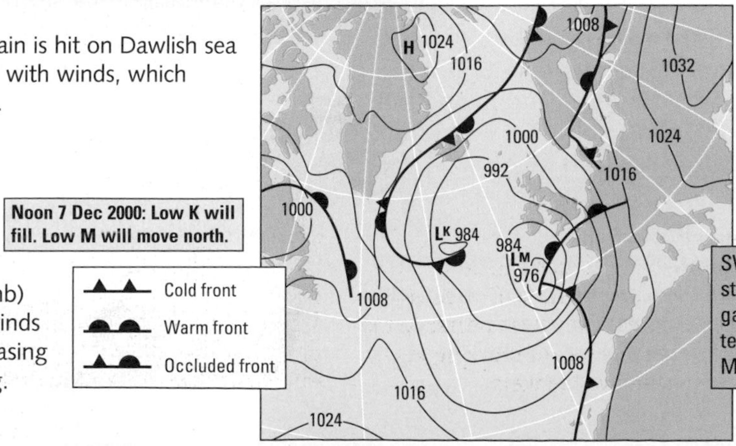

Noon 7 Dec 2000: Low K will fill. Low M will move north.

Cold front
Warm front
Occluded front

SW England: Heavy rain and strong winds with severe gales by the afternoon. Max temp 10–12°C. Tonight, rain. Min temp 8–10°C.

▶ **Figure 2.12b**
A deep depression (below 976mb) and its associated storm force winds were tracking northwards, increasing the risk of more coastal flooding.

In contrast, strong westerly winds cannot create damaging waves along the east coast of Britain because they are blowing offshore. Dominant winds (winds that produce the largest waves along a coast) are more significant here. The most damaging waves that affect eastern Scotland and England are driven by winds from the east and north. Being dominant as opposed to prevailing winds means that they exert control over wave size on a smaller number of occasions during the year. There is no land on the direct northerly route from East Anglia to the North Pole to interrupt movement; therefore northerly winds originating in the Arctic Ocean can drive waves on to the exposed north coast of Norfolk with the second longest fetch in the British Isles. In extreme circumstances these produce tidal storm surges, which are short-term increases in sea level. They can be responsible for considerable physical changes to the coastline and great damage to property (see page 27).

Tides

Tides have a more regular energy input into the coast system than do waves. Tidal fluctuations depend upon the relative positions of moon and sun. Tides are caused by the gravitational pull of the moon and to a lesser extent that of the sun. This results in two great bulges in the oceans in line with the moon and the sun. These bulges move around the Earth as it rotates, giving two high tides per day. Twice a month shortly after new moon and full moon, when sun, moon and Earth all lie in a straight line, the gravitational pull of the sun and moon work together to cause especially high and low tides known as spring tides (Figure 2.13). The name spring tide does not seem very appropriate for an event which happens twice a month. Its origins lie in what happens in spring and autumn at the time of the Equinoxes when the sun is overhead at the Equator. There is a boost in the sun's gravitational pull which leads to the highest and lowest tides of the year at these two times (around 21 March and 21 September). For any given place tides can be forecast years ahead with great accuracy. Tides are not an unpredictable input into the coastal system in the way that wind strength and wave size are. However, for low-lying coastal regions spring tides are a worry, especially when river levels are high, but their time and height can be forecast and precautions (where possible) taken.

Low tide
High tide
North Pole
Earth
High tide
Sun
Moon
Low tide
Note: Spring tides also occur when the moon is on the same side of the Earth as the sun.

▲ **Figure 2.13** How spring tides are formed

Tidal range can be significant; this is the difference between the mean levels of high and low tides. Enclosed seas, such as the Baltic and Mediterranean, have very small tidal ranges, which restrict wave action to a much narrower width in the coast zone. Whereas tidal ranges are high in the British Isles, particularly along the North Sea and Channel coasts. Here a combination of narrowing areas of sea water and increasingly shallow sea beds leads to the rapid build up of water at high tide by funnelling and accumulation thus increasing the distance between the peak high and low tides. A high tidal range leads to a broad zone of wave attack on cliff faces, in places favouring the formation of wide rocky wave-cut platforms, which are given maximum exposure during low spring tides. The long funnel shape of the Severn estuary causes the advancing tide to develop a steep front which causes a tidal bore, seen on the River Severn as a wave which moves at about 30kph, on occasions travelling almost to Gloucester.

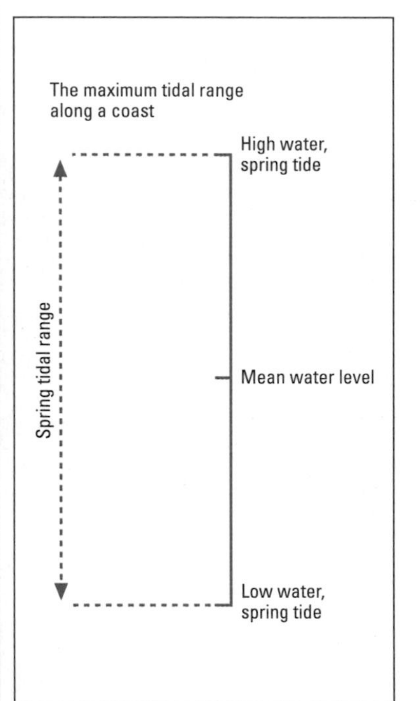

From time to time other conditions work together to give much higher water levels at high tide than those predicted. Storm surges are caused by extreme meteorological conditions, usually strong winds, especially when these have a long fetch. Where the configuration of coastline and sea is favourable, water piles up, which becomes especially dangerous for densely populated areas when it coincides with particularly high tides. Therefore the most likely conditions for the generation of a storm surge is when the impact of a high tide is magnified by a strong onshore wind. The southern part of the North Sea is an example of an area at risk from storm surges. When two or more favourable conditions for their formation combine, the flooding that results can create mayhem for those living in the coastal areas affected. The North Sea storm surge of 31 January and 1 February 1953 lives in folk memory, despite having happened some 50 years ago. It is on a par with other extreme events such as the Lynmouth flood in August 1952 and south-east England's 'hurricane' in October 1987. Another part of the world vulnerable to storm surges is at the head of the Bay of Bengal where low-lying Bangladesh suffers most (page 67).

The North Sea storm surge of 1953

Case Study

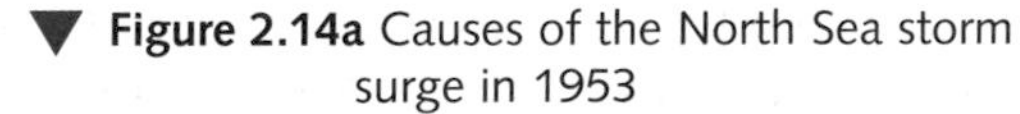

The circumstances which combined to make this such a notorious storm surge were as follows:

- an already deep Atlantic depression crossed Scotland, deepening all the time giving violent gales. It then veered south eastwards to lie in a position off the coast of Denmark where its central pressure fell to 970mbs
- at the same time the anticyclone lying in the Atlantic west of Ireland built up and its pressure increased to 1032mbs
- the great pressure difference over such a short distance between the centres of areas of low and high pressure created a very steep pressure gradient. The anti-clockwise circulation around the low sucked down air from the Arctic Ocean, a long way north of the British Isles, which produced vicious northerly gales. Gusts up to 160kph were recorded. Gale force winds whipped up enormous seas
- the long journey of the winds across open water gave the maximum fetch possible for the east coast
- tides in the southern North Sea and Straits of Dover were particularly high, up to two metres higher than the already higher than average spring tide level.

▼ **Figure 2.14a** Causes of the North Sea storm surge in 1953

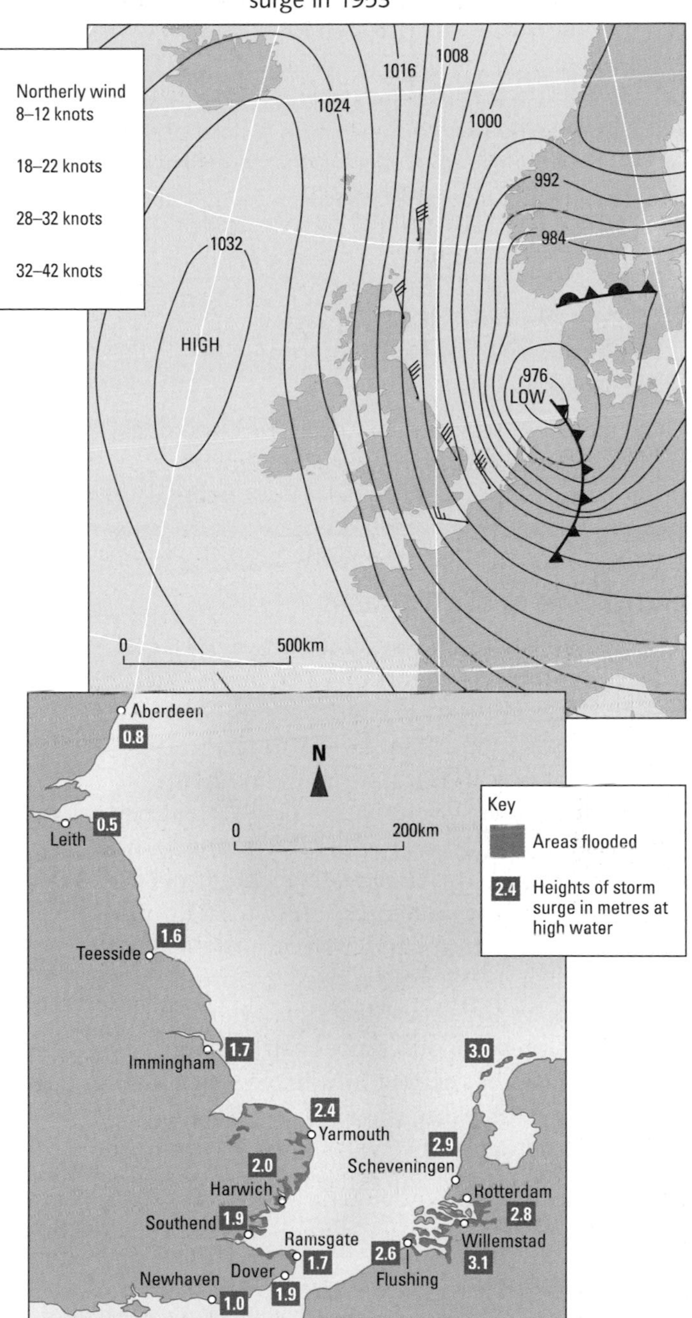

▲ **Figure 2.14b** Heights of the storm surge and areas flooded

The result was that water, which piled up in the southern end of the North Sea at the point where it narrows, then created a bottleneck near the Straits of Dover. In places along the east coast of England water levels were between two and three metres higher than the already high predictions for high tide (Figure 2.14b). The Dutch coast was even more exposed with water levels about three metres higher along most of its coastline. In the worst recorded case, water level in one estuary was more than five metres above the height expected.

The storm surge had dramatic consequences, both physical and human. Cliff lines were driven back everywhere down the east coast of England, by as much as three metres at Herne Bay in Kent. Remember that this was the result of just one night's work by the waves. Sand dune systems along the length of the east coast were breached. Many sea defences were unable to take the strain and 64,000ha of low-lying land between the Humber and Thames estuaries were flooded, causing nearly 300 deaths, as well as great damage to property and huge losses of livestock.

Bad as the consequences were in England, they were on a much smaller scale than the devastation and destruction in the Netherlands. Three times as much land was flooded, including almost one tenth of the country's agricultural land. Nearly 1,800 people were drowned and more than 50,000 had to be evacuated from their homes. The dyke systems around the islands in the delta region of the Rhine and Maas in the province of Zeeland ('land of the sea') in the south west collapsed and 67 breaches occurred. A total catastrophe was narrowly averted. The embankment on the Hollandse Ijssel, a small river east of Rotterdam, held; otherwise salt water would have flowed by the back door over the main area of polderland which contained the agricultural and urban core of the country. The scale of the disaster was too great for it not to provoke a reaction. The Dutch response was the Delta Plan (page 67).

Questions

1 Define fetch and explain its geographical significance.

2 a Distinguish between prevailing and dominant winds.

b

Mean percentage frequency of winds in the British Isles											
N	NNE	ENE	E	ESE	SSE	S	SSW	WSW	W	WNW	NNW
7	5	6	7	5	8	9	9	14	15	8	7

Draw a wind rose to show these percentages.

c Outline the effects of relative frequencies in wind direction upon coastal processes around the British Isles.

3 Figure 2.15 shows longshore drift and general directions of movement around Britain.
Explain what Figure 2.15 shows in relation to prevailing and dominant winds.

4 Why are tides considered to be less important than waves in the formation of coastal landforms?

5 a Outline the characteristics which distinguish destructive waves from other waves.

b Discuss the factors favourable for their formation.

6 Make notes for a case study of the storm surge in the southern North Sea in 1953.

a State the key facts in an organized manner (for example, when, where, spatial variations in size, physical effects and human impact).

b Outline the permanent features of the southern North Sea which makes it more vulnerable to storm surges than most other coastal zones around the British Isles.

c Explain the immediate meteorological causes of the 1953 storm surge, illustrating your answer with a sketch map.

7 Why do extreme events, such as storm surges, only occur when a combination of factors favourable to their formation are present?

High and low energy coasts

High energy coasts are ones in which wave power is strong for a significant proportion of the year. The distribution of these coasts is largely controlled by the climate and the direction they face. Strong winds capable of generating the largest waves are more frequent in areas of the world with a Cool Temperate Western Maritime (CTWM) type of climate than with any other type of climate. High average wind speeds are associated with the frontal depressions which form over the oceans at the junction between warm tropical and cold polar air masses. They often deepen as they move eastwards driven by the prevailing circulation from west to east. Big pressure differences can develop between the centres of the low pressure systems and any intervening or blocking ridges of high pressure. Exposed coastlines experience gales often, storm force winds regularly and hurricane force winds from time to time. The storm wave environments found in areas with CTWM climates are shown in Figure 2.16. They occupy similar positions on the western side of continents between 45° and 65° north and south of the Equator. In the northern hemisphere they extend from Alaska to British Columbia in North America and from northern Norway to northern Spain in Europe. Atlantic islands such as Iceland are also included within this zone. Wave height, and therefore wave energy, are potentially greater in the southern hemisphere. Westerly winds, depressions and ocean currents (the Antarctic Drift) have largely uninterrupted passages around the globe because so little land extends south of 45°. Waves hitting southern Chile are driven by winds which have the world's longest fetches.

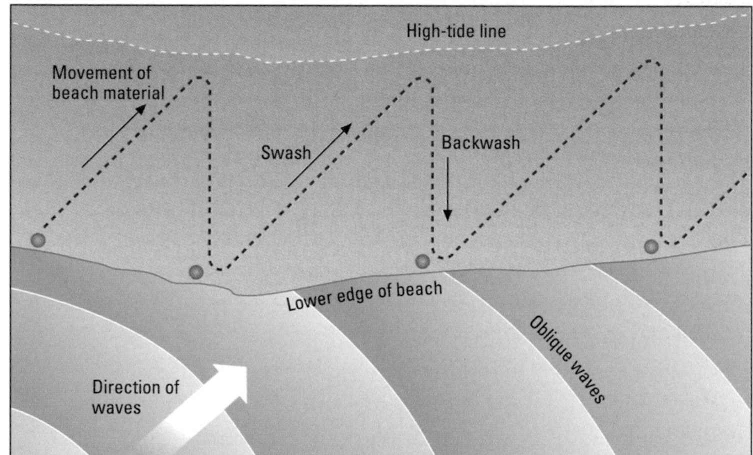

▲ **Figure 2.15a** Longshore drift

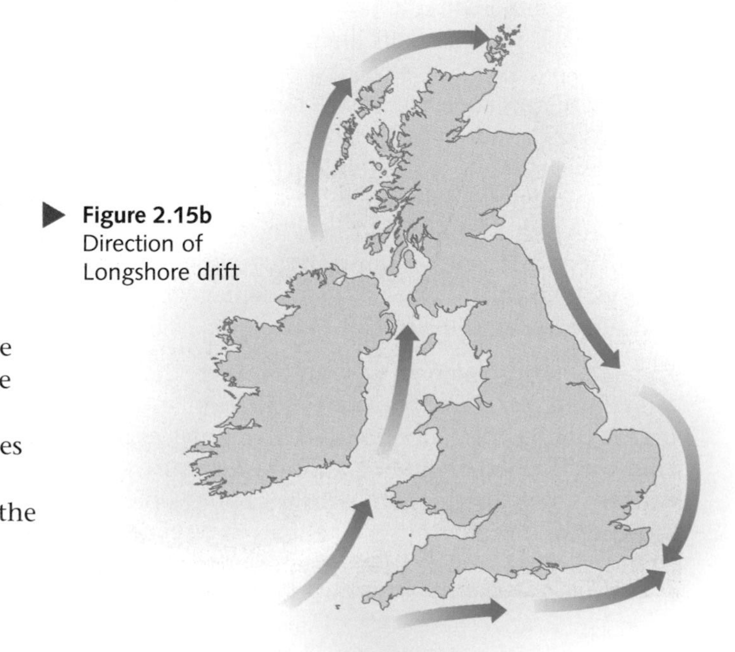

▶ **Figure 2.15b** Direction of Longshore drift

In tropical latitudes the position of the high energy environments switches to east-facing coasts of continents and islands reflecting the directions from which the prevailing trade winds blow, from the north east in the northern hemisphere and from the south east in the southern hemisphere. These winds have long been noted for their reliability, hence the name 'prevailing', which was given to them in the days of sailing ships. They blow persistently outwards from the high pressure horse latitudes and towards the thermal lows around the hot Equator. They are on average less strong and less subject to extremes than westerlies in temperate latitudes because they are not part of swirling low pressure systems. Along east-facing tropical coasts they are noted most for the size of the swell they create, although this is sufficient to create some rugged stretches of coast, especially where the fetch is long as on the eastern side of Easter Island in the middle of the Pacific Ocean. Harbour sites on tropical islands are more frequently located on sheltered western sides as a result. From time to time cyclones are responsible for very significant coastal change in the tropical zone, because they are capable of generating winds of a ferocity rarely recorded anywhere else on earth. A wall of water can be pushed onshore causing total destruction. One such cyclone devastated Orissa in India in 1997 (see **AS Level Geography**, pages 70–71).

Figure 2.16 The distribution of strong wave environments

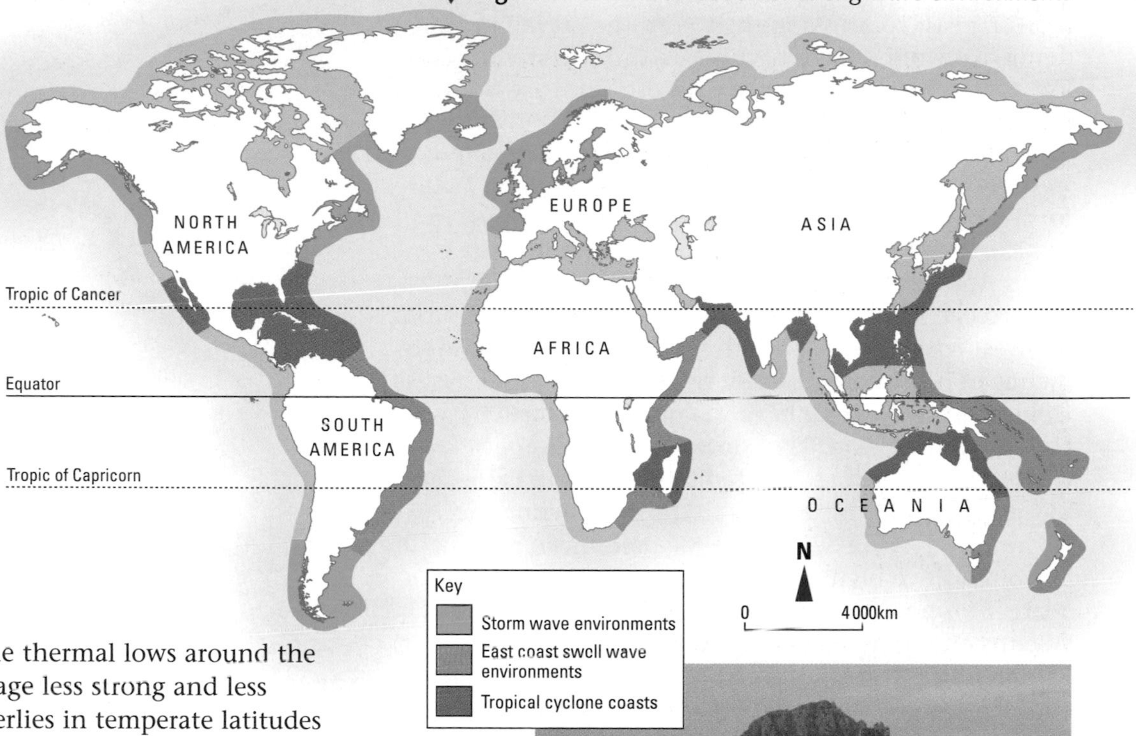

NORTH AMERICA
EUROPE
ASIA
AFRICA
SOUTH AMERICA
OCEANIA
Tropic of Cancer
Equator
Tropic of Capricorn
N
0
4000km
Key
Storm wave environments
East coast swell wave environments
Tropical cyclone coasts

Figure 2.17
Cape Horn. For sailors it is one of the world's best known and most feared natural landmarks. Few passages around the Cape are in seas as slight as the one shown. The waters off Cape Horn are notorious for mountainous seas in which waves can reach twice the height of the maximum recorded in Atlantic waters west of Britain.

Figure 2.18
The north-east corner of Easter Island. Lying 4000km away from the nearest inhabited land, this coast is exposed to trade winds with a long fetch.

Within the UK, the west coast is a higher energy coast than the east coast. Westerly is both the prevailing and dominant wind direction; it is also the direction of longest fetch. Maximum wave heights decrease from west to east and from north to south across the British Isles away from exposure to the open ocean and onshore westerly winds (Figure 2.19). Fetch is the limiting factor for the height of waves generated by easterly winds in the North Sea. No matter how long an easterly gale blows, the waves breaking against the east coast can never reach the height of those from westerly gales along the west coast. However, with waves of fifteen and more metres in height occasionally recorded along the coast of Holderness, waves still have the power to cause considerable erosion. The shores of Europe's almost enclosed seas, such as the Mediterranean and Baltic, are low energy coasts in relation to those bordering the Atlantic and North Sea. In the Mediterranean gales occur less often since high pressure dominates the weather for a larger proportion of the year and strong low pressure systems only track south with any regularity during winter. In the Baltic Sea some of the longest examples of constructional coastal landforms in Europe have been formed, mainly because both sheltered waters and low tidal ranges are present (Figure 2.53).

On a smaller scale some estuaries, inlets and bays provide more sheltered environments in which the average wave energy is lower than on the headlands and the more exposed coastal zones are on both sides of them. A change in coastal direction can also reduce average energy levels. Along coastlines that are irregular, waves approaching the headland feel the effects of frictional drag at their base before those which approach the bay. Those in the bay continue to move relatively freely shorewards for longer. Waves around the headland turn inwards and concentrate their attack upon them (this bending of the waves around a headland so that they approach almost parallel to the coast is known as wave refraction, Figure 2.20); whereas waves in the bays spread outwards and dissipate their energy. Differences in wave energy levels are thereby created at the local scale. However, the size of the differences changes with time; as headlands are worn back, less shelter is offered to bays and wave energy again increases.

▼ **Figure 2.19** Maximum wave heights recorded around the British Isles

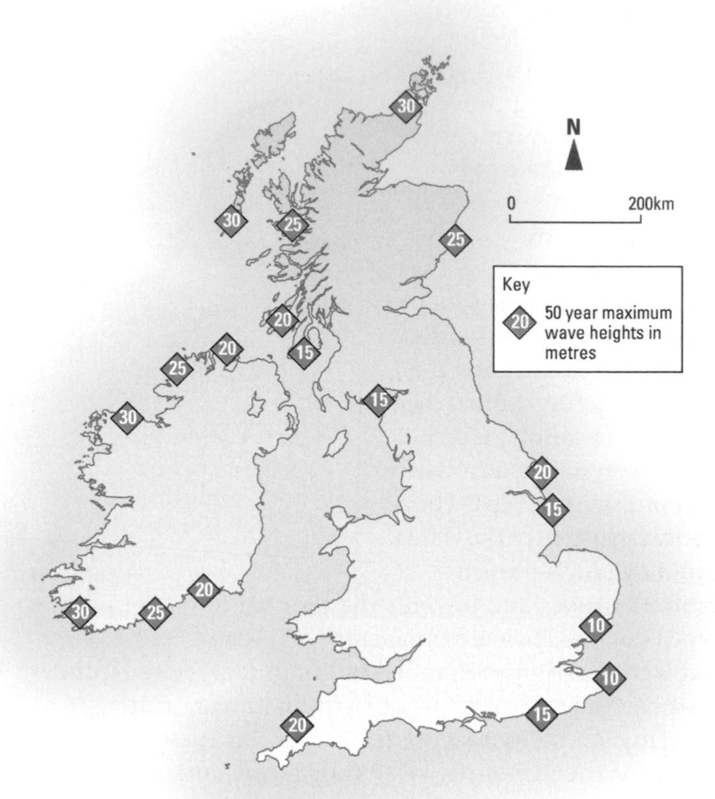

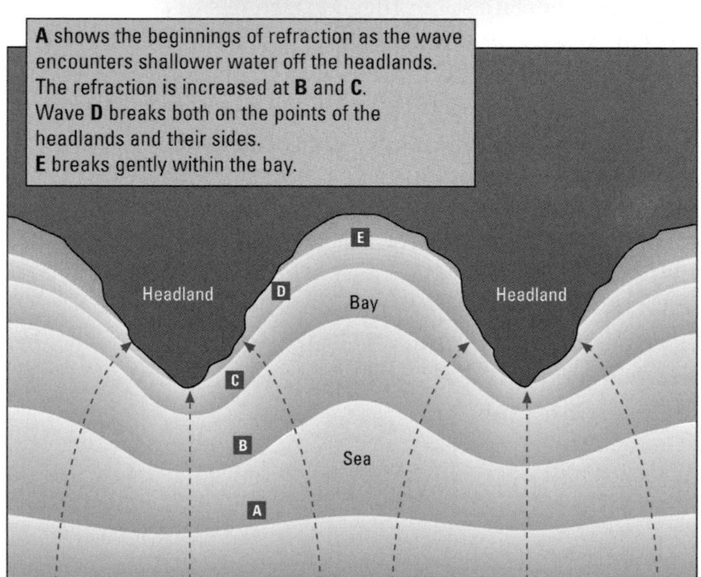

▲ **Figure 2.20** Wave refraction

Other factors influencing coastal erosion

A strong association between high energy coastal environments and high rates of coastal erosion exists. However, wave power alone is insufficient to explain the varying rates of retreat of cliffs and coastlines. Of the other factors that need to be taken into account, rock type is the most important. Is the rock hard or soft? Is it well jointed or well bedded, or is it massive? Is it consolidated or unconsolidated? Is the rock susceptible or not to chemical weathering? There are many permutations. A well-jointed hard rock can be as vulnerable to erosion as an inherently much softer rock which outcrops in a massive block without significant weaknesses. Ancient igneous and metamorphic rocks outcrop along much of the high energy Atlantic coast of the British Isles. These have only survived in their present positions due to their resistance to erosion; otherwise the islands which make up the British Isles would have disappeared millions of years ago. Younger and generally weaker sedimentary rocks outcrop around the coasts of lowland Britain. Of these, chalk resists erosion longer and more successfully than most of the others; weakest of all are the unconsolidated deposits such as boulder clay.

Figure 2.21 Cliff extremes

▶ **a** Land's End, one of the most exposed places to the high energy of Atlantic storm waves. The granite rock is well jointed. It might be expected to be the site of rapid coastal erosion, but the rate of retreat is probably a matter of a few centimetres a year because granite is a hard and tough rock.

▶ **b** Part of the coast of Yorkshire, where the weak boulder clay (glacial till) cliffs are being undercut by waves from below and washed away from above. Annual rates of retreat are measured in metres rather than centimetres.

Structure is another factor. Where major structural weaknesses exist along the west coast, large coastal indentations can be seen. The great inlet of the Bristol Channel occupies a structural depression which has been eroded and infilled by younger sediments, most recently from rivers such as the Severn. To the north, the Pembrokeshire peninsula shows the influence of old hard rocks and powerful folding in the Hercynian mountain building period. To the south, there is the South West peninsula with its strong backbone of granite. In north-west Scotland the presence of faults helps to account for the size of some of the lochs and the separation of the Hebridean islands from the mainland.

Other physical factors that affect rates of marine erosion are cliff height and coastal alignment. The higher the cliff, the greater the pile of loose material is left at its base after every cliff fall. This rock debris offers protection to the base of the cliff preventing further undercutting by the waves until all of it has been removed. Stretches of coast which are aligned so that they face onshore prevailing winds are likely to suffer attack from storm waves more frequently than those which face only dominant winds. This is especially true of west-facing locations where the direction of the prevailing wind and longest fetch coincide. At the local scale humans can speed up erosion. Extending jetties, breakwaters and groynes out to sea deprives the litoral (along the shore) waves of load and increases their potential to erode coasts further down drift.

▲ **Figure 2.22**
Recent rockfall near Ramsgate in Kent affording temporary protection to that part of the cliff against further wave attack

Questions

1 a Make a list of the physical factors that affect rates of marine erosion.

b Explain why
- **i** the British Isles is an area of the world associated with high energy coasts
- **ii** coasts with the highest energy are located on the western sides of the British Isles
- **iii** some of the highest rates of cliff erosion are recorded along the east coast of England.

2 Where and why are low energy coasts present
- **a** within the UK
- **b** elsewhere in Europe, and
- **c** in other parts of the world?

3 **Extended prose**

Explain the causes and effects of spatial and temporal variations in wave energy.

Erosional processes and landforms

Several processes of wave erosion are responsible for undercutting cliff faces. In those places where no beach is present to absorb wave energy, waves break directly against the cliff for a longer period before and after the time of high tide. The hydraulic effect, which is the impact of the water itself, is the basic process. The shock pressure from the weight of water as it is forced forwards and downwards by the breaking wave is enormous. Each breaking event may last for only one or two seconds, but it is not long before the next breaking wave repeats the punishment on the rock face. Since wave energy is proportional to the height of the breaking wave, average pressures are greatest along high energy coasts and greatest of all under storm conditions. All types of rock weaknesses, whether joints, bedding planes or faults, are ruthlessly exploited until blocks of rock are loosened and break away. Softer materials such as deposits of boulder clay and glacial sands can simply be washed away during periods of high wave energy.

A second process, considered by some to be responsible for the greatest coastal erosion, is abrasion. Pebbles, stones and smaller sized particles are stirred up and moved by waves. Breaking waves fling these against the rock face, knocking off protruding edges in hard rocks and loosening outer edges in weak rocks. The greater the size of the breaking wave, the larger its potential load and the greater the damage it can cause. During storms boulders are added to the list of missiles that the waves throw at cliff faces.

Other processes of coastal erosion also contribute. Attrition is the process whereby particles are reduced in size and rounded off by colliding with one another as they are washed along in the waves. Attrition's influence is seen in the smooth appearance of many cliff faces below the high tide mark. It is also thought to be the main process responsible for the rounding off of boulders lying at the head of the beach after detachment from the cliff. The effect of compressed air, sometimes labelled cavitation, is believed to add to the pressures exerted on rock faces by breaking waves. Pockets of air in joints, notches and caves are trapped by the great speed at which waves break. The resulting compression forces out powerful jets of spray upwards on to the rock faces above. Its most likely contribution is to the weakening and break up of jointed rocks. Taken together, marine processes of erosion are so efficient at picking out differences in resistance between soft and hard bands of rock that, by removing the soft rock, the otherwise more resistant bands of hard rock become more exposed and subject to increased levels of wave attack.

Figure 2.23
The effects of wave processes upon Corallian limestone rocks in Filey Bay, Yorkshire

All landscapes are affected by weathering processes. In the coastal zone their main effect is to speed up coastal erosion. The outer surfaces of many coastal cliffs are weakened by chemical and mechanical weathering over many years and although the immediate cause of any cliff collapse is wave erosion by undercutting at the base, the resulting rock fall happens earlier and more abundantly because of these other weathering processes acting as well. The chemical effect of sea water upon rocks merits some consideration, even if its role in landform formation is difficult to gauge and impossible to measure. Basalt is believed to weather more quickly in proximity with sea water than fresh water, which may speed up the formation of the distinctive coastal scenery that it produces (Chapter 3, page 88). So many caves are present around the bases of limestone cliffs that it seems likely that coastal solution plays some part in their formation, even though wave action is undoubtedly the major factor. Chemical weathering helps create the fretted surfaces on many rock platforms (wave-cut platforms) that are made of limestone in the inter-tidal zone.

▲ **Figure 2.24**
Marsden Rock north of Sunderland is made of magnesian limestone. The base shows all the signs of wave erosion, although it is possible that chemical weathering also contributes to its appearance.

▲ **Figure 2.25**
Flamborough Head. At this point the chalk outcrop is thinner. Mass movements have already carried boulder clay down to shore level. Scars on the slopes on the cliff top indicate that mass movement is still occurring, despite the continuous cover of vegetation.

Non-marine processes

The effects of non-marine processes in the coast zone can be observed most clearly on cliff tops. Here various types of weathering and mass movement are the main determinants of morphology, although undermining by waves at the bottom of the cliff encourages earlier and more rapid movement at the top. These are grouped together under the label sub-aerial processes, which literally means 'those occurring at the base of the atmosphere'. In Figure 2.25 the appearance of the cliff top is different from that of the rest of the cliff. The break in angle of slope shows where the dominant influence of sub-aerial processes above is replaced by marine processes operating below. Weathering and mass movement are given separate and more detailed study in Chapter 3 on pages 99–110, so coverage at this point is restricted to the consideration of the ways in which they directly affect landforms in the coast zone.

Heavy rainfall is the trigger for many movements. In coast zones where weak or unconsolidated clays and sands form the surface outcrops, heavy rainfall alone can lead to direct erosion on the cliff face from sheet wash and the flow of rivulets, where surface water movements are concentrated (Figure 2.21b). In times of stronger flow this leads to gulleying. Water seeping into the ground during and after periods of rain produces a saturated mass which slides down the cliff, leaving a pile of loose material at the bottom of the cliff, which the waves at high tide soon remove. In the UK most cliff tops are vegetation covered, which delays but does not stop mass movements. Soil creep is taking place on even the gentlest of slopes, albeit slowly and often imperceptibly. Slides occur from time to time on slopes where surface layers of grass and soil are thin. After periods of prolonged and heavy rainfall, when the ground has absorbed all the water it can take, the weight of the saturated soil becomes too great and it tears away the grass near the top of the slope. Once its hold upon the top of the slope is broken, the mass easily slides over the wet surface below, particularly where it overlies unconsolidated rocks such as boulder clay and glacial sands. This is what is happening in several places on the cliff tops in Figure 2.25.

Slumping is another type of mass movement that occurs in the coast zone. Slumps are distinguished from slides by the element of rotation in the flow of the mass as it moves down a curved slip plane. Many slumps are triggered off by undercutting at the base of the cliffs, so that the mass becomes unsupported. Movement of the mass is encouraged by previous saturation from heavy rains creating a well lubricated plane of movement. Along certain stretches of the English coast local geology is favourable to slumping. At Barton-on-Sea east of Bournemouth in Hampshire sand overlies clay. Rainwater seeping downwards through the sand lubricates the junction with the clay, which encourages slides and slumps. A great series of movements east of Folkestone in 1915, resulting in many thousands of tonnes of chalk collapsing on to the land below and into the sea, altered the appearance of a 500m stretch of coastline (Figure 2.26). The cliffs shown at Beachy Head in Figure 2.1 include a section that has slumped down from the top of the cliff.

▲ **Figure 2.26**
Rotational slumping at Folkestone Warren in Kent. The geology is favourable to movement because unstable Gault clay underlies chalk. After prolonged wet weather, both rocks become saturated and movements are lubricated by underground springs. Massive blocks of chalk moved by spectacular landslides over the years form an undercliff below the main chalk face.

Questions

1. **a** Explain how the different processes of marine erosion operate.
   b Describe and comment upon the effects of marine processes on the rock faces in Figures 2.23 and 2.24.
   c Discuss the factors which lead to high rates of marine erosion along a section of coastline.
2. **a** Define 'sub-aerial processes'.
   b Outline the nature of sub-aerial processes which operate in coastal zones in the UK.
   c From Figures 2.21, 2.25 and 2.26, describe and comment on the evidence for the operation of sub-aerial processes.
   d Give reasons why major cliff collapses, such as the one at Beachy Head in 1999, occur as a result of the combined effects of a number of factors.

Landforms of coastal erosion

The sea cliff is the main landform along coasts where marine erosion is dominant. The basic formation of a sea cliff is the same everywhere. Waves attack the base of newly exposed rock faces. By hydraulic action and abrasion, and the other processes of coast erosion, the base of the cliff is undercut to form a wave-cut notch. The rock face above the effects of wave action begins to overhang. As waves continue their relentless attack upon the base of the cliff, the size of the overhang increases until the weight of the rock above can no longer be supported and a section of the cliff face collapses (Figure 2.22). Active marine erosion begins again at the base of the cliff after the waves have removed the loose rock, leading to further collapses and the gradual retreat inland of the position of the cliff. Therefore every cliff coastline is a sign that land is being lost.

As a consequence of cliff retreat another landform, the wave-cut platform, is formed. This is the rock exposed in the inter-tidal zone at low tide, which slopes gently towards the sea. Its surface is well planed but broken up by numerous furrows, trenches and hollows running in different directions across and through it. The detailed form of the platform is related to the qualities of the rock. On chalk, a relatively soft and homogeneous (uniform) rock, the surface tends to be even with only one or two minor furrows etched into its surface and the platform can be quite broad. Whereas below the granite cliffs of Cornwall, where hardness and massive jointing are the main rock characteristics, any platforms produced are small and irregular due to attacks on the joints. Where rocks have been tilted and folded, and especially if they contain well marked bedding planes, platforms have corrugated surfaces, with ribs of rock standing up a metre or more above the general level of the platform (Figure 2.27a). As the cliff retreats, the platform widens, but at the same time the washing of the waves over the surface, armed with boulders, pebbles and sand, is reducing its level by abrasion. The great selectivity of wave action exploits lines of weakness in the rock and eats into them more quickly. Any trapped deposits of boulders and shingle are reduced in size by attrition which makes their removal easier by the backwash. A wide wave-cut platform affords protection to the cliff faces behind because some of the energy of the waves is consumed before the base of the cliffs is reached. However, this gives only temporary relief because protection is lost after the level of the platform is reduced by abrasion.

Figure 2.27 Landforms at Flamborough Head

◀ **a** Wave-cut platform viewed from near the water's edge at low tide

▼ **b** Natural arch viewed from the same position, but looking towards a promontory of rock leading into the sea

Every rock outcrop has points within it where wave attack is faster and more pronounced. These usually coincide with lines of weakness, notably joints within rocks and faults or bedding planes between bands of rock. Vertical weaknesses such as joints and faults are often starting points for the formation of caves. Having formed a hole in the base of the rock along the weakness by hydraulic action and abrasion, the area of wave attack is widened to the rock on either side, which increases the cave's width. The effects of compressed air are probably significant in extending the height of the cave upwards following the line of weakness. Well-jointed limestone and chalk rocks are often lined by caves at their bases (Figures 2.24 and 2.25).

Where a more substantial weakness is present, usually a fault line, the upward extension of the cave may place so much pressure on the roof that it collapses. Along reasonably straight stretches of coastline the surface collapse leads to long holes called geos and to blow holes. Where the rock outcrops as a promontory into the sea, an intermediate stage occurs when wave attacks on the back of the cave eventually lead to daylight showing through creating a natural arch (Figure 2.27b). The sequence of erosion continues as the base of the arch is subject to wave attack on both sides. This increases the pressure on the top of the arch causing its eventual collapse, particularly if the original line of weakness extends well into the rock which forms the arch. After collapse the seaward support of the arch, which resisted erosion longest, is left as an upstanding outcrop of rock, known as a stack. It is isolated from the mainland and surrounded by sea at least at high tide. A sea stack is therefore the end product of a sequence of erosion which began with the formation of a small cave. As adjacent cliff coasts continue their retreat, stacks are subject to more continuous wave erosion, which eventually leads to their collapse as their bases are sheared off at the level of maximum wave attack. Such rock stumps at or near sea level are great hazards to shipping.

Questions

1 Study Figure 2.28 on page 36.

  a From the photograph of cliffs used in this chapter, choose one example of each of the three types of cliff profiles 1–3 in Figure 2.28

  b For each one, **i** draw a labelled sketch of the cliffs **ii** give reasons for their form.

Figure 2.28 Cliff profiles. Variations in cliff profile reflect:

- rock type and resistance to erosion
- presence or otherwise of lines of weakness
- coastal structure
- whether the cliff is active or inactive.

d Stacks are common showing the same profile, such as the Old Man of Storr in north-west Scotland, made of 600 million-year-old Torridonian sandstone.

1 Vertical cliffs

Few weaknesses are exposed to wave attack. The slow rate of collapse means that rock broken off in cliff collapses can be removed quickly to leave a clean face.

a In homogeneous, hard rocks or resistant rocks such as chalk

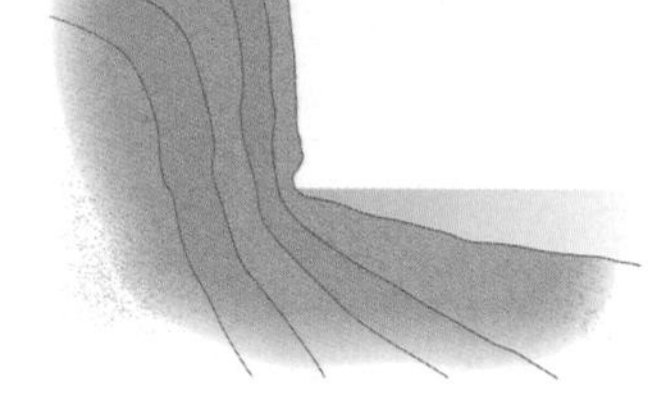

b In resistant rocks with a steep angle of dip towards the sea

c In hard rocks with horizontal beds which lead to jagged, vertical cliff faces

2 Cliffs with variations in steepness

These cliffs are composed of layers of rock with different resistances to erosion.

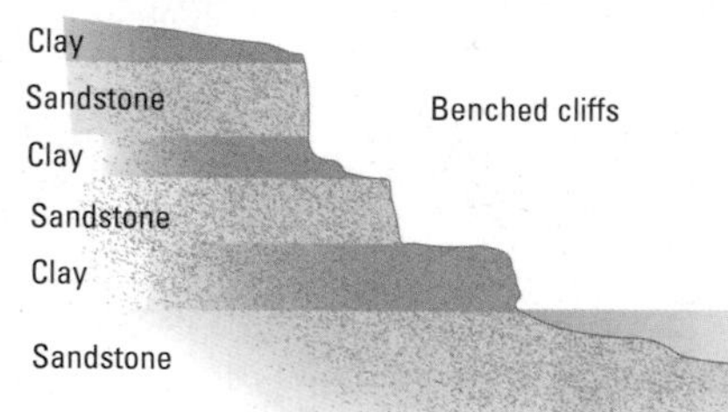

a Benched cliffs with steeper profiles where resistant rocks outcrop. The slope at the base tends to be kept steep by wave action, irrespective of rock hardness.

b Weak rock above and more resistant rock below. The low angle at the top of the cliff is a reflection of weathering and mass movement, whereas the vertical face of the cliff below reflects active undercutting by waves on a more resistant rock upon which a steeper angle can be maintained.

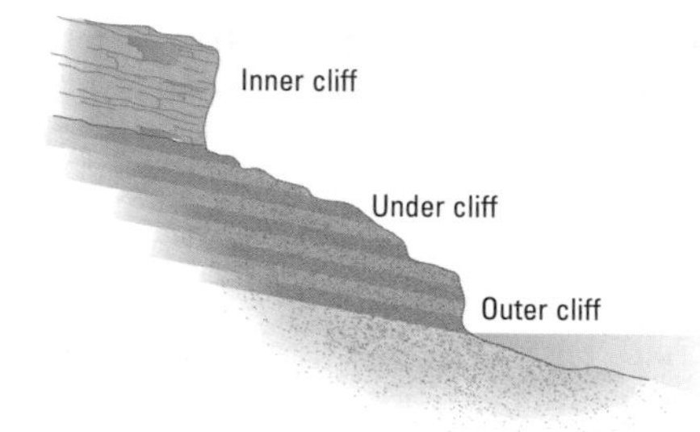

c Resistant rock above and weak rock below. Examples of these cliff profiles are found along the south coast of England and on the Isle of Wight where chalk overlies clay. Water percolates through the chalk to keep the clay below saturated, which provides a lubricated surface along which landslips occur from time to time. Conditions are especially favourable where the dip of the rocks is towards the sea. The chalk forms a more vertical inner cliff than the gently sloping undercliff of clay, which is vertical only on the outer cliff where it is steepened by active wave action.

3 Cliffs with low angles

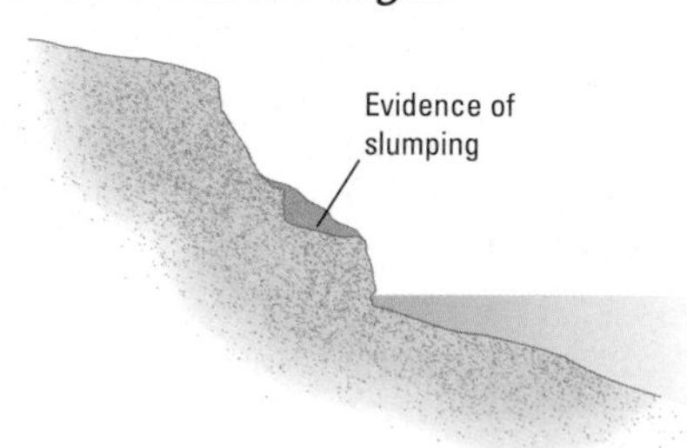

a Outcrops of weak, soft or unconsolidated rocks, such as sands or boulder clay. The rock does not possess the strength to maintain a steep angle. The face often shows evidence of slides and slumps so that the angle of slope varies from top to bottom, as well as from place to place along the same stretch of coastline.

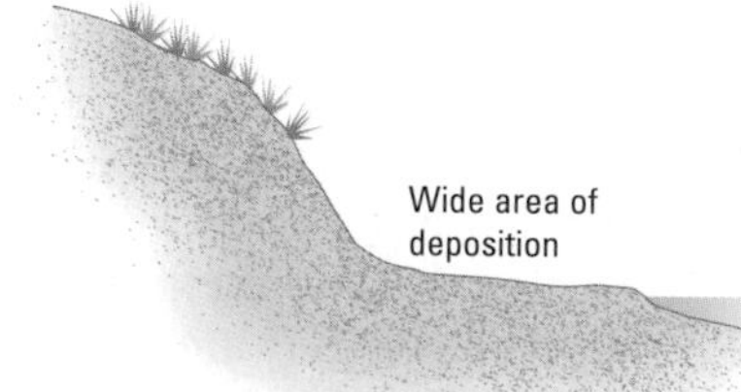

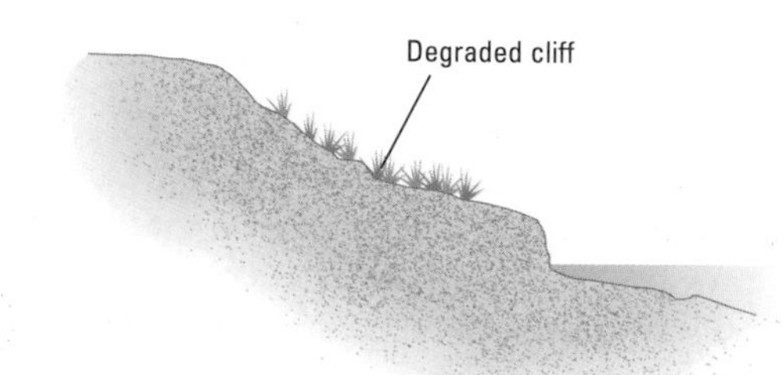

b Inactive cliffs little or unaffected by present wave action. Increasing freedom from wave attack results in a decline in profile steepness.

i Not affected by waves, but still subject to change by weathering and mass movement. However, increasing vegetation cover helps to stabilize the old cliff. The fossil cliffs behind Romney Marsh, a wide zone of deposition, are examples.

ii Only a small part still affected by waves. Present wave action is achieving little beyond steepening the base before the degraded inactive cliff face is reached. This type is sometimes labelled a hog's back cliff.

Coastal plans

Profile is the side view. Plan is the map or aerial view. Both the national and local plans of the coast strongly reflect spatial variations in rates of erosion. Straight coastal plans are most common along stretches of coast dominated by deposition; however, they do occur along coasts of erosion where only one type of rock outcrops. The coast of Holderness is a good example. Deposits of boulder clay, reasonably similar in depth and composition, outcrop along about 60km of straight coast. The coastal plan is also remarkably straight along that stretch of the Sussex coast known as the Seven Sisters. Where dry valleys reach the coast the cliffs are less high, but there has not been the bay development that would normally have been expected in this type of location. In the absence of surface streams and active fluvial erosion, the relief factor has been outweighed by the homogeneous nature of the chalk, which is the dominant factor controlling the coastal plan along this part of the Channel coast.

However, much more common in the British Isles are irregular coastal plans. The irregularity is a reflection of geological structure and variations in rock resistance, which result in the formation of headlands and bays. Geological structure is the basic reason for the great number of headlands and bays around the British coasts. It is predominantly discordant to coastlines so that bands of rock in most places meet the coast at right angles. This is one of the general characteristics of those coastlines which border the Atlantic Ocean. The consequence is that variations within and between bands of rock are open to selective wave attack and differential erosion. Flamborough Head is such a prominent feature along the east coast of Yorkshire, extending the land by ten kilometres, because of chalk's greater resistance to erosion compared with boulder clay, which outcrops to the south in Holderness. However, Flamborough Head is not the one smooth headland that it appears to be on atlas maps. There are several individual headlands and bays within it due to variations in the thickness of the chalk and in the closeness of joints and bedding planes (Figure 2.29). Caves, arches and stacks are other prominent landforms of erosion commonly associated with headlands. The bay is often the larger and more visible sign of coastal erosion, formed where a weaker rock is sandwiched between two more resistant outcrops of rock. Rock weakness is often a direct reflection of relative hardness, but any combination of other factors such as well bedded, heavily jointed and severely folded or faulted rock may also contribute and on occasions be more important. Figure 2.30 shows the geological control over the formation of Swanage Bay.

▼ **Figure 2.29** Headlands and bays within Flamborough Head

Questions

1 **a** Explain the formation of sea cliffs and wave-cut platforms.
b Examine ways in which geological structure can speed up cliff collapse and retreat.

2 **a** Identify three factors which affect cliff profiles.
b For each one, analyse its effects.

3 **a** Study Figures 2.27a, 2.27b and 2.29. Describe the coastal features of Flamborough Head.
b Explain the presence of a variety of cliff profiles and landforms around Flamborough Head.

The Purbeck coast of Dorset

Case Study

dominated by erosion

▼ **Figure 2.30** Simplified summary of the geology of the area

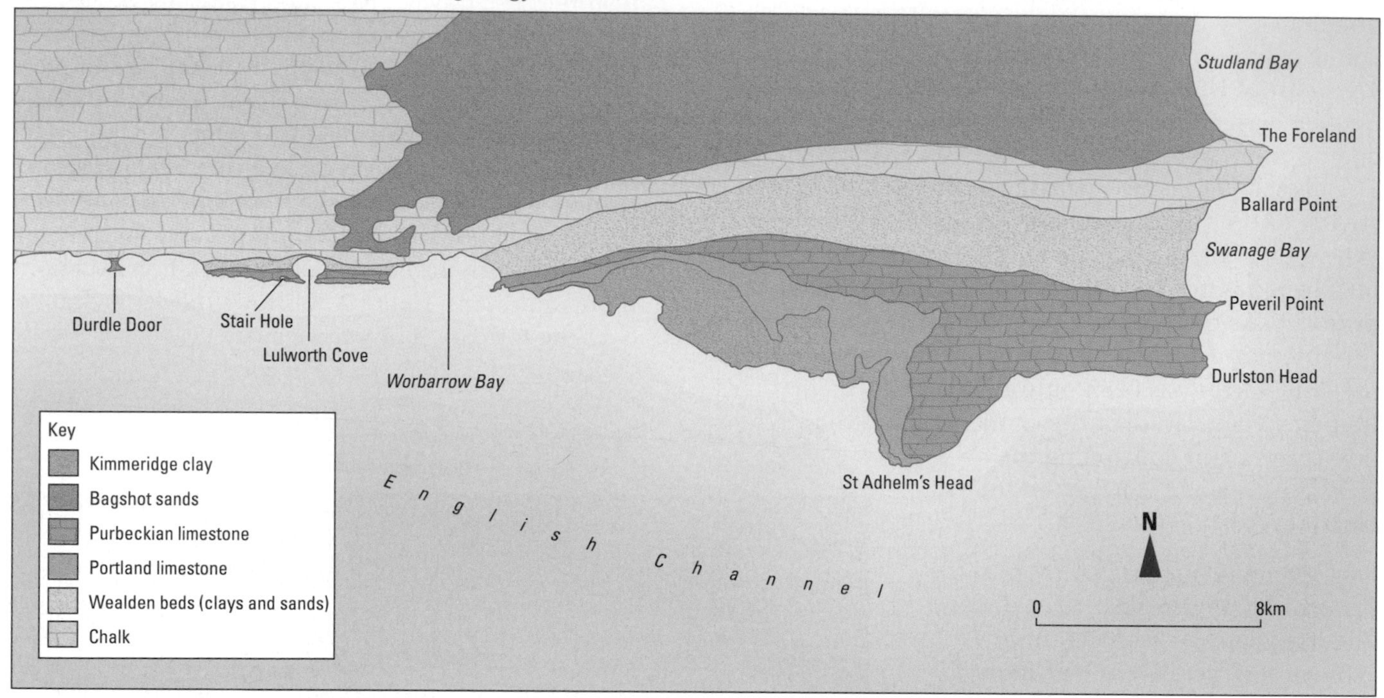

Discordant coastline

▲ **Figure 2.31** The Purbeck coast of Dorset

Questions

1. Study the OS map in Figure 2.32.
   - **a** Draw an annotated sketch map to show the main coastal landforms.
   - **b** Indicate on it the variations in height of the sea cliffs.
   - **c** Draw a sketch profile of Ballard Cliffs.
2. Study Figure 2.31.
   - **a** Identify the map locations of the features shown on the photograph.
   - **b** Draw a sketch profile of the cliffs shown.
3. Explain the inter-relationships between geology, inland relief and coastal landforms.
4. As a brief summary, explain why this is a coastline of headlands and bays.
5. Measurements of erosion rates at Ballard cliffs indicate an average rate of retreat of 0.23m per year. The equivalent rate at Beachy Head is 1.06. Suggest why rates of erosion for the same type of rock are different.

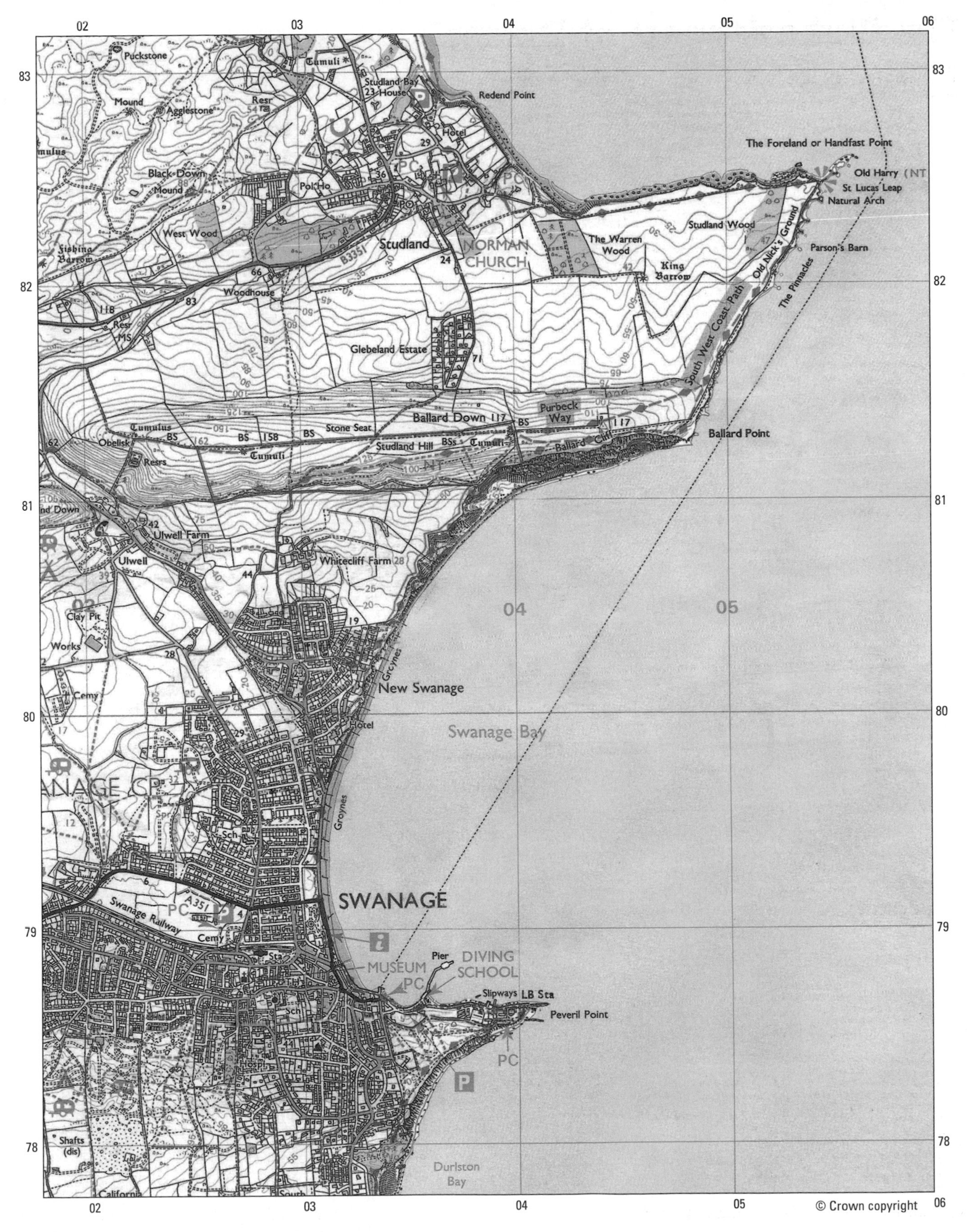

▲ **Figure 2.32** 1:25,000 OS map of Swanage Bay

Concordant coastline

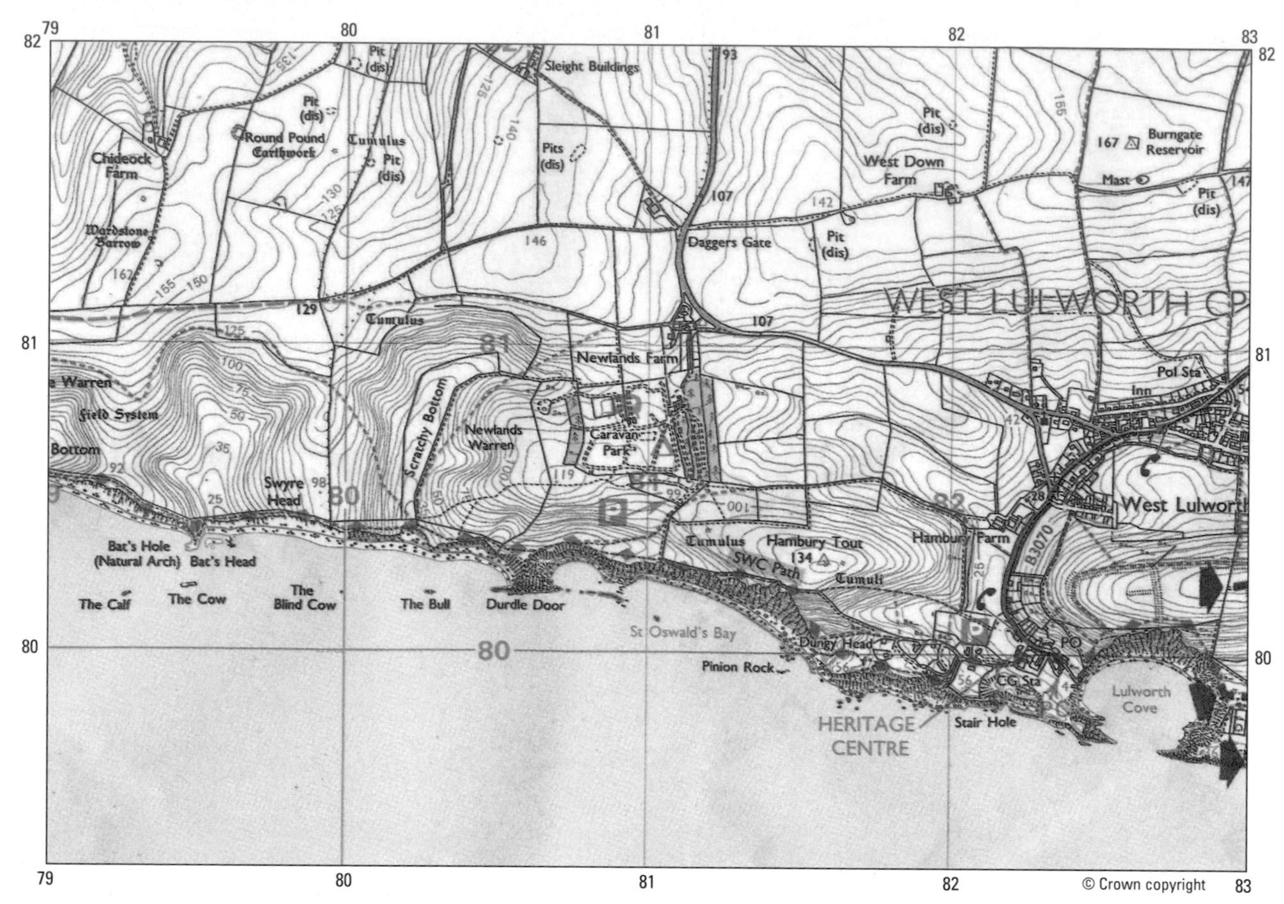

▲ **Figure 2.33** 1:25,000 OS map of the Dorset coast near Lulworth

▶ **Figure 2.34** Stair Hole

◀ **Figure 2.35** Stair Hole and Lulworth Cove

There are relatively few examples within the British Isles where the geological structure is concordant to the coast, but the Dorset coast west of Swanage is one of them. The alignment of rock outcrops (such as the Bull and Calf rocks) parallel to the shoreline is more typical of coasts which border the Pacific Ocean. Although many similar coastal landforms of erosion are produced, there are some differences in appearance. A study of the Dorset coastline is made all the more interesting because it is possible to observe the stages in the sequence of coastal erosion at different points along the coast which are relatively close to one another.

The early stages can be seen in that stretch of coastline near Lulworth Cove. Find the Stair Hole in Figure 2.33 first. Here the limestone ridge has been breached, but not removed. Weaknesses in the ridge were exploited by waves, which opened up access to the next layer of rock which is softer. The limestone has been left exposed as a narrow ridge while the less resistant Wealden sands and clays behind it have been more rapidly eroded (Figure 2.34). Wave erosion is now concentrated in a west to east direction following the line of the weaker Wealden beds. Inland the cliff tops are being attacked by sub-aerial processes leading to gulleying and slumping in the weak sands and clays (Figure 2.35).

Next examine Lulworth Cove on the map. This symmetrical bay is more circular and more enclosed than those typically found along discordant coastlines. This is because it has been easier for the waves to extend it in a west to east direction following the line of the less resistant Wealden beds. The gap in the limestone across the entrance is its narrowest part, while rates of erosion on the chalk at the back of the bay are lower than those on the sands and clay at the sides. Further west St. Oswald's Bay shows what happens next. This is a double bay formed by the amalgamation of two coves. The only sign that remains of the limestone barrier that formerly protected the coast from erosion is the line of rock stacks east from Durdle Door. The final stage, the return of an almost straight coastline, is exemplified by the stretch of coast west of Durdle Door. Apart from the rock promontory and natural arch at Durdle Door (Figure 2.36), the only remnants of the limestone ridge are out to sea in the Bull and Calf rocks (Figure 2.37). So much of the Wealden beds have gone that the face of the chalk ridge is being attacked in what is virtually a uniform manner.

▲ **Figure 2.36** Durdle Door

▲ **Figure 2.37** The Bull and Calf rocks

Questions

1 What is the difference between 'plan' and 'profile' in the study of coasts?

2 a Why do stretches of coast with irregular plans dominate in many places in the British Isles?
  b Explain how and why irregular coastal plans often become straighter with time.

3 Study Figure 2.38 which shows a section of the coast of Northumberland near St. Abb's Head.
  a Describe the characteristics of the coastal rocks as far as they can be observed from the photograph.
  b Draw labelled sketches to show cliff profile and coastal plan.
  c Suggest reasons for what you have described and drawn.

▲ **Figure 2.38** Coast of Northumberland

Sea level changes and coastal landforms

Worldwide climate change during the last ten thousand years has meant rising sea levels. This is the result of ice melting after the Great Ice Age had released its grip upon the northern parts of North America, Europe and Asia. In areas of higher relief in the British Isles the effects of sea level changes are confined to valleys. Here, drowning has created more heavily indented coastlines and increased the number of islands. Where the coastal structure is discordant, rias (drowned river valleys) and fiords (drowned glaciated valleys) are the two principal landforms. Along coastlines with a concordant structure, the most distinctive feature formed by drowning are islands aligned parallel to the coast. The clearest example is the Dalmatian coast in the Adriatic Sea, most of which is now included within the republic of Croatia (Figure 2.39c). The simple separation into discordant and concordant coasts works for the majority of examples of drowned coastlines, but not for all. In southern Chile, the Andes mountains run north to south parallel to the Pacific Ocean in a concordant manner. Rises in sea level have created masses of islands. However, deep, penetrating fiords are also present, carved by ice when the glaciers and ice caps of Patagonia were more extensive than they are today. So broken is the coastal relief that land communications within Chile between the southern city of Punta Arenas and all other regions north of it are impossible.

Drowned river valleys – rias

Ria estuaries are dominant features of the coastal plans of south-west England, south-west Ireland and Brittany. The form of each ria is largely controlled by structure. Long, simple inlets are found where rivers follow the lines of weak beds of rock as in south-west Ireland, whereas many branched estuaries are frequent in Cornwall. For the latter, the course of the main river valley was cut across rocks of varying resistance. This forms the ria's straight main arm; the courses of tributary rivers, which followed beds of weaker rocks and flowed at right angles to the main river, form the branches.

▼ **Figure 2.39** Form (morphology) of different types of drowned coastlines

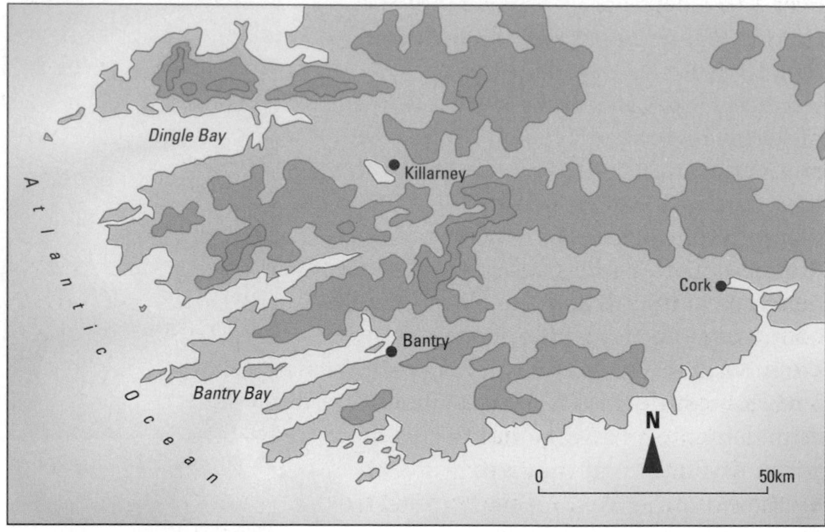

a South-west Ireland

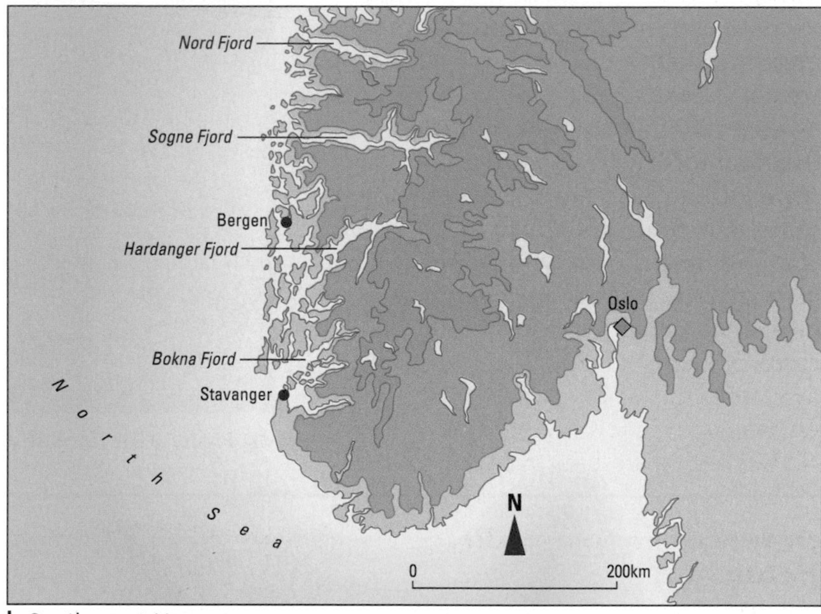

b South-west Norway

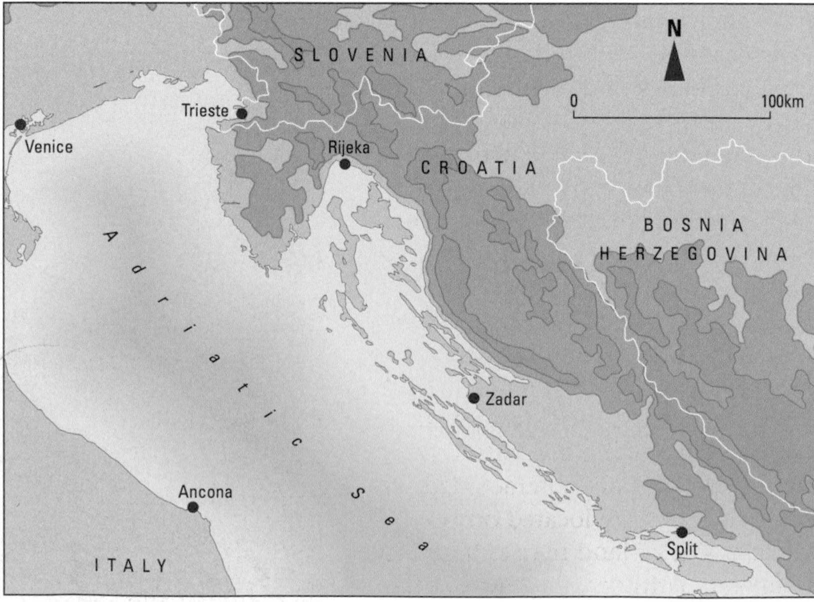

c The Dalmatian coast of Croatia

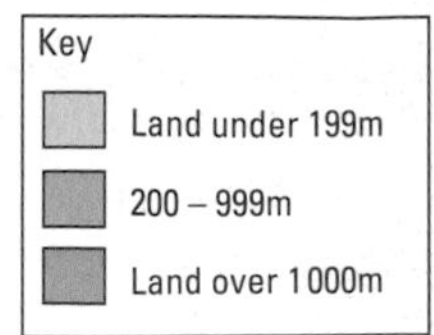

Relief and rates of deposition are the important controls over a ria's depth and its prominence as a landscape feature. Rias in south-west England are large; their length, width and depth make them significant coastal features. Slopes above are often quite steep. The majority of the rivers flowing through them are draining granite moorlands; the resistance of granite to erosion greatly restricts the size of river loads. Limited estuarine deposition means that many deep natural harbours are present, although width, depth and distance of penetration inland pose considerable problems for land communications. In contrast rias in south-east England are less impressive landscape features. In Essex and Suffolk most rias are nothing more than broad shallow estuaries, composed of a maze of creeks and shallow winding inlets. At low tide their appearance is dominated by the exposure of extensive tracts of mud and marsh. Deposited materials are widely and readily available for transport by rivers. Estuaries along the south coast, such as those of the Adur and Ouse, have been infilled by great thicknesses of alluvium derived from tributary streams flowing across clay vales. What were once estuaries now contain fifteen metres or more of river deposits; the flat areas created look more like flood plains. Therefore deposition leading to aggradation is an important process in and around the ria estuaries of southern and eastern England. Marine transgressions associated with rising sea levels have contributed to the deposition of extensive areas of silts and muds by carrying onshore fine sediments which are plentifully available on the bed of the North Sea. In these wetland environments the accumulation of peat and spread of marshland vegetation are favoured.

Drowned glaciated valleys – fiords

The basic morphology of a fiord is that of a glaciated valley. Therefore it is characterized by a U-shaped valley cross section and a markedly irregular long profile. The only difference is that the lower part of the valley has been drowned, often to a considerable depth. Rock basin measurements in some Norwegian fiords have revealed depths over 1000m. The seaward limit of fiords is marked by shallower water above a rock threshold. Fiords have a specialized world distribution, which gives clues to the formation of such large-scale coastal landforms. One significant common characteristic is position. They are located on the western side of land masses in temperate latitudes. Another is that they are on the edge of mountainous areas. Such areas are thought to have coincided with the areas of highest snowfall during glacial periods. Mountain glaciers were thick because of plentiful snow and ice accumulation. Speed of descent towards sea level was rapid because of high ice budgets and steep relief. Additional ice was likely to have been supplied from ice sheets covering plateaus in the adjacent mountains. Therefore for a variety of reasons, the glaciers which carved these valleys were of exceptional depth and velocity, which made them capable of selective and intense erosion by the glacial processes of abrasion and plucking (Chapter 4, pages 130–31). Removal of so much rock from valley floors and sides would have triggered the operation of the pressure release mechanism, thereby further weakening the surface rock and making it even more susceptible to plucking.

The presence of some of the deepest fiords probably coincides with the existence of lines of geological weakness, notably fault lines. Post-glacial infilling from river deposition occurs and can be noticed most at the heads and sides of fiords through the presence of alluvial fans and deltas. Here the velocity of streams cascading down the steep fiord sides is reduced where it meets a large water mass – the ocean – leading to deposition. Fiords, however, are on a different scale to most rias, which means that infilling is restricted to certain favoured locations and rugged relief continues to dominate, especially on the edge of mountainous areas where glaciers are still present.

▼ **Figure 2.40** Drygalski fiord in South Georgia in the South Atlantic – wide, deep, rugged and coloured by glacial moraine

Submerged valleys in low-lying Denmark (maximum height is less than 200m above sea level) are called fjards. It seems most likely that these long valleys were eroded by meltwater streams flowing in tunnels under the ice. Their morphology has more in common with British rias than Norwegian fiords. The Frisian Islands off the northern coast of the Netherlands are remnants of a belt of sand dunes which formed an old coastline. They were breached by the post-glacial rise in sea level to leave the current line of sandy islands, separated from the mainland by either shallow sea water or marsh. River estuaries further east, such as those of the Ems and Weser, are large and out of proportion to the size of the streams which occupy them today, suggesting drowning.

▲ **Figure 2.41**
A group of 'A' level Geography students undertaking fieldwork on the raised beach in Arran. The former line of sea cliffs is visible behind them.

Exposed coastal landforms

Flooding obscures many minor relief features, whereas relative rises in land levels expose small-scale coastal landforms previously partly or totally covered by sea water. It appears contradictory that sea lochs drowned by rises in sea level should be present in the same areas in western Scotland as raised beaches and fossil cliff lines from rising land levels. However, the eustatic and isostatic processes responsible for changes in relative levels of land and sea operate independently of one another (page 23). Post-glacial isostatic recovery has exceeded general eustatic sea level rises in northern and western Scotland because of the thickness of the ice sheets that covered the area during the Pleistocene ice age. The most prominent and widely observable landform in the British Isles (and elsewhere) is the raised beach. Average height increases northwards from just one or two metres around the sides of Morecambe Bay in Lancashire to a general height of between eight and ten metres in northern Scotland. The narrow coastal platform created is widely used as a site for roads and settlements. There is a marked contrast between its level surface and the rugged and steep relief which characterizes the coast of the Scottish Highlands. In places fossil beach deposits can be found, although these are not usually preserved for a long time. More easily recognized are the fossil cliffs located a little way inland from the present shoreline. Despite having lost some of their vertical form through the action of weathering processes, their marine origins are confirmed by the signs of caves and notches at their bases.

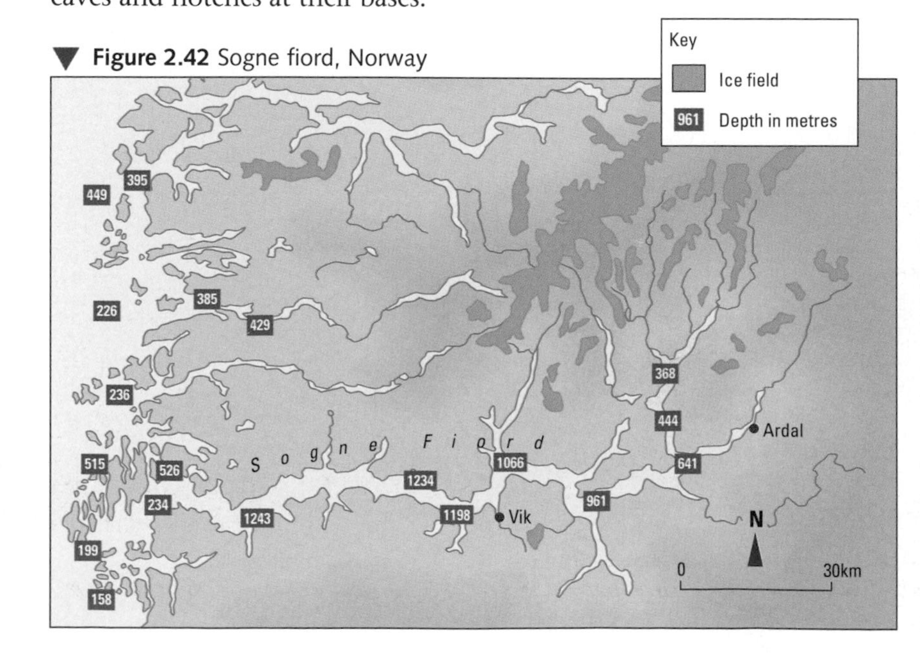

▼ **Figure 2.42** Sogne fiord, Norway

Questions

1 Study a physical map of the world in an atlas.
   a On an outline map of the world, show the distribution of fiord coastlines and name them.
   b Describe the common features of their locations.
   c Explain the world distribution.

2 Study the maps of the Sogne fiord in Figure 2.42 and the coast of southern Norway in Figure 2.39b.
   a i What is the evidence for the existence of a threshold at the mouth of the Sogne fiord?
   ii State some significant dimensions to illustrate this fiord's great size and scale.
   b Outline and comment on the main physical features of this part of Norway's fiord coastline.
   c Investigate the opportunities and problems of the fiord coastline for Norway and its people.

3 Identify the similarities and differences between the coasts shown in Figure 2.39 and suggest reasons for them.

Depositional processes and landforms

To visitors to the coast, landforms of deposition such as beaches and spits have a look of permanency about them. They have taken many years to form. However, coastlines of deposition are no less dynamic than those of erosion; it is simply that short-term changes are not so obvious and less easy to observe. Beach deposits are continually reworked by waves, tides and currents. Along every coast there is a preferred direction of sediment movement or litoral drift (Figure 2.15). Within the general pattern there are variations where the local operation of tides and currents over-rides the general direction of movement; for example, along parts of the north Norfolk coast, drift is from east to west (page 28). Constructive waves are the ones most associated with deposition (page 52). Along any stretch of coast, a constructive wave has the same amount of total energy as a destructive wave; but because it is a longer wave, it arrives over a longer period of time so that the energy released upon breaking is more dispersed. By breaking gently forwards the swash up the beach is emphasized and the backwash is reduced. Constructive waves are present for a greater proportion of the year along those coasts which do not face prevailing or dominant wind directions.

Load availability is an important control over the amount of deposition. Within the British Isles, it is greatest along those parts of the east coast where rapid erosion of the boulder clay cliffs is combining with high rates of deposition by rivers crossing lowland areas of weak rocks and plentiful surface deposits. Even human actions have helped, as for example where waste from the coastal coal mines in County Durham was for a time tipped directly into the North Sea. Deposition begins at a bend or a break in the coastline commonly associated with an estuary, inlet or bay. How quickly sediment accumulates depends upon the complex inter-relationships in any locality between amount of load, strength of currents, tidal movements, and depth of water. Sediment deposition is likely to be most rapid and more permanent in those locations where load is large, currents are weak and the water offshore is shallow. The direction of deposition is largely a reflection of coastal alignment and the strength of inshore currents. Along some coastlines deposition follows and hugs the coast, whereas in others it is directed outwards into the open sea.

Landforms of coastal deposition

The basic landform is the beach. The beach is the zone of deposition between high and low tidal limits, which shelves downwards towards the sea. In theory it can be made of anything left behind by the waves at the point where the tide turns. On British beaches the turning point is often marked by a line of plastic bottles, tin cans, driftwood and shells in varying proportions. The nature of beach deposits is also on occasions a direct reflection of local economic activity, hence the former black (coal) beaches of County Durham and the present timber and log beaches found around some shores in the Baltic. But most commonly the two deposits are sand (with grains between one sixteenth and 2mm in size) and pebbles (above 4mm and up to 64mm or more). Granule sizes between sand and pebbles are poorly represented.

The idealized model splits a beach into two parts. The lower beach is characterized by a gentle gradient, often as low as 3 degrees or less, because it is most likely to be built of fine grained sand and mud. Minor features include ripples, ridges and runnels. Ripples form patterns in the sand which indicate where sand is moved to and fro by waves and currents. Ridges of sand tend to run parallel to the shoreline and are separated by elongated puddles of sea water in the runnels, which are left exposed as the tide goes out.

The upper beach can usually be distinguished by its steeper profile. Gradients in the order of between 10 and 20 degrees are more typical which reflects its

▲ **Figure 2.43**
The lower beach on Studland spit, lying on the southern side of the entrance to Poole Harbour in Dorset

composition of coarser sediments such as shingle and pebbles. Ridges form in the shingle and maintain their position longer than minor features in the sandy part. Highest of all is the storm ridge, lying above the level reached by highest spring tides. Below at different levels are beach ridges called berms. Where the shingle and sand parts of a beach meet, beach cusps form, although these are more temporary features. These cusps, or 'headlands' of shingle, sometimes protrude down the beach and are about a metre higher than the 'bays' of sand that form in the lower beach between them.

Figure 2.44
Sandwood Bay in north-west Scotland, looking northwards in the direction of Cape Wrath. Both the upper and lower beaches are built of sand, which makes for similar profiles.

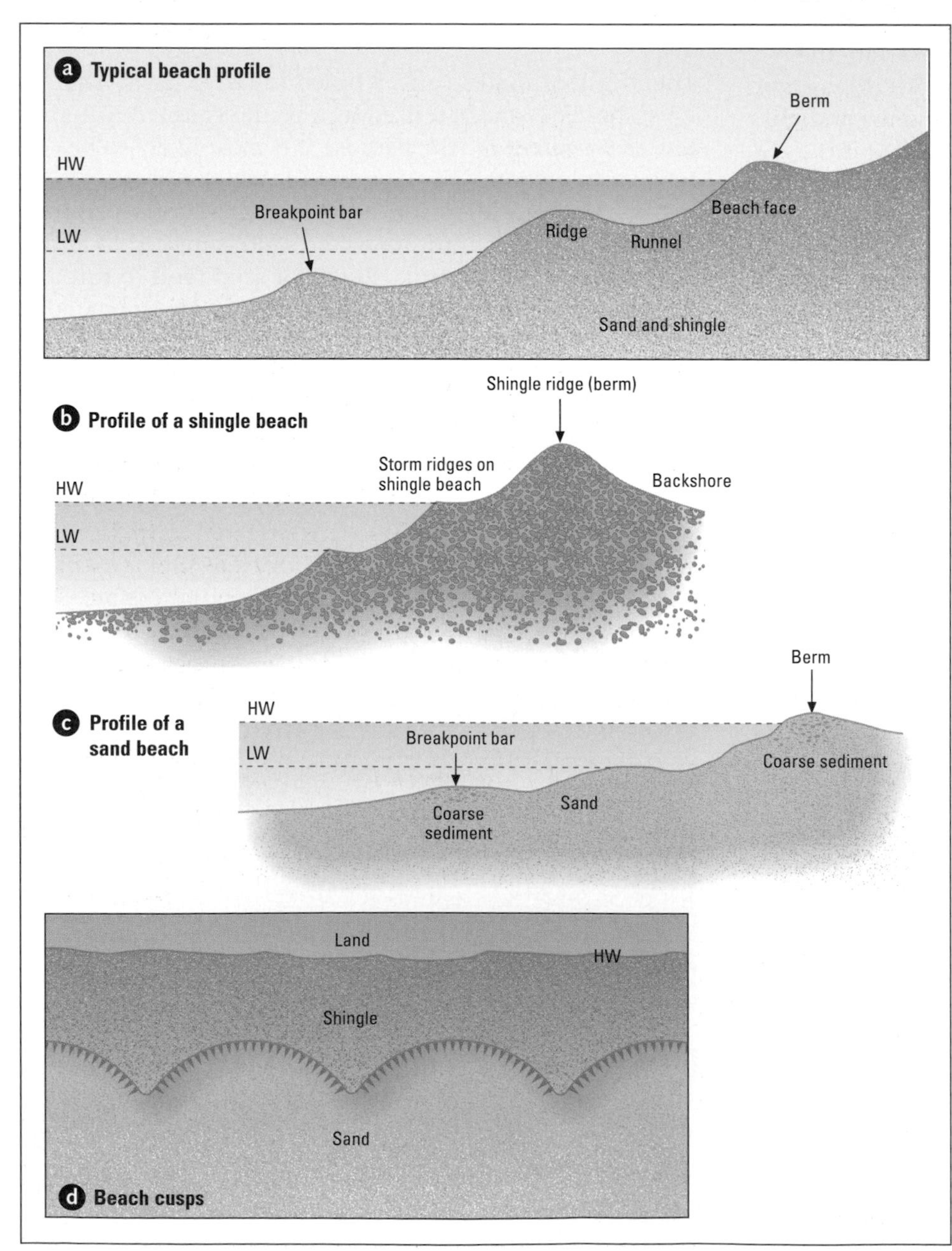

Figure 2.45 Beach profiles and beach features

In practice many beaches are all sand or all shingle rather than a mixture. Some sandy beaches are almost flat. Waves break some distance away from the shoreline at the break point bar and the swash travels up the beach as surf. Any significant steepening of the beach profile is always more likely to occur near the head of the beach, because deposition of coarser materials is more likely to occur at points where high tide waves break. A wide area of exposed foreshore, which allows the sand to dry out at low tide, forms a perfect environment for onshore winds to have an impact by building up sand dunes beyond the tidal limit. Whereas all-shingle beaches, such as Chesil Beach in Dorset, are steep and ridged in form (Figure 2.45b). Ridges occur at significant points for wave activity, such as around the mean turning points for high and low tides, and at positions where notable storms, driven by onshore winds, have reached. However, on Chesil Beach there is also a spatial variation with mean pebble sizes increasing from about pea size in the west to an average of 50mm in diameter in the east, probably in accordance with greater exposure to storm waves. In the east this results in the beach slope increasing to the high angle of 26° at the point near to Portland, where the top of the beach is more than twelve metres above the mean high water mark.

Beach profiles also change between summer and winter in the British Isles. The summer beach is wider and has a more generous cover of sand or shingle. Storm waves are less frequent which gives more time for constructive waves to re-nourish the beach. In winter, deposits which form the lower beach are more vulnerable to removal by destructive waves, although the area above the inter-tidal zone can be attacked under storm conditions. This area of summer deposition and winter removal is known as the sweep zone. One big winter storm can have a tremendous impact. Within 24 hours many east coast beaches were lowered by one metre or more during the notorious North Sea storm surge of 31 January 1953 (page 27).

▲ **Figure 2.46** The steep profile and ridges of shingle beach east of Bournemouth

▼ **Figure 2.47** Robin Hood's Bay, a few kilometres south of Whitby

a Part of the wide rocky platform exposed at low tide. Note the dip of the rocks towards the left (north).

The commonest location for a beach is at the head of a bay, where a natural sediment trap for material drifting from both directions is formed by the enclosing headlands. Accumulation continues for as long as the headlands remain sufficiently prominent to give protection. Not all bays therefore have a beach, however. The entire length of Robin Hood's Bay on the Yorkshire coast, for example, is subject to erosion; every high tide reaches the base of the cliffs at the back of the bay which makes significant sediment accumulation impossible. The most imposing landform in the inter-tidal zone within the bay is the wave-cut platform, with its rock scars domed according to structure (Figure 2.47).

b Although the cliffs that form the headland on the northern side of the bay are tall and impressive landscape features, the horizontal layers of shale and sandstone of which they are composed are highly susceptible to marine erosion. The headland gives only limited protection to the boulder clay deposits which form the bay. Coastal defence works are also visible (see page 61).

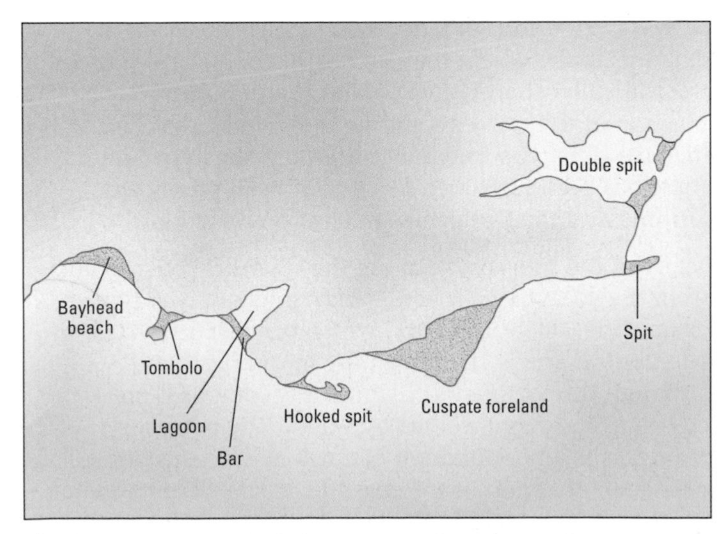

▲ **Figure 2.48** One classification of coastal landforms of deposition

Spits and bars

Spits and bars are long ridges of sand and shingle. A spit is attached to land at one end, the proximal end, and finishes in open sea, the distal end. A bar extends across the mouth of a bay, sometimes reaching the other side and sealing off its entrance. However, there are many variations upon this simple two-fold classification. Spits vary in both shape and alignment (see below). The entrance to Poole harbour in Dorset is unusual in having a spit extending from both its northern and southern sides, which forms a double spit. Chesil Beach is called a tombolo because its shingle ridge links the mainland to an island (Portland). Some ridges are more clearly separated from the mainland and form offshore spits and bars such as Scolt Head Island off the coast of Norfolk (page 53). All spits and bars interfere with free drainage from the land behind them. At first lagoons are formed; however, in these sheltered environments the continued build up of sand and mud is encouraged, which in turn allows vegetation growth and the evolution of marshland communities. The net result can be significant seaward extensions of land, as at Dungeness along the Channel coast, where the name cuspate foreland is used for the triangular shaped area of land that has formed. The position of the former coastline is indicated by a line of inactive cliffs. The wetland of Romney Marsh in front of these has been reclaimed for human uses, principally farming and the Dungeness nuclear power station.

▲ **Figure 2.49**
View looking towards the mainland from the offshore bar in Virginia, USA. This forms part of the prominent landform which runs for much of the length of the east coast of the USA.

Many of the spits visible along the Channel coast diverge from the coast to grow at a marked angle to it. A classic example is Hurst Castle spit, which has reached a state of equilibrium and is changing little in overall shape, although the sediments of which it is composed are constantly being re-worked by waves. The two classic pre-requisites for the formation of a spit exist at this point. The change in direction of the coastline at the western end of the Solent encouraged initial deposition. A well loaded longshore drift, carrying sediments gained from erosion of sandy rock outcrops further west, allowed continued accumulation. The main part of the ridge, aligned basically from west to east, is about two and a half kilometres long and is well adapted to the prevailing winds from the south west. The distal end is hooked and contains several recurved ridges of shingle. This end is subject to stronger wave action in progressively deeper sea water. Additionally its exposure to occasional winds from the north and north east which blow down the Solent is responsible for the recurving. However, this widens its adaptation to physical conditions and increases its stability. It remains a permanent feature of today's coastline, although minor adjustments, notably a gradual shift eastwards in its position, are continuing.

Spits found along the east coast of England more characteristically run approximately parallel to the coast, which enables them to build up ridges of greater length. One example is Orford Ness in Suffolk, which is over 15km long. The course of the slow-flowing River Alde has been extended southwards over the centuries by the same amount (Figure 2.51). This form of spit is not unique to the east coast. At Shoreham on the Channel coast west of Hove, the course of the River Adur is diverted eastwards by the spit growing from the west across its mouth. The longer this type of spit grows, the less stable it becomes. The likelihood of breaching by vigorous wave attack during storms and by river flood water becomes increasingly likely. If a breach is not rapidly healed by the longshore drift and waves of a constructive nature, the broken end of the spit in open water is eventually washed away by the wave action.

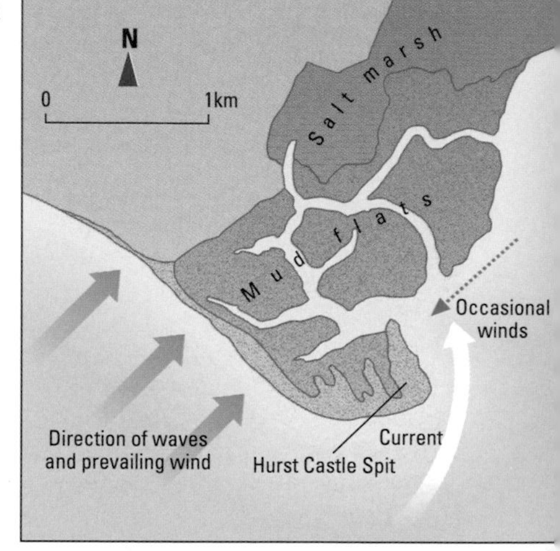

▲ **Figure 2.50**
Hurst Castle spit

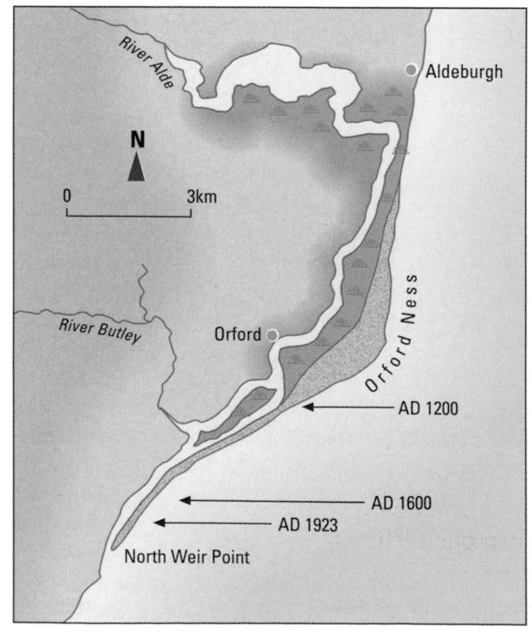

◀ **Figure 2.51**
Orford Ness. The spit grew first across the mouth of the River Alde and later that of the River Butley. Before about 1200 Orford was a sea port facing the open sea.

> **Spits and bars**
>
> *Favourable conditions for growth:*
> - *bend or change in direction of the coastline*
> - *plentiful load*
> - *active longshore drift*
> - *environments favouring constructive waves.*
>
> *Factors for reducing or stopping growth:*
> - *reduction in the supply of sand and shingle*
> - *deeper water*
> - *stronger river and tidal currents*
> - *more exposure to storm waves.*

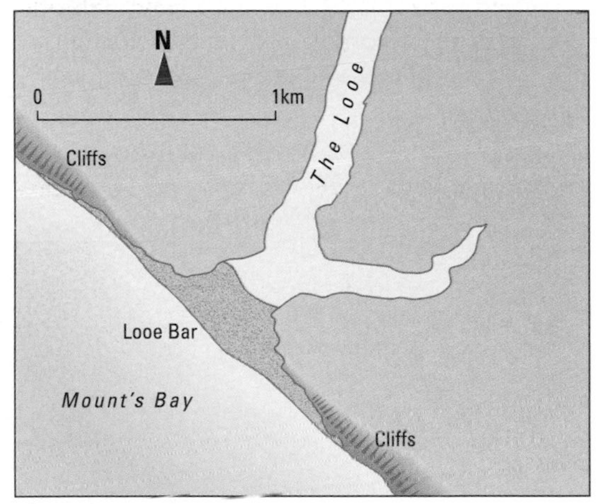

▲ **Figure 2.52**
Looe Bar. The shingle ridge completely encloses the Looe (or Pool), the water escaping through an artificial tunnel. The ridge lies appreciably above the level reached by the highest tides, which suggests that the shingle deposition by the longshore drift was supplemented by shingle flung onto it by storm waves.

Questions

1 Identify and comment on the factors used to classify coastal landforms of deposition in Figure 2.48.

2 Describe the general characteristics of coastal locations favourable for the formation of landforms of deposition.

3 a Outline the main elements of a beach profile.
  b Explain why beach profiles vary
   i between winter and summer in the same location
   ii between one section of coastline and another.

Methods of formation for bars are similar to those for spits, except that highly sheltered coastal environments are favoured where any streams flowing into the bay are small and have weak flows. This allows rates of sediment accumulation to exceed those of removal by river and sea currents. Small examples are found in many places around the British coast; perhaps Looe Bar in Cornwall (Figure 2.52) and Slapton Ley in Devon are among the best known nationally. Much longer spits and bars form along the southern shores of the Baltic Sea (Figure 2.53), where average wave energy is reduced by its enclosed nature and tidal ranges are low. Coastal deposition is making the coast of the Baltic smoother and straighter.

It is less easy to offer fully satisfactory explanations for the double spit at Poole Harbour and for the offshore features along the north coast of Norfolk. One explanation suggested for the former is longshore drift that is operating from two directions. The normal Channel drift from west to east is responsible for the larger spit growing from the south and a local drift from east to west is forming the smaller northern spit. In such a sheltered environment as this, the relative effects of the westerly winds may be diminished and those of the easterlies would be enhanced beyond normal levels. However, given the difficulty of finding other evidence to prove the existence of an easterly drift in the area, an alternative theory is that it represents the remains of a bay bar that was later breached by storm waves.

Along the north Norfolk coast there are spits and bars both onshore and offshore. Scolt Head Island is the most fully developed offshore feature (Figure 2.59). This low ridge of sand and shingle appears to have grown from east to west and therefore in the opposite direction to the general longshore drift down the east coast of England. Further east the spit at Blakeney Point is another westward pointing spit. The great mass of offshore glacial deposits are thought to be the principal sediment source. On a gently sloping shoreline such as this, waves break long before they reach the coast. The waves' rotating action excavates material from the sea bed, from which bars are built offshore. These are ultimately built up to a point where their tops are above sea level. As waves erode and re-work material from the outside of the bar, there is a tendency for the bar to move inland, gradually silting up the lagoon behind it and encouraging marsh development. It is possible that the westward pointing spits are built from sediments already present offshore that are being re-worked by local marine currents and drifts, rather than from newly supplied drift sediments from elsewhere along the east coast.

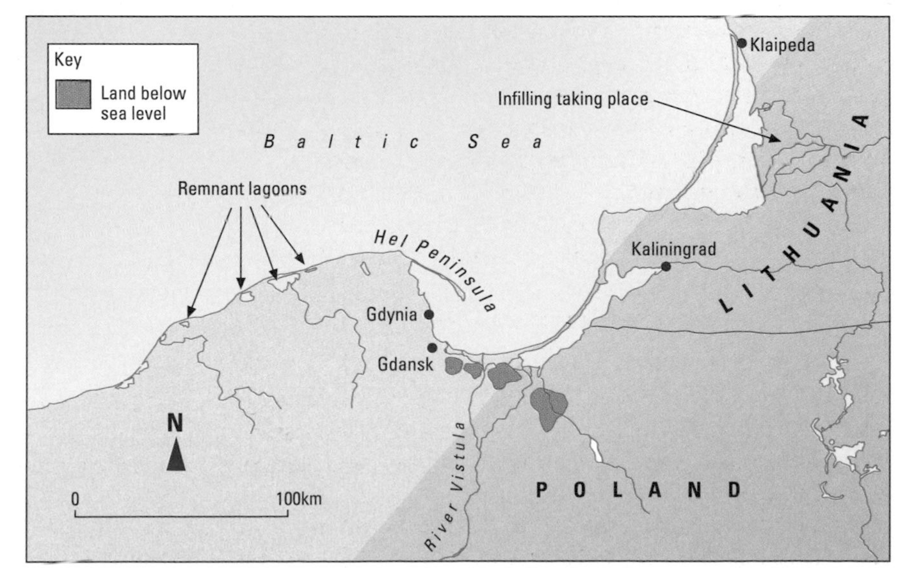

▲ **Figure 2.53**
Coastal deposition in the Baltic Sea. The map shows spits and bars at different stages of formation. Similarly the lagoons in the estuaries and bays are at different stages of infilling. Lagoons are replaced by marsh with time and eventually disappear.

Spurn Head, an example of an unstable spit

Case Study

Spurn Head is the classic example of an unstable spit. There is no more natural position for the formation of a spit than the northern side of the wide Humber estuary. The longshore drift from north to south carries a particularly heavy load because of the rapid rates of erosion along the 60km length of boulder clay cliffs in Holderness to the north. This helps to explain Spurn Head's considerable length of about eight kilometres. The fact that the dominant wind direction here is from the north east not only keeps the alignment parallel to the coast but also curves the distal end of the spit back into the Humber estuary. The spit's growth has created still waters behind it, in which finer sediments have been deposited; at the same time the deep water channel in the estuary is being pushed southwards. Historical records suggest that once Spurn Head becomes five kilometres long or longer it becomes unstable. The vulnerability of narrow points in the central section of the spit to storm waves from the east and south east increases. There are records of breaches that occurred in the fourteenth, seventeenth and nineteenth centuries. After every breach, the spit begins to reform, because all the favourable conditions for the formation of a spit in this position continue to exist. However, new growth begins further west, a reflection of the retreat westwards of the boulder clay coastline to the north, to which the new spit's formation is inextricably linked.

At the start of the new millennium Spurn Head is currently longer than earlier spits that were broken. Between the 1850s and 1950s the policy was to protect it. A concrete wall, built by the army when Spurn was owned by the Ministry of Defence, was meant to stop erosion and wooden groynes were intended to trap and hold the sand in place. At that time it was not realized that Spurn Head needed to move for survival. Now official policy has changed. Parts of the wall have collapsed and many of the groynes are in a state of disrepair. Narrow sections on the spit are exposed and very vulnerable to erosion during northerly gales because Spurn Head is now in the wrong place. Its position has remained stationary while the rest of the Holderness coastline has retreated.

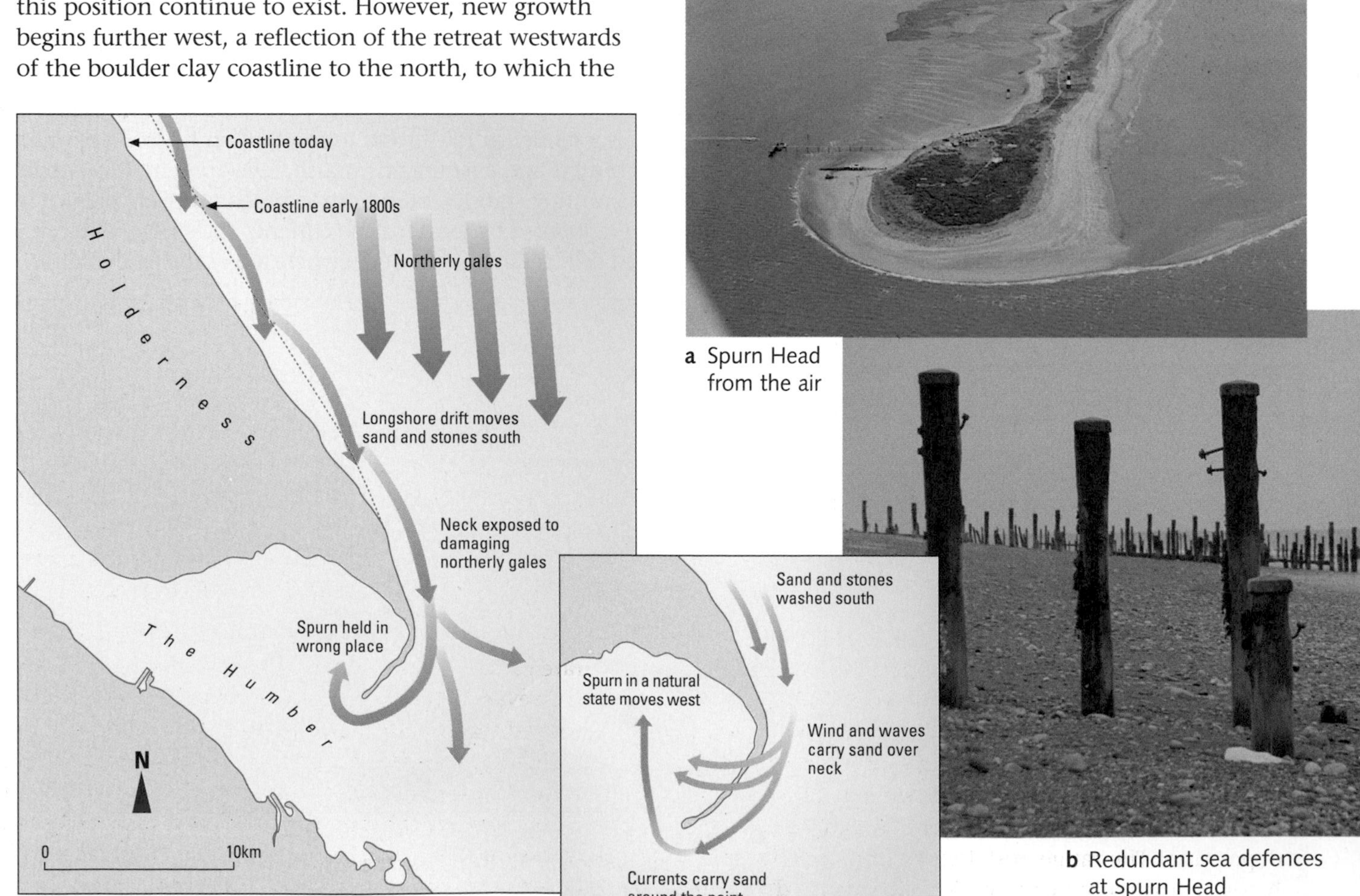

▲ **Figure 2.54** Spurn Head

a Spurn Head from the air

b Redundant sea defences at Spurn Head

Questions

1 a i Describe the similarities and differences in form between beaches, spits and bars.
ii To what extent is their formation identical?
b i Identify ways in which spits and bars vary in form, size and stability.
ii Give reasons for these variations.

2 Refer back to the diagram of the coast system (Figure 2.9, page 24). Make a larger version of the systems diagram (about one side of A4) by making boxes for the two inputs, three processes and three outputs. Within each of the eight boxes, add further information about the inputs, processes and outputs named.

Sand dunes and salt marshes

Sand dunes and salt marshes are formed in association with the landforms of coastal deposition referred to before. Primary dune formation, regularly leading to sand accumulations up to fifteen metres high, usually begins at the head of a beach. A major requirement is frequent and strong onshore winds. Although widespread along stretches of the east coast of Scotland and England, some of the largest sand dunes are on the west coast of Britain, such as at Braunton Burrows in Devon and around Southport in Lancashire that are both exposed to prevailing westerly winds. Another need is a wide foreshore exposed at low water, so that there is more chance of the sand drying out, and leaving more time for onshore winds to carry the sand inland beyond the mean high tide mark. A third requirement is the presence of a trap for the blown sand to encourage its accumulation. This trap can be shingle, or tufts of grass, or drifted debris dumped by waves in a storm. Early colonization by vegetation of the sand as it accumulates is essential otherwise wind or high tides will quickly lead to its removal. The first stage in the psammosere succession is colonization by marram grass, which has a deep branching root system that binds together the loose dune sands. However, marram grass only thrives on dunes where new sand is being supplied; once the supply of fresh sand ceases, dunes are liable to 'blow outs' in stormy conditions. Many dunes in eastern England and the Netherlands were destroyed by the storm surge of 31 January/ 1 February 1953. The sand dunes which line almost the entire length of the Dutch coast need to be well managed because of their importance as the first line of defence against the sea. Inhabited areas are as low as 6.7m below current sea level (page 66). They survived the storm surge relatively intact.

Salt marsh formation begins after mud and other fine sediments have been deposited by tides in locations sheltered by sand dunes, spits and bars from direct wave attack. Initial colonization by halophytic (salt loving) plants helps to trap seaweed, which acts as a further check upon water movement, encouraging more deposition. The range and density of plants living in the halosere gradually increases. This builds up the level of the marsh until it is only during the high spring tides

▲ **Figure 2.55** Sand dunes in southern Chile where prevailing westerly winds blow onshore, as in Britain

that it will be covered by water. By this stage it is possible for farmers to reclaim the marsh for grazing land, usually for sheep. In between areas of concentrated vegetation growth there are small channels of deeper water; these are the creeks kept free of vegetation by tidal scour. Marshes are equally as impermanent as sand dunes because they can survive only as long as the protective barriers of sand and shingle remain in place.

Marshes can survive rising sea levels provided that the rate of rise is slow enough for new growth to keep pace. However, there are risks to all depositional landforms and related features in the coast zone from the speed at which current rises in sea level are happening. Rising water levels extend the height of the zone affected by the tides. The coastal zone that was previously above the mean high tide mark becomes more vulnerable to destructive waves driven onshore during storms, to which the depositional landforms have little resistance.

The coast of Norfolk

Case Study

between the Wash and Great Yarmouth

This is a good choice of coast for studying the results of many of the processes operating in the coast zone for the following reasons:

- There are examples of landforms of both erosion and deposition.
- There are examples of constructional landforms, notably the barrier beaches and extensive marshland areas.
- There is an example of the clear reversal in direction of the longshore drift.
- The coast is undergoing constant modification.

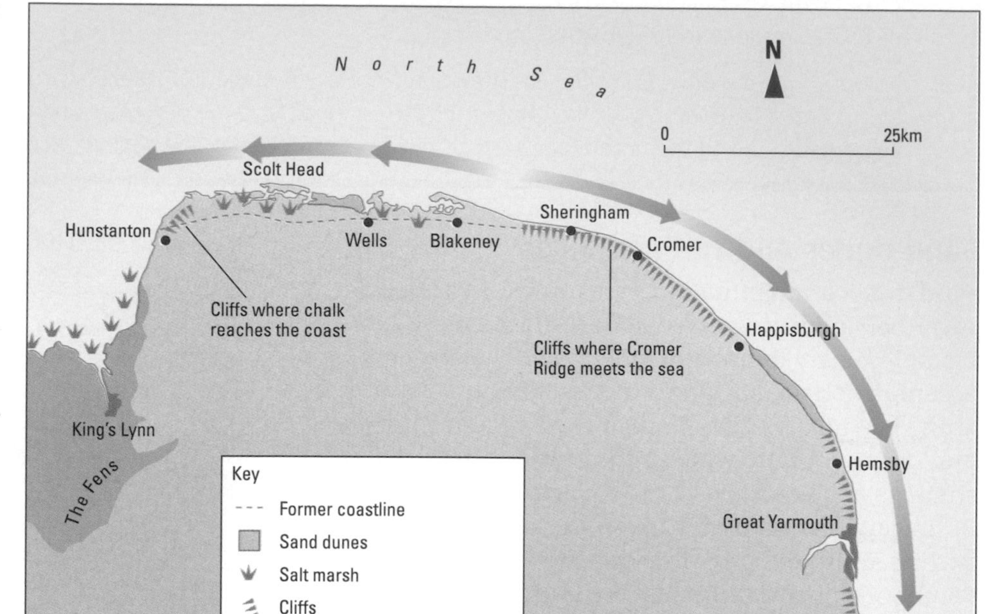

▲ **Figure 2.56** The Norfolk Coast

a Erosion

The main sections with cliffs are shown in Figure 2.56. Those near Hunstanton are formed where the solid geology outcrops at the coast; they are capped by chalk. Those on both sides of Cromer form where the conspicuous terminal moraine of boulder clay reaches the sea. North of Cromer the cliffs are made from sandy and gravelly material; south of Cromer clays dominate. There are many signs of slumping, slides and gulleying. Near Cromer the coast is open to waves with the longest fetch when the dominant northerly winds blow; some high rates of erosion are recorded here. The cliffs near Hemsby are low and easily eroded.

▲ **Figure 2.58** The effects of coastal erosion at Hemsby

Who pinched the Queen's bottom?

As implacable coastal erosion reaches critical proportions in Norfolk, some are blaming the dredgers which shovel up sand from the Crown-owned sea bed.

In 1980, you could see 53 bungalows along the top of a bank of three dunes in Hemsby. Today only six are left. Each winter, surge tides eat six metres of beach a year. There are no sea defences and insurance companies now decline to take on home-owners close to the encroaching sea.

A retired scientist, whose beloved bungalow 'Riskit' crashed into the sea eight years ago, suspects that he has the answer, human greed. 'The primary cause of erosion here is the marine dredging.'

Not far out to sea, dredgers shovel up millions of tonnes of sand and gravel, with 40–60p per tonne going to Her Majesty's Government owing to Crown Rights over 'the Queen's Bottom' – the seabed stretching from the shoreline to twelve miles out. Last year 26.1 million tonnes of marine aggregate was dredged from off the shores of England and Wales, 16 million tonnes of it from the North Sea. As a result the power of the winter waves is no longer broken by the sand banks underneath the sea and coastal erosion gets worse.

▲ **Figure 2.57** An extract from *The Observer*, 4 August 1996

b Deposition

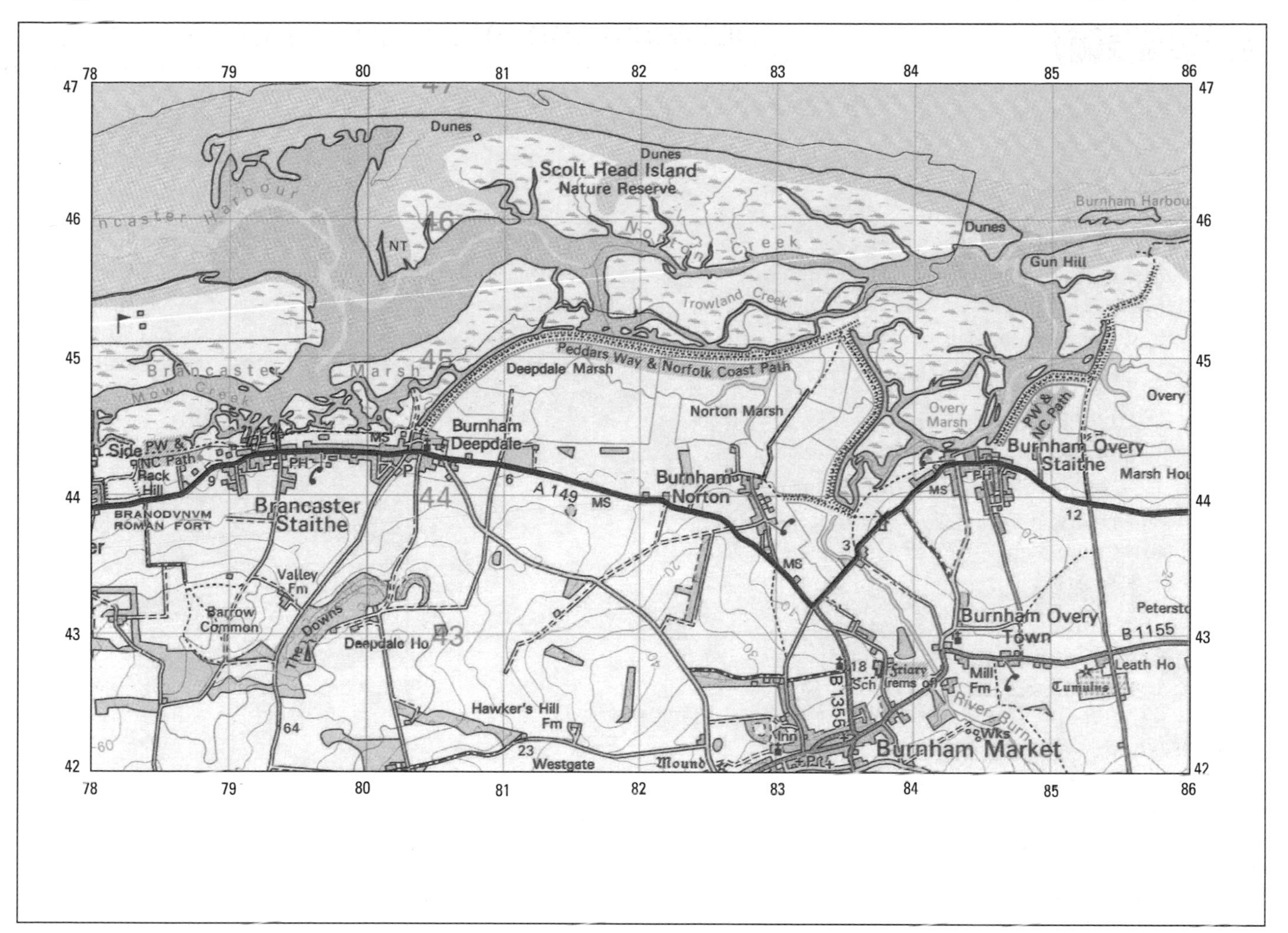

▲ **Figure 2.59** 1:50,000 OS map of part of the north Norfolk coast

A study of beach deposition reveals a change in direction of the longshore drift west of Cromer. The effects of big waves hitting the coast from the dominant northerly and north-easterly directions is thought to be responsible for causing the local direction of the litoral drift to go from east to west towards the Wash, contrary to the national trend. Blakeney Point is a spit, built of shingle, which confirms this local direction of the drift. Scolt Head Island is an offshore bar which forms a low ridge of shingle and sand; it also has a westward facing spit growing out from its western edge. Scolt Head's northern side is lined with sand dunes, as also is the coastline eastwards towards Wells. The sand dunes here are prograding, which means they are gradually growing seawards; the foreshore in front of them is wide and sandy and slopes extremely gently to the sea. In the shelter of the dunes is a wide zone of salt marsh and creeks. The resort town of Great Yarmouth is built on a spit. The Yarmouth spit across the Yare estuary faces south, in the same direction as spits further down the coast, such as Orford Ness in Suffolk.

Questions

1 a Draw a frame and grid of the same size as that in Figure 2.59. Sketch on it and label the location and extent of landforms and other features of coastal deposition.

b State and explain the map evidence for each of the following:

i Scolt Head is an offshore bar

ii the longshore drift is from east to west

iii the former (old) coastline ran along or just to the north of northing 44.

2 a Explain why deposition is an important process along the north coast of Norfolk.

b Why has it created a variety of coastal landforms?

3 a On a sketch map, identify the areas along the Norfolk coast where erosion is an important process.

b Explain the physical and human factors responsible for high rates of coastal erosion in Norfolk.

Coastal problems

The root cause of many of the current physical problems for people in the coast zone is that we are living either in an inter-glacial or a post-glacial period. Whichever one it turns out to be, and only time will tell, the results are the same. The mean temperature of the Earth is rising and more ice is melting each year than is accumulating; therefore world sea levels are rising. It is estimated that sea levels have risen by 15–25cm in the last century. The present rise is 1–2mm per year, which does not seem very much, but the effects are cumulative, and in areas subject to flooding small differences in height assume great significance.

The last few million years have witnessed great and frequent fluctuations in sea level. The Great Ice Age, which began about two million years ago, consisted of up to four major ice advances in the northern hemisphere, during which land-based water stores in ice sheets and valley glaciers increased greatly. A higher proportion of global precipitation fell as snow. This snow was locked up as ice due to freezing temperatures, which reduced the amount of run off via rivers into the sea. Further precipitation in the form of snow resulted in the transfer of more water from seas to glaciers, to the point where the eustatic fall in relative sea levels during the maximum ice advance is estimated to be in the order of 145m. Large areas that are now part of the continental shelf around the British Isles would have been revealed as land. In contrast, some of the inter-glacial periods were particularly warm. About 100,000 years ago in the last major inter-glacial, the Ipswichian, it is believed that maximum sea levels reached some fifteen metres higher than those of today. In other words, those parts of the UK which lie below the fifteen metre contour line today would have been under sea water 100,000 years ago.

The last major ice advance across Europe, known as the Devensian in the British Isles, is estimated to have reduced sea levels by between 100 and 125m. Once the ice sheets began their retreat, the mass of water released by melting produced a post-glacial marine transgression, i.e. sea water infringing upon and flooding low-lying land. During early de-glaciation water release was very rapid, but from about 6,000 years ago, by which time most of the ice caps formed during the Devensian had melted, the marine trangression slowed appreciably (Figure 2.60). At the end of this period of rapidly rising sea levels, the southern North Sea Basin and English Channel were flooded. The Straits of Dover were cut by this event, known as the Flandrian transgression, to give the British Isles a coastline similar to today's. Relative stability in sea levels during the last five to six thousand years has given constructive landforms, such as beaches, sand dunes and salt marshes, the time they needed to form in low energy coastal environments.

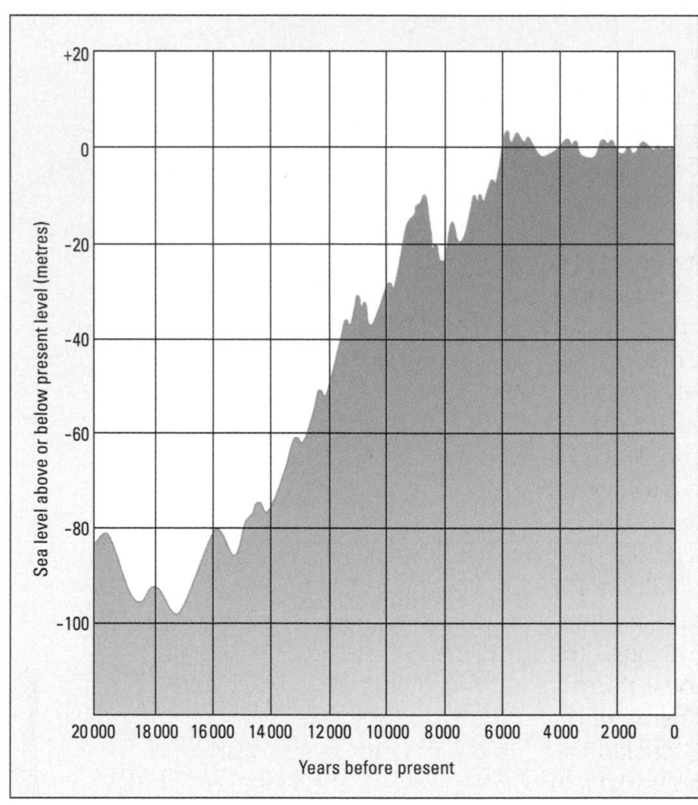

▲ **Figure 2.60** Eustatic rises in sea level since the last glacial advance in the Devensian

Even within the general pattern of global warming during the last 10,000 years, there have been many short-term climatic fluctuations of heat, cold, drought and wetness. For two or three hundred years before AD1300 the climate of the British Isles became warmer and drier, favouring farming and allowing population increase. After 1350 temperatures fell and rainfall increased; some medieval villages were 'lost' as farmland was abandoned and populations became less healthy and declined. There are good historical records for cold winters in the years after 1550 in the UK until the global trend towards rising average world temperatures was felt more strongly as the twentieth century progressed. Of the ten hottest years, the years with the highest mean world temperatures, four were in the late 1980s and six were in the 1990s.

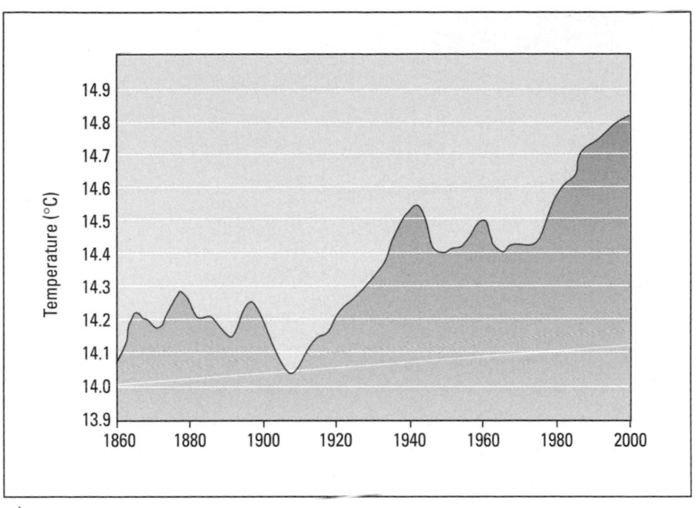

▲ **Figure 2.61** Mean world temperatures 1860–2000

The most noticeable meteorological signs of climatic change from global warming in the British Isles have been greater mildness and lower snowfall in winters. Winters have been dominated by depressions transferring warmth from the Atlantic Ocean rather than by anticyclones sucking in cold polar air masses from the continent or the Arctic. This could just be a UK phenomenon; however, the same reduction in winter snowfall has been noticed in other areas with a CTWM climate, such as in southern Chile and on the island of Tierra del Fuego. Based on the latest global temperature trends, the middle forecast for eustatic rise in world sea levels is half a metre between 2000 and 2100. The combination of increases in the volume of water already in the seas is due to temperature increases and from extra water as land ice stores continue to melt. To make their predictions realistic, forecasters have to take into account from where meltwater may come. Although the ice in the Arctic Ocean is known to be thinning, it is already floating on the sea. Therefore the ice cap and valley glaciers in Greenland are regarded as more significant potential contributors. More icebergs will break away from Antarctica, but it will take a much longer time period for widespread break up because of the great thickness of the ice. Accurate prediction is made more difficult because of other potential interactions between different elements. One example is the cold desert environment of Antarctica. If it were to warm up, increased precipitation in the form of snow would be likely for a time, which, at least in the short term, could offset any melting through global warming.

Coastal flooding and erosion

Coastal flooding is usually a short-term problem, confined to coastal plains, as a result of temporary increases in water levels, which are substantially above normal high tide levels. However, in this time of rising sea levels the likelihood of longer term and more extensive flooding is increasing. It is becoming a major international issue. Among those most concerned are small island states such as the Maldives and Seychelles in the Indian Ocean and Tonga, the Marshall and Cook Islands in the Pacific, part or all of which are built of coral. Atolls are rings of live coral reef around a lagoon. The sand islands which accumulate on the edges make a precarious place for plants and people to live since many are only one or two metres above present sea levels. Already coral can be destroyed by storms, hurricanes and El Niño events and global warming is not going to reduce the risks. Certain particularly densely populated parts of the world are at high risk, notably delta regions like the Nile in Egypt, the Ganges in Bangladesh and the Rhine-Maas in the Netherlands. The scale and effectiveness of coastal defence works already in place are much greater in the Netherlands, one of the world's wealthiest countries, than in the two LEDCs, although they have much higher populations. Estuaries are also highly vulnerable. The Thames is one of them. After the east coast floods from the 1953 storm surge, it was recognized that the protection for London needed to be greatly improved, for which the Thames Barrier was completed in 1982.

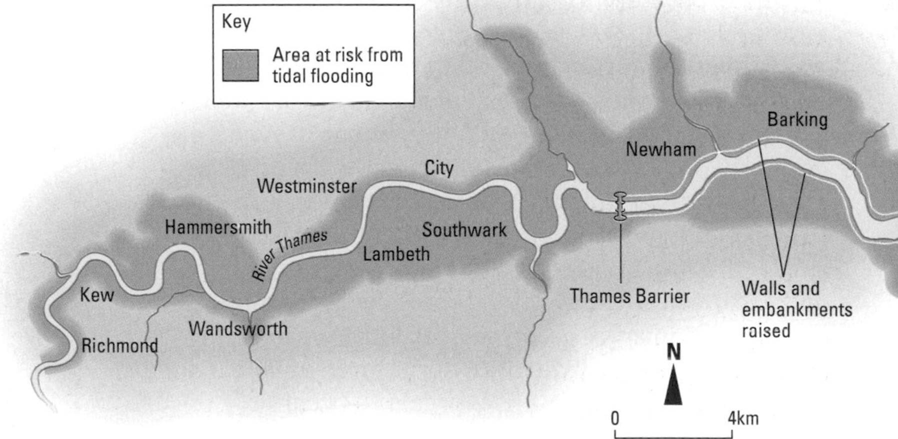

▲ **Figure 2.62**
Areas of London at risk from tidal flooding. The potential cost of a flood disaster is incalculable – in terms of loss of life (over one million people live in the shaded area and there are more than 50 underground stations) and of disruption to commerce, trade and industry.

Questions

1 a Distinguish between eustatic and isostatic changes in relative land and sea levels.
  b Why are the isostatic changes less global than the eustatic.

2 To what extent are current rises in sea level similar or unique compared with those that have happened before?

However, MEDCs do not have all the solutions. Even though vulnerable coastal locations are well known, it is impossible to predict exactly where flooding will happen next along a section of coast. The small North Wales town and resort of Towyn had the misfortune to hit the national news headlines in 1990. On 26 February a storm surge, caused by the strong onshore winds of a deep depression, coinciding with exceptionally high tide levels, breached the sea wall at Towyn and flooded over six square kilometres. In the centre of town flood waters rose to more than five metres above normal sea level. Domestic and commercial properties in Towyn itself were ruined and caravan parks in the surrounding coastal lowlands were destroyed. The sea walls and groynes along this stretch of coast attest to the recognition of its vulnerability to flooding. It was known from the beginning that the railway line, running along the coast and built in Victorian times, interfered with coastal movements of sediment. The Clwyd lowlands around Towyn are reclaimed land mainly below five metres above sea level. The shingle ridge, which gives some natural protection to the coastline further east, peters out before it reaches Towyn. Although groynes were placed in front of the sea wall at Towyn, little sand accumulated there, which helps to explain why the sea wall felt the full force of the breakers, which was sufficient to lead to the breach.

Future danger to people, property and land does not come only from direct sea flooding. It also comes from the increased frequency of dangerous high water, high energy marine events. Extreme events are major causes of coastal flooding and erosion. Some are tectonic, notably the formation of tsunamis (tidal waves) after earthquakes. Areas at risk from strong earthquake shocks are well known (Chapter 3, page 93), but earthquake events are impossible to predict. Many are climatic; deep depressions in temperate latitudes, cyclones in the tropics and El Niño events in the Pacific are all capable of generating storm surges. Cliff and coast erosion are increased considerably during these events and they are expected to increase as a result of global warming. Events, such as the North Sea storm surge of January and February 1953, which were expected to occur only once in 100 years, might become a 50-year, 20-year or even a 10-year event. So much damage is accomplished during these special events where coastal defences are tested beyond breaking point, that rates of coastal erosion might exceed previously recorded levels. However, surprise cliff collapses can occur after much less extreme weather events. The wet autumn of 2000 in the UK was blamed for the rash of landslides and another coastal location in North Wales hit the headlines (Figure 2.65).

▲ **Figure 2.63**
The Thames Barrier. Gates are raised to form a barrier across the river during flood and storm alerts. Walls and embankments have been raised along the sides of the Thames.

▲ **Figure 2.64**
The Chester to Holyhead railway line, believed to be one of the contributory factors to the severity of the flooding at Towyn in February 1990, with the flooded caravan park behind it

▼ **Figure 2.65** Adapted extract from *The Guardian*, 3 January 2001

Woman killed by car park landslides

An elderly woman was killed and her husband was seriously injured yesterday when their car was sent crashing on to a beach as landslides struck a car park below cliffs on the coast of North Wales. Four other cars were hit by landslips on the 40m sand and clay cliffs near the village of Nefyn, a popular holiday resort on the Lleyn peninsula.

Council officials reported that the cliffs had been made unstable by three months of torrential rain followed by several days of sub-zero temperatures. Two cottages had been damaged in another slip a few weeks ago. One of the cars damaged yesterday belonged to an insurance company's loss adjuster who had arrived to inspect the damage.

It is believed that the couple had driven down the narrow winding road to a car park where they sat admiring panoramic views over the Irish Sea. Their silver coloured vehicle was struck by the first slip and pushed towards bollards at the edge of the car park. The second slip struck the car five minutes later and forced it and another car to plunge a further ten metres on to the beach.

Local cliff paths had been closed for several days before yesterday's slips. 'This was bound to happen because the cliff face is in such a perilous state,' said a local retired teacher. 'What can you possibly do when the earth is saturated after 100 days of incessant rain?' a council spokesman said. 'The problem with all the coast in that area is that it is composed of clay and sand, so you can imagine the effects of the tremendous rain over the last few months.'

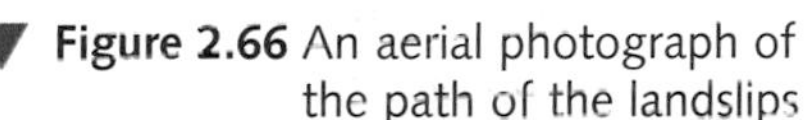

▼ **Figure 2.66** An aerial photograph of the path of the landslips

The lesson that must be learnt is that coastal erosion is a natural process. Erosion is a vital part of the dynamic coast system. Difficulties arise because the impact of natural changes upon people is now much greater than ever before. Over half the world's population (a total of six billion in 1999) live within 300km of the sea. Many of the world's big cities are coastal. The coast is a tremendously attractive location for many human activities. Ports and harbours offer global links for the movement of goods. Continental shelves contain resources of fish and in some places oil and gas. Tidewater locations are attractive for many heavy industries notably oil refining, petrochemicals, steel making and heavy engineering (including shipbuilding). The coastline is a magnet for tourists and recreational activities. Upon coastal lowlands there is a high chance of the availability of productive farmland and they offer easy building for houses and lines of communication. It should not come as a surprise that some human activities are contributing to coastal problems by both deliberate and accidental alterations. Potentially the most serious problems are likely where there is a coincidence between coastal flooding and high rates of erosion on the one hand and dense human settlement and intensive use of the coastal strip on the other.

Questions

1 Study one named example of each of the following: coastal flooding; coastal cliff collapse.
For each one,

- **a** describe the nature of the problem and its local impacts
- **b** give reasons why it is occurring in the area named
- **c** discuss the relative contributions of physical and human factors to its occurrence
- **d** assess what, if anything, is likely to change in the future.

2 Essay

'Coastal erosion is a natural process speeded up by humans'. Discuss this statement, supporting your answer by reference to examples.

Human activities and coastal problems

One effect of human activities is the disruption of coastal sedimentation. This is done in a variety of ways. Building groynes for tourist beaches and breakwaters for harbours disturbs the natural patterns of wave movement which changes the distribution of sediment stores. Cliff protection schemes do the same by inducing accelerated rates of erosion for natural cliffs elsewhere on the down drift side. Farmers and residents living south of Mappleton along the coast of Holderness are convinced that the recently enhanced protection given to that village is accelerating erosion further south. Frequent groynes, piers and breakwaters in the resort towns and ports along the Channel coast are responsible for the local reduction of sediment inputs into the coast system further east, reducing beach widths and exposing cliff bases to higher wave energies. By building upon cliff tops and by altering ground water levels, people reduce the stability of coastal cliffs leading to cliff collapse, which is most serious where the geology naturally favours movements. Shipping channels are kept open by dredging which is another means by which sediment is artificially removed from the coast system. Sand and gravel are economic resources that are removed from beaches and the seabed offshore often with more of an eye on economic gain than on natural consequences. Actions of people inland can also have an effect on the coast system. By building dams and trapping sediment, river loads are reduced. Accelerated rates of coastal erosion are a product of both increased wave energy and reduced sediment availability and humans can contribute to both, albeit unwittingly in some cases. Occasionally people's actions favour deposition. For many years coal wastes were tipped directly into the North Sea from coastal mines in County Durham. The rate of tipping, because it exceeded the capacity of the waves to remove it, created black beaches; for many years they afforded protection against active wave attack to the magnesian limestone cliffs between Seaham and Blackhall.

▼ **Figure 2.67** The coast of Holderness

a Sitting on the beach at Mappleton on a summer's day

b Holiday homes south of Mappleton at risk from accelerated erosion

▲ **Figure 2.68** Cattle grazing in the same area shown in Figure 2.55

Some coastal environments are particularly fragile and are highly vulnerable to even small-scale human impact. Examples include sand dunes, salt marshes and coral reefs. All are dynamic coastal landforms. Sand dunes, for example, rely upon fresh supplies of sand for survival against wind and wave erosion. Along low-lying coastlines they are a vital element in coastal protection, as the Dutch recognize better than any other people. Dunes, however, attract people and have a variety of uses, many of which can be classified under the heading of leisure and tourism. Land uses include golf courses and camping and caravan parks; popular recreational activities are walking, horse riding and biking. In certain places dunes are reserved for more specialized use such as for military training and exercises, or for the extraction of sand and fresh water supplies. Elsewhere, in areas where the dunes have not been afforested with conifers, grazing is a common activity. Unfortunately, the majority of these uses involve disturbance by trampling, which can lead to blowouts and the eventual disintegration of the dunes. Blown sand can cover valuable agricultural land behind the coastal zone in an uncontrolled manner, removing the coastal protection to settlement that the dunes previously afforded. By planting trees and incorporating them as golf links, dunes are taken out of the natural dynamic coast system and turned into fossil landforms.

Wetlands

Wetlands also have an important role in coastal protection. They dissipate wave energy before it can reach and attack sea walls placed on their inland sides. However, reclamation for agricultural land (their main human use) usually involves the construction of embankments around their edges; having protected part of it, the remaining marshlands lower down the estuary are subject to increased wave energy and erosion. Rising sea levels are expected to erode marshes towards the outer areas of estuaries and replace them with more restricted habitats of sand and gravel. Otherwise, without human interference, many marshes can keep pace with rising sea levels by natural growth. Recognition of the importance of marshes as a natural defence against rising sea levels has triggered greater levels of interest in techniques to stimulate new marsh growth. One policy being more readily considered is 'managed retreat', or 'retreating the existing defence line' (page 61). This works by abandoning and removing old sea walls and defences in poor states of repair and allowing a wider area to be flooded, which will be reclaimed naturally over time by marsh plants as they grow. This is the preferred policy on some of the Essex marshes.

Coral reefs

Corals require specific environmental conditions for growth. Reef-forming corals only thrive where sea water temperatures are above 25°C. Nevertheless, they are of widespread occurrence, being found offshore in more than a hundred countries in the tropics. An additional requirement for growth is a coastal platform of less than 100m deep. They are killed off by sediment and pollution, which is why they are absent from the mouths of large rivers such as the Amazon. The majority of reefs in the Pacific Ocean are described as being in 'good condition' because island populations are low and they are remote from the world's well populated regions. In contrast off the coasts of densely populated South East Asia about two thirds of the reefs are described as 'sick'. Although subject to natural disturbances from cyclones which can destroy the living corals and throw them on to the flat reef tops, and from the changes in ocean temperatures and currents due to El Niño, human disturbance is the main enemy of coral. Some of this human disturbance is indirect and results from land-based activities, for example deforestation which has increased sedimentation in coastal waters. The effects of other human activity are more direct. There has been a massive increase in the amount and extent of offshore pollution from sewage and other waste disposals, including oil pollution from land, shipping and offshore drilling. Coral reefs teem with fish, but locally there has still been overfishing, accompanied in some areas by the use of damaging fishing techniques notably dynamiting. Along coasts frequented by tourists, without the strict supervision and enforcement of regulations, visitors trample on reefs and remove corals as souvenirs, while boat owners attach anchors to the live coral. Regulations are less likely to be applied in LEDCs.

▲ **Figure 2.69**
Australia's Great Barrier Reef, one of the natural wonders of the world. It is protected as a Marine Park, in which restricted human uses are confined to designated areas only. It is a habitat of great marine bio-diversity, a great absorber of wave energy (protecting the coast behind) and a major tourist attraction.

Global warming itself brings two threats. One is an increase in the scale of coral bleaching from warm waters; the second is that sea levels may rise too fast to enable coral growth to keep pace. Therefore, in many different ways human settlement and activities are disturbing the equilibrium of coast systems in many parts of the world, with locally serious consequences.

Questions

1 Make amendments to the physical coast system in Figure 2.9 to take account of the effects of humans.

2 Identify and outline with examples the following:
   a the attractions of the coastal zone for human settlement and activities
   b the problems for those living in or using the coastal zone.

3 Why is there an uneven spatial distribution of coastal problems **a** worldwide and **b** within Britain?

4 **Essay**

Discuss the evidence for the view that the coast is both a resource and a hazard for humans.

5 **Investigation**

For a stretch of coastline of up to 10km long (either the one closest to where you live, or one which you have visited or studied):
   a Outline its main physical features.
   b On a sketch map,
      i locate the settlements
      ii show and label the human land uses in the coastal zone (within 1km of the coastline).
   c Give reasons for the presence of human settlement and land uses.
   d Explain why some sections of this coast are more attractive to people than others.
   e Identify and comment upon any coastal problems.

Coastal management strategies

Coastal management

What does it mean?

Management means controlling development and change in the coastal zone and undertaking work according to agreed principles and criteria. Good management involves taking account of both physical and environmental considerations, as well as the different views of residents and other interested groups, in order to create a balanced policy. Priorities usually need to be established to ensure that maximum benefit is achieved for the available resources.

Stages in management

1 Understand the causes of the problems.

2 Undertake works to reduce or solve the problems.

3 Improve prediction and make contingency plans.

Some parts of the UK coastline have long attracted people; they have also attracted human interference. Promenades, protected by sea walls, mark the divide between land and sea in most resorts. Groynes trap sand and shingle to maintain the beach. Breakwaters extend into the sea to increase shelter and water depth in ports and harbours. Local need used to be the controlling factor; the consequences for coastlines down-drift, or for the coastal environment in general, were rarely considered by the councils and port authorities paying for the coastal works. Therefore it is not surprising that there are places where human actions have created or worsened coastal and environmental problems. Accelerated rates of coastal erosion and rising sea levels are forcing a reconsideration of coastal management techniques. A more 'hands off' approach is being adopted. For most of the British coastline the official management policy is to 'do nothing', which means leaving the coastal zone to be shaped by the forces of nature.

Whatever the main purpose of coastal works, whether for flood control, coastal protection or economic gain, most use hard engineering structures, of which the sea wall is the one used most widely. Sea walls are usually placed on the seaward side away from the base of the cliffs; in effect, the result is to 'advance the coastline' because the new line that is being defended is in front of the cliffs. It is also an example of 'coastal squeeze', as the width of the foreshore is reduced by building the defence works. Natural features on the foreshore are lost or drowned. The foreshore is being narrowed further by rising sea levels. Many sea walls are subject to enormous, and increasing, wave pressures. Take Scarborough as an example. The long, wide sea wall, on top of which Marine Drive runs around the base of Castle Headland, is the vital link between tourist beaches in the North and South Bays. It was built to secure the otherwise vulnerable bases of the shale and sandstone cliffs below the castle and fix the coastline. The narrow rock platform that remains between it and the sea is completely covered during high tide right up to the walls of Marine Drive. Defence levels are now inadequate for high seas and storm tides which leads to frequent overtopping and road closures (Figure 2.70), despite a regular programme of remedial work.

▲ **Figure 2.70** Marine Drive, Scarborough. Sea overtopping is so regular that the warning board and road barriers are permanently in place.

Building and maintaining sea walls is expensive; the cost can only be justified if what is being defended has high benefit value (residential, commercial, cultural, heritage etc.). Other hard engineering structures widely used for defending short sections of coast are armour blocks of rock, gabions, revetments and groynes. Blocks of hard rock such as granite are often placed in front of weak cliffs to break the force of the waves. Where sea walls need an additional advanced line of protection, rocks are placed on their seaward side. Gabions are cages enclosing shingle or small blocks of rocks. They tend to be used in similar ways, but where the amount to defend is less. Revetments is a general term for defences that are aligned parallel to the shore, including posts, pillars or walls of rock placed on the foreshore. They are intended to break the force of the waves before they reach the fixed coastline. Groynes are timber posts and boards, or low broad walls, which run out to sea at right angles to the shore to trap sediment drifting along the coast. This may be for coastal protection, or for the economic advantages that a wide beach brings to a resort, or for both purposes. Each one interferes with natural coastal processes and they are not always visually attractive (Figure 2.71).

Greater encouragement is being given to councils and planners to move more towards soft engineering solutions, which work with the forces of nature and are therefore likely to be sustainable in the long term. One method is beach nourishment; sand and shingle brought from elsewhere are added to beaches to maintain their breadth and depth in an attempt to try to ensure continued coastal protection by natural means. Another is planting grasses, bushes and trees, already widely practised in sand dune environments. Along many coasts the preferred policy has changed from 'holding the line' to one of 'managed retreat', in which a new line of defence is fixed further inland, allowing the sea to win back some land. It is argued that this will make it easier to hold the new line, because it involves the creation of a wider inter-tidal zone that is able to absorb much of the wave energy. Less money will be spent (and probably wasted) on sea defences with only limited life expectancies. However, the policy of abandoning the line and managing retreat is not popular among farmers and property owners, partly because there is no compensation for sea losses at the moment. On the other hand, it does find much favour with environmentalists who appreciate the creation of new wildlife habitats and foresee an end at last to the continued disappearance of coastal wetlands (Figure 2.73).

Figure 2.71 Hard engineering structures being used for coastal defence at Robin Hood's Bay, Yorkshire

a The old properties next to the shore forming the historical centre of the former fishing and smuggling village of Robin Hood's Bay (now a tourist resort) are protected by a small concrete wall, apron and ramp. The massive, unattractive concrete retaining wall behind and to the right was built in 1975 to prevent further cliff collapses and housing losses above the unstable tall cliffs composed of shales and sandstones with a capping of boulder clay.

b Benefits of coastal protection here have been assessed as high. In late 2000 new coast protection and cliff stabilization works began at a cost of over £1 million.

c Use of armour blocks of rock is the main method being used here to protect the soft boulder clay outcrops.

Call to buy out people living on eroding coasts

Parts of the coastline should be abandoned to the sea, but planners are avoiding making the right decisions because there is no legislation to allow them to compensate the owners who face ruin as a result. Rising sea levels and more frequent storms mean that it is more and more difficult and expensive to defend parts of the coast. Improvements in science also show that extra defences in one area mean erosion in others so those adversely affected should receive compensation.

A test case is Medmerry Beach at Selsey, near Chichester, where the largest caravan site in Europe – which has 10,000 residents in summer – was sheltering behind a shingle beach that was being washed away by the sea. Each year the environment agency is waging a losing battle against the elements by spending £500,000 a year replacing shingle on the beach. Basically the right thing to do is to let the shingle beach move inland. Eventually the sea will win, but there is no proper way of compensating those who suffer. The environment agency said it was hoping for permission from MAFF to move back the line of Medmerry Beach. 'Three homes will be lost and part of the caravan site and it will cost millions to complete, but at least we will have a beach we think we can hold,' said a spokesman.

A lot of radical decisions need to be made. Unstable cliffs cannot be defended and must be allowed to fall into the sea. Low-lying land in north Kent, Essex and Norfolk must be abandoned to allow salt flats to develop. Small schemes, mostly in harbours such as Chichester, have already been successful, but they are needed on a much larger scale. Developments should not be allowed where there are no adequate sea defences. Hundreds of houses are still being built at Sovereign Harbour on Pevensey Bay in East Sussex where there is danger of inundation by the sea. Councillors often overruled the advice of coastal engineers, their own officers and the environment agency and allowed development in dangerous places.

▲ **Figure 2.72** Adapted extract from *The Guardian*, 5 January 2001

Weatherwatch

Britain's tidal marshes and mudflats are one of our most important habitats for birds. Every winter they play host to huge flocks of waders. In spring and autumn migrating waders stop off at estuaries like the Wash and Solway. But now these places are under threat. Sea level rises endanger much of our coastline, according to a study by the Royal Society for the Protection of Birds. With levels predicted by some to rise by an average of 25cm by the year 2050, the problem is an urgent one. Saltmarshes are already being lost to the sea at alarming rate and there is nowhere else for the birds to go.

But it's not all bad news. Saltmarshes and mudflats actually help protect the coastline, by acting as a safety valve when high tides and storm surges lead to floods. The RSPB has identified almost 100 sites around the country where existing sea defences can be set back, allowing land to flood. This would benefit the birds by creating new areas of mudflat and marsh; and ourselves by reducing the costs of sea defences and protecting homes and people.

One area in which there may need to be a change in coastal defence policy is at Pett Level east of Hastings. The land has been drained for farming since medieval times. Due to draining, the sediment contracted; lying at or below current sea level, it is becoming increasingly expensive and difficult to defend. The large embankment of earth built to keep the sea out itself needs to be protected by groynes and revetments, and in places where there are caravan sites, by a sea wall as well. The embankment has also been capped by concrete on the seaward side. The beach needs regular artificial nourishment with quarried shingle. Despite the enhanced scale and greater range of the defensive measures, the embankment has suffered from accelerated erosion since 1987, not helped by the sediment trap formed as a result of harbour works at Hastings. At what stage does it become economically unviable, or impossible in engineering terms, or so environmentally unfriendly, to maintain a fixed line of defence? When should some managed retreat be allowed?

▲ **Figure 2.73** Adapted extract from *The Guardian*, 18 January 2001

In the UK, MAFF (Ministry of Agriculture, Fisheries and Food) is responsible for the management of coastal flooding in Britain; since 1985 it has also managed coastal protection works, which includes erosion control. Shoreline Management Plans (SMPs) have been produced on behalf of local councils, government agencies and other interested parties, to co-ordinate planning along designated sections of coastline. The aim of each SMP is to provide the basis for sustainable coastal defence policies and to set objectives for future management of the shoreline. It is a requirement that physical, environmental, engineering and planning constraints are taken into account. MAFF guidelines identify four coastal defence options:

1. Do nothing – carry out no new coastal defence activities (except for safety measures).
2. Retreat the Existing Defence Line – to move by intervention the existing defence landward.
3. Hold the Existing Defence Line – by intervention, with additional defences where and when necessary.
4. Advance the Existing Defence Line – by intervention to move the existing defence seaward.

Questions

1 **a** What is meant by coastal management?
b Outline the differences between hard and soft engineering responses to coastal management.

2 With reference to the UK,
a describe the different types of hard engineering methods used
b outline where and why they are most likely to be used
c evaluate, with reference to examples, the advantages and disadvantages of their use.

3 For a named section of coastline, present the arguments for and against
i undertaking defence works to maintain the position of the coastline
ii allowing some managed retreat from the previous position.

Coastal schemes

One of the few countries with a national coastal defence policy is the Netherlands. The Dutch have fought the sea for thousands of years, learning how to build dykes to keep the tide out. If the sea had been allowed to have its way, the country would be about half its current size. Whenever possible the Dutch work with the sea. This approach is seen in the care with which they maintain the sand dunes as their first natural line of defence (Figure 2.78); soft engineering techniques are supported by lines of groynes. From time to time in this age of rising sea levels the Dutch have had no choice but to resort to strong measures that physically keep the sea out, especially after existing coastal defences in the Delta were overwhelmed by the North Sea storm surge of 1953 (page 27). The Zuider Zee and Delta Works are examples of ambitious, hard engineering coastal schemes, in scale well beyond anything ever attempted in the UK.

From time to time the possibility of major schemes has been mooted in the UK, such as an enclosing dam to seal off the Wash and barrages across the Severn estuary and Morecambe Bay. Potential purposes were varied, mainly land reclamation and fresh water storage. The environmental lobby is so much stronger today that they are less likely than ever to be resurrected. One coastal scheme that has recently been completed is the Cardiff Bay barrage, but not without protests from conservationists, who disliked it for wiping out mudflats and who claim that blue-green algae will form in the stagnant water of the lake that forms its centrepiece. It also ran greatly over budget. Its enormous cost was justifiable in the eyes of the Development Corporation by its great value as a catalyst for regeneration, both in the local area and for the region, and not for extra security against the sea in a location with a high tidal range of nearly fifteen metres.

Cardiff Bay barrage

Key facts

- *Cost – £196 million*
- *Dam length – 1.1km, exceeded in Europe only by the flood defences in Holland*
- *Fresh water lake – 200ha*
- *Office and industrial space – over 800,000sq/m*
- *New houses – 6,000*
- *Area renovated – 2,700ha of docks and former steelworks*

▲ **Figure 2.74** View of the Cardiff Bay barrage

The shoreline management plan

Case Study from Saltburn to Flamborough Head

A diverse range of physical, environmental and human considerations were taken into account for the stretch of Yorkshire coast between Saltburn and Flamborough Head. Option 1, 'do nothing', is the most common recommendation for the rural stretches, while Option 3, 'hold the line', is the most common for the settled areas with advice to the councils responsible for implementing coastal works.

Summary of suggestions for the 63 separate sub-cells investigated	
Option 1 - 'Do nothing'	27
Option 2 - 'Retreat the line'	9
Option 3 - 'Hold the line'	17

Figure 2.75 Summary of the Shoreline Management Plan from Saltburn to Flamborough Head

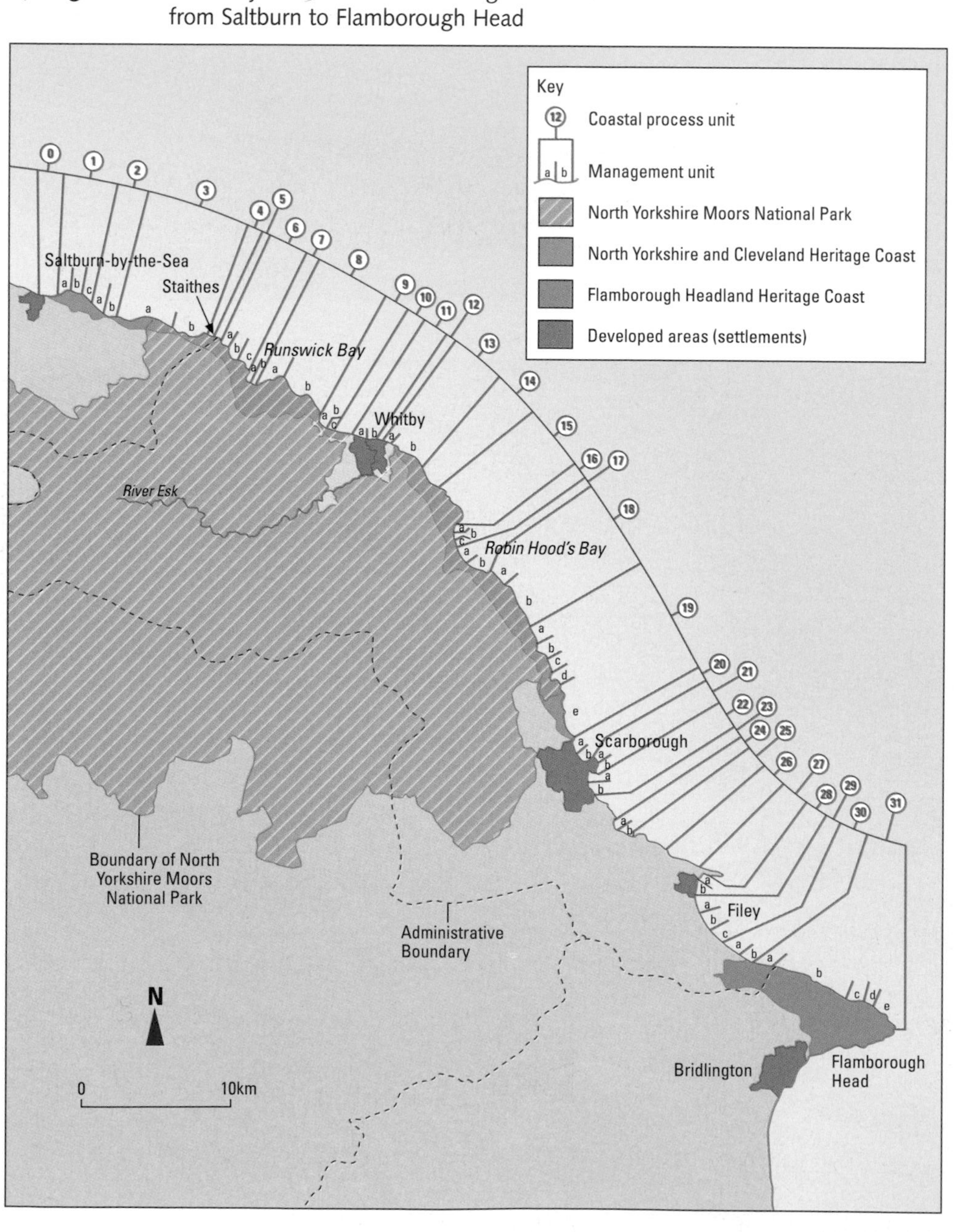

Examples of preliminary benefit analyses

Unit 4 Staithes

The unit contains the densely developed settlement of Staithes, its harbour and numerous listed buildings. It is given Conservation Area status. The benefit value of the unit has consequently been assessed as high suggesting that works to hold or advance the line, therefore increasing or maintaining the current level of defence, are justified.

Unit 5 South of Staithes

The unit is under agricultural management with the only property, that of Cliff Farm, located some distance back from the cliff top. This suggests a low cost/no intervention strategy for the management of this unit.

Physical considerations

The physical characteristics of this section of coastline include:

- high cliffs for the largest part
- cliffs made of Jurassic shale and sandstone in the north
- cliffs made of chalk at Flamborough Head
- soft boulder clay frontages which occur along its length
- sandy beaches mainly at Whitby, Scarborough and Filey
- smaller pocket beaches of sand and shingle, e.g. in Runswick Bay
- coastal erosion which is a danger along the whole coastline.

Human considerations

These include:

- the existing hard defences of settlements (sea walls constructed from masonry, concrete, and gabions, rock armour revetment systems, harbour structures and jetties)
- the low intensity of development, mainly farmland, between settlements
- the high environmental quality – North York Moors National Park, Heritage Coast, RSPB site at Bempton on Flamborough Head – and cultural heritage, e.g. Whitby Abbey
- the importance of tourism and recreation to the local population as well as fishing especially in Whitby.

Action plan to slow down coast erosion

The Government has been urged to set up a special commission to manage Yorkshire's crumbling coastline after a series of alarming landslides. During the past three months sections of the coastline have disappeared beneath the waves, following a pounding from the sea and the toll of heavy rains during the autumn.

Gravestones in St. Mary's Church in Whitby were left teetering on the edge of a cliff face and about 60 tonnes of earth was sheared away. The scenes were reminiscent of the spectacular collapse of the Holbeck Hall Hotel in Scarborough in June 1993. John Riby, Scarborough Borough Council's principal engineer, said millions had been spent on protection schemes in recent years but added: 'It's often hard to justify doing a lot of work in rural areas, where there is only land at risk and not expensive assets like property. ...We can't legislate for weather conditions and the very wet ground that our coastline has.'

Near the edge. Walkers on the coastal path in Whitby in 2000.

Landslide. The Holbeck Hall Hotel on Scarborough's South Cliff collapsed into the sea in 1993.

▲ **Figure 2.76** Adapted extract from *The Northern Echo*, 5 January 2001

Questions

For a case study for the Yorkshire coast between Saltburn and Flamborough Head:

1. Draw a sketch map to show the main coastal features.
2. Explain why it is mainly a coastline of erosion.
3. Make labelled sketches of the landforms of erosion at two or three places along the coast.
4. Outline where and why pockets of deposition occur.
5. State the main features of the management plan for this coast.
6. Present the arguments for and against spending more money on defending this coast.

Coastal management in the Netherlands

Case Study

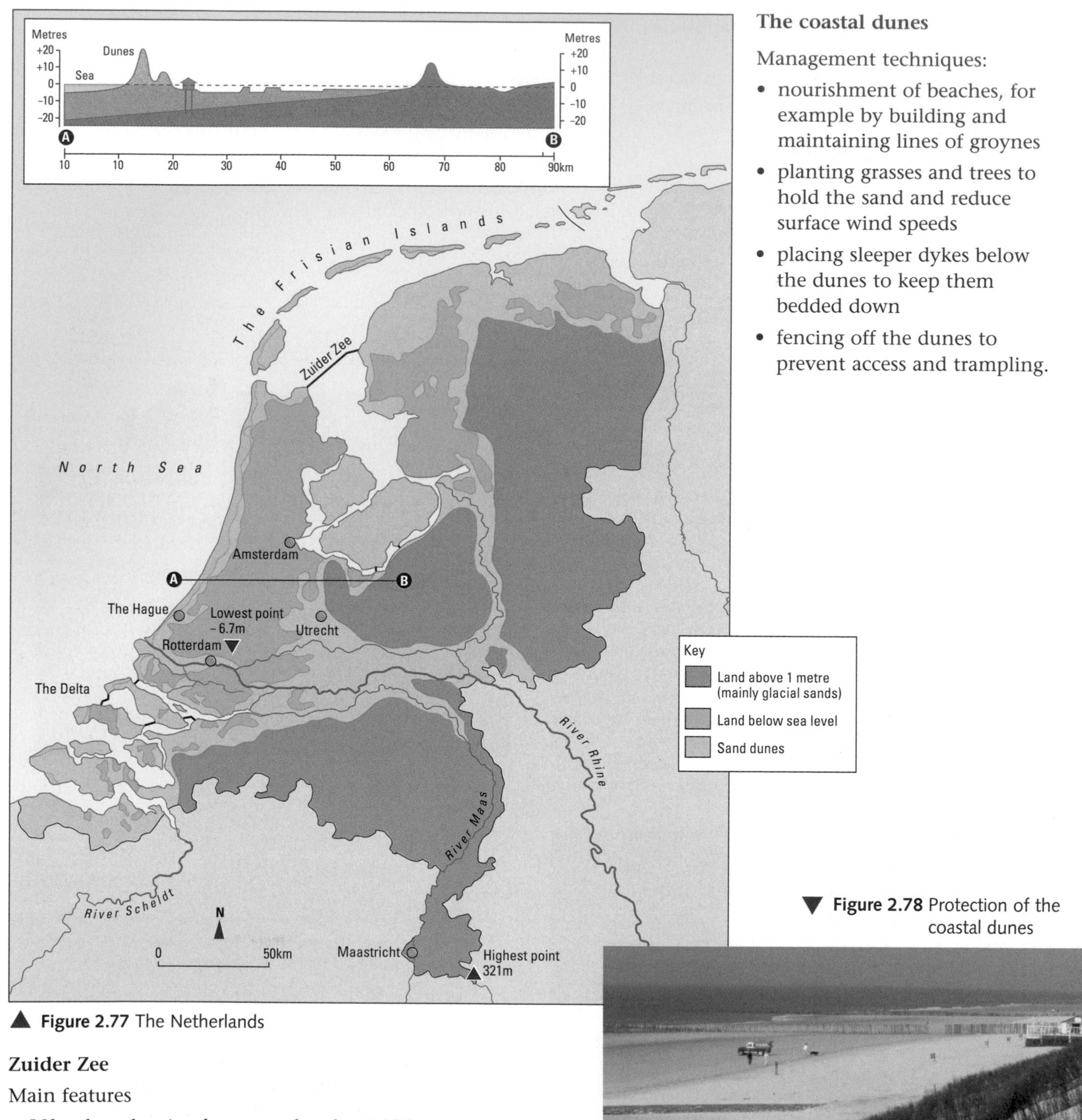

▲ **Figure 2.77** The Netherlands

Zuider Zee

Main features

- 30km long barrier dam completed in 1932
- It was built to remove the threat posed by high spring tides, backed by northerly winds, to hundreds of kilometres of low-lying shorelands
- Behind it is a fresh water lake, the Ijsselmeer, and reclaimed polders. The fifth and final polder, the Markerwaard, is unlikely to be reclaimed due to a combination of less need and increased concern for the environment.

The coastal dunes

Management techniques:

- nourishment of beaches, for example by building and maintaining lines of groynes
- planting grasses and trees to hold the sand and reduce surface wind speeds
- placing sleeper dykes below the dunes to keep them bedded down
- fencing off the dunes to prevent access and trampling.

▼ **Figure 2.78** Protection of the coastal dunes

The Delta

Main features

- In its natural state it consists of an area of islands and peninsulas, between which the distributaries of the Rhine, Maas and Scheldt find their ways to the sea.
- Over the centuries gains were repeatedly wiped out by fresh flooding.
- The scale of the flooding in 1953 forced the Dutch to divert financial resources and use modern technology to support their engineering skills and expertise of coastal management in a massive scheme.
- Ten dams seal off the channels between the big islands to keep the sea water out.
- Only two channels are left open for use by ships to reach the ports of Rotterdam and Antwerp.
- The longest dam, that across the East Scheldt, was built last in the mid-1980s, by which time pressure from environmentalists had increased. Instead of the fixed dams used elsewhere, a storm surge barrier with sluice gates that could be lowered in times of need was built so that it remained salt water preserving salt marsh and mudflats for wildlife.
- The length of coastline to defend in the Delta has fallen from 800 to 80km.

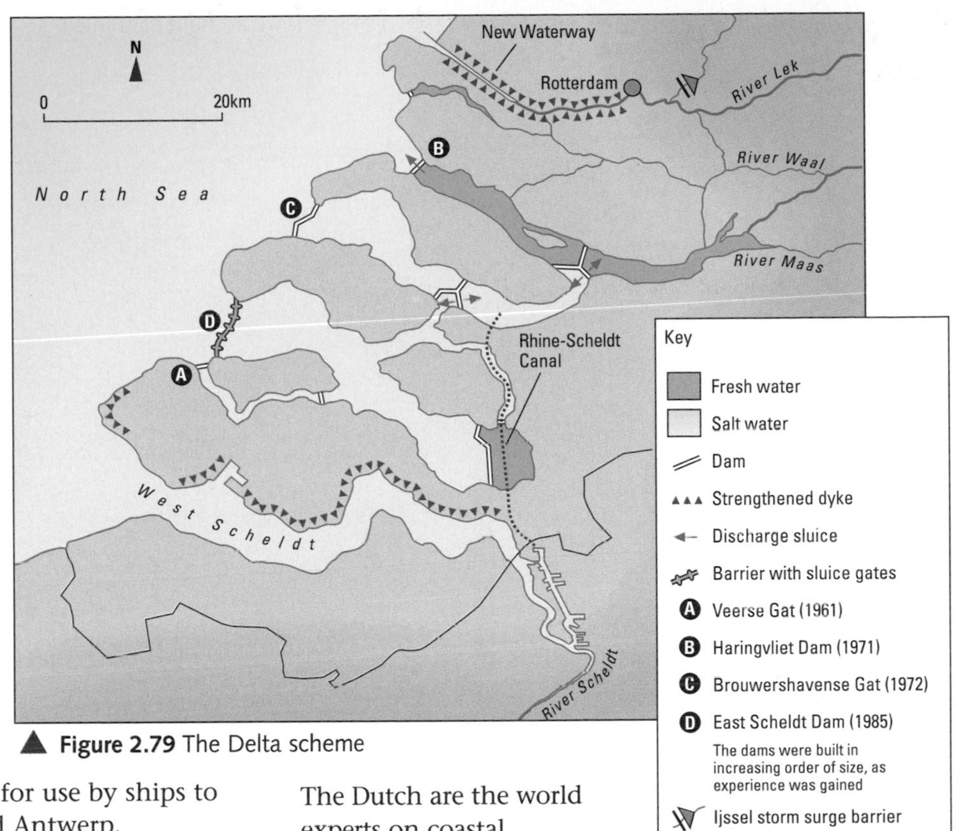

▲ **Figure 2.79** The Delta scheme

The Dutch are the world experts on coastal management. After centuries of rising sea levels they need to be. By 1985 the Dutch had won back virtually all the land that had to be abandoned to the sea during the course of the centuries, but at tremendous financial cost. Coastal defence is also a continuing burden; the Dutch government spends about £300 million a year on keeping the pumps working and maintaining defence works. The money comes from taxes.

Bangladesh

One country which badly needs a national scheme of coastal protection, but cannot afford one, is Bangladesh. A high proportion of the country's land area consists of delta land at or near sea level. The flat islands (chars) formed by deposition are ideal for rice growing, which helps to explain why at least 40 million people live in the region, making it one of the world's most densely populated rural areas. The funnel shape of the Bay of Bengal increases the height and likelihood of storm surges associated with tropical cyclones, a regular climatic hazard which affects the region during late summer and autumn. A tidal surge estimated at nine metres high and driven by 200 kph winds penetrated 150km inland across the flat delta region in 1985; at least 40,000 people were drowned, animals and rice crops were lost and fishing fleets were destroyed. Previous surges had resulted in even more deaths. The Coastal Embankment Project has been established to build embankments and a series of sluices. Mangrove trees have been planted to increase the spread of mangrove swamps as a natural buffer against sea incursions. More emergency shelters have been built on the higher land and flood warning systems have been improved. Appropriate management policies are in place, therefore, but the funding is not available to extend them to all parts of the coastline that need them.

Questions

1 a Draw a sketch map of the Netherlands to show the nature and extent of works to defend and protect the coastline.

b Discuss the relative use of hard and soft engineering techniques by the Dutch.

2 Give reasons why the amount of money spent on coastal protection varies greatly between countries.

3 **Essay**

'Coastal defence is just a matter of money'. Discuss.

Chapter 2 Questions

1 a Figure 1 shows two cliffs.

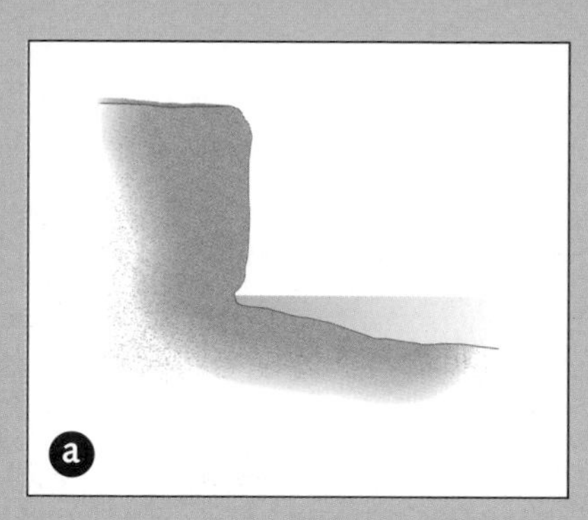

◀ Figure 1

Describe the cliff profiles and comment on their relationship with structure. (3 marks)

b For which one of the two cliffs would you expect the rate of erosion to be most rapid? Explain your answer. (3 marks)

c Outline the conditions that lead to the formation of waves that are particularly destructive along coastlines. (4 marks)

d Explain how sub-aerial processes speed up rates of coastal retreat. (5 marks)

Total: 15 marks

2 Synoptic essay

Explain why, for both physical and human reasons, some coastlines attract more human management than others. (30 marks)

Chapter 3 Geomorphological processes and hazards

Figure 3.1
Scenic beauty in the Andes along the border between Chile and Bolivia – an area of vigorous tectonic activity during the last 80 million years.

Plate tectonics and landforms

The theory of plate tectonics

Scientists now know that the narrow crust which forms the Earth's outer shell (or lithosphere) is composed of at least sixteen rigid plates, seven of which cover considerable areas (Figure 3.2a). The world map looks like a jig-saw puzzle of unevenly shaped pieces of plate. Many of the plates include areas of both ocean and land. What is of great importance is that these plates are continuously in motion – they are moving apart, or squeezing past and rubbing against each other, or crashing into one another. Typically the movement is only a few centimetres each year; however, after having been continuously on the move for hundreds of millions of years, today's world map is nothing like the one from 300 million years ago when scientists believe that there was just one 'super-continent' named Pangaea (Figure 3.2b).

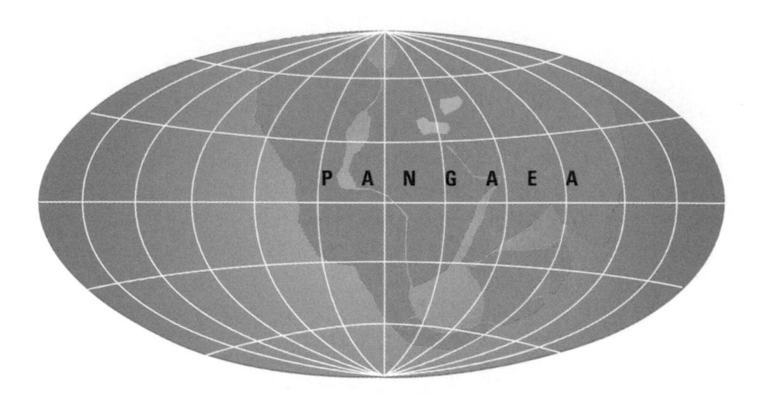

▲ **Figure 3.2b** What the world was thought to have looked like 300 million years ago

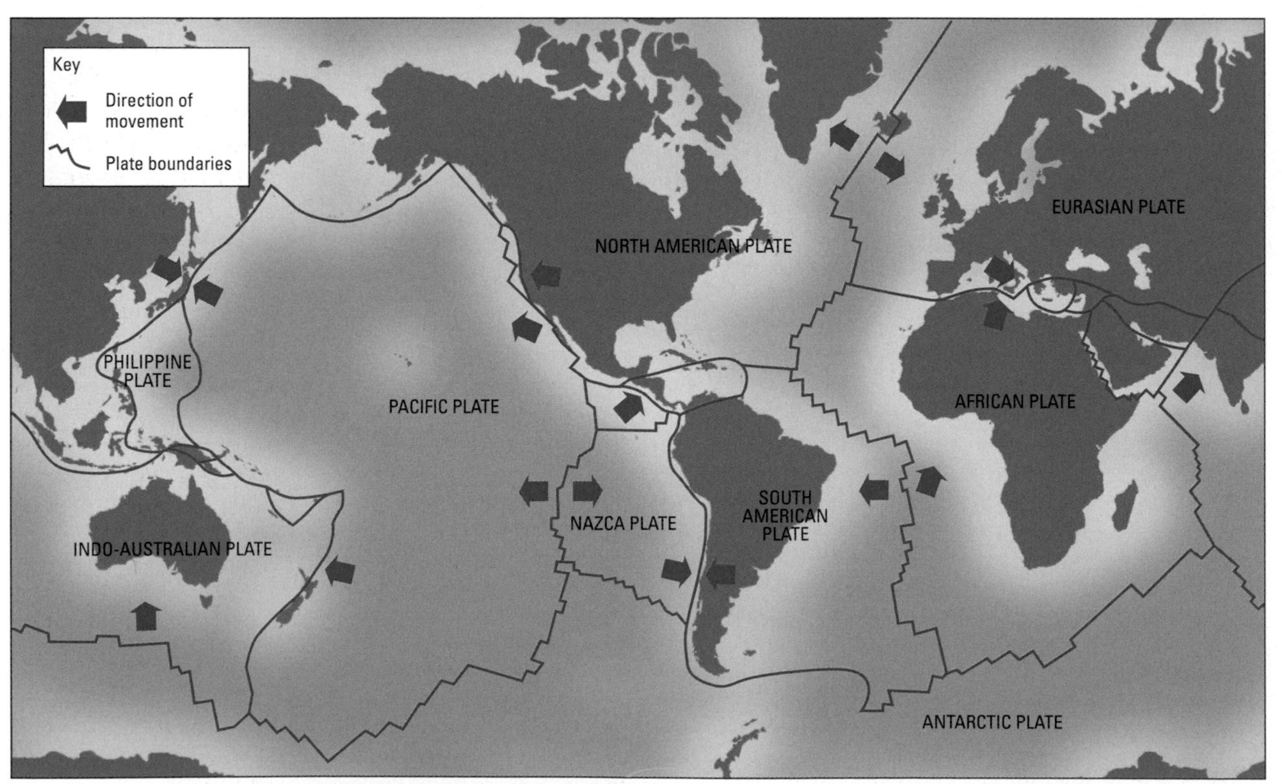

▲ **Figure 3.2a** The world distribution of major tectonic plates

The theory of plate tectonics helps us to understand:

- *the distribution of the world's major landforms*
- *where natural hazards such as volcanoes, earthquakes and tsunamis can strike*
- *the distribution of minerals and energy supplies.*

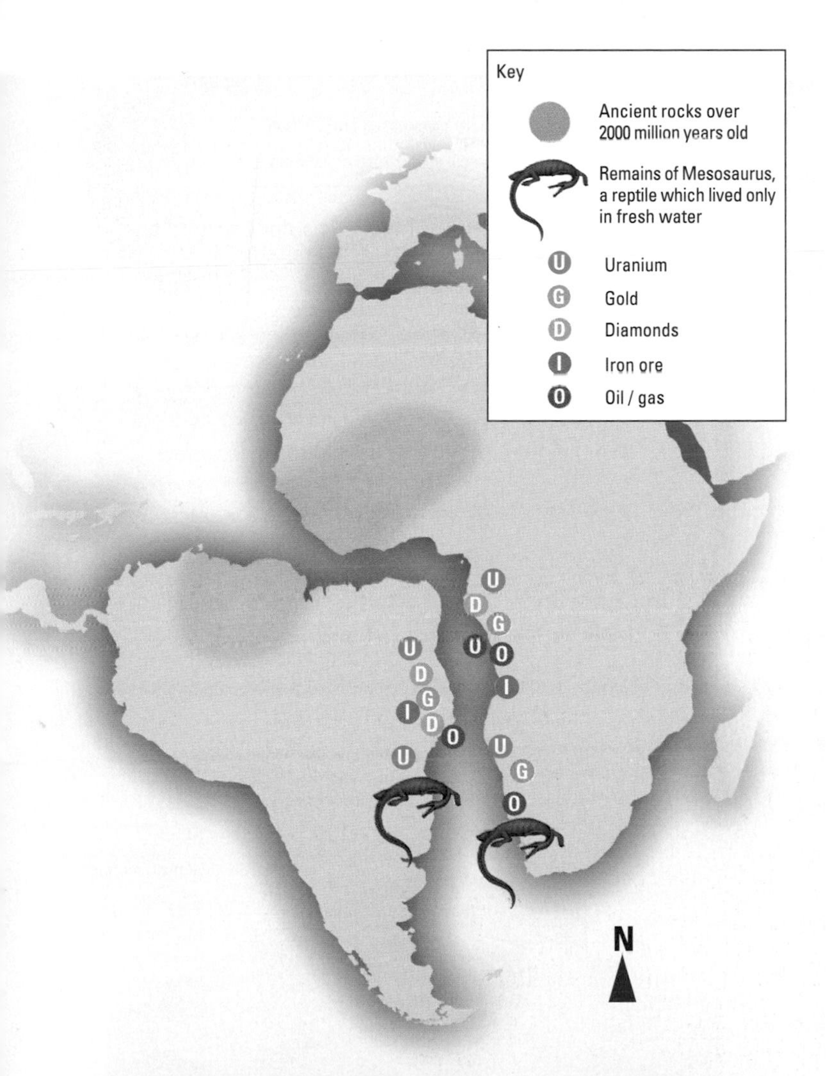

▲ **Figure 3.3** Evidence for the previous existence of Africa and South America as one continent

Essential terminology and areas of study

a Dictionary definitions

- ***Geology*** *Science of the Earth's crust, its rocks and their relations and changes.*
- ***Geomorphology*** *Study of the physical features of the Earth's surface and its geological structures.*

  Therefore through the study of geomorphology the geographical focus is upon surface landforms, although it is acknowledged that it is necessary to use geological evidence of rocks and structures to explain surface features.

Continental drift

During the twentieth century great strides forward were made in the geological and scientific understanding of the Earth. The good fit in the continental jigsaw between South America and Africa had long been noticed by explorers and early map makers. The various early ideas were put together as a theory of 'continental drift' by Alfred Wegener in a book published in 1915. He was trying to explain evidence for climatic change – for example, why fossils of tropical ferns should be found more than 50° north of the Equator in the British Isles and why remnants of glacial deposits should be present in tropical Brazil. Once the theory of continental drift had been suggested and provided a framework for study, others followed up the search for clues. More pieces of evidence were gradually assembled during the twentieth century which strongly suggested that South America and Africa had been one land mass – they are of identical ages, which can be supported by reliable fossil evidence and radio-active dating, and many mineral and glacial deposits are similar (Figure 3.3). Very old rocks, some over 2,000 million years old, are found both in Guyana and the Sahara. The geological column for South East Brazil is similar to that of South West Africa; both include similar mineral deposits, notably diamonds, as well as coal.

Whilst the evidence for continental drift is more varied and strongest for South America and Africa, it is also quite convincing for many of the other continents. Rocks of the same type and age and coal deposits are both present in eastern North America and Western Europe. The coal deposits in both were formed from wet tropical forests present about 300 million years ago. The evidence assembled was so overwhelming that by the 1950s few doubted that drifting of the continents had occurred. One problem remained. What forces or mechanism could possibly have been sufficiently powerful to move the massive block of rock that is a continent? The forces and mechanisms needed, and their causes, began to be understood only from the 1960s onwards by the development of the theory of plate tectonics.

Understanding plate tectonics

Scientific developments in palaeo-magnetism allowed great advances in knowledge of ocean floors. New molten basalt, upwelling from deep within the mantle onto the ocean floors, is magnetized in the direction of the prevailing Earth's magnetic field at the time when it is cooled and solidified. This magnetism is retained in the rock as part of the crustal record. Because the Earth's magnetic field keeps reversing at irregular intervals of a few hundred thousand years, a pattern of magnetic stripes like the one shown in Figure 3.4 is created. The black stripes date from times when there was normal magnetism from the north; the white stripes show times when magnetism was reversed from the south. Therefore the rocks on the ocean floors can be dated. Studies of palaeo-magnetism of these rocks revealed to scientists that rocks lying next to ocean ridges of basalt were the youngest, and that there was a progressive increase in the age of rocks with increasing distance from the ridge. Dating the ocean floor rocks by palaeo-magnetism demonstrated that most of them were young, having been formed within the last 80 million years. What had been discovered was sea-floor spreading. This is the mechanism whereby new ocean crust is continually being created along an ocean ridge from which it spreads on both sides at 1–10cm per year.

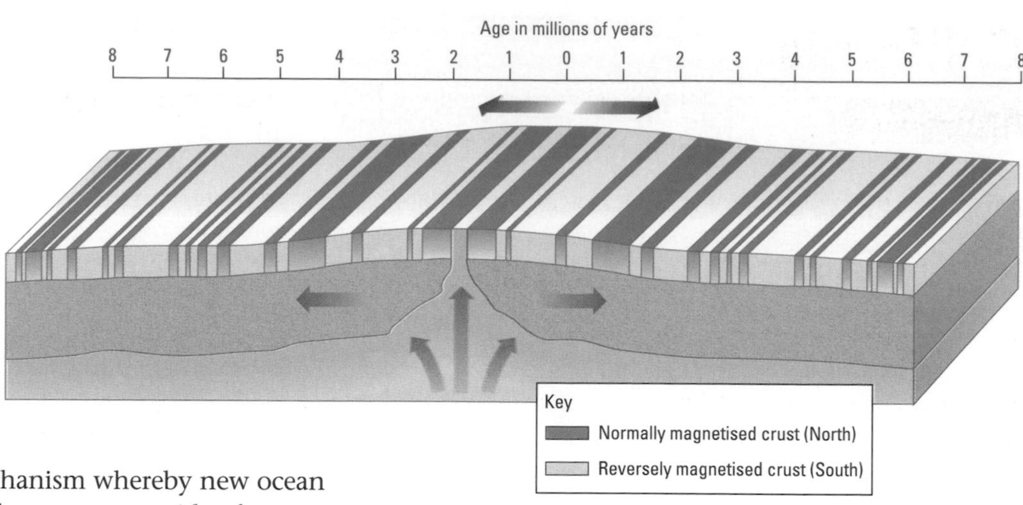

▲ **Figure 3.4** The pattern of magnetic stripes around an ocean ridge showing that sea floor spreading is taking place

Scientists also discovered more about what was happening in the mantle. Despite being made of rock, the mantle rock is under such great pressure that it is capable of flowing. Temperature differences produce convection currents within the mantle. The driving force for these currents is heat from the Earth's molten core. These convection currents carry mantle material up to the centre of the oceanic ridges from which new material is added to the Earth's crust. This pours out through the fracture created by the two plates moving apart. As the plates move apart they carry the continents with them.

The theory of plate tectonics has increased our understanding of the Earth and its landforms by providing us with an explanation for the theory of continental drift. Most scientific investigations now concentrate upon plate margins because these are zones of activity and change.

Questions

1 For the movements of the continents, show how:
   a the old theory of continental drift provided the evidence
   b the new theory of plate tectonics provided the explanation.

2 In what ways and why do the study areas of geography and geology overlap?

The different types of plate margins

Geographers are mainly interested in the surface landforms produced by tectonic activity and their effects upon people. Along constructive and destructive margins it is necessary to study what is happening under the crust, which is usually the preserve of the geologist, in order to understand what is happening on the surface and why it happens. However, conservative margins are different. No materials are being gained or lost along these margins and it is the surface movement that produces the significant results.

Conservative margins

In some places plates meet each other at an oblique angle so that they avoid collision and subduction cannot occur. However, this does not mean that the plates smoothly slide past each other like a well-oiled machine. Movement is erratic; the plates stick until the pressure builds up and one or both jerk forward and move again. Each horizontal change can cause earthquakes as powerful as anything generated along a destructive plate margin. The North Anatolian fault, which caused the devastating earthquake in Turkey in August 1999, is of this type (see pages 96–97).

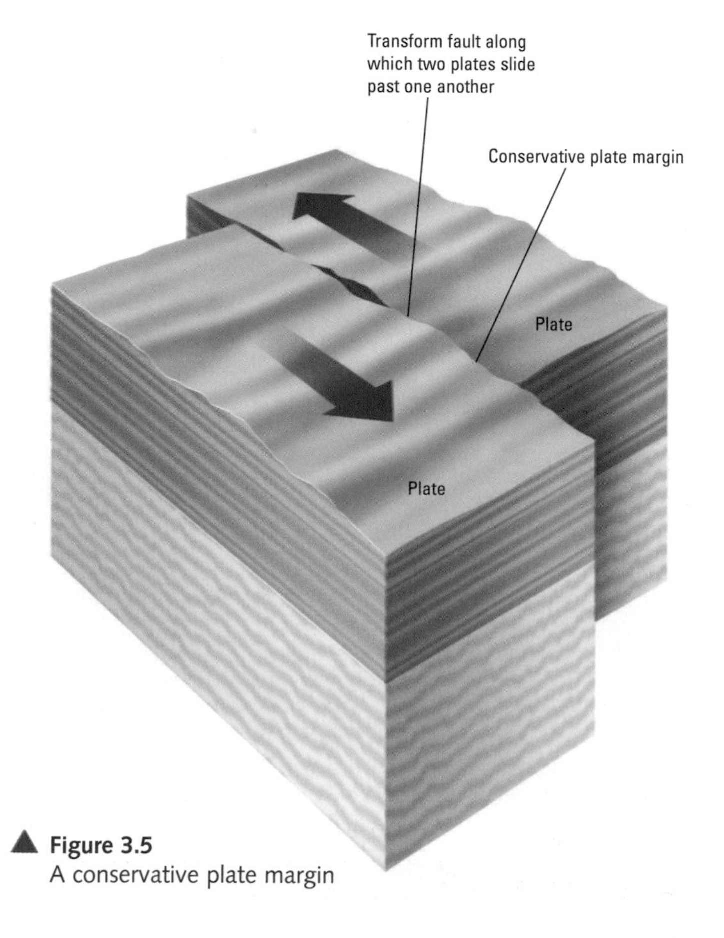

▲ **Figure 3.5**
A conservative plate margin

California: the conservative plate margin

Case Study

This is the conservative plate margin which receives the most publicity and greatest scientific study. The North American plate is almost stationary; if anything there is the gentlest of movements north westwards, but the Pacific plate is moving north westwards by up to 10cm per year. The San Andreas fault line is the largest and best known (Figure 3.6), but there is a complex pattern of faults running through some of the most highly populated areas in California. In recent years movements along the Hayward fault have been responsible for damage in the San Francisco region. Several smaller faults around Los Angeles have been much more active than the big fault line itself.

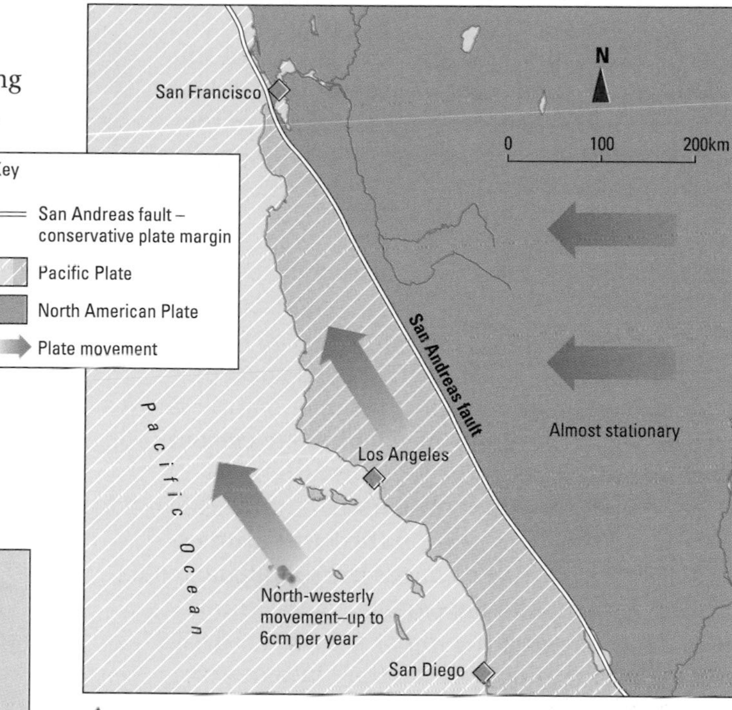

▲ **Figure 3.6** The conservative plate margin in California

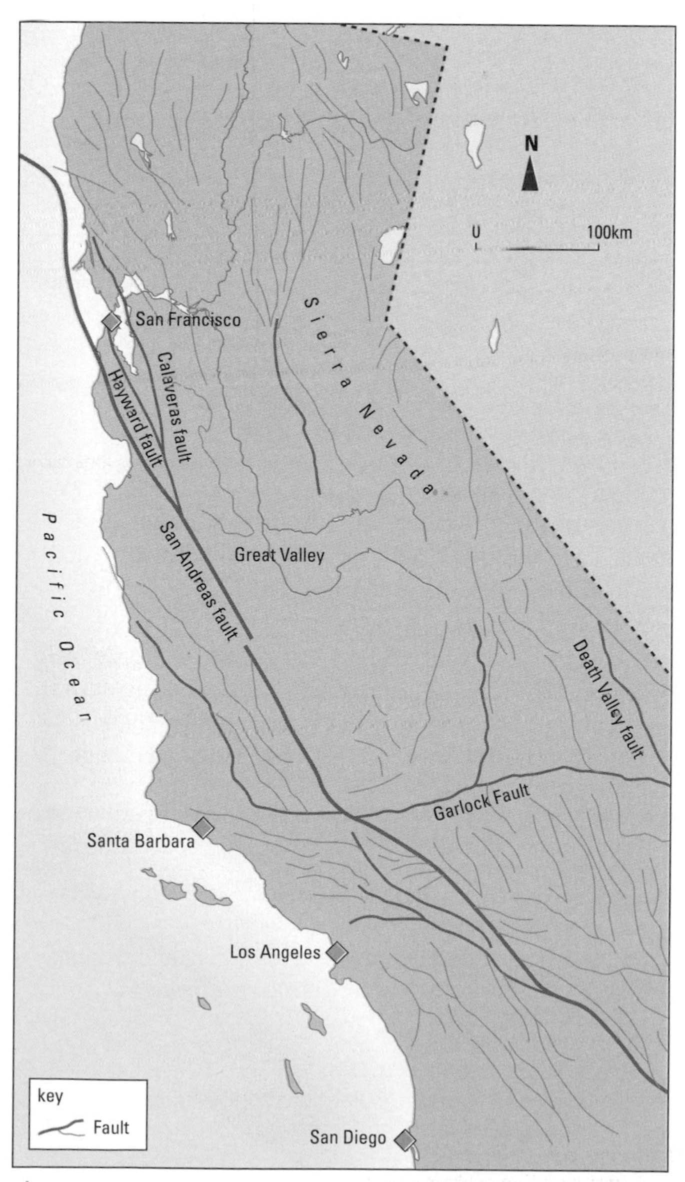

▲ **Figure 3.7** The main fault lines in California

▲ **Figure 3.8** In the Loma Prieta earthquake of 1989 the greatest loss of life occurred when a double decker segment of Interstate road 880 collapsed.

Constructive margins

These are located in the three main oceans – in the mid-Atlantic, eastern Pacific and central Indian – where new plate material from fissures on the ocean floors is being added before being carried away by sea floor spreading. Together the total length of all these constructive margins exceeds over 40,000km. The presence of the mid-Atlantic ridge, from which the occasional volcanic island protrudes above the ocean surface, makes the constructive margin running up the full length of the Atlantic Ocean the clearest of all. Iceland is the largest island on the ridge.

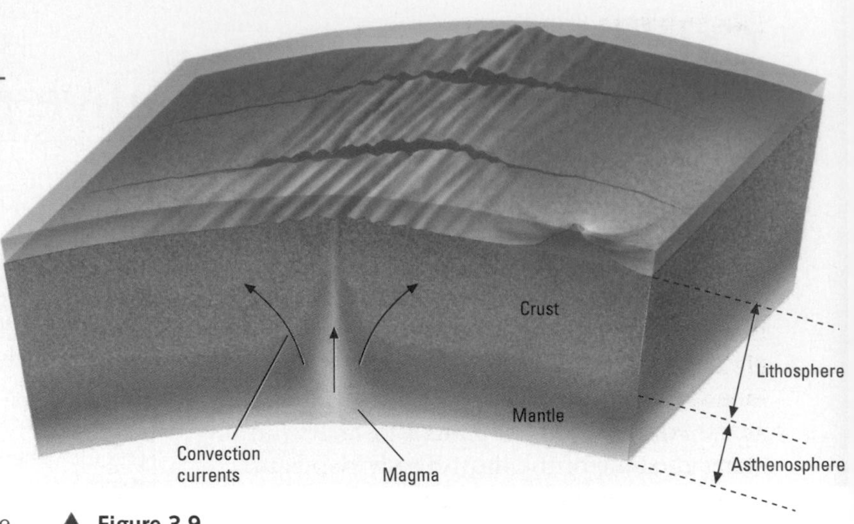

▲ **Figure 3.9** What is happening at a constructive plate margin

These margins are described as 'constructive' because molten magma rises from the mantle and reaches the surface as basalt, which adds new crustal material on the Earth's surface. The plates are being pulled apart by diverging convection currents in the upper mantle. As the two plates move apart, giant fractures are created through which the magma, being forced up by convection currents, reaches the surface as lava. This basaltic lava is the newest rock on the Earth's surface. The diverging plates cause rifting as the solid basalt splits and fractures into many long parallel cracks, known as fissures, which run along the top of the ridge. These fissures vary in width from 1m to 1km; in terms of length they can extend for many kilometres. Magma from the mantle is forced into the cracks as they develop and it solidifies. As the plates move large cracks, called transform faults, are created at right angles to the plate boundary. Some of the magma reaches the surface as basalt lava flows. Underwater lava soon cools in pillow-like lumps, but where eruptions occur above the ocean surface, lively fountains of red hot lava issue from fissures creating fast-flowing streams of glowing lava. Rifting causes earthquakes, but these rarely measure more than 6.0 on the Richter scale.

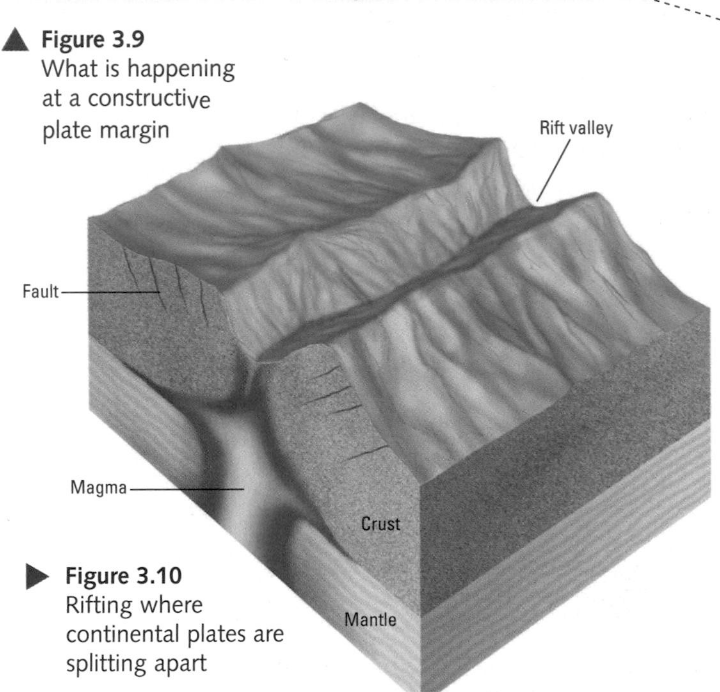

▶ **Figure 3.10** Rifting where continental plates are splitting apart

▲ **Figure 3.11** Lava flows from the volcano Hekla in Iceland

In summary the growth of oceanic plates along the constructive margins occurs continuously and is considerable in scale, producing rift valleys, oceanic ridges and volcanoes. However, it is all happening relatively gently so that violent eruptions or rapid earth movements are rare. One sub-type is where continental plates split apart; the major landform created by this separation is the rift valley, as in East Africa (see page 79).

Questions

1. a Outline the physical differences between conservative and constructive margins.
   b Explain briefly why spreading, divergent and tensional are alternative names for constructive margins.
2. For constructive margins:
   a describe their world distribution
   b explain why they are associated with the formation of:
   i ocean ridges,
   ii rift valleys.

Destructive margins

Destructive margins are concentrated around the Pacific Ocean. There are several different crustal plates within the Pacific Ocean. The largest of these is the Pacific Plate which is moving north-westwards before it eventually plunges most forcibly beneath the eastern edge of the Eurasian Plate and to a lesser extent the North American Plate. However, on the way it also interacts with the smaller plates such as the Philippine and Indo-Australian Plates producing the island arcs which are such a feature of the western Pacific from Alaska to New Zealand. Another destructive margin lies along the eastern Pacific where the Nazca and other smaller oceanic plates collide into the continental crust of Central and South America.

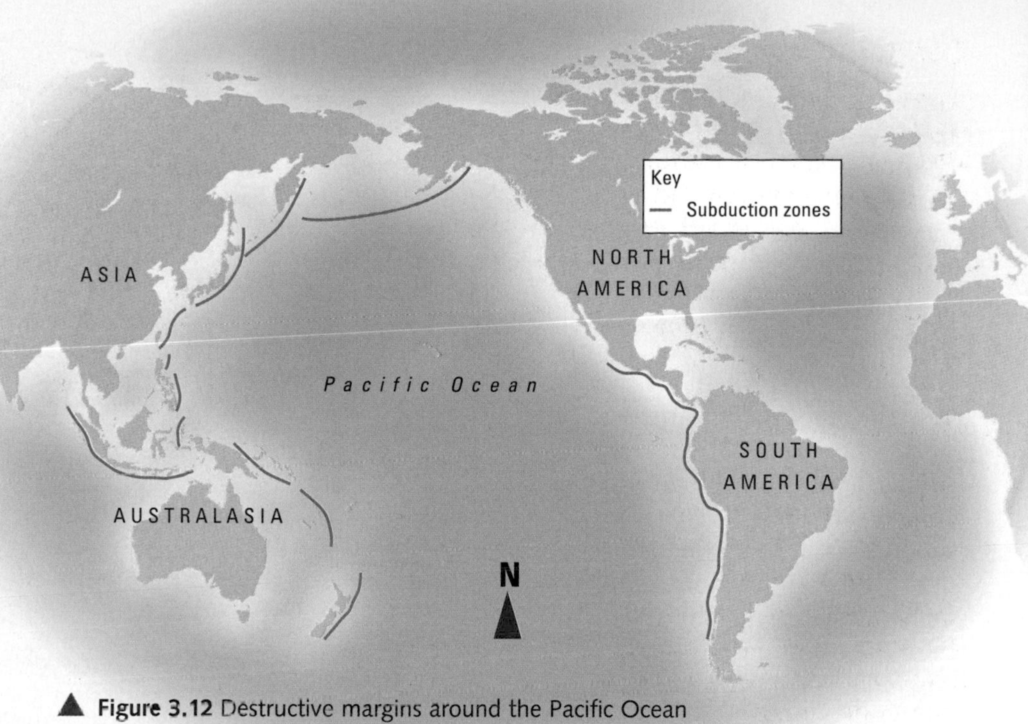

▲ **Figure 3.12** Destructive margins around the Pacific Ocean

	Oceanic crust	*Continental crust*
Density	*Denser (average 3.0)*	*Lighter (average 2.7)*
Thickness	*Greater and more varied (40–70km)*	*Smaller and more even (6–10km)*
Age	*Older (most over 1,500 million years old)*	*Younger (most well under 200 million years old)*

▲ **Figure 3.13** Differences between oceanic and continental crusts

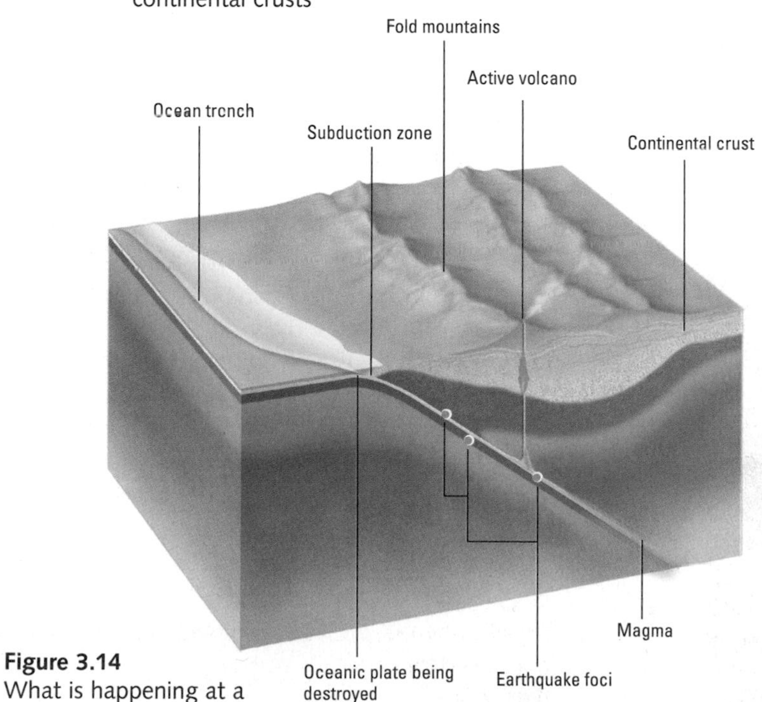

▶ **Figure 3.14** What is happening at a destructive plate margin

These margins occur where two plates converge. One plate is destroyed as it is forced down into the mantle to be reabsorbed. This is known as subduction and is the consequence of sea floor spreading. The other plate is forced up and over it. The subduction zone is an ocean trench with one wall formed by the subducted plate and the other by the overriding plate. These ocean trenches are very deep, usually 5,000–11,000m. Oceanic and continental crusts have different properties (see the Information box). The heavier oceanic crust sinks or subducts below the lighter continental crust at an average rate of 2–10cm a year, but the movement is jerky and this increases the already considerable strains and pressures as rock moves against rock. Also the leading edge of the overriding plate scrapes the sediments from its surface, piling them up, before pressure from the colliding plates causes the crumpling and folding of sediments to form mountain ranges. As a result of pressure and heat, magma is intruded, some of which reaches the surface in volcanic eruptions which are frequently violent. The friction created by the destruction of the plates generates earthquake shocks and therefore destructive plate margins are areas of intense seismic activity (see page 91).

In other words, destruction of plates is a much less gentle process than their construction. Great tectonic activity and major landform formation result. Associated with destructive margins are the world's highest mountain ranges, the majority of active volcanoes and the most damaging earthquakes.

One sub-type is where the two crusts which converge are both oceanic: because densities are similar, speed of movement controls which one of the two subducts. The faster one is destroyed and the molten crust material that rises up to the ocean floor as lava builds up island arcs (Figure 3.15).

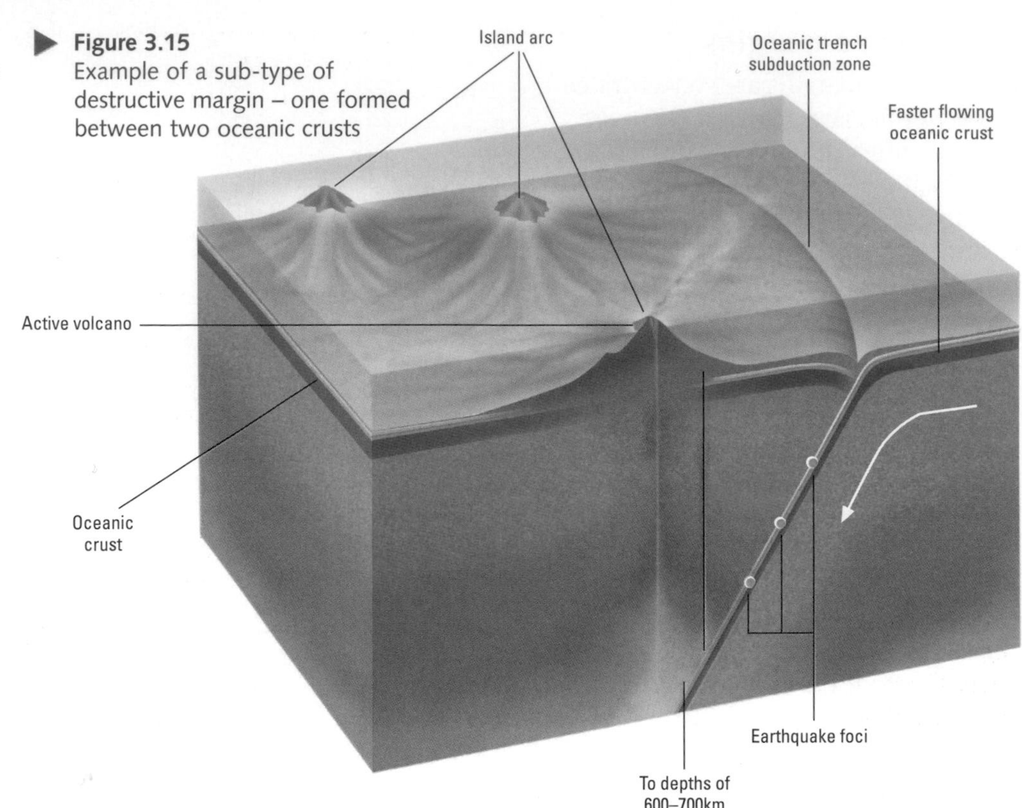

Figure 3.15 Example of a sub-type of destructive margin – one formed between two oceanic crusts

Hot spots

In examining the global distributions of major landforms and the reasons for them in the next part of this chapter, attention will be focused upon plate margins. However, a few active volcanoes do exist in locations well away from any plate margin. These are volcanic hot spots. They may be in the ocean, which is where the best known example, the Hawaiian islands, lies. Others are on land, for example the volcanic region around Rotorua in the North Island of New Zealand. As their name suggests, these are points where molten material from the mantle breaks through the rocks of the Earth's crust to reach the surface. They are caused by convectional plumes of very hot magma in the mantle which burn through the crustal rocks to reach the surface – in a similar way to burning through metal with a blowtorch.

The important point to understand is that the plume is stationary. The point where the hot material breaks out of the mantle and on to the surface stays in the same place. However, where it reaches the surface changes with time, because plates move, as the theory of plate tectonics tells us. Above the hot spot a volcano forms and grows and grows until the plate carries it away. Once the volcano has been carried away and no longer sits over its hot spot, it loses its source of magma. A new volcanic cone begins to form on top of the hot spot.

The Hawaiian islands are a perfect illustration of this. All the Hawaiian islands are volcanic. The nearest land is over 3,000km away. The islands lie on top of the Pacific plate which is moving north westwards by about 10cm a year. Volcanic activity today only takes place in the south-east corner of the island chain on the big island, called Hawaii (Figure 3.17). Mauna Loa is a huge volcano. It rises 9,000m from the floor of the Pacific Ocean to its summit, which itself is 4,170m above sea level. At its ocean base it is over 90km wide. Imagine how enormous this volcano would become if, without any plate movement, it remained over the magma plume for ever.

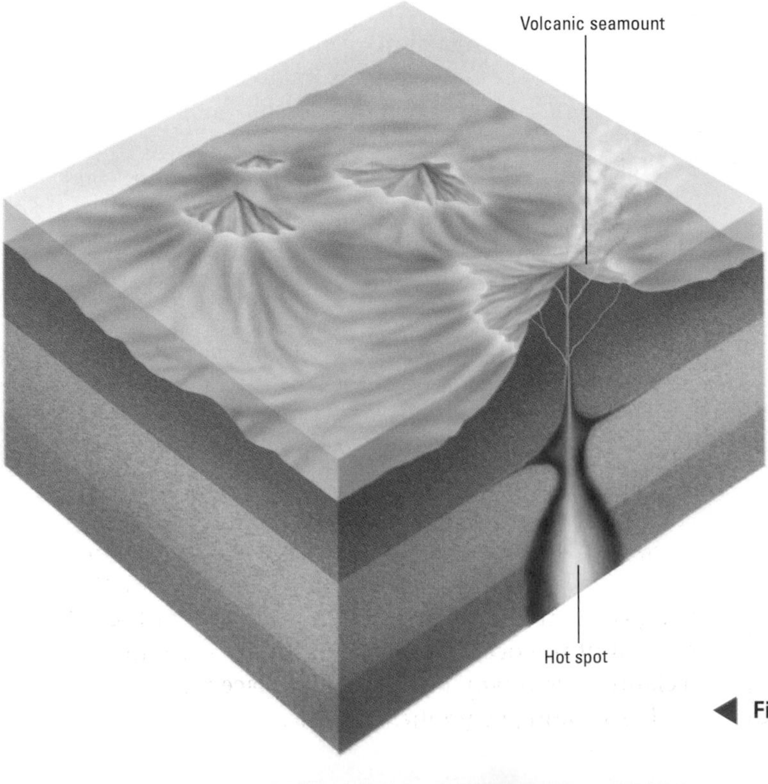

Volcanic seamount

Hot spot

Figure 3.16 Oceanic hot spot

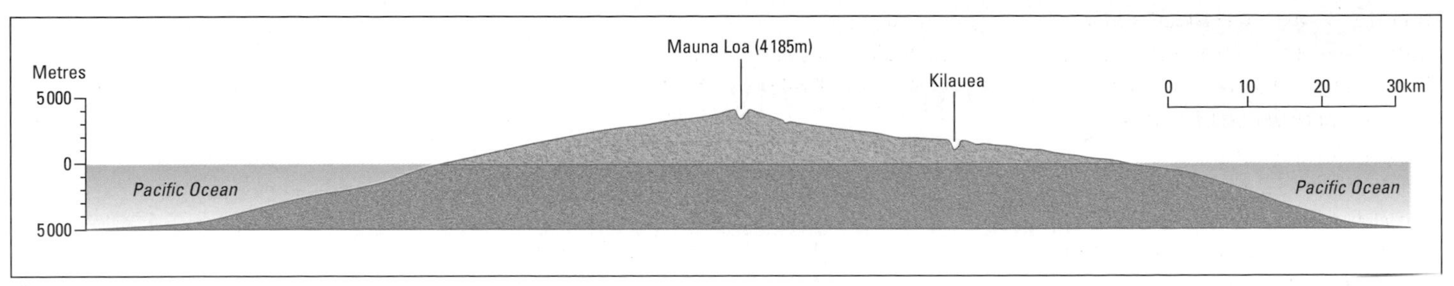

▲ **Figure 3.17** Mauna Loa

The source of the magma is in the mantle. This means that the plume is bringing new materials onto the surface, in the same way as along constructive margins. It is not surprising, therefore, that the type of lava erupted is also the same – very hot, runny basalt around 1,100–1,200°C. Its key features are identical to eruptions along constructive margins (see Information box below). Although these lava flows can do immense damage to buildings and crops in their path, only occasionally are they life-threatening. Kilauea, a subsidiary crater on the lower slopes of Mauna Loa, has been active for over 150 years. Its regular eruptions and magnificent firework displays, which happen on average every three years, are a major tourist attraction. Recent activity has been from two long fissures – the Great Crack and the East Rift (Figure 3.18).

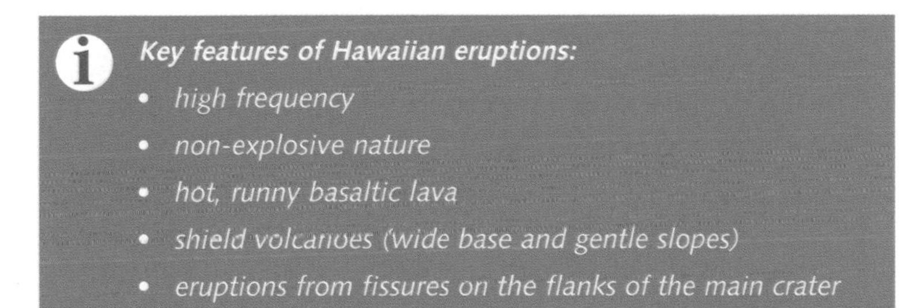

Key features of Hawaiian eruptions:

- *high frequency*
- *non-explosive nature*
- *hot, runny basaltic lava*
- *shield volcanoes (wide base and gentle slopes)*
- *eruptions from fissures on the flanks of the main crater*

Questions

1. a What is meant by a hot spot?
   b Explain what is happening at a hot spot.
2. a Draw a labelled sketch map to show the Hawaiian islands in relation to the plate margins.
   b For Hawaii, state and explain the evidence that:
   i hot spots are stationary and plates move
   ii many eruptions occur on the sides of shield volcanoes.
   c A sign in the Hawaiian National Park directs people to the eruption site. Why do people flock to eruptions instead of fleeing from them?

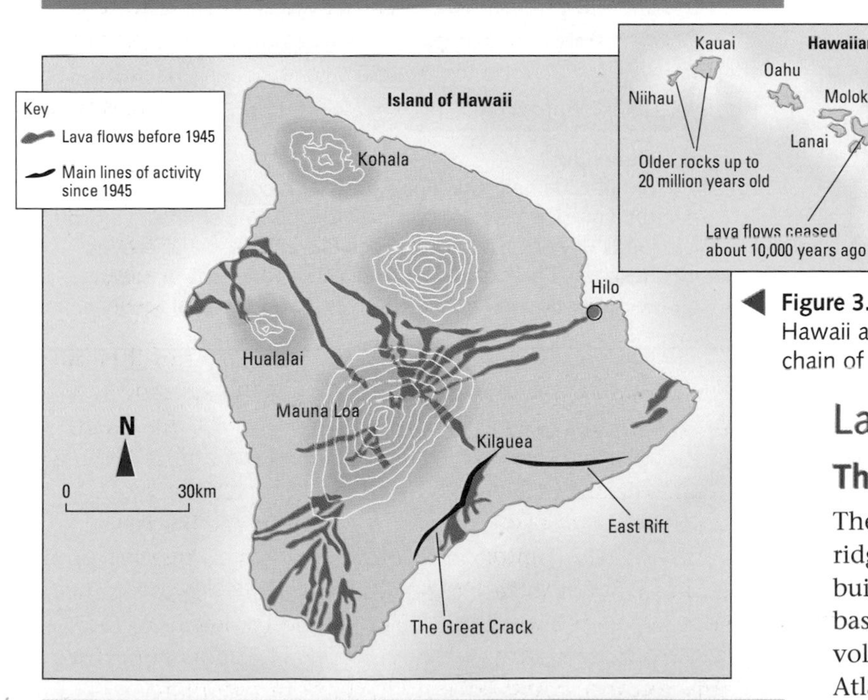

◀ **Figure 3.18** Hawaii and the Hawaiian chain of islands

Already the next Hawaiian island is being formed under the sea. It has been called Loihi and is located south and east of the island chain. It will be some time before it appears above the Pacific Ocean. At present eruptions are taking place some 1000m below the sea surface.

Landforms at constructive margins

The ocean ridge

The largest and most extensive landform is the ocean ridge, which is a mountain range on the ocean floor built by the continuous and massive outpourings of basaltic lava. Where the ridge reaches the surface volcanic islands form. The largest island on the mid-Atlantic ridge is Iceland. Where Iceland lies, that section of the mid-Atlantic ocean ridge is above sea level. Therefore the landforms typical of constructive margins, that are usually hidden from view at the bottom of the ocean, are present for all to see in Iceland. This is why it is a popular place for geologists and geographers to visit.

Iceland:

Case Study tectonic activity

Across the centre of the country following the course of the mid-Atlantic ridge are major fault lines, rifts and many fissures caused by tension as the plates moved apart. This central area of Iceland has the most tectonic activity; for example, earthquakes are more likely here than elsewhere. What Iceland is best known for are its active volcanoes and thermal areas, which are also located in this north–south corridor. Whilst most of the lava has spread out from massive fissures, there are some volcanic cones of the same type as on Hawaii. They have built up shield volcanoes. During the twentieth century there have been fourteen major eruptions, one of which in 1963 produced the youngest volcano of all, Surtsey, which lies off the south coast. On both sides of this central zone of current tectonic activity are basaltic plateaus, up to 5km thick, which are older and which have been carried westwards and eastwards by the American and Eurasian plates respectively.

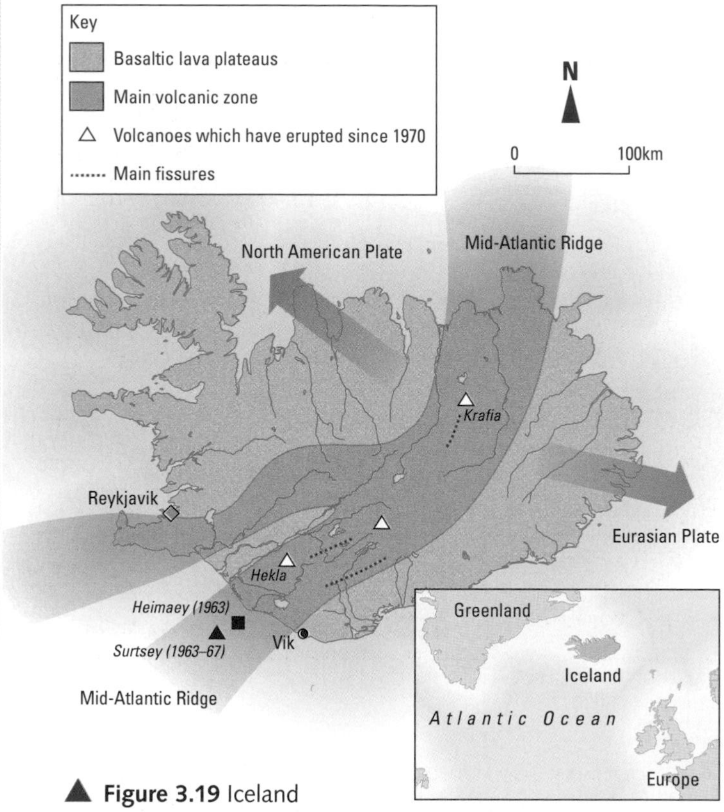

▲ **Figure 3.19** Iceland

▲ **Figure 3.20**
Basalt cliffs near Vik along the south coast of Iceland on the Eurasian plate. When basalt cools and shrinks, vertical joints develop. When the rock is weathered and eroded, hexagonal blocks and columns are prominent between these vertical joints, which gives unique coastal scenery.

The rift valley

The other major landform is the rift valley. The doming up of the crust, as a result of the intense pressure from the convection currents within the mantle, leads to rocks splitting along their weakest points. As the plates move apart, faults form and the fractures are widened by tension. Rift valleys occur where two parallel down-faults have produced a trough. In reality there are often several parallel faults rather than just two. The sides of the rift valley tend to be rugged and steep as scarp faces separate the faulted blocks of land. Again surface rift valleys are easier to study than those on the ocean floors.

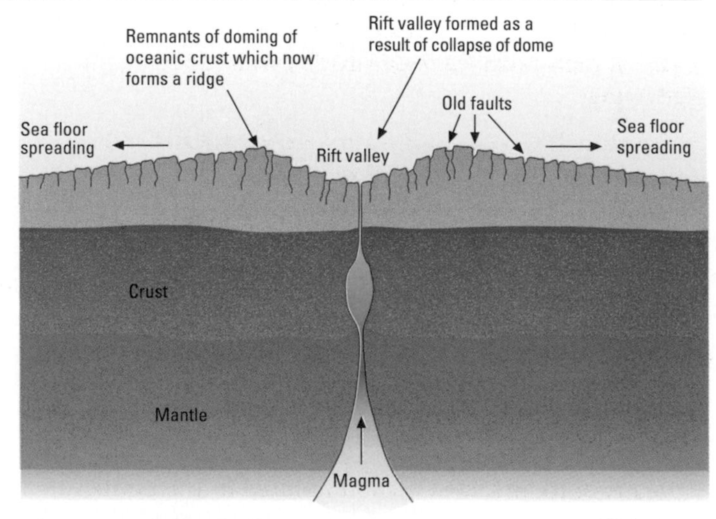

▲ **Figure 3.21** Rift valley formation

East Africa: the Great Rift Valley

Case Study

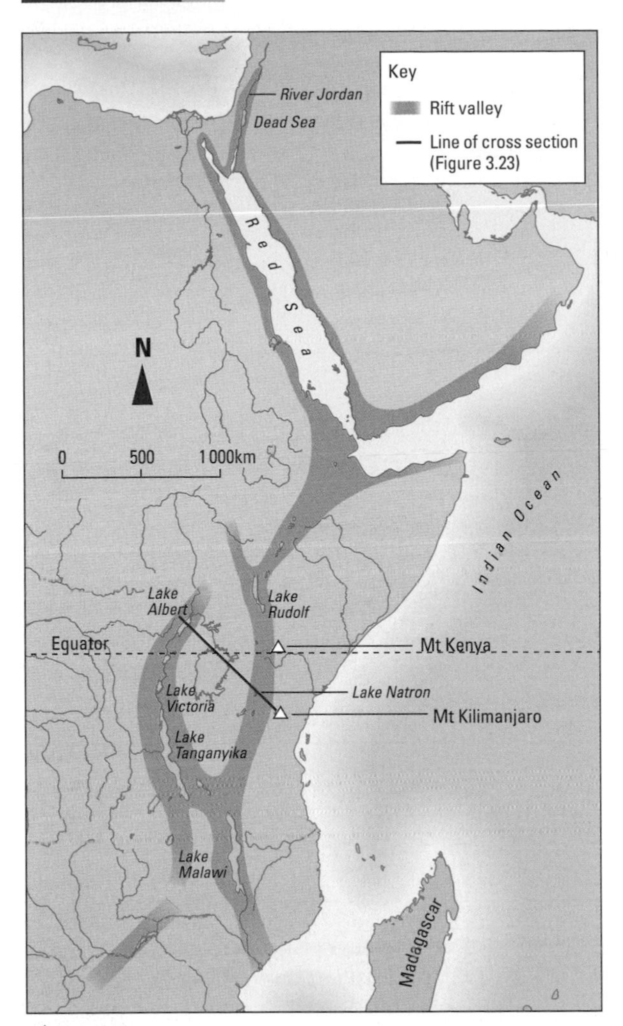

▲ **Figure 3.22** The Great Rift Valley

The rift valley system beginning with that of the River Jordan in the north stretches for over 4,000km through East Africa (Figure 3.22). The width of the rifting is greatest in the Red Sea where the Arabian plate has split apart from the African plate. Both arms of the Great Rift Valley of East Africa hold large ribbon lakes, with Lake Tanganyika close to an incredible 5,000m deep. These rift valleys almost encircle Lake Victoria, itself the world's second largest lake in terms of area, which occupies a broad depression where the surface has sagged (Figure 3.23). Volcanoes are associated with the eastern rift, mainly in Kenya and Tanzania, where the almost perfect cone of Kilimanjaro, Africa's highest mountain, is located. The faults are believed to create an easy route for lava to reach the surface.

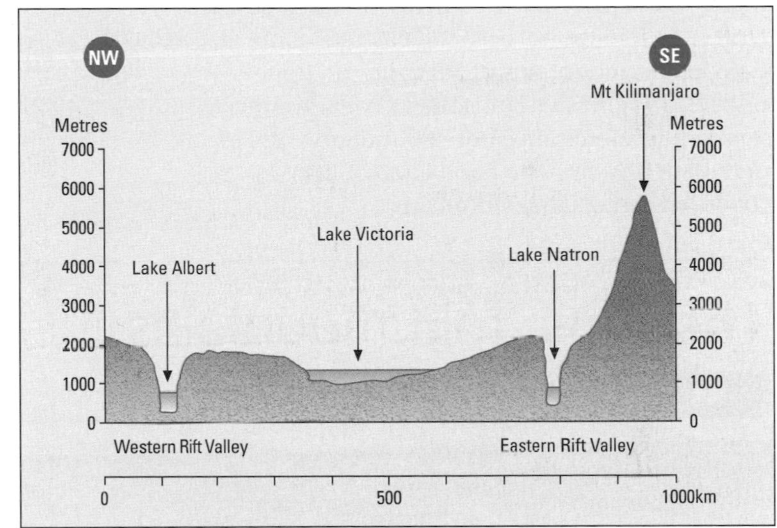

▲ **Figure 3.23** Cross section through part of East Africa

Landforms at destructive margins

The major continental landforms are the ranges of fold mountains which, because of the scale of the movements and their recent formation, form the highest points on the Earth's surface. They are the end result of a cycle of mountain building which involves the following:

- **Erosion** The rocks of the land are weathered and eroded by rivers, waves, glaciers and wind.
- **Deposition** Thick piles of sedimentary and volcanic rocks are deposited on the ocean floor where they accumulate and are carried along on the plate by sea floor spreading.
- **Deformation** As the crust of the ocean floor slides under the continent in the subduction trench, these materials are deformed.
- **Uplift** The pressure of colliding plates causes crustal material to be folded up and uplifted into mountain ranges.
- **Vulcanicity** Some of the crustal material which is melted by pressure and heat in the subduction zone is intruded as giant batholiths of granite into the core of the mountain range; the rest reaches the surface and builds up volcanic cones.

There is nothing accidental or haphazard about the distribution of young fold mountains (mountains formed mainly within the last 100 million years). They occur where subduction zones border continents. It is the theory of plate tectonics which provides us with the explanation for their uplift and growth. They run in lines along the margins of the plates which created them (Figure 3.24). There are two young fold mountain systems. One circles the Pacific Ocean reaching its greatest height in the Andes. The other extends in an east–west direction through Europe and Asia and includes the Alps and Himalayas, the latter forming the world's highest mountain range. Within each fold mountain range there is not just one line of mountains;

instead there are several long parallel ranges, separated by high plateaus and deep valleys. Many already impressive mountain landscapes have been made more rugged and even more spectacular by glacial erosion. Around the Pacific, snow-capped volcanic cones add to the scenic variety and beauty.

Old fold mountains were formed along old, previously active plate margins. The Caledonian mountains of Scotland, the mountains of Norway and the Appalachian mountains were formed as one mountain range before Europe and America drifted apart. Similarities between them was one of the strong pieces of evidence for the Theory of Continental Drift. Old fold mountains, such as the Caledonian mountains of Scotland, no doubt once had impressive landscapes similar to today's young fold mountains, but 400 million years of denudation (weathering and erosion) has produced today's low mountains.

▼ **Figure 3.24** The world distribution of fold mountains

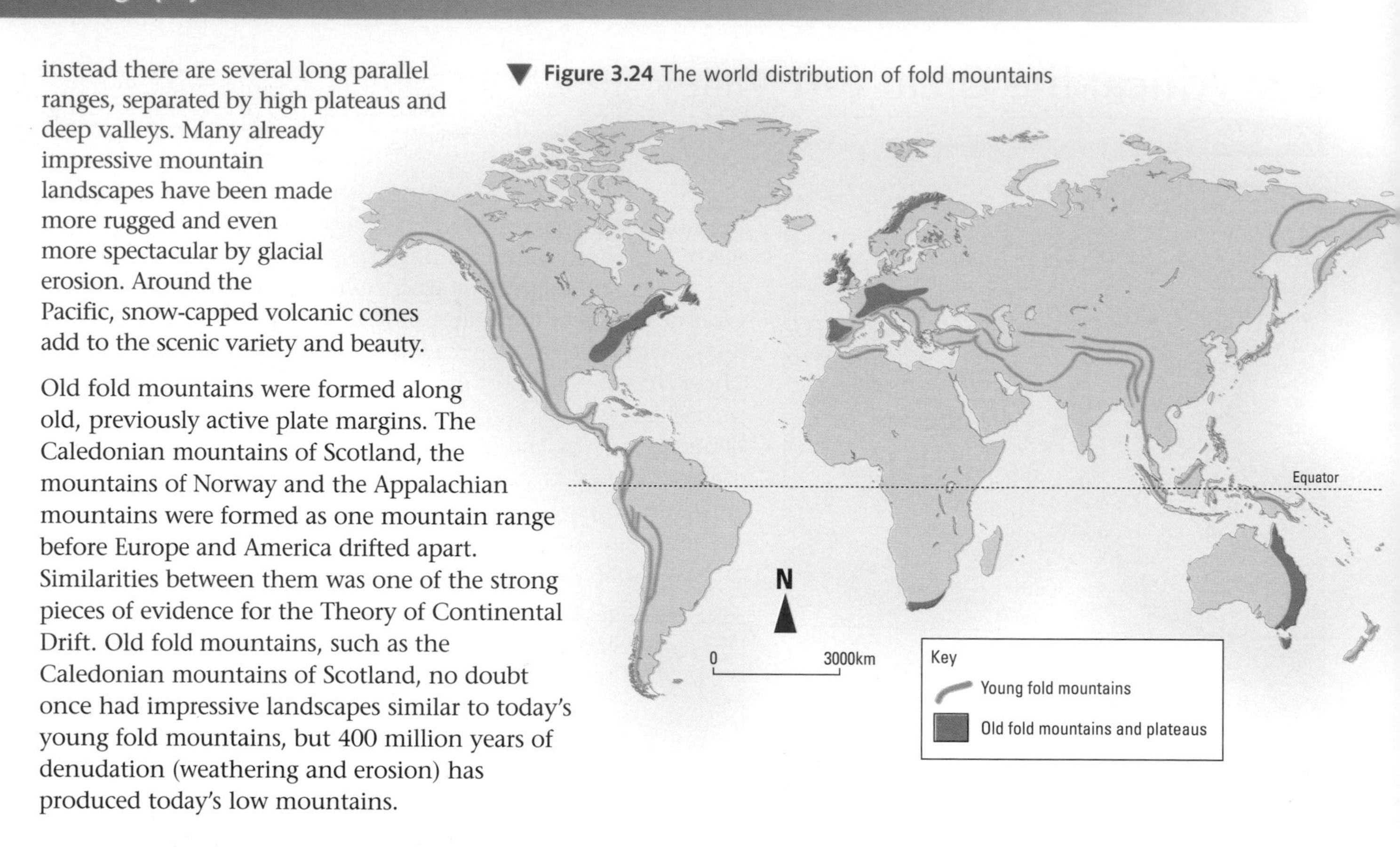

Case Study – The Alps: fold mountains

The Alps: fold mountains

Case Study

▲ **Figure 3.25** The Swiss Alps – there is a vertical difference of about 3,000m between mountain peak and floor of glaciated valley in the photograph.

The Alps were formed about 35 million years ago by the collision of the African and Eurasian plates. A vast amount of sediment had accumulated in the sea of Tethys by erosion after earlier periods of mountain building (orogenies). The most intense period of deformation and uplift led to complex folding which produced a line of high peaks from south-eastern France to Austria. Around the edges folding was more gentle; for example, in the Jura mountains of France and Switzerland simple folds of anticlines and synclines dominate. Such was the scale of the upheaval that even rocks in southern England were upfolded.

▼ **Figure 3.26** The formation of the Alps

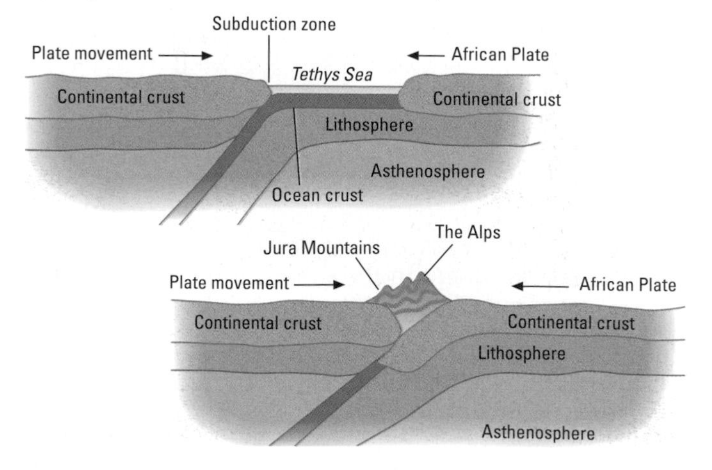

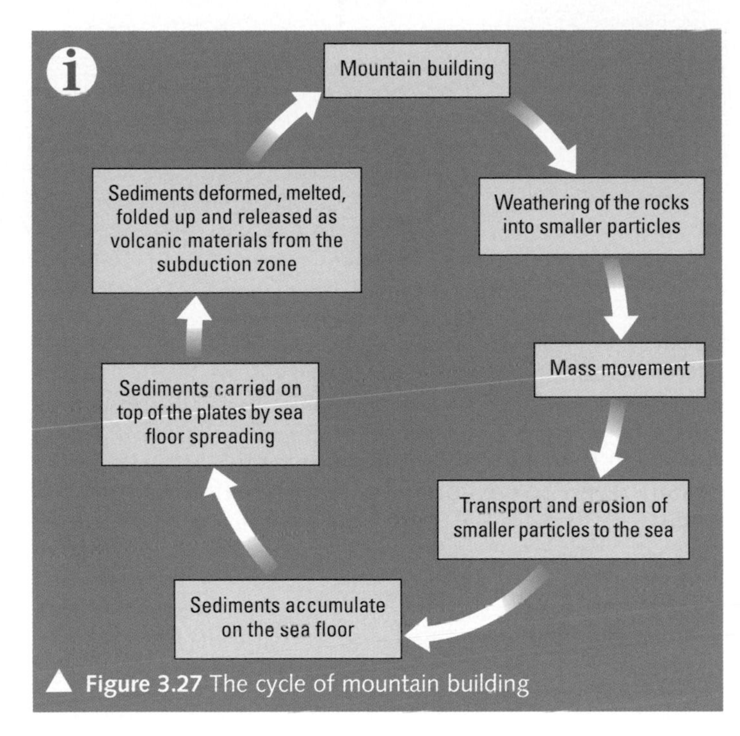

▲ **Figure 3.27** The cycle of mountain building

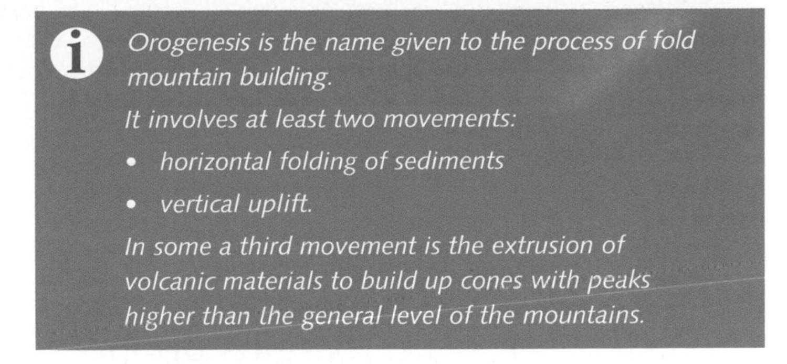

Mountain building is not on the same spectacular scale where two oceanic plates converge. Although sediments scraped off by collision contribute to the creation of land, it is the lava eruptions which are more significant for landscape formation. These build up chains of volcanic islands which form island arcs. The faster-moving plate is deflected downwards under the other plate where its oceanic crust is consumed in oceanic trenches, which take it back into the mantle. This happens in a subduction zone which is more steeply inclined than along continental edges. Most of the oceanic crust is melted or reabsorbed before reaching a depth of 300km (although the plate continues downwards to about 700km before breaking up). The molten crustal material is less dense than that of the mantle, which makes it rise up towards the ocean floor where much of it erupts as lava. The formation of island arcs can be viewed as an intermediate stage. What happens eventually, after further trenches and consumption zones have been made, is that the island arc is swept into the continent where its deformed materials will contribute to a new fold mountain range – perhaps in 100–200 million years' time.

The main band of island arcs stretches across the northern, and down the western, side of the Pacific Ocean from Alaska to New Zealand, including Japan, the Philippines and Indonesia. This is possibly the most active of all the world's tectonic zones with many active volcanoes and enormous numbers of earthquake shocks each year.

Questions

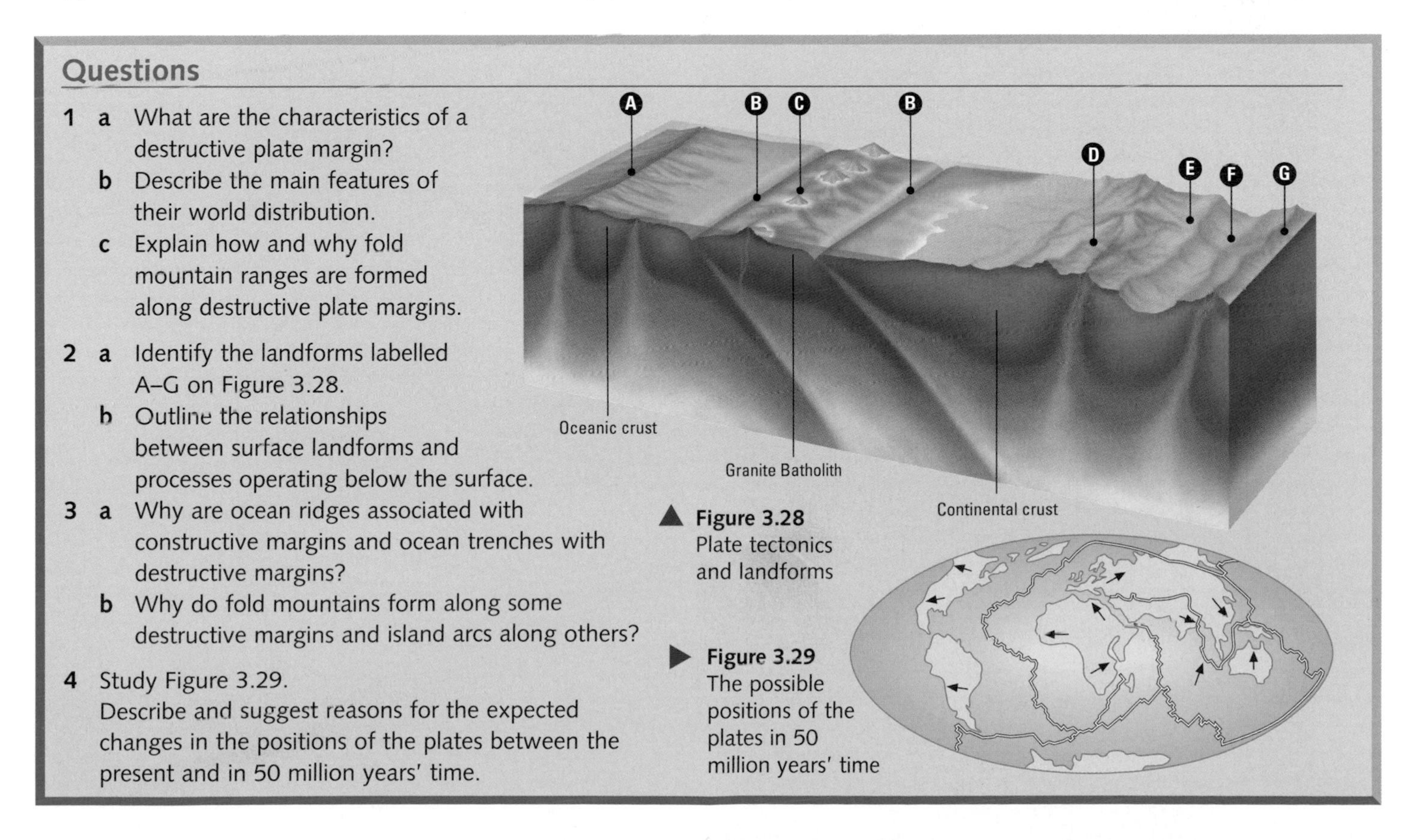

1 a What are the characteristics of a destructive plate margin?
  b Describe the main features of their world distribution.
  c Explain how and why fold mountain ranges are formed along destructive plate margins.

2 a Identify the landforms labelled A–G on Figure 3.28.
  b Outline the relationships between surface landforms and processes operating below the surface.

3 a Why are ocean ridges associated with constructive margins and ocean trenches with destructive margins?
  b Why do fold mountains form along some destructive margins and island arcs along others?

4 Study Figure 3.29.
Describe and suggest reasons for the expected changes in the positions of the plates between the present and in 50 million years' time.

▲ **Figure 3.28** Plate tectonics and landforms

▶ **Figure 3.29** The possible positions of the plates in 50 million years' time

Volcanic activity

The effects of plate margins upon volcanic eruptions

The world distribution of active volcanoes (Figure 3.30) shows mainly linear patterns following plate margins. The greatest numbers are located around the edges of the Pacific Ocean where they form what is known as the 'circum-Pacific ring of fire', which coincides with the presence of destructive plate margins. Surface volcanoes are not as clearly associated with constructive margins. Most of the outpourings of lava take place unnoticed on the ocean floors. Where the oceanic ridge reaches the surface, as in Iceland, a cluster of volcanoes is visible, which in itself is an indicator of the number of volcanic eruptions that must be taking place within the world's oceans. There are large areas of the Earth's surface, away from the plate margins, where current volcanic activity is non-existent. The UK is one of them, although it does not mean there are no volcanic landforms (see pages 88–89). A few active volcanoes can be noticed in the middle of plates as a result of the presence of hot spots, such as in Hawaii (see page 76), and along continental rifts, as in East Africa (see page 79).

Volcanoes transfer magma (molten material) from within or below the Earth's crust on to the Earth's surface. When magma reaches the surface it becomes lava. Constructive and destructive plate margins produce different types of lava, which leads to different types and frequency of eruption. In turn the forms of the resulting volcanic cones are also different. These differences are summarized in Figure 3.31.

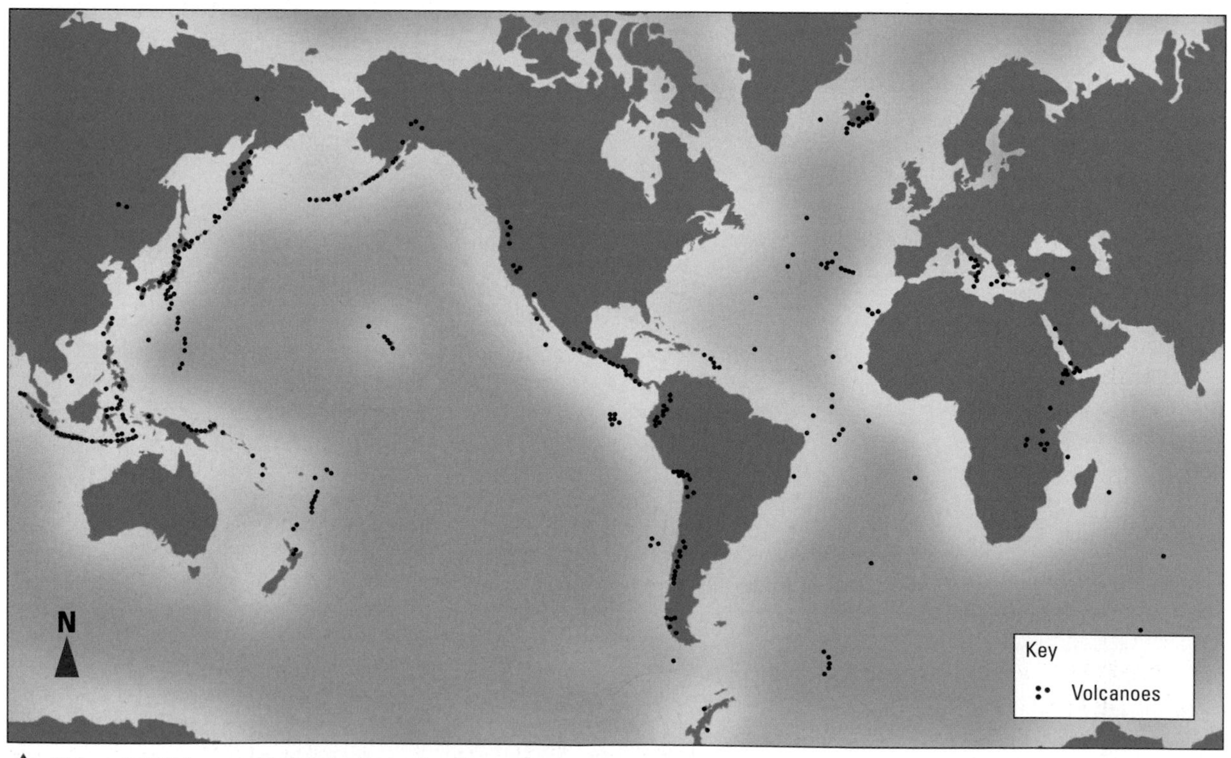

▲ **Figure 3.30** The world distribution of active volcanoes

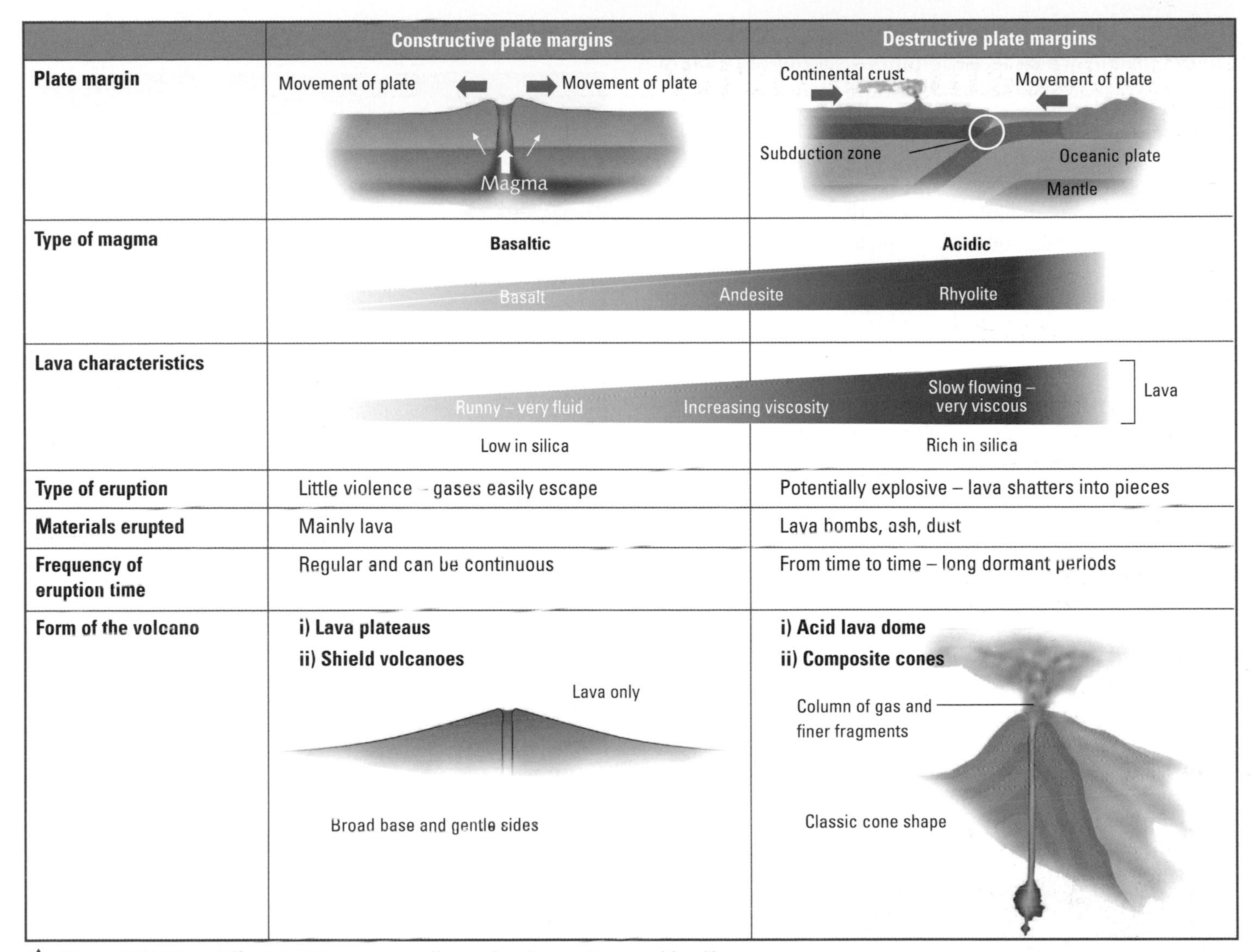

	Constructive plate margins	Destructive plate margins
Plate margin	Movement of plate; Movement of plate; Magma	Continental crust; Movement of plate; Subduction zone; Oceanic plate; Mantle
Type of magma	**Basaltic** — Basalt → Andesite	**Acidic** — Rhyolite
Lava characteristics	Runny – very fluid; Increasing viscosity; Low in silica	Slow flowing – very viscous (Lava); Rich in silica
Type of eruption	Little violence – gases easily escape	Potentially explosive – lava shatters into pieces
Materials erupted	Mainly lava	Lava bombs, ash, dust
Frequency of eruption time	Regular and can be continuous	From time to time – long dormant periods
Form of the volcano	**i) Lava plateaus** **ii) Shield volcanoes** Lava only; Broad base and gentle sides	**i) Acid lava dome** **ii) Composite cones** Column of gas and finer fragments; Classic cone shape

▲ **Figure 3.31** How different plate margins affect volcanic eruptions and landforms

The landform associated with the volcanic eruption is the cone-shaped mountain (Figure 3.32), because the magma forces its way out through a central pipe (vent) and out of a single crater. Erupted materials build up first around the crater which makes it the highest point. The lava flows out in all directions from the central point which gives the circular shape.

▲ **Figure 3.32** Volcanoes in the Andes

Questions

1. a In what different ways is it possible to make a classification of volcanoes?
   b Choose the way you consider best and outline the classification it gives.
2. a Draw a labelled sketch and describe the features of the volcanoes shown in Figure 3.32.
   b What type of volcanoes are they? Justify your answer.

Volcanic landforms and materials erupted

Molten magma which feeds volcanoes is a combination of lava and volcanic gas. At the beginning of an eruption, when the pressure suddenly drops, the gas separates out. How easily the gas escapes is a major influence upon how violent the eruption is.

When gases in the magma escape with ease, eruptions are usually non-violent. The type of magma and its chemical composition are important. When the proportion of silica in the lava is below 55 per cent, gases easily escape; the basaltic lava is fluid and very hot and flows for long distances before cooling. Cooling forms a skin on the surface under which the red hot lava continues to flow (Figure 3.34). Also important is the supply of magma. New magma from the mantle is readily available along constructive margins and above hot spots. Frequent or almost continuous eruptions keep the volcano's pipes and tubes open, which makes for easy out-pourings of lava. The landform which results when the lava is erupted from a single vent is a cone-shaped mountain with gentle slopes (2–10°) and wide bases. It is known as a shield volcano. When runny basaltic lava is erupted from long fissures, extensive level surfaces composed of great thicknesses of lava are built up. These lava plateaus form as the lava fills up the valleys and covers the hills and flows outwards over great distances to produce extensive areas with little variation in height. The great size of volcanoes such as Mauna Loa (see page 77) and the extent of lava plateaus such as the Deccan in India are testimony to the amount of new magma released onto the Earth's surface from inside the mantle along constructive margins.

▼ **Figure 3.33** Andes landscape – geysers at 4000m with mountains in background

Viscosity of lava

Viscosity is the stickiness of the lava or its resistance to flow. It increases as lava spreads from the vent and cools. Rhyolite with over 70 per cent silica content is the most viscous lava of all.

▲ **Figure 3.34** Lava flow on Hawaii

When the gas cannot escape easily, it explodes. This shatters the lava into pieces, forming everything from volcanic bombs to ash and dust. Sometimes the force of the explosion is directed skywards expelling dust and ash upwards where they are picked up by the air flows of the upper atmosphere, which circulate around the world. More commonly the explosion is directed sideways and downwards and a mixture of lava and gases flows downhill at speeds of up to 200km per hour in glowing clouds (*nuées ardentes*). These ash flows, known as pyroclastic flows, result from the frothing of magma in the vent, which leads to the gas bubbles expanding explosively and shattering the lava. Silica-rich lava, with 55–70 per cent silica, is thick, pasty and explosive. Magma which rises from the subduction zones at destructive plate margins produces lava of this type and composition. Volcanic activity usually occurs for only short periods for a few months, or from time to time during one or two years. Between eruptions the volcanoes lie dormant for long periods, anything from several years to several hundred years or even several thousand years. As the eruption ends the remaining viscous lava often oozes out of the vent and piles up as a dome above it. While dormant, lava in the crater solidifies and plugs the vent. This solid material needs to be cleared before the next eruption can take place; when pressures for an eruption are again building up within the volcano, the need to open up the old vent or create a new one contributes towards the violence of the eruption. Therefore these strato-volcanoes are characterized by their non-predictability.

Volcanic mountains which form along destructive margins characteristically have tall cones with steep sides of up to about 30°. The cones consist of a mixture of lava flows and beds of ash which is why they can be called composite cones. The solid fragments from the explosion collect around the crater; the pasty lava forms short and thick flows which also accumulate more around the vent and crater, hence the height and steepness of the cone. The larger explosions blanket the lower slopes with lava and rock fragments. Again the supply of magma is important. Unlike at constructive margins, magma only surges upwards from time to time with variations in supply that are difficult to understand and explain. Look at the eruption styles of the three neighbouring volcanoes in southern Italy (Figure 3.36).

Gases	***Liquids***	***Solids***
Water vapour/steam *Hydrogen* *Hydrogen sulphide* *Sulphur dioxide* *Chlorine*	*Runny – Basaltic lava* *Viscous – Andesitic lava* *Very viscous – Rhyolitic lava*	*Dust (flour size)* *Ash (sand size)* *Lappilli (little stones)* *Cinders (rough clinker)* *Bombs (up to 1m or more in diameter)*
Comment *Ease of release affects degree of violence of an eruption. Presence of sulphur leads to the smell of rotten eggs associated with most volcanic regions.*	***Comment*** *Type of lava has a large influence on the shape of the cone. The more viscous the lava, the higher the cone, the steeper the sides and the narrower the base.*	***Comment*** *Light materials such as dust and ash can become airborne and sometimes travel great distances in the upper atmosphere. Larger materials accumulate around the crater and increase cone height.*

▲ **Figure 3.35** Volcanic materials

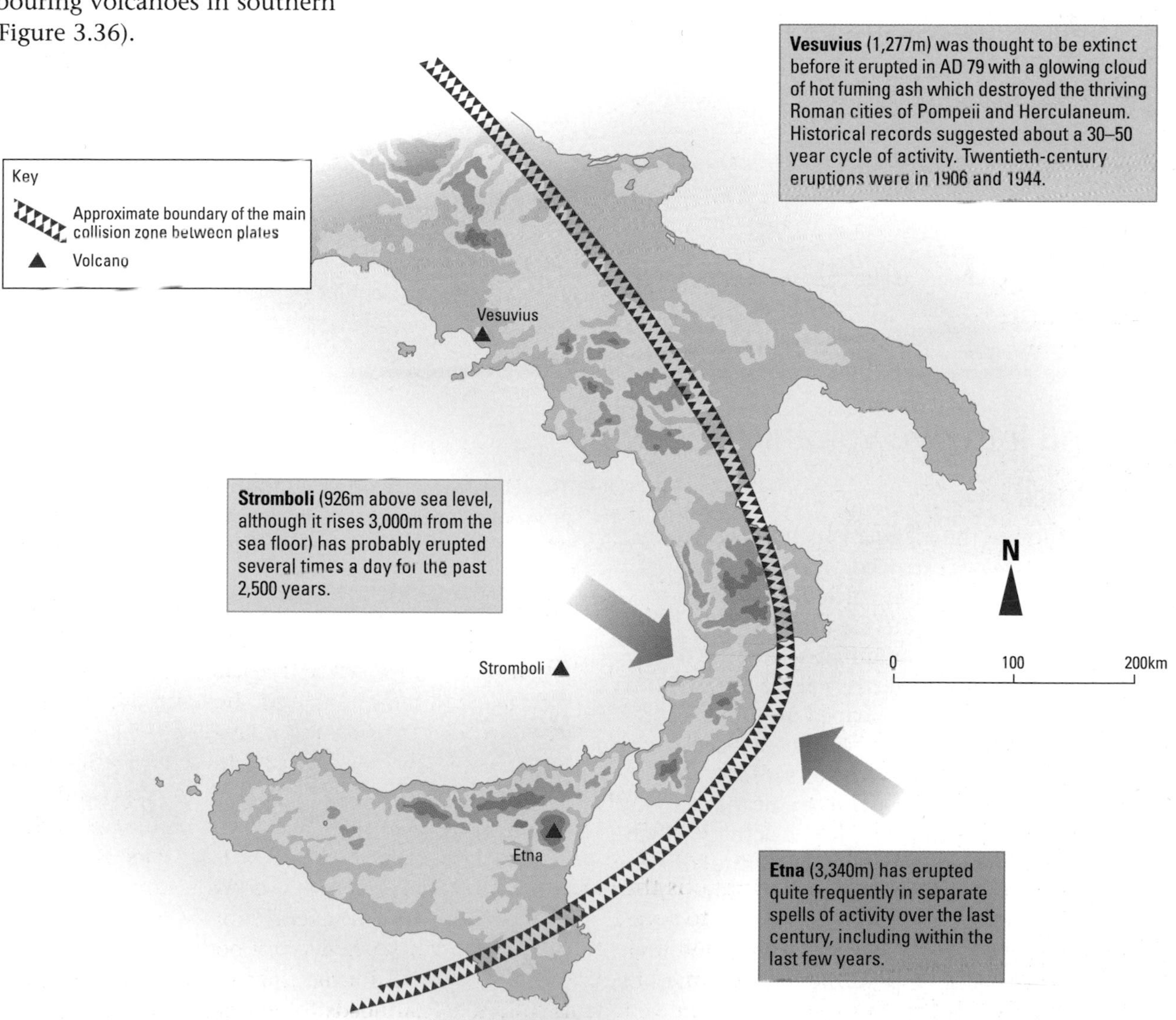

▲ **Figure 3.36** Italy's active volcanoes

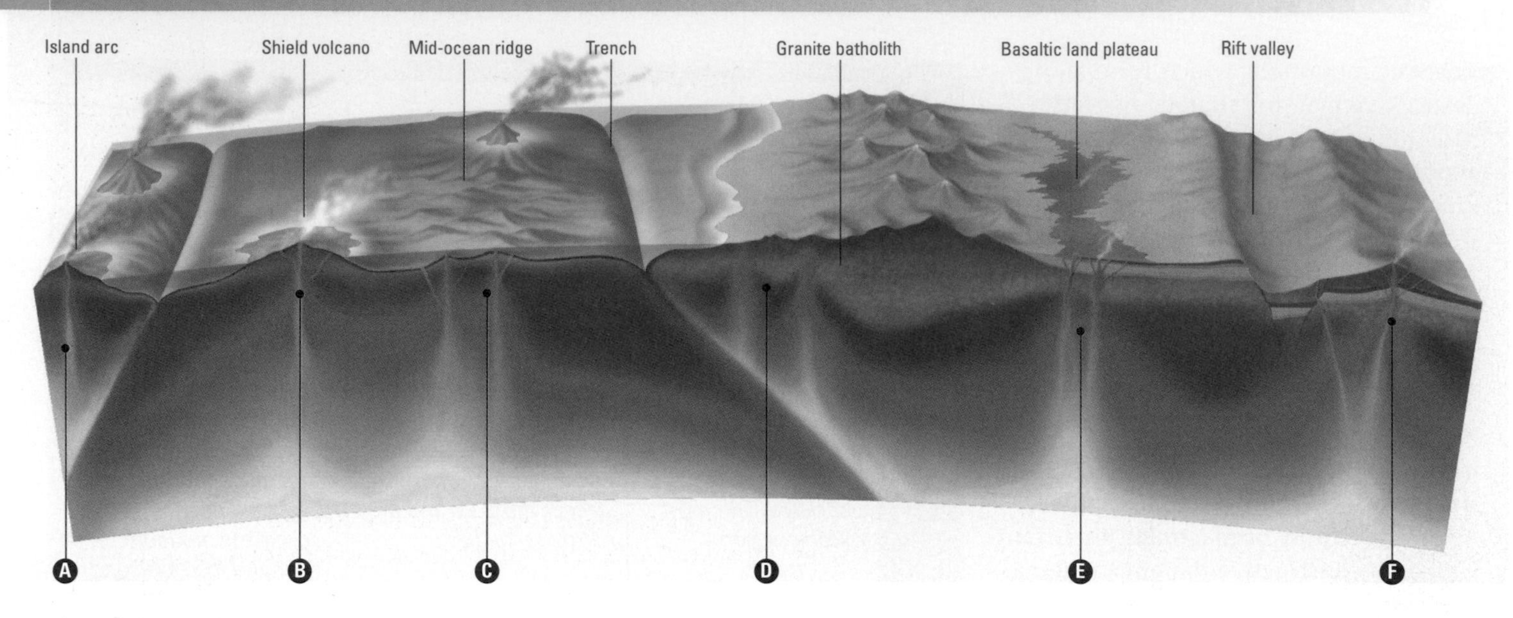

▲ **Figure 3.37** Areas of volcanic activity

Questions

1 a On an outline world map:
- **i** sketch the distribution of active volcanoes
- **ii** name five of them in different areas of the world and of different types
- **iii** add labels which describe their distribution.

b Give reasons why active volcanoes occur in greater numbers:
- **i** in Asia than in Europe
- **ii** in South and Central America than in North America.

2 a Draw annotated sketches of the volcanic eruptions shown in Figure 3.33 and Figure 3.34.

b Explain how and why the styles of their eruptions are different.

3 Figure 3.37 summarizes locations where magma reaches the surface leading to volcanic activity. These have been lettered A–F. For each one of the areas lettered A–F:
- **a** explain why magma reaches the surface
- **b** outline how the characteristics of the magma affect the surface landforms produced.

Extrusive and intrusive volcanic landforms

Extrusive features

Only a tiny proportion of the magma which forces its way upwards through the crust is extruded onto the Earth's surface as lava, either erupted from volcanic craters or poured out of long fissures. Despite the impressive appearance and size of volcanic mountains, they are the exception rather than the rule as far as magma release from the mantle is concerned. The cone-shaped mountains and lava plateaus built of basalt, which have already been referred to, are examples of extrusive landforms, because they were built up on the surface by direct volcanic activity. There are also some minor forms of volcanic activity which lead to surface features of a more temporary nature such as geysers, hot springs and boiling mud pools. When water infiltrating from the surface comes into contact with the hot rocks below the surface, it is converted into steam. The presence of a fissure may allow a powerful jet of boiling hot water to rise periodically many metres into the air as a geyser. Although the name of the feature is derived from the Great Geyser in Iceland, none is more famous than the Old Faithful geyser in the Yellowstone National Park. With less pressure there are bubbling hot springs and mud pools. These features are often all that remains when a volcano is approaching the end of its active life. Or they may be one of the features of a volcano's dormant period (Figure 3.39).

▲ **Figure 3.38**
Old Faithful, noted for the height of the water jet and the regularity of eruption (almost every hour)

▲ **Figure 3.39** The volcano Poas (2,700m above sea level) near San Jose, the capital city of Costa Rica in Central America. On the sides of this dormant volcano's crater lake an active fumarole has formed above a vent emitting steam and other vapours.

Intrusive features

Most of the magma upwelling from the mantle cools and solidifies within the crust and never reaches the surface. It is forced into or between existing rocks; it has therefore been 'intruded' into the pre-existing rocks. The resulting intrusive features which form below the Earth's surface include batholiths, laccoliths, dykes and sills. Intrusions vary greatly in size, shape and depth. Largest and deepest of all are batholiths which are gigantic masses of igneous rock, such as granite, many of which were intruded into the roots of fold mountain ranges during periods of mountain building. Batholiths have irregular dome-shaped roofs, from which the walls plunge downwards for many kilometres; the size of the intrusions enlarge with depth and many have no visible foundations. Although they do not align with the rocks around them, they extend in the same direction as the general trend of the mountain ranges in which they are found.

The other three intrusive features are classified according to shape and alignment. Sometimes the magma follows the strata as it is forced along the more or less horizontal lines of weakness between and within the beds of rock. If the magma forces its way along a bedding plane, making room for itself by uplifting the overlying rocks, the resulting flat, table-like sheet of igneous rock is known as a sill. Instead of spreading widely as a relatively thin sheet more viscous lava may have found it easier to arch up the overlying strata into a dome-like shape. The thicker, more rounded mass of igneous rock, which is still concordant to the rock layers, is called a laccolith. One of the commonest signs of former igneous activity is the dyke, which is a vertical wall-like intrusion of igneous rock. It is discordant in structure cutting across the layers of rocks. The magma is forced up through vertical fissures forcing the rock walls apart as it pushes through. On cooling it becomes a vertical sheet of rock cutting across the existing strata.

Underground these intrusive igneous features are of little interest to the geographer. However, once the surface rocks above have been eroded away, the exposed rocks create landforms of interest to the geomorphologist. They also have an impact on human activities. This even applies to the UK which is today located well away from any active plate margin and is, in fact, being carried further away from the constructive margin in the centre of the Atlantic Ocean by sea floor spreading and the resulting eastward movement of the Eurasian Plate.

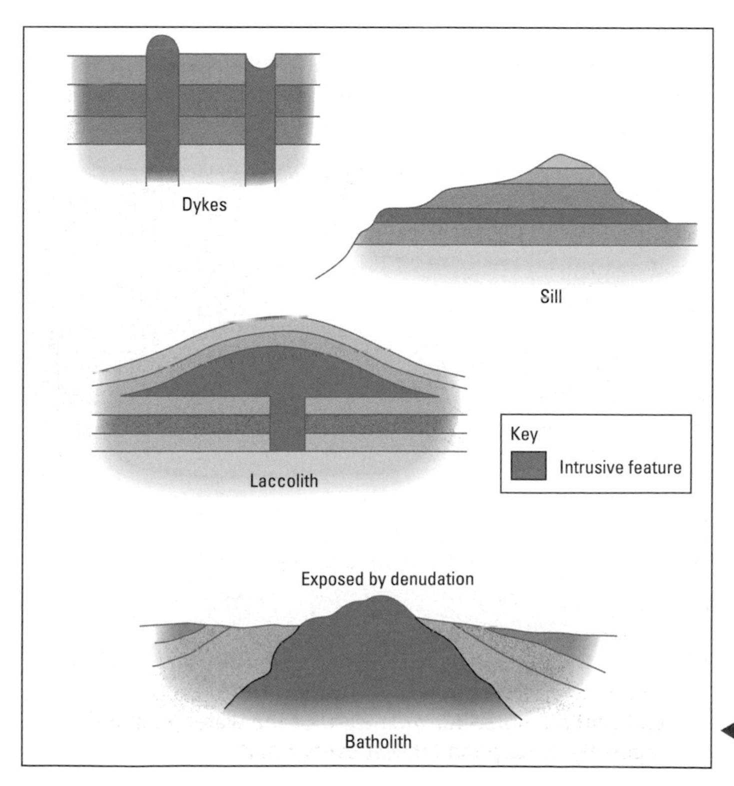

◀ **Figure 3.40**
Intrusive igneous features

The UK: landforms related to igneous activity

Case Study

Although the nearest active volcanoes to the UK today are in Iceland and Italy, there are abundant remains from earlier periods of mountain building and its associated volcanic activity. The British Isles experienced a major period of mountain building and vulcanicity 400 million years ago during the Caledonian folding which created the mountains forming the present Scottish Highlands. Along today's destructive plate margins, lava and ash were erupted from volcanoes active at that time. These influenced landscapes as far south as the Cheviots in Northumberland. Edinburgh Castle is perched on the plug of an extinct volcano dating from volcanic activity 325 million years ago. All that is now left is the hard lava from the base of the vent, which provided the prominent landmark now that the large lava and ash cone, which surrounded it, has been eroded away.

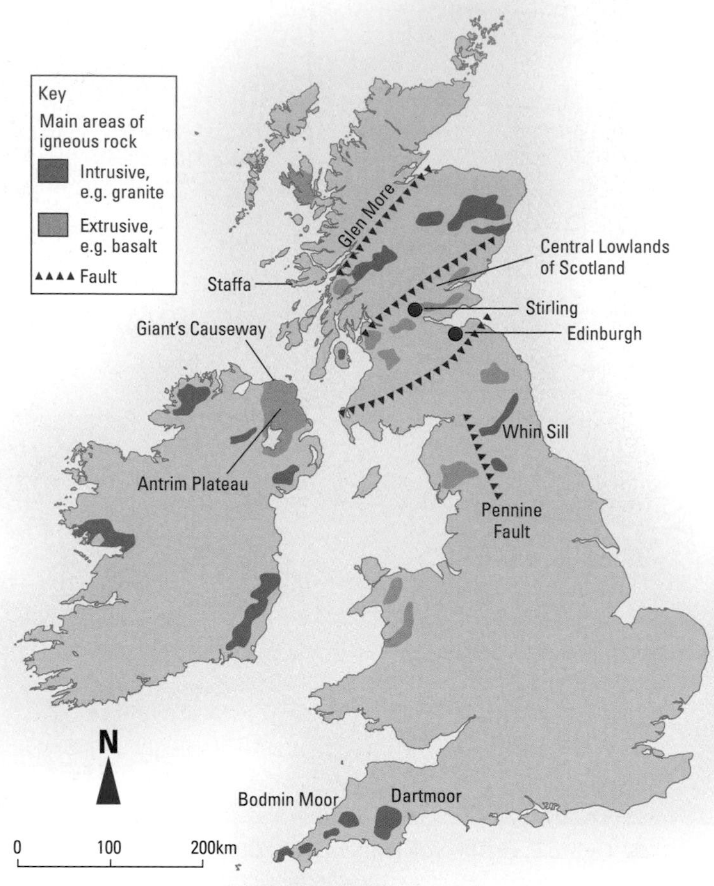

▶ **Figure 3.41** Landforms from past intrusive and extrusive igneous activity in the UK

▲ **Figure 3.42** The Giant's Causeway, Northern Ireland

As what is now the UK was moved further away from the destructive margin about 300 million years ago, a major mountain building period, the Hercynian orogeny, occurred in what is now Central Europe. The only part of the UK affected was south-west England, where part of the giant batholith of granite was intruded into the base of the mountains that it formed. In places the granite is now exposed on the surface. Weathering and erosion have combined to give distinctive landscapes of upland plateaus capped by rock outcrops and tors, such as Dartmoor, and rugged sea cliffs, as at Land's End. The last time magma was pouring out over the British Isles was some 50 million years ago. Floods of runny basaltic lava poured out along a belt running through the Inner Hebrides and Northern Ireland creating a plateau of enormous extent with remains as far away as Greenland. Part of this is the Antrim lava plateau. During cooling vertical cracks developed in the lava from which hexagonal columns of basalt have been exposed by erosion at the Giant's Causeway and around the Isle of Staffa – identical to those in Iceland (see page 78).

▲ **Figure 3.43** An eroded dyke outcropping on the coast of Arran, Scotland

The example of Devon and Cornwall shows how former intrusive volcanic activity can have an impact upon landforms and landscapes. Dykes are numerous in many places in western Scotland. One 'swarm' of dykes is on the Isle of Arran where over 500 can be seen along a 20km stretch of coast. When the igneous rock which forms the dyke is more resistant to erosion than the rock which surrounds it, it stands out as a prominent ridge and sometimes runs across the countryside like a wall. When less resistant, it is selected for greater erosion, such as by sea waves, which leads to a long narrow trench (Figure 3.43).

A classic example of a sill is the Great Whin Sill which underlies many parts of the north of England. Whin is a term used by quarrymen for any dark coloured rock suitable for road building, in this case dolerite. Near Durham it is over 300m below the surface and its presence was only of concern to coal miners. However, there are many surface outcrops, swinging in a great arc from near the Scottish border to the upper course of the River Tees in the Pennines, resulting in considerable landscape effects (Figure 3.44). It forms the Farne Islands (a nesting haven for sea birds). It is the base upon which past defensive works were constructed, including Hadrian's Wall and Bamburgh Castle. Its outcrops in the valley of the River Tees have interrupted the river's long profile and created Cauldron Snout and High Force waterfalls, the latter the highest in England. All the places mentioned are important visitor attractions.

In the UK where great tectonic activity ceased millions of years ago, the present landscapes and landforms reflect the long periods of denudation (weathering and erosion) since first formation. The Caledonian old fold mountains are low and rounded compared with the young Alpine fold mountains where sharp edged peaks above 3,000m are a common sight. So little remains today that the shape of the original volcanoes in and around Edinburgh and Stirling can only be guessed at. However, post-1960s advances in scientific understanding, allowed for by the theory of plate tectonics, have greatly increased knowledge of past geological events, which allows the geology and landscapes of the UK and Europe to be placed and understood quite accurately within a world context.

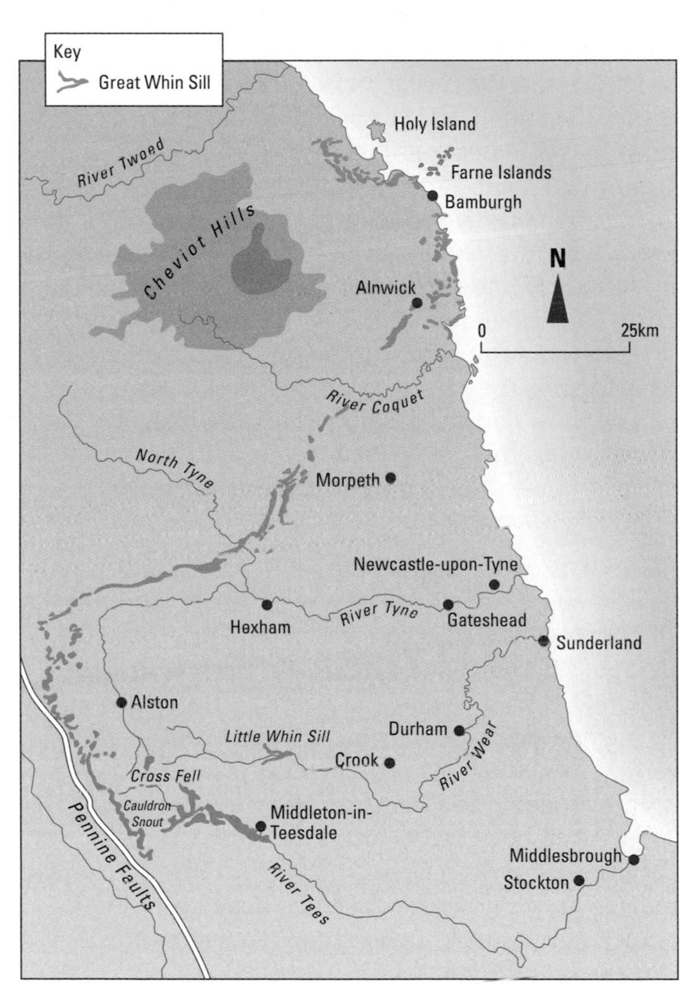

▲ **Figure 3.44** Outcrops of the Great Whin Sill across northern England

Questions

1 a Distinguish between intrusive and extrusive volcanic activity.

b Suggest and justify a classification of intrusive volcanic features.

2 a Comment upon the distribution of landforms derived from previous igneous activity in the British Isles.

b By reference to examples, explain in what ways and why intrusive features of volcanic activity can affect both inland and coastal landscapes.

Earthquakes

Characteristics and measurement

An earthquake is the sudden and violent movement of the rocks of the Earth's crust which causes surface vibrations. The rocks of the Earth's crust are always under tremendous strain. When the rocks are distorted beyond the limit of their strength they give way along a fracture or fault so that the rocks on either side suffer a sudden dislocation. The point underground where the first movement occurs is the focus. At the source the movement may be over in a few seconds, but the vast amount of energy released travels through the rocks of the Earth's crust as seismic waves, which cause the surface vibrations. The point on the surface immediately above the focus is the epicentre where the vibrations are greatest and most damage usually occurs. The waves become weaker as they spread out from the focus. It has been likened to what happens after a stone is thrown into a pond of water.

Some waves pass through the body of the Earth and are called body waves. Primary, or 'P-waves', travel fastest of all and they are the first to be registered on a seismograph. These are longitudinal waves and cause the rocks to vibrate forwards and backwards in the direction of wave movement. Secondary, or 'S-waves', are transverse waves which disturb the rocks from side to side at right angles to the direction in which they are travelling. When body waves reach the Earth's surface, much of their energy is reflected back down into the ground. How much vibration is caused depends on the type of rock. A solid rock such as granite vibrates much less than alluvial silts and sands.

Other waves are surface waves. They arrive shortly after the body waves and travel through the crust close to the Earth's surface. Longitudinal waves push the rocks upwards in the line of travel producing ripple-like waves. Transverse waves push the rocks sideways at right angles to the direction in which they are travelling producing a shearing motion which causes much of the surface damage.

All in all this means that there is an intricate pattern of waves up and down and from side to side, producing both horizontal and vertical vibrations, which test natural and human structures alike, often beyond their limits. Rugged fault scarps are one of the natural features created. Wrecked buildings are one of the legacies from earthquakes in urban areas. Figure 3.46b shows

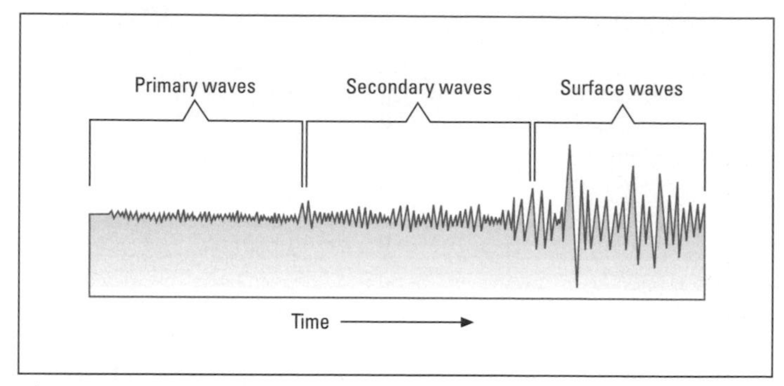

▲ **Figure 3.45** Earthquake waves

seismograph readings taken as the Turkish earthquake struck in August 1999. The great increase in movement was associated with the arrival of the surface waves.

The magnitude of an earthquake is measured by the Richter scale. It measures the energy released by an earthquake. The scale is logarithmic – an earthquake measured at 6.0 is ten times greater than one measured at 5.0; therefore one measured at 7.0 has one hundred times the magnitude of the one measured at 5.0.

Although the Richter scale measures the energy released from an earthquake, it does not necessarily indicate its effects on people. There is an alternative, the Mercalli scale, which assesses the degree of damage in built-up areas and changes in the natural landscape on a scale from I (felt only rarely) to XII (total damage). VIII on the scale is described as 'damaging' which would typically coincide with a magnitude between 6.0 and 6.9 on the Richter scale. However, the Mercalli scale is subjective and the point on the scale can only be gauged after the event. The damage done depends upon a variety of factors, both physical and human, and the ways in which they come together (see page 95). A measurement on the Richter scale, on the other hand, is immediately available, is measured in the same way everywhere and is universally understood. Magnitude is also a reasonable indicator of an earthquake's potential for damage.

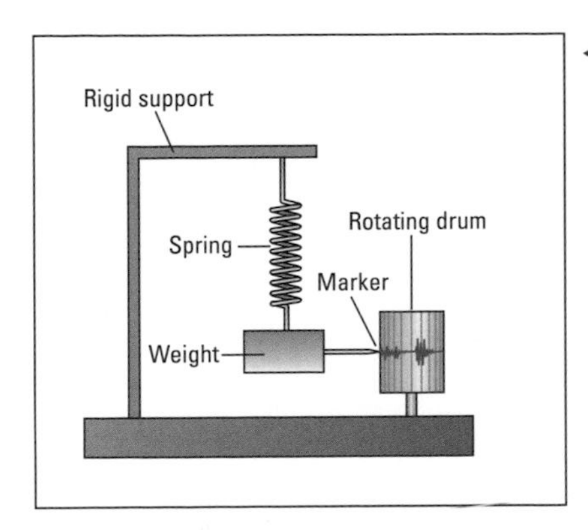

Figure 3.46a
How a seismograph works: an earth tremor agitates the spring causing the weight to go up and down. As it does so, the ink marker leaves a record of its vertical movements on the paper around the rotating drum. Without ground movements the ink marker leaves a straight line.

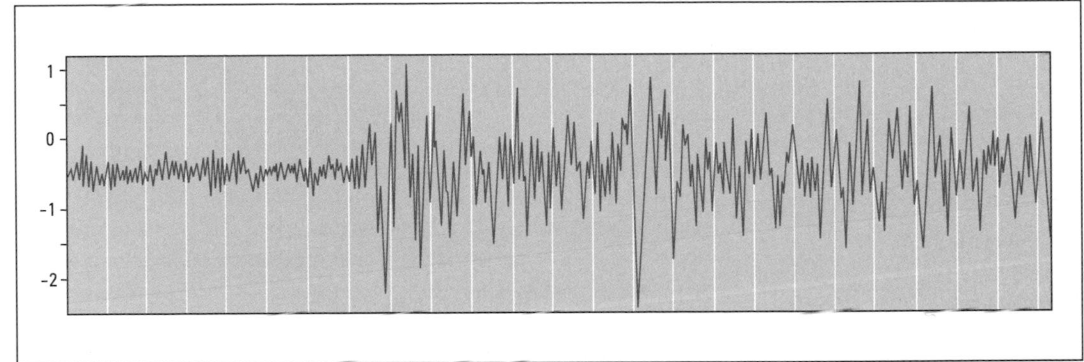

Figure 3.46b Seismograph reading, August 1999 from the Turkish earthquake

Magnitude on the Richter scale	Comments	Average number per year (approx.)
less than 2.5	Rarely felt by people	1 million
2.5 - 3.9	Minor earthquakes felt by some	100,000
4.0 - 4.9	Light earthquake felt by all	10,000
5.0 - 5.9	Moderate earthquake with some damage	1,000
6.0 - 6.9	Strong earthquake with much damage	180
7.0 - 7.9	Major earthquake – very destructive	18
8.0 - 8.8	Great earthquake – much devastation	1 every few years
8.9 and more	The really 'Big One'	?

Figure 3.47 Number of earthquakes at increasing magnitudes

Formation of earthquakes

People use phrases like 'as solid as rock' or ' as hard as rock' without realizing that rocks everywhere are cracked, fractured and faulted and that these lines of weakness within and between rocks are the result of the Earth moving. It is not the presence of a fault line which causes an earthquake, but movement along it. Most of the vibrations caused by these movements are too small to be felt by people; but what is clear is that even in areas, such as the UK, that are currently tectonically inactive because of their locations some distance away from plate margins, earthquakes can occur.

Figure 3.48 shows that some large faults exist in the British Isles. The most notable landform created by faulting is the rift valley that has formed the Central Lowland of Scotland. From time to time movements occur along these faults as stresses on the rocks are released – movements which can only be measured by sensitive seismographs. Movements felt by people in the UK are rare. They are most likely when they occur along fault lines passing through the densely populated West Midlands, but they do confirm that there remains a possibility of a light or moderate earthquake occurring in the UK, even if the chance of it happening is very low. The Warwick earthquake on 23 September 2000 measured 4.2 and was felt widely, although there were no reports of damage. This was because it was deep, some 13km down. One of a similar magnitude (4.7) near Colchester in 1884 damaged a large number of buildings because it was relatively shallow. Less of the energy of the shock was absorbed on its way to the surface. The loose, light soils of East Anglia almost certainly shook like jelly to amplify the seismic waves.

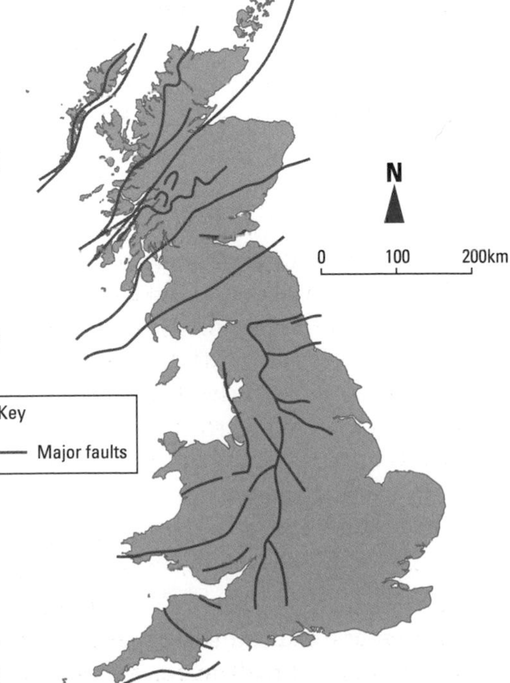

Figure 3.48 Major fault lines in the UK

▼ **Figure 3.49a** Adapted extract from *The Guardian*, Tuesday 7 May 1996

Earthquake rattles crockery in the Potteries

The earthquake that rattled crockery in the Potteries, set off security alarms and shocked people awake at Burslem at 4.50am yesterday, registered 2.6 on the Richter Scale. This is about eight times smaller than the 3.4 earthquake which rattled teacups in Shrewsbury, Telford and Oswestry in March, but the effects were more dramatic because the focus of the earthquake was only 2.6km below the surface. Yesterday's shock was felt as far away as Crewe in Cheshire. In Burslem, pictures fell off walls and ornaments were shaken off shelves. Police at Newcastle under Lyme felt the tremor and received reports of 'loud bangs'.

Seismologists at the British Geological Survey (BGS) in Edinburgh said: 'That is a classic description of a primary wave, reflecting into a sound wave and causing the bang. It was followed by a secondary wave which caused shaking and rattling.'

Britain is not – like Japan, California and New Zealand – on a tectonic frontier, but it does have between 300 and 400 earthquakes a year. Very few of them cause damage and only about 12 people are thought to have been killed by them in the last 500 years. There have been a number of magnitude 6 earthquakes in the North Sea, but the largest earthquake on land – at 5.4 – was in Gwynedd in 1984.

Most earthquakes occur where large stresses build up either where crustal plates collide along destructive margins, or where plates grind past each other along conservative margins (pages 72–76). As two plates are subducted into the ocean trench, the tremendous friction resulting from rock being forced against rock generates earthquake shocks. This is an area of intense seismic activity. The foci (points of origin) of the earthquakes are in the subduction zone, frequently at depths up to 70km, although they can be much deeper in what is called the Benioff zone (Figure 3.50). The ones which originate near to the surface usually cause the most damage. Earthquakes along conservative margins can cause just as much damage when the rock masses of two adjacent plates cannot move freely past each other. Stresses build up over a long period until crustal materials slip suddenly and release stored energy in a series of seismic shockwaves (page 73). Constructive margins also generate earthquakes because stresses and tensions build up in the crustal material as the two plates move apart. Fractures and faults result from this movement, but the scale and intensity of the movement are much lower than at destructive margins. As a result earthquakes are of lower frequency and magnitude (usually below 5.5) than along the two other types of plate margin.

The world distribution of earthquakes (Figure 3.51) reflects the dominant role of plate margins in their formation and the importance of destructive margins above all others.

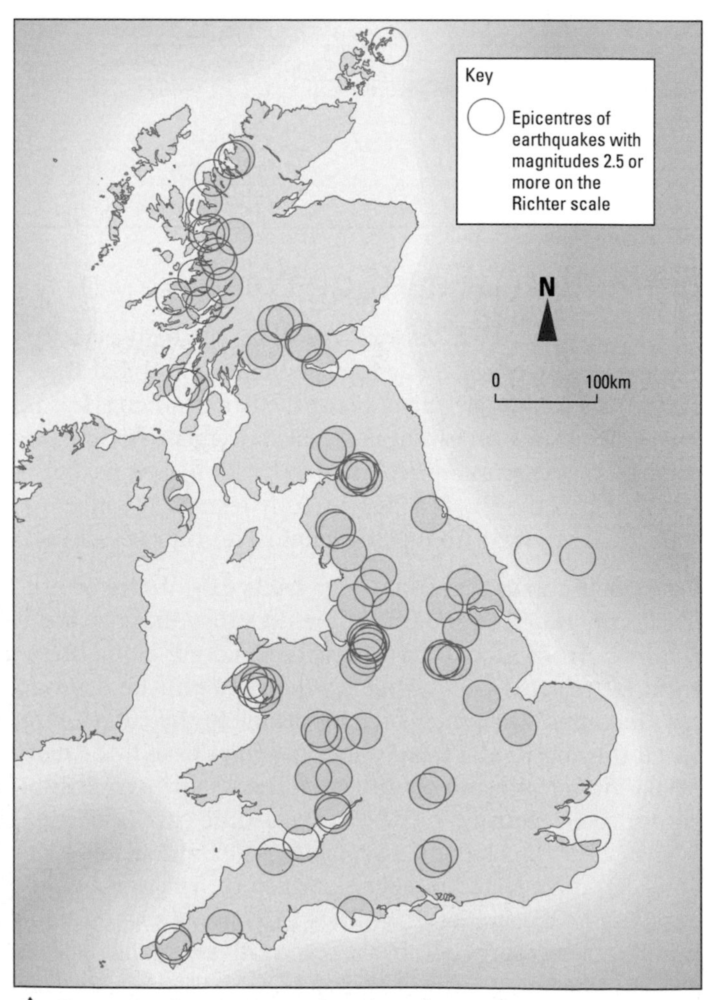

▲ **Figure 3.49b** Epicentres of earthquakes in the UK

Questions

1. Describe the ways in which the world distribution of earthquakes is:
   a. similar to
   b. different from

   that of volcanoes.
2. Explain why:
   a. earthquakes are formed along all plate margins
   b. earthquakes are more frequent along some types of plate margin than others.
3. a. Describe the distribution of earthquake epicentres shown on Figure 3.49b.
   b. Suggest reasons for the uneven spatial pattern shown.
4. a. Explain the statement that the earthquake in Burslem was eight times smaller than the earlier one in Shrewsbury, but was felt more strongly.
   b. Show how the different types of earthquake waves contribute to the effects that earthquakes have upon buildings and people.
5. Examine and comment upon the earthquake risk in the UK in world terms.

▼ **Figure 3.50** Earthquake formation at a destructive margin

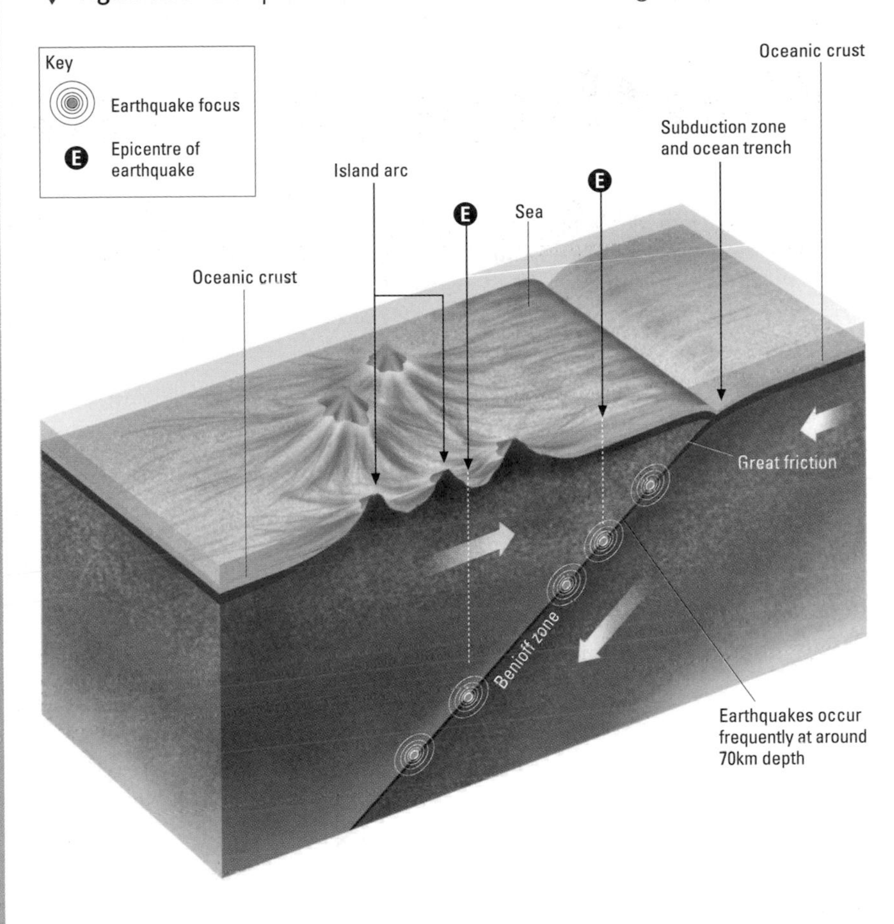

▼ **Figure 3.51** Distribution of earthquakes

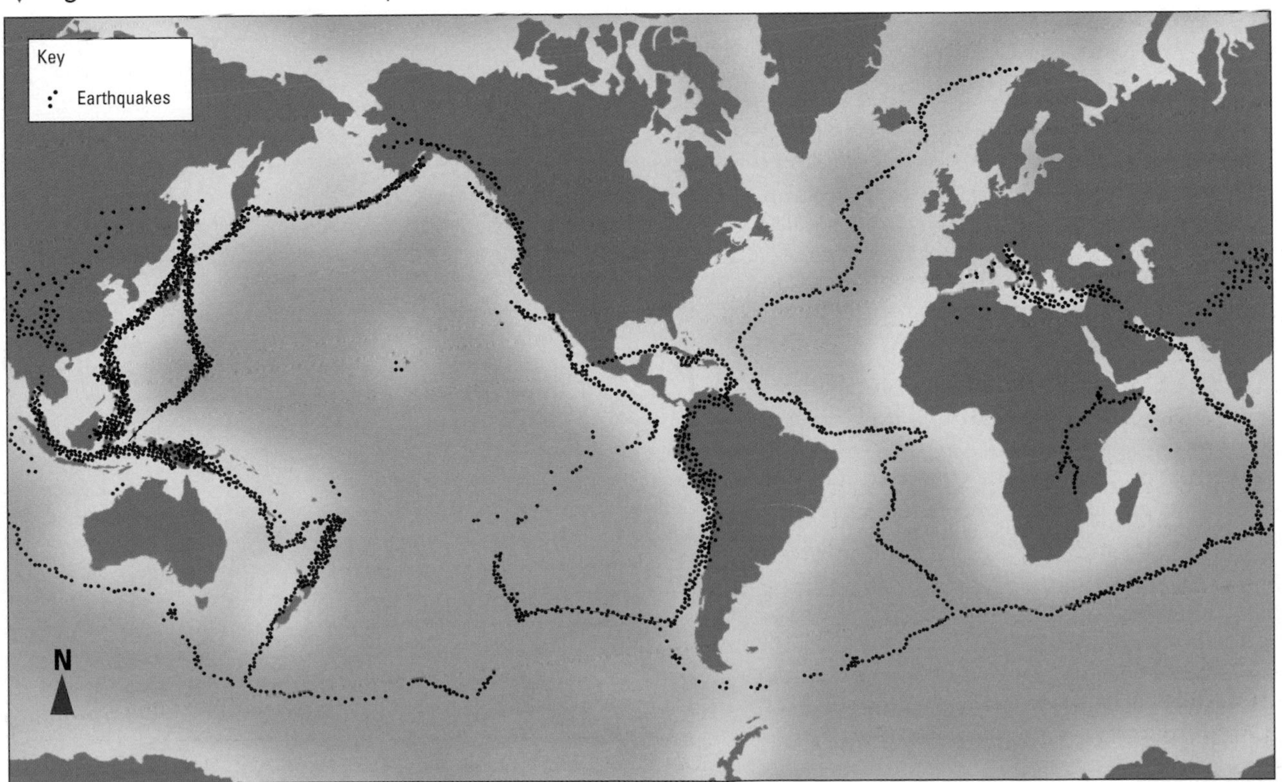

Human involvement, impacts and responses

Many have claimed the ability to predict the occurrence of an earthquake. They have tried everything. Some attempts are rooted in the scientific such as monitoring for signs of pre-shocks, observing levels of ground water and detecting electrical signals from underground. Others involve studying changes in animal behaviour. The Chinese approach to prediction has been a mix of the two. When in 1976 one of the Chinese disaster scientists correctly predicted an earthquake near Tangshan in north-eastern China, he received worldwide publicity, even though he greatly underestimated the strength of the shock wave. This was not followed up by other successes, which suggested that luck played its part in that prediction. The real truth is that humans cannot predict with any accuracy when and where a major earthquake will strike.

The high risk zones near to plate margins and faults, where a strong earthquake may occur at any time, are known. However, some have occurred along fault lines that scientists did not even know existed until the earthquake occurred. This is why earthquakes are one of the most dangerous of natural hazards. Some people have suggested that by building enormous structures, such as large dams which retain great reservoirs of water, seismic activity in the areas has increased due to the increased weight and pressure on the Earth's crust. Nevertheless human causation of earthquakes remains as unproven as human prediction.

Primary and secondary impacts upon people

Earthquakes have both primary and secondary impacts. The shock waves damage buildings to varying degrees – dislodging masonry, collapsing floors and facades, tilting the building or destroying it totally. Pillars which support bridges and elevated roads shear and cause spectacular damage as sections collapse (Figure 3.8). People are killed in their homes, places of work and cars. Many more are injured or trapped. These are primary effects.

In urban areas fire is the most widespread secondary effect. Gas hissing out of broken gas pipes and fractured mains leads to explosions and fires; sparks can often be seen flying from damaged electricity cables. Water with which to fight the fires is not usually available because the water pipes have also been broken by the earthquake. In many city earthquakes, such as San Francisco in 1906 and Kobe in 1995, fires caused far more damage than did the earthquake shocks themselves. In rural earthquakes landslides and avalanches sometimes pose the greater threat to people and property. People living in villages at the foot of steep valley sides are vulnerable, as are those living in areas where slopes are composed of weak sands and clays. In these areas only the slightest vibration can bring down a whole slope. A particularly devastating example occurred in Peru in 1970 when vibrations from a severe earthquake disturbed the glacier ice from a mountain summit in the Andes. Shortly afterwards rock and melting ice began to move down valley. A flow of rock, ice and mud travelling at up to 350km per hour gave the 20,000 inhabitants of the small town of Yungay no chance.

If the majority of primary effects of an earthquake are small and local, one secondary (indirect) effect can be enormous and worldwide. This happens when earthquake movements unleash a tsunami (sometimes also called a tidal wave). These are huge seismic sea waves capable of crossing ocean areas as wide as the Pacific. Ninety five per cent of them are caused by earthquakes, the remainder by volcanic eruptions. They are caused by rapid sagging and rising of the sea floor during an earthquake. Sea water pours into the void formed by sagging before being forced out again. This produces a surface wave. In the open ocean, although they travel up to 750km per hour, they are virtually undetectable because they are only a metre or two high. As they approach a coastline the story is different. The friction with the sea bed slows down the wave but increases its height. Wave heights of 10m or more are common. Walls of water that break and crash against the shore line at speeds of around 60km per hour are not unknown. Destruction in the coastal zone can be total and loss of life enormous. Three quarters of tsunamis which cause damage to coastal areas are in the Pacific.

▲ **Figure 3.52** Tsunami damage in Kodiac, Alaska

▼ **Figure 3.53** Causes and effects of the tsunami which hit Papua New Guinea in 1998

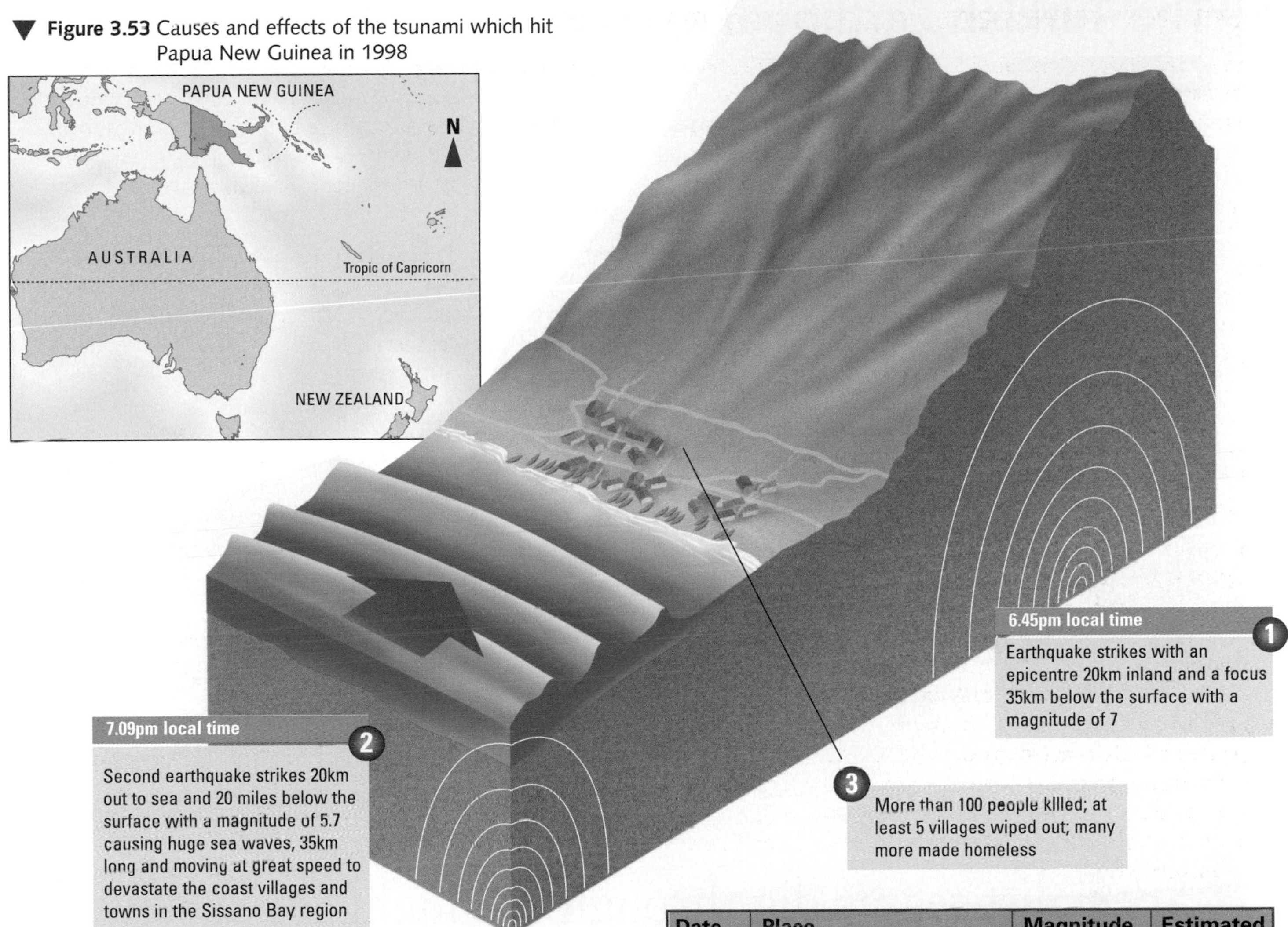

In general there is no direct relationship between the magnitude of an earthquake and loss of life as the earthquake selection in the table shows.

However, once the magnitude of the earthquake exceeds 6.0 on the Richter scale, the potential for great loss of life and damage exists. It increases considerably with a magnitude of 7.0 or more. What actually happens is controlled by how a variety of physical and human factors combine (see Figure 3.55).

Date	Place	Magnitude	Estimated deaths
1964	Anchorage, Alaska	8.4	131
1970	Ancash, Peru	7.8	66,000
1976	Tangshan, China	7.8	500,000
1985	Mexico	8.3	7,000
1989	Loma Prieta, California	7.1	62
1993	Maharastra, India	6.4	13,000
1995	Kobe, Japan	7.2	5,500
1997	Eastern Iran	7.1	1,500
1999	Turkey	7.8	15,000

▲ **Figure 3.54** Loss of life in earthquakes

Physical factors	The worst scenario – causing greatest damage and loss of life:
Magnitude of the earthquake	high
Its depth of focus	shallow focus
Number and intensity of aftershocks	frequent and strong
Time of occurrence	chance – most people near the epicentre at the time it happened
Nature of the surface rock	buildings with foundations on sands and clays vibrate more than those on solid rock
Human factors	
Density of population	high density urban area
Building and construction standards	old buildings not designed to be earthquake proof, blocks of flats, self-built houses
Degree of preparedness of people	absence of earthquake drills or trained emergency teams

▲ **Figure 3.55** Physical and human factors affecting aftermath of earthquakes

The Turkish Earthquake, August 1999

Case Study

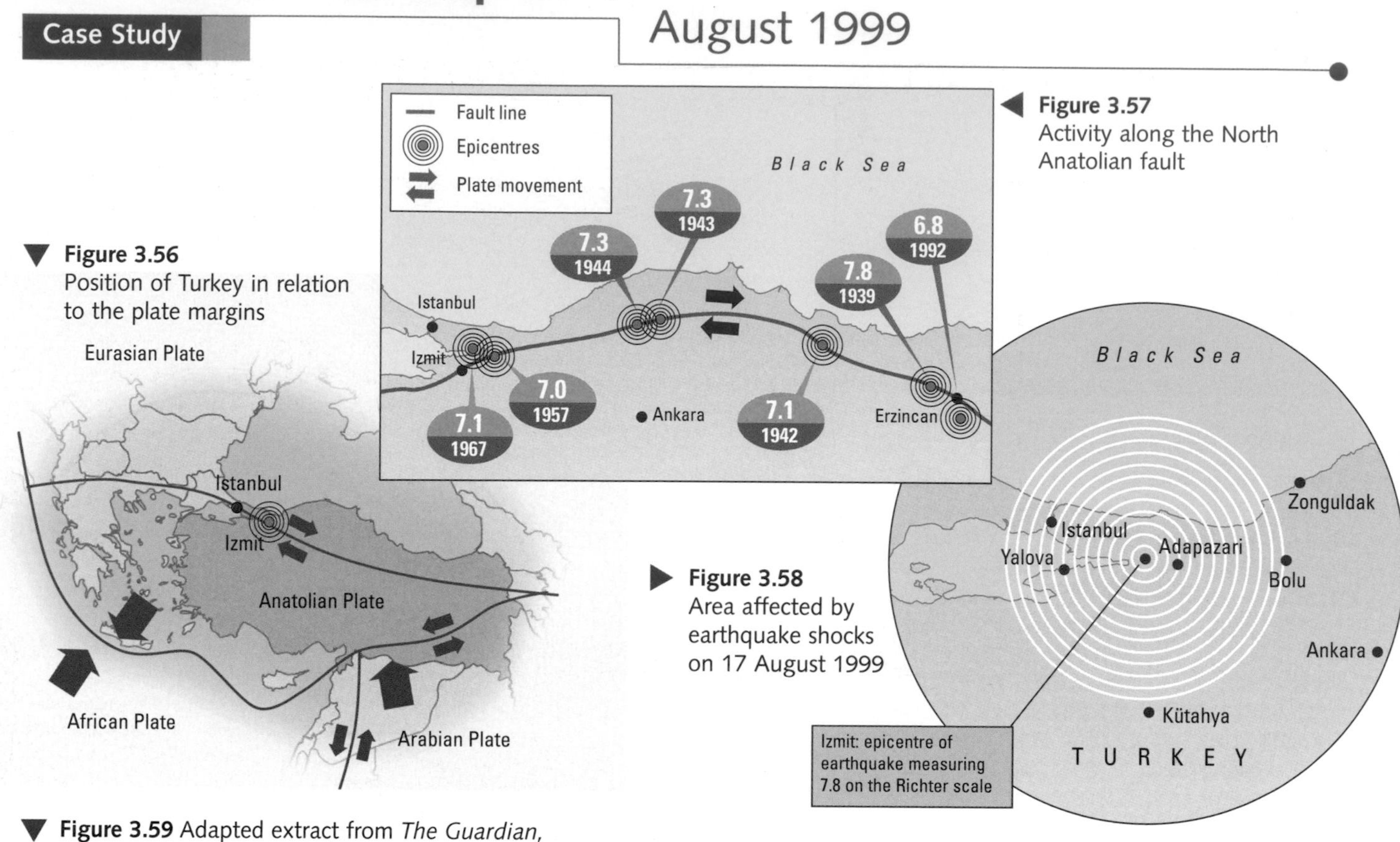

Figure 3.57 Activity along the North Anatolian fault

Figure 3.56 Position of Turkey in relation to the plate margins

Figure 3.58 Area affected by earthquake shocks on 17 August 1999

Figure 3.59 Adapted extract from *The Guardian*, Wednesday 18 August 1999

Specialist teams dig through the night for survivors

Rescue workers were still tearing at the rubble early today, some with their bare hands, in a desperate attempt to save thousands of people believed to be trapped in collapsed buildings across western Turkey, after one of the most devastating earthquakes to strike the region in 20 years.

The death rate last night stood at 2,000, but was rising steadily as aid workers in some of Turkey's most populated and urbanised districts continued to pull bodies from the wrecked buildings.

The earthquake lasted just 45 seconds. It happened at 3.02 am, as if to strike its victims – many of whom lived in poor districts where building regulations are often ignored – when they were at their most vulnerable. The epicentre was near the industrial city of Izmit, about 55 miles east of Istanbul. (The area affected contributes over one third of Turkish GDP).

American geologists recorded a magnitude of 7.8 on the Richter scale, making it the strongest since the Mexico earthquake disaster of 1985 that killed 9,500 people. Buildings shook up to 200 miles away from the epicentre.

A massive rescue effort was in full swing throughout the night. Recovery teams often appeared overwhelmed by the enormous scale of their task. Multi-storey apartment blocks were reduced to piles of rubble in a matter of seconds. A huge fire was still raging at an oil refinery near Izmit last night, while roads and bridges were destroyed and power lines were cut across wide areas of the country.

Specialist teams moved into the worst affected areas with sophisticated listening equipment and highly trained sniffer dogs. Medical services in the region have been stretched to the limit. Makeshift hospitals were set up among the ruins to care for thousands of injured people.

Turkey sits on an active geological fault line, but there was no obvious warning of the impending disaster. Hundreds of aftershocks yesterday provoked widespread unease and occasional panic. The blame may not be nature's alone. In many areas buildings survived the full force of the tremor, while others crumpled into heaps of metal and concrete.

Most people detected the hand of greedy building contractors, who had used widespread corruption to ignore what should be tough regulations to make sure buildings meet safety standards. The Izmit region has experienced a building boom in recent years as migrants have flooded in from the east of the country in search of work.

▼ **Figure 3.60** Adapted extract from *The Financial Times* Thursday 19 August 1999

'Corruption kills, not earthquakes'

More than half of all buildings in Turkey are built in violation of construction regulations and are prone to collapse in an earthquake, according to the country's architects.

'We know how to build earthquake resistant houses,' says Chairman of the Architects' Chamber of Turkey 'This is the first thing they teach us at university. We have first rate experts in every field related to construction. Yet Turkey is full of *kacak* buildings'.

Kacak means contraband – buildings built without permits, or architectural plans which do not conform to building regulations. They are erected in places such as riverbeds where they should not be, and in which the requisite amount of cement and iron is not used.

Their builders are often people with political connections who put profit above safety. Because Turkey's per capita income is less than US$ 2,500, many buyers tend not to be too choosy. 'Most of the buildings which collapse in the earthquake are in this category'.

Aerial television footage showed many apartment blocks which collapsed only metres away from others which remained intact. Under Turkish law it is up to the municipal authorities to ensure that buildings are erected according to regulations after proper permits are obtained, but it is always possible to find corrupt officials who will look the other way. Government inspectors are aware of what is going on but their reports are invariably disregarded when they come to public notice.

Despite the fact that Turkey has suffered a deadly earthquake on average every 18 months this century, it is unlikely that building regulations will be tightened up. 'The earthquake has given us a lesson in how to build, the chairman added. 'But whether we learn anything is another matter'.

The Financial Times, Thursday 19 August 1999

▲ **Figure 3.61** One building remains intact surrounded by collapsed buildings.

Questions

1 Identify the key facts about the Turkish earthquake. Examples: date and time; strength; location of epicentre; area affected; effects.

2 Turkey is a 'high risk' earthquake country.
  a State the evidence for this.
  b Explain how its position makes it high risk.

3 **a** Describe the economic effects of the earthquake on Turkey.
  b Why economically could it not have happened in a worse area?

4 **a** How strong was the relationship between the strength of the earthquake and its effects?
  b To what extent do you agree with the Turkish architect's view that 'Corruption kills people, not earthquakes'?

Human responses to earthquakes

These can be sub-divided into immediate, short-term and long-term. The most immediate need for those still able is to get out of buildings and into the safety of as large an open space as possible, out of range of falling objects, and before aftershocks bring down buildings and structures already weakened by the main shock. After this, there is the urgent need to treat the injured and rescue the survivors who are trapped, often whilst aftershocks are occurring. The survivors suffer from a mixture of shock, panic, fear and stress. The worst stress often comes from the frantic search for friends and families and the inevitable feeling of helplessness which takes over when nothing can be done. The process of rescue usually lasts for three to four days until the hope of finding anyone else alive is so slight that the next phase of the response begins – clearing up the mess. Often this stage involves the use of heavy machinery such as bulldozers and cranes. Utility workers struggle to repair pipes and wires to try to resume supplies of essential services such as water and electricity, without which the return to normality is impossible. In the short term, people made homeless need to be given temporary shelter, food, water and in some cases medicines. Hunger and illness are widespread. Shelter usually means tents; how urgent the need is depends greatly upon weather conditions in the area affected. In MEDCs emergency supplies are routinely stockpiled, but the only recourse for most LEDCs is to seek international aid, which increases the lag time before help arrives. In the chaos which follows the event, and with the breakdown of public services and particularly reliable supplies of clean water, there is the ever-present risk of the spread of water-borne diseases, notably typhoid and cholera, to add to the survivors' misery.

Some of the short-term effects can become long term. It may take many months, or even years, for the scars from losing home, possessions, relatives and friends to be healed, or for new homes to be built for all. What were intended to be temporary 'tent cities' may become semi-permanent residential areas. There may be significant economic effects in the long term, both local and national. The cost of re-building the local infrastructure of roads and supply lines can be an enormous burden on the economy of a LEDC at a time when income from factories and commerce has been reduced by the earthquake. The early estimates for the amount of destruction after the Turkish earthquake in 1999 were anything up to US $10 billion. The earthquake shook Istanbul and Izmit, both major industrial and financial centres, and affected that part of the country responsible for one third of the country's manufacturing output. The totally destroyed oil refinery near Izmit accounted for more than 40 per cent of Turkey's total oil-refining capacity. Economists pointed to some of the negative effects that would continue to drag down Turkey's economy for some time into the future such as:

- key industrial plants, other than Turkey's largest oil refinery, were damaged, notably tyre and engineering plants
- companies in the earthquake areas had lost many of their skilled workers
- destruction of public utility networks (power, water and communications) would reduce industrial output in factories throughout the country
- people would be consuming less.

Despite the risks, there is a tendency to re-build in the same area after an earthquake. This is partly because people have always lived in the regions. Where could they move to? It is partly because many other areas of a country are likely to share a similar earthquake risk as well. Managua, the capital of Nicaragua in Central America, was destroyed by an earthquake in 1931, rebuilt, and destroyed again in 1972. It is often said that 'lightning never strikes the same place twice', but unfortunately earthquakes do.

Wednesday 18 August 1999

- 2000 die in Turkish earthquake
- Desperate struggle for survival as tremor devastates sleeping cities
- Specialist teams dig through the night for survivors
- Aid effort - Greece buries differences to help old enemy

Thursday 19 August 1999

- Toll nears 4000 as thousands lie trapped
- Rescuers race against time
- Scale of crisis becomes clear
- Poor pay price for cheap houses
- Health — water and power loss poses threat

Monday 23 August 1999

- Official death toll now over 12,000
- Alive... after five days in the darkness
- Foreign rescue teams pulling out
- Medical aid now pouring into Turkey
- Focus switches to medical care for the living
- Slow, helpless and disorganised — Turks accuse their leaders

Tuesday 24 August 1999

- Rescued — Pulled from the rubble after 150 hours
- Tent cities turn foul in the torrential rains
- The homeless — Leaking shelters, damaged drains and a deluge of mud are adding to the fears of deadly epidemics

Monday 6 September 1999

- Aftershock — Still reeling from the 'quake, Turks and their leaders agree on one thing: a different Turkey must emerge from the devastation

▲ **Figure 3.62** How the newspaper headlines for the Turkish earthquake changed

Questions

1 a For the earthquake in Turkey, identify:
  i the short-term effects
  ii the long-term effects.
 b Explain how and why people's responses changed with time.

2 How true is it that short-term effects of an earthquake are mainly social while long-term effects are mainly economic?

Weathering and mass movement

Different types of weathering

One definition of weathering is 'the decomposition or disintegration of rocks *in situ* at or near the Earth's surface'. *In situ* refers to the fact that the breakdown of rock takes place where the rock is sited. When weathering takes place, rock changes occur without involving any movement or transport, whereas erosion only takes place with movement. Processes of erosion (abrasion, corrasion, corrosion, attrition and plucking), undertaken by the agents of erosion (rivers, waves, glaciers and wind), rely upon movement for their effective operation. Once movement of water, ice or wind breaks off pieces of rock, the rock particles are further reduced in size during transportation by processes such as attrition. Although separate definitions for weathering and erosion are possible, in practice they work together to lower the height of land surfaces. Weathering speeds up rates of erosion. Particles and pieces of rock disintegrated or decomposed by weathering become subject to the operation of mass movements down-slope under the influence of gravity, before being transported by agents of erosion. Eventually they all end up in the sea. This is why it is often more accurate to use the term 'denudation', which includes the results of both weathering and erosion, to refer to the wearing away of rocks exposed on the Earth's surface.

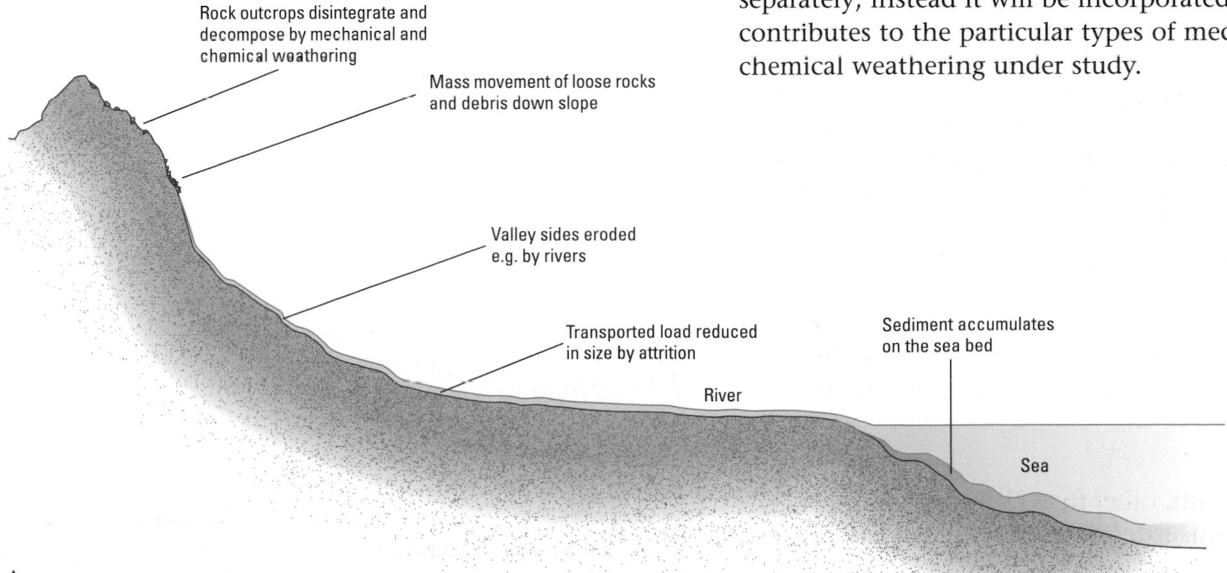

▲ **Figure 3.63** Denudation

It is traditional to sub-divide weathering into three main types – mechanical, chemical and biological. Mechanical (or physical) weathering breaks up the rock without any alteration to its existing mineral structure. Mechanical processes such as freeze-thaw, or alternate heating and cooling, or pressure release once rocks on top have been removed lead to the disintegration of rocks. In contrast, chemical weathering produces a change in the composition of the rock which speeds up and leads to its decomposition. These chemical reactions usually involve rainwater. Some minerals dissolve even in generally pure rainwater. This is known as solution. Sometimes there is a chemical union between water and the minerals in the rock to form solutions which are carried away, known as hydrolysis. Calcium carbonate, of which limestones are made, dissolves in rainwater that is acidic. This is limestone solution or carbonation. Water can cause other minerals to expand, known as hydration, which sets up stresses within the rock leading to its decomposition. Another type of chemical weathering is oxidation when the oxygen ions readily available in water combine with metallic ions; this happens most readily in rocks containing iron.

Biological weathering is a distinctive type of weathering only in the sense that its direct cause is plants and animals. Otherwise this third type of weathering represents a mixture of processes of mechanical and chemical weathering. As a result, it will not be discussed separately; instead it will be incorporated where it contributes to the particular types of mechanical and chemical weathering under study.

Mechanical weathering

Changes in temperature are mainly responsible for mechanical weathering. The most widespread type in temperate and polar zones, with results on the landscape that are easily observable, is frost action or freeze-thaw. Its operation depends on the fact that ice occupies nine per cent more volume than an equivalent mass of water. Its occurrence is controlled by climate; ideal conditions exist in places where there are frequent changes in temperature above and below freezing point during most of the year, such as in mountainous areas in temperate latitudes and in coastal locations in polar regions (Figure 3.64). These places have the additional advantage of limited vegetation cover, which means that weaknesses in the rock, the presence of which contributes greatly to the speed and effectiveness with which the process operates, are fully exposed to the elements. Rocks which contain many cracks, joints or fissures, or ample pore spaces, offer opportunities for water to collect when the temperature is above freezing point. Once the temperature drops below 0°C, freezing of the trapped water occurs from the top downwards which increases the pressures on the rock sides. This is repeated many times until the pressure exerted splits the rock along the line of weakness so that angular pieces of rock are broken off. The amount of scree below the rock outcrop in Figure 3.64 testifies to the effectiveness of frost action as a type of weathering as well as to its operation over a long period of time.

▲ **Figure 3.64**
Steep scree slopes on South Orkney. It lies almost 60° south in the sub-Antarctic polar zone where climate and active weathering restricts vegetation cover to orange coloured lichens as the pioneer plant species.

In hot and arid environments, mechanical weathering resulting from large diurnal changes in temperature is generally considered to be the most common type of weathering operating there. Day-time heating on exposed rock surfaces as a result of high rates of solar insolation is the main cause. Where spheroidal boulders are present, the outer layers expand under the sun's heat and are pulled away from the cooler core during the day, only to contract again each night. This leads to the process of exfoliation in which the outer layers of rock are peeled away. Where rocks composed of a variety of minerals are exposed, varied rates of expansion and contraction occur. The rock minerals of different colours respond at different rates to the effects of intense day-time solar heating. This leads to granular disintegration. However, some research work has suggested that both of these processes operate much more quickly in arid areas where water is present, such as on shaded sides and on surfaces close to the ground. This is where the results of night-time condensation are most likely to lead to the presence of moisture. Therefore features which for many years were considered to be the result only of mechanical weathering may in fact also be caused in whole or in part by the presence of water and associated chemical weathering. This is an example of how weathering processes are interrelated which makes it difficult to study them separately.

On a much larger scale there is more agreement that pressure release has been responsible for causing the fractures, which have resulted in surface sheeting, on exposed domes of granite rock. This rock was originally intruded at depth under great pressure. It was crystallized under temperature and pressure conditions very different from those found on the surface. As the overlying rocks were worn away, the rock expanded and split into sheets along the outer layers forming joints which run parallel to the surface of the rock. The creation of joints near the surface increases the vulnerability of the rock to further mechanical and chemical weathering, which creates an exfoliation dome.

Biological weathering that may be considered mechanical only operates at a local, very small scale. Roots of plants and trees, as well as the work of burrowing animals such as rabbits, are capable of disintegrating the rock physically. Thus the roots of the ash tree in Figure 3.65 are widening the joint in the Carboniferous limestone rock in which it is anchored as part of its desperate search for water and nutrients for survival. However, how much of the widening may be due to chemical attack on the rock as well? Again this highlights the difficulty of trying to isolate the role of individual types of weathering.

Chemical weathering

This is widespread in occurrence and responsible for the decomposition of many types of rock on a massive scale worldwide. The relationship between the presence of water and most types of chemical weathering has already been mentioned. The rate of chemical weathering increases with temperature. Therefore the highest rates of chemical weathering are experienced in the hot, wet tropics. Another factor contributes here. The hot, wet tropics have the greatest vegetation cover on Earth, with the highest net primary productivity and the highest and most rapid rates of vegetation decay and nutrient recycling. Therefore many organic acids are released by the vegetation on the forest floor to speed up the processes of chemical weathering. Outside the humid tropics the end products of chemical weathering are sand and clay, which are left unchanged and therefore described as stable. It is a different story within the humid tropics as both of these become unstable and are removed. Also unstable are the silicates, which are the commonest rock-forming minerals. Aluminium and iron are the most stable minerals and they remain as heavy rains leach away other minerals, mainly silica. Oxides of aluminium and iron become more concentrated. Sesquioxides of iron (Fe_2O_3) and aluminium (Al_2O_3) in the soil give tropical soils their characteristic red and yellow colours. Hydrated aluminium oxides form deposits of bauxite, commercially the raw material for making aluminium. Iron oxides become concentrated in laterite horizons within the deep tropical soils. These laterite horizons, which form hard, almost rock-like layers, up to 10m thick, are not soil but iron in its ferric (O_3) form. These can have a profound influence impeding drainage and limiting penetration by plant roots. Below the soil is a deep layer of weathered and partly weathered material (the regolith). Chemical alterations to the parent rock regularly take place at depths of 100m or more, such is the effectiveness of chemical weathering in a hot, wet climate.

The maritime nature of the UK's temperate climate provides the water necessary for the operation of most chemical processes, although lower temperatures mean reduced rates of operation both generally and seasonally

▲ **Figure 3.65** Biological, mechanical or chemical weathering? Ash tree growing from the sides of Bar Pot in the Yorkshire Dales

than in the tropics. Despite the amount of rock decomposition for which chemical weathering is responsible and its widespread worldwide effects, only the process of carbonation leads to distinctive landscapes and unique landforms. Limestone rocks have a widespread global distribution. Again it is believed that limestone solution is speeded up by the heat and moisture in humid tropical locations, leading to faster destruction than in temperate latitudes. This produces landscapes dominated by upstanding limestone towers between which are depressions in the rock enlarged by solution, called cockpits. In parts of Europe, such as the Balkans, the southern part of the Massif Central in France and within the Yorkshire Dales and Peak District National Parks in the UK, the outcrops of Carboniferous limestone are sufficiently thick to dominate the relief. Carboniferous limestone is a massive, well jointed and strongly bedded rock, which naturally gives upstanding relief; however, the presence of so many lines of weakness increases its vulnerability to the effects of carbonation, or limestone solution. The result is a combination of distinctive surface and underground features placed under the collective heading of karst scenery. As a result of the dominance of solutional processes, these areas are noted for their lack of surface drainage, surface streams disappearing underground down swallow and sink holes, dry valleys and gorges, surface rock pavements and underground cave systems. Solution is equally important in weathering the other softer limestones and chalk, even if such distinctive landscape features do not result from it.

▲ **Figure 3.66** The tropical red earth soil or latosol, whose great depth and makeup are a reflection of the operation of chemical weathering under humid conditions

Questions

1. Sketch and label the main features shown in Figures 3.64, 3.65 and 3.66.
2. Explain the role of weathering in the formation of the features shown.

Some examples of types of chemical weathering:

a ***Hydrolysis*** *The chemical union between water and minerals of the rock*

Example: (orthoclase) feldspar, one of the mineral constituents of granite, is broken down into the clay mineral kaolinite by hydrolysis. Kaolin is a stable clay mineral under temperate conditions.

b ***Oxidation*** *The chemical reaction between metallic ions and oxygen to form oxides.*

Example: 'rusting' of rocks by reddish-brown discoloration showing that elements of iron within the rock have been oxidized. Although this seems to be only a superficial change, there may also be changes in the chemical structure of the rock making it more vulnerable to attack.

c ***Carbonation*** *Carbon dioxide in the atmosphere and stored in plants and soils mixes with rainwater to form the weak carbonic acid (H_2CO_3) which reacts with carbonate minerals, notably limestone, to form calcium hydrogen carbonate, which is soluble. It is carried away in solution.*

$$CaCO_3 + H_2CO_3 \rightarrow Ca(HCO_3)_2$$

Economic effects of chemical weathering

- *Occasional droughts in the otherwise wet UK can have unpleasant side effects.*
- *In normal years water is absorbed into clays and shales (by up to 60 per cent) by the process of hydration.*
- *In times of drought these rocks dry out leading to shrinkage.*
- *In the drought years of 1975/6 and 1995/6 shrinkage of the clay led to partial foundation failure for houses and other buildings.*
- *This has increased the costs of buildings insurance especially in the most vulnerable areas in southern England.*

Summary of factors which influence the types and rates of weathering

Large scale factors

The two most important factors are rock structure and climate. For erosion, whether the rock is hard or soft is often the most significant factor. For weathering, what is more important is whether the rock has any chemical and physical weaknesses that make it susceptible to one or more types of weathering. Granite is a strong, resistant rock, but because one of its minerals is (orthoclase) feldspar, it is affected by hydrolysis and breaks down chemically. Limestone is vulnerable to carbonation. Physical weaknesses such as joints, lines of cleavage or bedding planes give easier routes into the rock which are exploited by various weathering processes. The importance of vertical hexagonal jointing in an igneous rock such as basalt and the frequency of joints and bedding planes in sedimentary Carboniferous limestone have already been referred to and exemplified.

References have been made to the effects of climate throughout. It has been estimated that the speed of a chemical reaction increases at least two-fold with each rise in temperature of 10°C. Rates reach their maximum in Equatorial regions where the mean annual temperature is 27°C and at least 1,500mm of rain falls per year (Figure 3.67a). Since silicates form over 90 per cent of all rock-forming minerals on the Earth's surface, it is particularly significant that they are unstable in the humid tropics. The one type of weathering known to be more effective in temperate latitudes is frost action. As was emphasized earlier, frequent fluctuations above and below freezing point are extremely effective in speeding up the weathering process. This means that areas of extreme cold are not the best climates for weathering (Figure 3.67b).

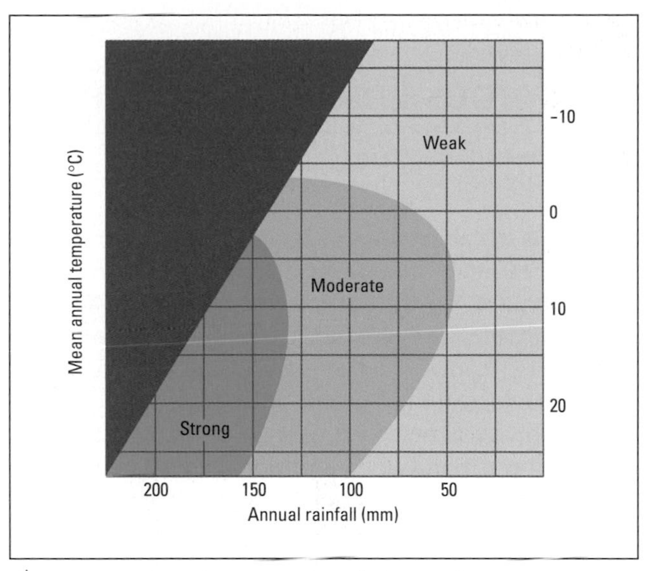

▲ **Figure 3.67a** Average rates of chemical weathering in relation to climate

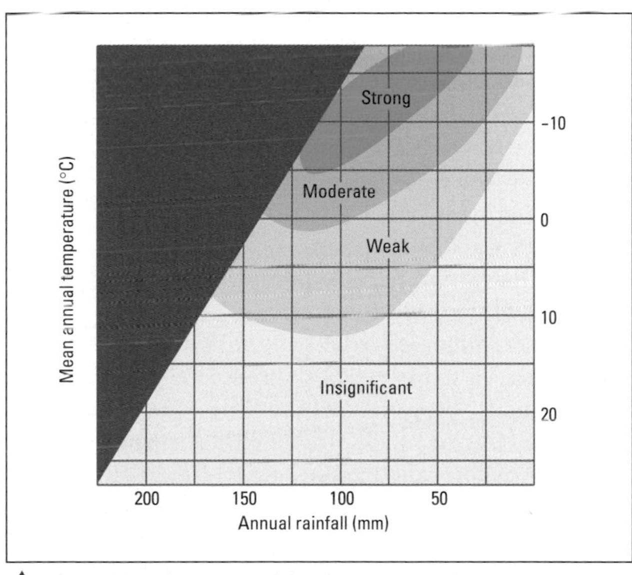

▲ **Figure 3.67b** Rates of frost action in relation to climate

▲ **Figure 3.68** Urban air pollution and its effects on old buildings – York Minster

Small scale factors

Smaller scale factors have an important role to play at the local level. One factor is microclimate. Differences in rates of weathering are often noticed between the sunny and shaded sides of a rock outcrop or at different heights within a few metres of the ground surface. Another is soil and vegetation cover. This may be providing protection by sheltering and shading the rock from the direct effects of weathering. Alternatively plant roots may speed up the rate of mechanical weathering and vegetation when it decays and releases organic acids leading to chemical weathering. Relief is a third factor. The aspect of the slope links in with the climate factor. In steep-sided glaciated mountain regions in the northern hemisphere frost shattering is greater on north and north-east facing slopes, which are in almost permanent shadow. Relief has a strong influence upon the speed of mass movement. The steeper the slope, the more rapidly loose weathered materials are likely to be removed and the more quickly the newly exposed rock face can be attacked again by weathering.

By what means and how quickly weathered materials are removed by mass movement leads us naturally into the next section. However, before leaving weathering as a separate study, mention must be made of human involvement in weathering processes. As with everything else, human involvement is increasing. Polluted air in urban areas speeds up the rate of rock weathering on buildings and statues. Since the early days of the Industrial Revolution falling rainwater has been combining with the emissions of carbon and sulphur dioxides present in the atmosphere to produce dilute solutions of carbonic and sulphuric acids. Under this persistent onslaught in the UK's humid climate stonework and brickwork have rotted and crumbled away. Limestone rocks, of which the Houses of Parliament and several cathedrals are built, are particularly sensitive and have required regular cleaning and restoration (Figure 3.68). This is not just a UK problem. The 'export' of acid rain to cities in Scandinavia is increasing the rate of decay of old buildings there. The outward spread of Cairo into the desert to the edge of the pyramids at Giza and the Sphinx has carried polluted urban air with it and brought concerns for the health of the ancient monuments that have been used to clean, dry desert air. In broader terms humans increase, either accidentally or intentionally, the number of bare rock surfaces. In quarries many layers of rock, previously deep underground and safe from most surface weathering, are exposed to direct attack after top soil and rocks have been removed. In the tropics overgrazing and overcropping can strip the land of its cover of vegetation exposing it to the rapid chemical weathering.

Questions

1 a Distinguish between mechanical, chemical and biological weathering.

b Evaluate the extent to which it is justified to study each type of weathering separately.

2 Identify and explain the relationships between weathering and:

a rock type and structure

b climate.

Near Ingleton, Yorkshire: Carboniferous limestone scenery

Case Study

The causes and results of chemical weathering

Rainwater flowing over the surface of the impervious millstone grit, which caps Ingleborough Hill and the shales of the Yoredale series below it, joins up and forms surface streams. These begin to disappear underground once they have passed on to the area below where the Carboniferous limestone outcrops. Rainwater contains some CO_2 from the atmosphere; more CO_2 is taken from passing through the soil and rock, which aids the rate of solution and increases the amount of calcium concentrated in the water after solution. It is at the soil-bedrock interface that most solution is believed to take place. Many joints, gaps and pores in the limestone are widened to allow surface water to pass underground in an unspectacular way. The loss of water from Fell Beck is more concentrated – travelling down the swallow hole at Gaping Gill and falling over 100m into the giant cavern that has been hollowed out below. A funnel-shaped depression is left above (Figure 3.69). Surface depressions are quite a feature of limestone areas and are formed either by solution on the surface working downwards or by the collapse of cave passageways from below. As the operation of chemical weathering and the work of streams have increased in extent with time, former holes down which water used to flow, such as Bar Pot (Figure 3.65), have been abandoned and now lie well beyond the points at which water disappears underground under normal weather conditions. There is an extensive system of underground passageways ending with Ingleborough Cave, which is open to the public, as the varied lime creations formed by stalactites and stalagmites are attractive to visitors. Water falling on the limestone itself passes into the rock, making use of the multitude of gaps provided by the joints and bedding planes. This may eventually join the stream water in the form of drips from cave roofs. Calcium bicarbonate is unstable and is redeposited in the caves as calc-tufa reversing the carbonation process. The water re-emerging from Ingleborough Cave at Clapham Beck is carrying as much calcium as the carbon dioxide present in the water allows. Parts of the limestone outcrop below Ingleborough Hill are covered by boulder clay; however, where the rock itself is exposed, limestone pavements have formed. The surface of the limestone is broken up into fretted blocks, called clints, separated by grooves, called grykes, which range in depth from a few centimetres to a few metres. The effects of solution by carbonic acid are concentrated in the joints and along the bedding planes, the size and closeness of which control the degree of separation and depth of the grykes (Figure 3.69b).

▼ **Figure 3.69a** Limestone pavement

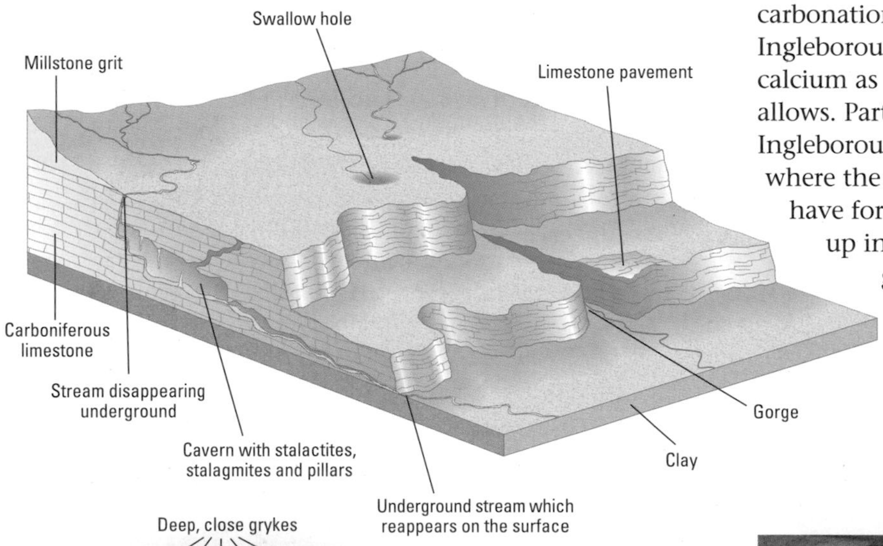

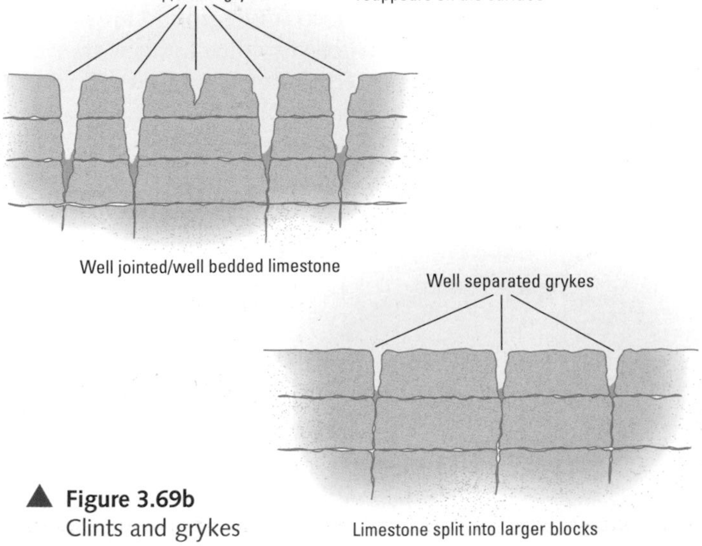

Swallow hole
Millstone grit
Limestone pavement
Carboniferous limestone
Stream disappearing underground
Cavern with stalactites, stalagmites and pillars
Underground stream which reappears on the surface
Gorge
Clay

Deep, close grykes
Well jointed/well bedded limestone
Well separated grykes
Limestone split into larger blocks

▲ **Figure 3.69b** Clints and grykes

▲ **Figure 3.69c** Grykes below Ingleborough

▲ **Figure 3.70** 1:25,000 OS map of Ingleborough

Questions

1 Draw a labelled cross-section due west from the top of Ingleborough to the western edge of the map.

2 Identify and comment upon the map evidence for each of the following:

a Carboniferous limestone outcrops on land below 460m above sea level (approximately).

b The course formerly taken by Fell Beck between Gaping Gill and Ingleborough Cave.

c Mechanical and chemical weathering both of which operate in the area covered by this map extract.

Causes and consequences of mass movements

Mass movement is the transfer downslope of loose rocks, rock debris and soil as a result of gravity. It should be viewed as the link between weathering on one hand and transport by agents of erosion on the other. The force of gravity acts constantly on all rocks and debris. The downslope force of gravity increases with increasing steepness of slope. The greater the slope, the increased tendency for loose material to move down it. Whilst gravity is forcing all loose materials downslope, there is resistance to movement from friction and cohesion. These have to be overcome before any movement can take place. Indeed mass movements only begin once the forces for movement are greater than those against it. More rapid movements need to be 'triggered-off' by either a natural or a human factor. Examples of natural factors are earthquakes or earth tremors, an intensive rainstorm or rapid snow melt. In terms of human factors, the vibrations from passing heavy traffic may be sufficient, although people undertaking work on hillsides is perhaps more common. Alternatively the factors favourable to eventual mass movement may have been building up for a long time. From above, there may be the further accumulations of loose debris or an increased presence of snow and water. From below, there could be the removal of material by agents of erosion such as streams or waves to undermine the supports. On occasions humans are responsible by creating changed circumstances through construction work for roads, houses and dams. Water is often an important factor in promoting movement. It can lubricate movement by reducing the effects of friction. It certainly increases the actual weight of the materials to be removed and adds to their stress which makes movement more likely. Once the forces against movement have been overcome, the mass of the material on the move helps to prolong the movement since the weight of material from above acts as part of the downslope force.

The relative importance of these processes of mass movement varies. For example, in a rockfall, once the piece of rock has become detached, gravity becomes the dominant factor. This is because these occur only on the steepest slopes with angles of between 70° and 90°. The top of slopes from which rockfalls occur are steep with bare faces of hard rock. In the UK these have been exposed to frost action for many years and still are. As soon as the piece of rock breaks off, it goes into free fall, bouncing along until the point is reached on the slope below where forces cease to favour movement. This normally means that the slope angle has become sufficiently shallow for the rock to come to rest. If the fallen angular pieces of rocks are not removed, they develop into a scree slope, which can be of substantial size, especially when the rocks above are heavily fissured, bare of vegetation cover, high above sea level and have undergone frost action for thousands of years (Figure 3.71). Often there are preferred channels down which many rockfalls are directed and in which avalanches of loose rocks periodically occur forming large scree cones at their bases.

Figure 3.71
The scree slopes on the north-facing side of Wastwater

One classification of mass movements uses the different types of transport down the slope. By ignoring falls, this produces a three-fold division into slides, flows and heaves. The classification allows different movements to be represented not only according to speed of movement but also by the extent to which water is involved in the transport of materials (Figure 3.72). In a river there is great dominance of water over debris. In mass movements debris is more dominant than water. At one end of the scale soil creep and rockfall have an abundance of debris and very little water. These are examples of heaves and falls. At the other end of the scale are the flows such as mudflow and earthflow with more water present, which makes them some of the faster forms of mass movement. In between are the slides. In those forms of mass movement with more water present, the form of movement is flowing while the drier types undergo sliding. The difference between flowing and sliding is illustrated in Figure 3.73.

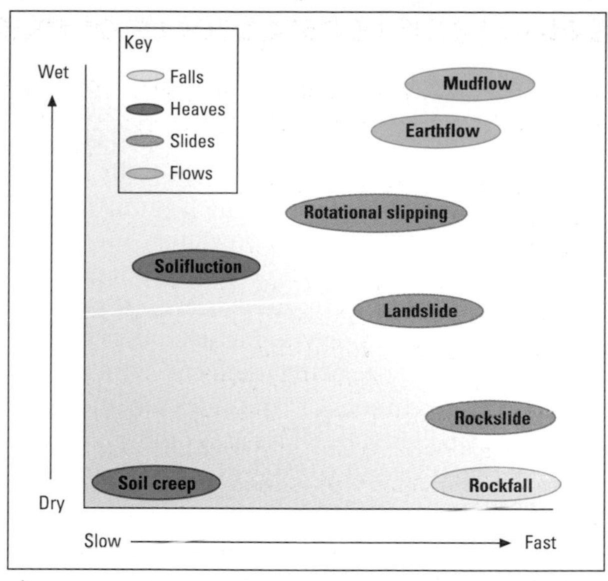

▲ **Figure 3.72** Mass movements in relation to speed of movement and water involvement

▼ **Figure 3.73**
Flows and slides. In a flow, velocity is greatest at the surface and decreases to (almost) nothing at the bottom. In a slide there is equal velocity from top to bottom of the moving mass.

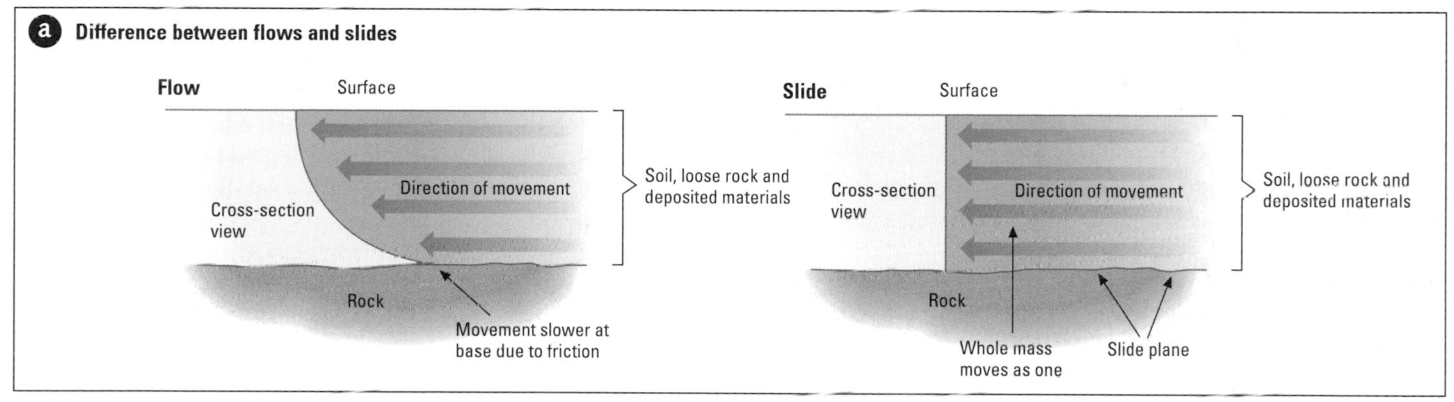

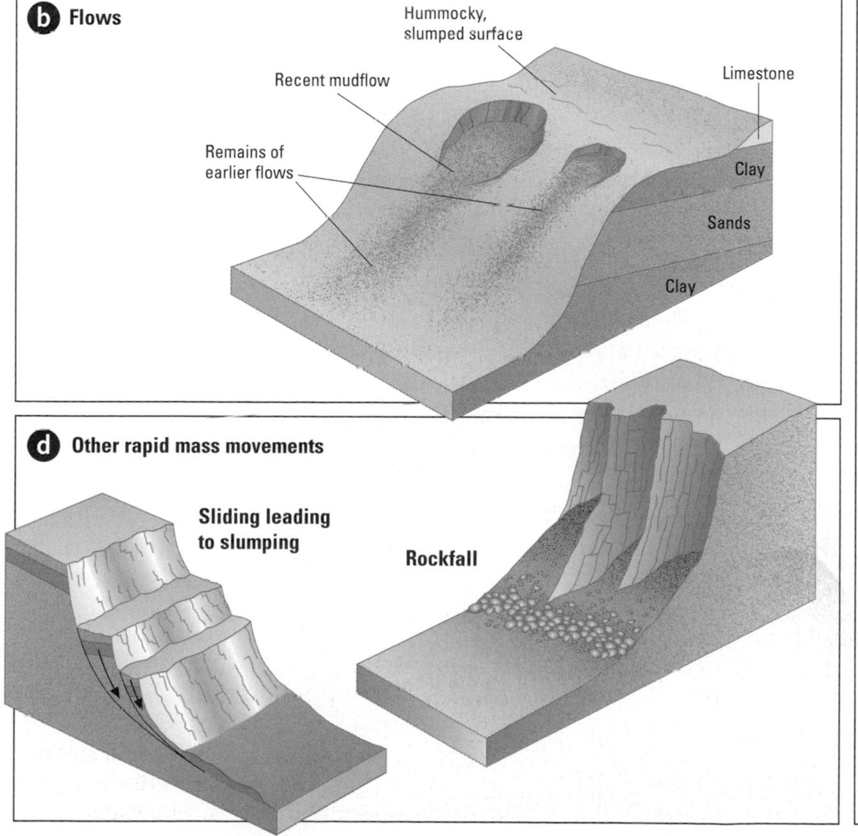

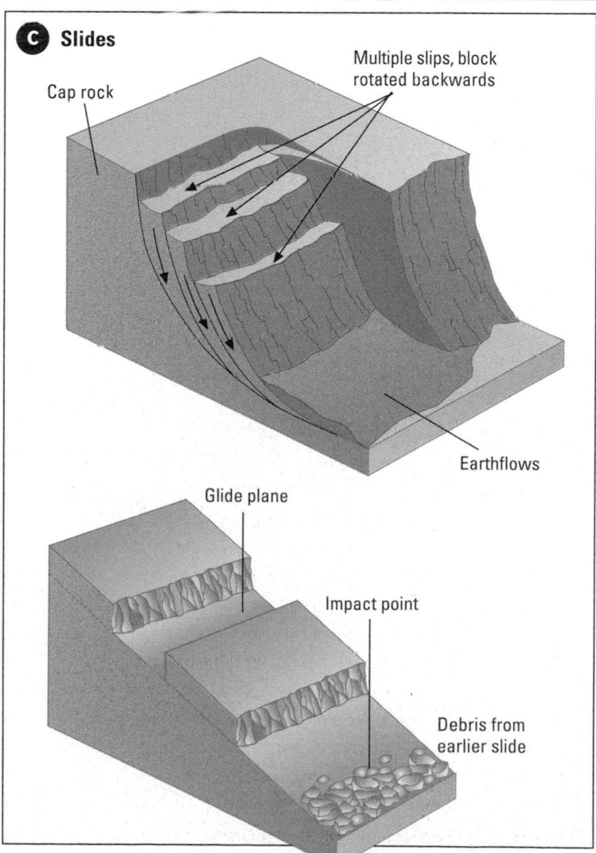

Slides

The standard type of slide is just given the label landslide. It is the movement of any mass of material along a slip plane. If the mass of material consists almost entirely of loose rocks, it could technically be distinguished as a rock slide, which is only a little more organized than the rockfalls previously mentioned. More usually regolith and rock will be mixed together. Given that the amount of water present is on the low side, landslides are most likely to happen on steep slopes and particularly on those being undercut, which is why many of the recent examples of landslides are in coastal locations. Smaller scale slides are common in non-natural locations such as on the sides of railway and motorway embankments.

In a slide the entire mass of material will move along a slip plane. As it moves it largely retains its shape and structure; only at the end of the slide as it comes to a halt does it suffer any deformation. Suitable slip planes include junctions between rocks, bedding planes and fault lines. Slides happen only occasionally, but when they do, movement is fast. The pressure for movement is likely to have been building up for some time before movement is triggered off. Three examples of possible triggers for movement are the increased presence of water, very cold weather causing movements within the soil or waves undercutting steep sea cliffs.

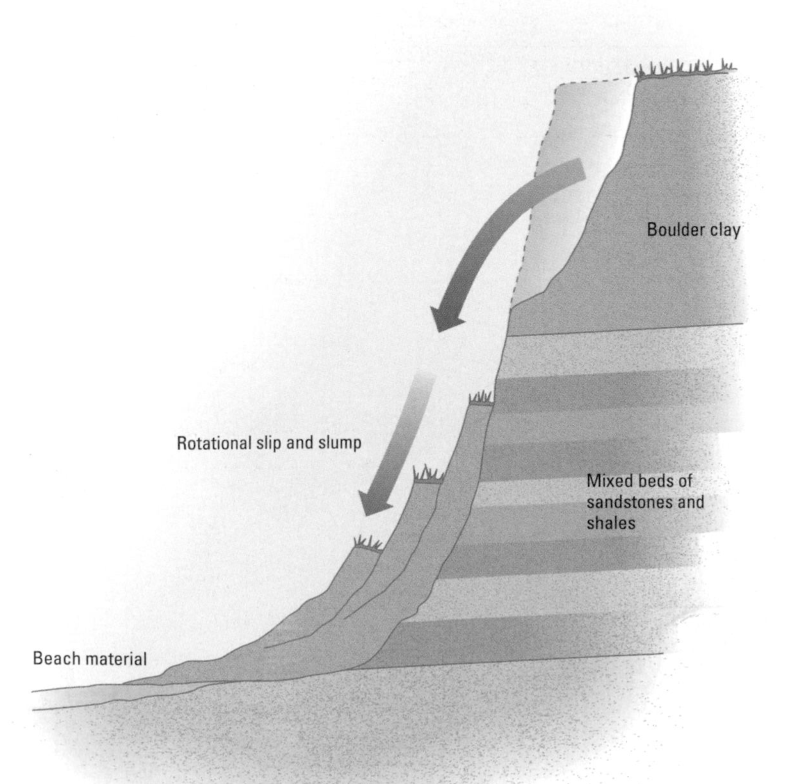

▲ **Figure 3.74** Rotational slipping

When the slip plane is more of a concave curve, the moving mass is rotated backwards. This produces rotational slipping. These can occur on slopes composed of just one type of rock. Weak rocks such as clay are very vulnerable to the development of slip planes. The result of the movement is to produce a scar. In these the initial form of the mass may be more readily destroyed so that what began as a slide ends as a slump. In some examples the presence of large amounts of water may lead to the slump becoming a flow. Figure 3.74 shows the profile of the many rotational slumps that occur where boulder clay overlies rock which is being rapidly eroded along the North Sea coasts in Yorkshire and Norfolk. The strongest slides happen after periods of heavy rain and north-easterly gales. The former thoroughly saturates and lubricates the boulder clay; the latter undercuts the cliff supports below.

Flows

Flows are more likely to occur than other types of mass movement when the slope materials contain a high proportion of fine particles, mostly no larger than sand size. In order to become mobile under its own weight the mass needs to become saturated with water. Although they occur only occasionally, the effects of mudflows and earthflows can be quite devastating. This is because, once they are on the move, water and smaller sized materials become more concentrated in their base and at the front of the flow, which allows them to spread out over more gentle slopes than those needed for the movement to begin. Mudflows are the fastest. Ideal conditions for their occurrence are little or no vegetation cover in areas subject to occasional torrential downpours. Some hot desert locations, such as on the sides of wadis, offer these ideal conditions. Earthflows are thicker in consistency which means that the proportion of debris to water is slightly higher. The most tragic earthflow in the UK occurred in October 1966 in the mining village of Aberfan in South Wales. The waste tip from the coal mine, about 250m high, was located at the top of a valley on slopes of about 14°. It had been there for many years and was part of the landscape. An exceptionally wet autumn raised the water content levels within the waste heap. On the morning of 21 October the liquid limit needed for movement was exceeded and the mass of saturated pit waste 'flowed' down the slope. It gave no chance of escape to the children in the primary school below. This may have happened almost forty years ago, but the name of Aberfan remains well known after this man-made natural disaster as do places such as the village of Lynmouth in Devon, the scene of another exceptional natural event.

▲ **Figure 3.75** The destructive earthflow at Aberfan in 1966

▲ **Figure 3.76** Aerial view of Aberfan today with the now landscaped slopes above the village

Heaves

Heaves or creeps are the slowest but most widespread types of mass movement. Soil creep is the slow downslope movement of soil and debris under the influence of gravity. It takes place on slopes as low as 5° and speeds up noticeably as slope angles increase. Bare soil marks to be seen on the faces of most slopes indicate that it is happening (Figure 3.78), although pieces of evidence for its presence can be quite numerous (Figure 3.77). Operating on such a small scale it does not need much to trigger the creep off. Large droplets of rain may be sufficient to dislodge soil particles downslope. More creep probably occurs in winter when localized expansion and contraction of the soil due to freezing and thawing is added to the less seasonal alternate wetting and drying. Due to the growth of ice crystals below soil particles when freezing occurs, any frost heaving will lift the soil particles up at right angles to the slope; however they then fall back in a direct line to the ground, which places them in a downslope position compared to the one occupied before the heaving began.

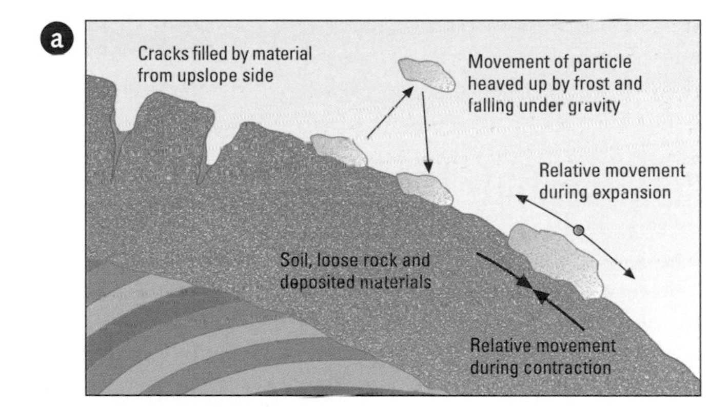

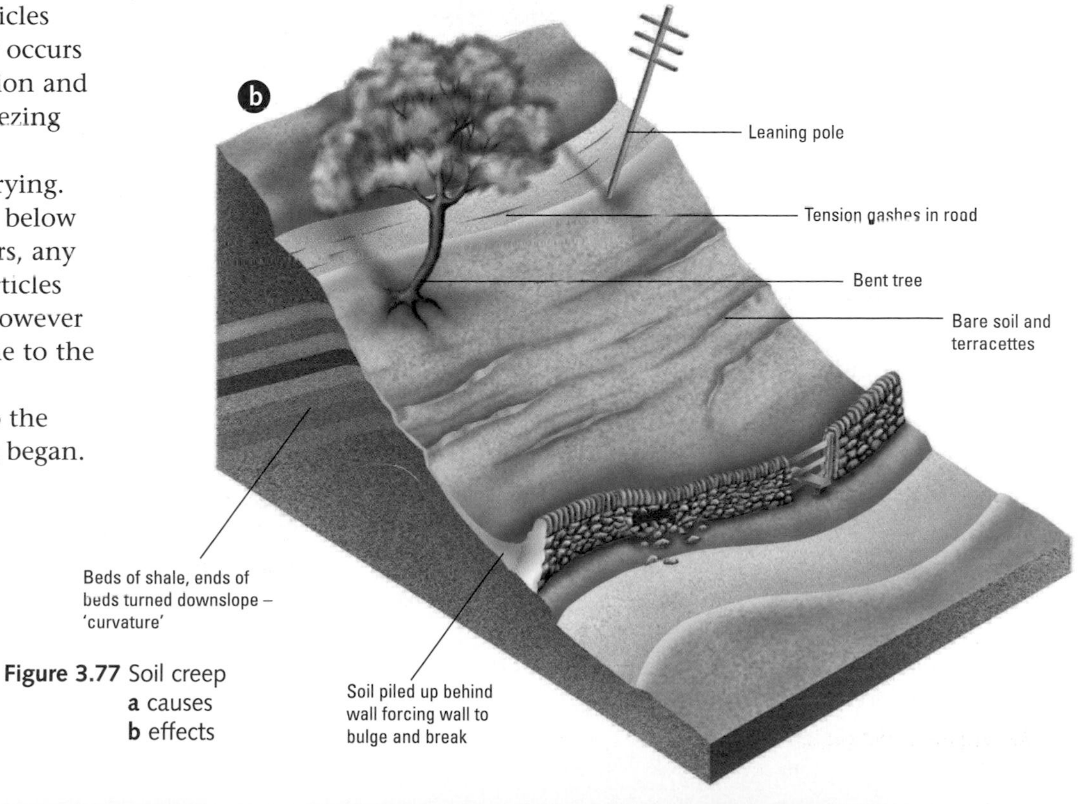

▶ **Figure 3.77** Soil creep
a causes
b effects

Solifluction

Solifluction is a flow (though slow enough to be also classified as a heave) confined to tundra and other periglacial environments. Its occurrence is dependent upon the presence of permafrost. When surface temperatures rise above freezing point in summer the meltwater, prevented from downward movement by the permanently frozen sub-soil, saturates the active surface layer which becomes highly mobile even on quite gentle slopes of 2–3°. The main surface landform created is solifluction lobes – small step-line terraces upon the backs of which the thin mat of vegetation cover has been moved (page 146).

▲ **Figure 3.78** Evidence of soil creep and mass movement in a valley in Northumberland

Relationships between weathering, mass movements and erosion

After mountain building and uplift of land from the sea, it is the processes of weathering, described earlier under the headings of mechanical and chemical, that are mainly responsible for the early stages in the denudation of the new land surfaces. It is rare for a rock to be attacked by a single weathering process; the different mechanical and chemical processes work together, although their relative importance varies from one rock to another and between one climatic region and another.

Mass movements are the next stage in the denudation process after weathering. Their role is to transport the pieces of rock and all the other debris caused by the disintegration and decomposition of rocks by the different weathering processes. Some movements act very slowly but almost continuously such as soil creep. Others cause sudden movements of large masses of material, such as earthflows, followed by long periods of inactivity. By falls, heaves, slides and flows loose materials move downslope until they are in a location where one of the agents of erosion is able to transport them further on their journey towards the sea. Unlike mass movements, agents of erosion such as rivers and glaciers erode and break down further the materials being transported as load. By the time most rocks reach the sea they have been reduced to sand and silt-sized particles by processes such as abrasion and attrition.

On reaching the world's seas and oceans, the load of sediment falls to the sea bed. Here it accumulates over millions of years until it is transported towards a destructive plate margin, where Earth movements upfold the sediments into the Earth's new fold mountains. Then the cycle of weathering, mass movement and erosion starts all over again.

Questions

1 With the aid of labelled sketches and examples, distinguish between heaves, slides and flows.

2 Discuss the natural factors which favour mass movements.

3 As contributors to the occurrence of mass movements analyse the role of:
   a people
   b tectonic activity.

4 Investigation
   a Search for, sketch and explain the evidence of mass movements in the region where you live.
   b Research the origins of tors emphasizing the importance of rock characteristics and the role of weathering.

The impact and response to geomorphological processes and hazards

Impacts on the natural world

Mountain building and rifting lead to landforms that are major landscape features. In some areas they are continental in scale extending for thousands of kilometres; however, their formations do not have the same dramatic and immediate impact upon the landscape as does a volcanic eruption (Figure 3.79). Despite the scale of death and destruction wrought by a large earthquake hitting an urban area, earthquakes leave only small scale physical scars on the landscape. Cracks open in the ground, small scarps form and blocks of rock are uplifted further. The face of slopes may be altered by landslides. Land or lake levels may rise or fall by a few metres, which might be of great significance locally, but only locally.

Figure 3.79
The cone of Mt Eldfell and its lava flows were formed by the 1963 eruption on Heimaey off the south coast of Iceland. All that can be seen on the left of the photograph is new land from that date. About one third of the houses of the settlement were destroyed under the lava flows.

Figure 3.80
A one way street to nowhere in Flores in Guatemala, a town sited in the middle of a lake, the level of which has risen as a result of tectonic activity

At the local scale volcanic eruptions destroy the vegetation cover, whether natural or human. A bare ground surface is created. Once the lava cools and hardens, small plants, typically mosses and lichens, begin to colonize the new surface. These form the first stage in a plant succession, a lithosere. If left uninterrupted by further eruptions or human activities, it can be expected to lead eventually to the return of climatic climax vegetation – the most complex community of plants that the climate of that place will allow. The presence of small plants, accompanied by weathering of the new volcanic rock, leads to the formation of a deeper and richer soil which can support a greater variety and taller plants. Climate is an important control on the speed of progress towards climatic climax. In Iceland's cool climate mosses may only grow by one centimetre in a hundred years. Figure 3.81 shows the densest natural vegetation cover found on the lava flows from Eldfell in 1963. After more than 35 years, some bare surfaces remain. A careful study of Figure 3.79, however, shows grass-covered slopes near and above the settlement. These are not natural. Grasses were artificially laid on top of the lava to stabilize the new volcanic deposits near to the houses which survived the eruption.

▲ **Figure 3.81** Lava flows from the Eldfell 1963 eruption are mainly moss covered.

Figure 3.82 is a time column for the plant succession on what remained of Krakatoa after the 1883 eruption. Krakatoa is located near the Equator with a hot, wet Equatorial climate. Since it lies only 40km from mainland Java, it could be reached reasonably quickly by wind-dispersed seeds and these formed the majority of the plant species present in the first fifty years. However, the number and variety of species remains much less rich than in an old established rainforest, where typically there are between 40 and 100 species of tree within just one hectare. It may be thousands of years before the great bio-diversity of the climatic climax rainforests is recovered.

Early 1883	Tropical rainforest
Late 1883	Covered by a layer of ash up to 100m thick No vegetation
1884	Slimy film of cyanobacteria covering the ground Grasses and ferns Small bushes
1893	Some tree saplings
1933	Mantle of trees covering the island (36 species of tree)
1980	Trees up to 30m tall in places (60 species of tree)
1983	After 100 years, it is described as secondary forest because of the limited diversity of plants

▲ **Figure 3.82** Vegetation succession on Krakatoa

Whilst the physical effects of most volcanic eruptions are also restricted to the local area, some from strato-volcanoes have had global impacts. The greatest in recent recorded history was that of Krakatoa. Over one hundred years ago, however, the ability to record and measure the worldwide effects of a major eruption was limited. The effects of the eruption of El Chicon in Mexico in the late 1980s were carefully monitored as the dust from it was carried around the globe by the wind circulation in the upper atmosphere. This dust reduced the amount of incoming solar radiation and led to lower temperatures in the northern hemisphere at a time when global warming was otherwise taking place (Figure 3.83). Therefore the awesome power of some volcanic eruptions causes impacts which are truly global.

Eruption of Krakatoa 1883

August 1883

- *Explosion blew away the top of the mountain and left a caldera*
- *Heard over 4,500km away*
- *Tsunamis up to 30m high smashed against the coast of Java*
- *Over 36,000 people were killed*
- *Ash and gas sent 36km high into atmosphere*
- *There were two days of darkness over western Java*
- *The dust circled the world for several years, reducing temperatures.*

Impacts on human activity

It is reasonably safe to live in those areas (near to constructive margins and hot spots) where volcanoes emit basaltic lava. Eruptions may cause damage, but are rarely life threatening since people have plenty of time to move away. When Eldfell erupted in 1963, there was time to evacuate most inhabitants of Heimaey to mainland Iceland. It was even possible to spray the front of the lava flow with cold sea water to increase the rate of cooling and slow it down. This successfully reduced the amount of damage to the harbour and town. This artificial, human induced cooling helps to explain the height of the lava wall shown in Figure 3.79. However, people living on the slopes of potentially explosive strato-volcanoes have higher risks. When located in MEDCs, active strato-volcanoes, such as Mount Etna which erupted again in 1999, are monitored by scientists. Although it is impossible to predict exactly when an eruption will happen and what form it will take, the advance warning signs are clearer than for an earthquake. In LEDCs monitoring is rarer and many eruptions come as a complete surprise to local people. Even so, often the secondary effects, such as mudflows, many of which are utterly impossible to predict and prevent, kill more people than the lava flows or ash clouds.

Questions

1. Draw a labelled sketch of Figure 3.79 to show the physical and human effects of the 1963 eruption of Eldfell.
2. Outline the different reasons why so few people were killed in the eruptions of Eldfell, Krakatoa and Mount St Helens
3. What does the Mount St Helen's example indicate about human ability to predict volcanic eruptions?
4. Evaluate the extent to which volcanoes and earthquakes can have effects beyond their origins.
5. Put together a case study of Krakatoa. Suggested headings are 'location'; 'reasons for an explosive eruption'; 'primary effects of the eruption'; 'secondary effects'; vegetation changes.

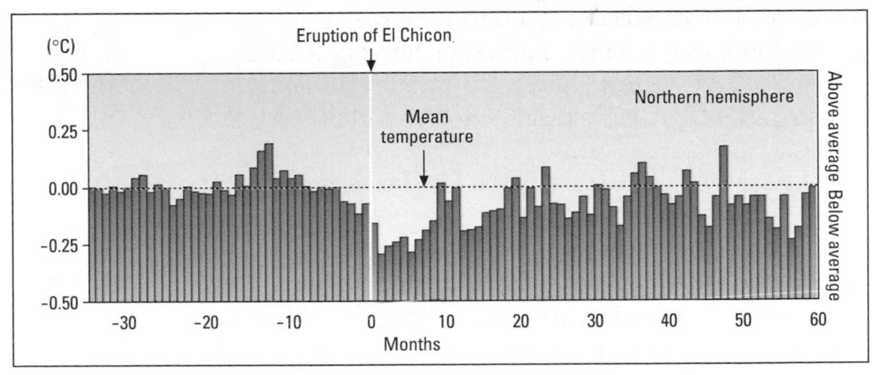

▲ **Figure 3.83** The effects of the El Chicon eruption on temperatures in the northern hemisphere

	Physical warnings	Human responses
March	Small earthquake shocks Black ash emitted Northern sector bulged outwards	Residents and loggers evacuated and visitors restricted
April	Earthquakes continued	No entry zone of 5–13km created around the volcano
Early May	Quiet period without earthquakes, eruptions or further bulging	Residents allowed back under supervision to claim belongings
18 May	Suddenly a 5.0 earthquake destabilized the bulge and created a massive landslide Exposed magma exploded Blast devastated the forests around the volcano and sent ash and dust high into the atmosphere	Great damage, only 1 person killed

▲ **Figure 3.84** Warnings before the eruption of Mount St Helens, 1980, USA

Prediction and preparation for volcanoes and earthquakes

As magma rises up into and through the volcanic cone, there are warning signs. Small earthquakes occur, water is heated giving off more steam and there is a greater release of the gases commonly found in magma such as hydrogen sulphide. Technology is also helping with prediction: satellites can be used to monitor heat changes, which is most valuable in remote locations or in LEDCs without ground monitoring stations.

Much more worrying for people living in areas subject to tectonic activity are earthquakes. Without any even partly effective method of prediction, the best people can do is prepare for them and put strategies into place which are designed to reduce their impact. High buildings such as skyscrapers are much more likely to remain standing if they are built using the following: steel caged structures, only small areas between each support, deep foundations on solid rock and a rubber pad placed between the building and its foundations. Making already existing buildings and structures earthquake proof is more difficult and expensive; the Americans call this 'retrofitting'. Clearly the richer the country and the higher its level of development, the greater the need for preparation and the more possible it is. For many people in LEDCs there can be only one priority – survival now. In this respect the study of a Californian earthquake below provides quite a contrast to what happened in an earthquake in Turkey (pages 96–97).

Quake rocks California

7.0 trembler is felt from LA to Las Vegas

It wasn't the Big One but it was bad, and it could have been a lot worse. A magnitude 7.0 earthquake centred in the southern California desert rocked buildings from Los Angeles to Las Vegas, shaking an Amtrak train from its tracks and knocking out power to more than 90,000 customers.

The quake was centred 100 miles east of Los Angeles and 32 miles north of the remote desert town of Joshua Tree, where nerves remained frayed yesterday after shock waves jolted many from their sleep. There were no reports of serious injury or damage in the 2:46am quake, although crockery broke and pipes burst near the epicentre, while 150 miles away, gamblers in Las Vegas were distracted suddenly, if only for a moment. 'I saw the leaves on the fake palm trees rustling so I guessed it must be an earthquake' said one Las Vegas gambler, who added 'If I am up, I might as well lose some more change'.

In intensity, yesterday's boomer actually was stronger than the 6.7 magnitude quake that levelled the Northridge area of Los Angeles in January 1994, killing 72 people and causing an estimated $40 billion in damage. But because of the epicentre's remote location yesterday, damage was far more limited.

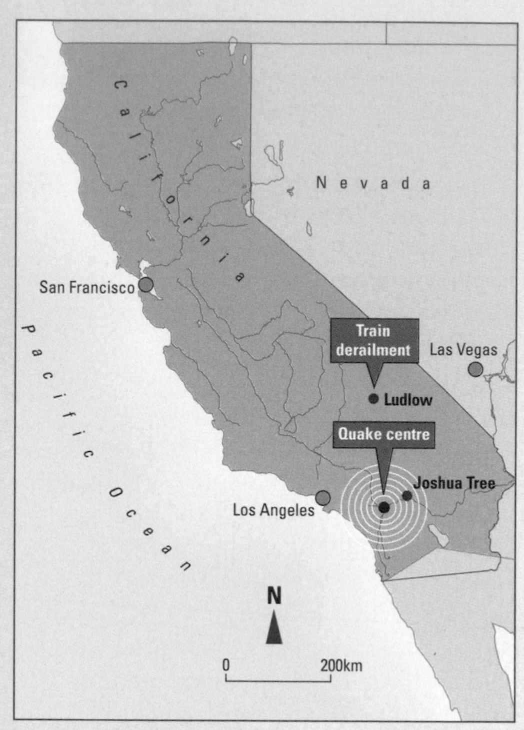

▲ **Figure 3.86** California

▲ **Figure 3.85** Adapted extract from *Daily News*, 17 October 1999

READY OR NOT, THE BIG ONE IS COMING

Quake-proofing the S.F. area is very slow, very expensive task

As bad as it was, the 1989 Loma Prieta earthquake wasn't the 'big one' that the Bay Area has dreaded ever since San Francisco was virtually wiped out by the monster which struck in 1906. The epicentre of the 6.9 magnitude quake in 1989 was 60 miles south of Oakland near Loma Prieta peak in the lightly populated Santa Cruz mountains. Still the quake was powerful enough to resonate north, killing 68 people and causing $7 billion in property damage.

Two reports released Thursday emphasize that, bad as the Loma Prieta earthquake was, it was not as bad as it could have been. A theme running through both reports is – the big one is coming, yet much of the Bay Area still isn't prepared, despite a decade of lessons from Loma Prieta.

Loma Prieta and the 6.7 magnitude Northridge quake in southern California five years later energized a statewide effort to make homes, commercial buildings, highways and bridges more quake-proof. But retrofitting remains costly and is far from complete. Surveys found that most Bay Area homeowners are not bolting the frames of their houses to the foundation or shoring up chimneys. The highest percentage of homeowners doing this in any area was 38 per cent in Berkeley. The region's infrastructure is being slowly strengthened. More than 500 bridges have been retrofitted and Interstate 800 was rebuilt as one level. However, retrofitting the Golden Gate bridge is less than half finished and the rapid-transit rail and subway system still needs to raise $810 million to complete its work. San Francisco Airport's new international terminal is one of the structures using a new technique of building on giant ball-bearings. The structures don't shake in a quake; they roll gently.

Yet science reveals the urgency because researchers have determined that Loma Prieta did little to relieve the seismic pressure building since 1906. Pressure is building throughout the Bay Area's entire fault network, like a wooden ruler being bent. The more the ruler bends, the more stress builds along its length. Where the ruler finally breaks, the stress is released. 'All the faults are part of the same ruler. We just don't know where it will snap next.'

▲ **Figure 3.87** Adapted extract from *USA Today*, Friday 15 October 1999

Questions

1 **a** What is retrofitting?
b Outline the ways in which buildings and structures can be made earthquake proof.
c Describe the features of buildings in Turkey which led to their collapse.

2 Compile a case study: California – earthquake country.
Suggested headings:
- why the earthquake risk is high
- experiences from previous earthquakes
- degree of preparedness for future earthquakes.

The role of aid

Outside aid is desperately needed by local people, irrespective of whether they are rich or poor, in the immediate aftermath of a natural disaster. In rich countries such as the USA and Japan it is expected that the local and national authorities will have the resources and organization to undertake and finance the rescue operations. Emergency procedures for known hazard risks such as earthquakes are practised in advance. With a high level of advanced preparation and modern communications, specialist rescue and medical teams can be expected to be on the scene within hours, even in relatively remote locations. In less wealthy countries, such as Turkey, national organizations may not be able to cope with the disaster tasks allocated to them after a major event, as the case study of the earthquake in Turkey in 1999 showed (pages 96–97). The poorer the country, usually the lower its preparedness and the greater its reliance upon aid from other countries. For many LEDCs the only source of short-term aid is from overseas. NGOs (Non-Governmental Organizations or charities), such as Oxfam, Christian Aid or the French medical charity *Médecins sans Frontières*, are often the ones first to reach the scene of the disaster. They may already have members working in the country and they can respond quicker and more flexibly than can governments and international bodies such as the UN and EU. Individual governments in MEDCs can be effective at organizing relief supplies of food, medicines and equipment, particularly if it is a country within their own sphere of interest, but they are often incapable of distributing it adequately. One positive outcome of the Turkish earthquake was that Greece sent immediate aid to Turkey putting aside their traditional hostility to each other.

In this era of global communications, world TV news teams flash back pictures to people in their home countries in the MEDW usually within twenty four hours of the event happening, and people are often willing to contribute generously to the relief needs. However, surface communications are often found wanting when needed to bridge the gap between pledging money and giving equipment and its receipt by people overcome by disaster.

Important as immediate relief aid is to save lives, many people would argue that longer term aid to repair and replace what has been lost and to lessen the likelihood of another disaster striking is even more important. As a result some charitable organizations have re-focused their giving upon development instead of disaster aid.

EU guilty of aid budget bungling

Clare Short, the UK's international development secretary, is to challenge international institutions including the UN, the World Bank and the EU to reassess the way they manage their aid programmes in the wake of growing criticism of inconsistency, poor coordination and life threatening delays. Ms Short's outburst comes as MPs prepare to deliver a scathing attack on the bureaucratic incompetence of the EU's £7.5 billion-a-year aid budget.

Accusing Brussels of 'Kafkaesque' delays – including the need for up to 40 official signatures before emergency relief can be despatched – the cross party select committee on international development will tomorrow reveal that, nearly two years after hurricane Mitch killed almost 7,000 people in Central America, the EU's promised £175m has yet to arrive. The report will underline how it takes an average of four years and two months to deliver EU aid to survivors of a global disaster.

The Commons committee will also argue that too much EU aid – about half – goes to countries in southern and eastern Europe or north Africa, areas strategically important to the EU, instead of highly indebted countries in sub-Saharan Africa and in Asia. The report comes as Ms Short prepares a white paper defending globalization as a shift in world affairs as profound as the change from feudalism to industrialization in the seventeenth and eighteenth centuries. Ms Short wants a higher profile for so-called graduation policies, under which countries receive more aid if they follow sensible development paths.

▲ **Figure 3.88** Adapted extract from *The Guardian*, Monday 7 August 2000

◀ **Figure 3.89** Cartoon which accompanied the article in *The Guardian*

Questions

1 Look at Figure 3.89. Comment on what it shows.

2 a What is meant by geomorphological hazards?
  b To what extent is it possible to predict and prepare for them happening?

3 For one example of an area struck by a geomorphological hazard:
  a outline its impacts on the area and the people
  b comment on the responses of the people living there.

Positive impacts on people

Mineralization is associated with many of the great Earth movements and their related igneous activity. The economies of countries in the Andes, notably Chile (copper), Bolivia (tin) and Peru (a variety including lead, zinc, copper and silver) still depend heavily upon exports of metals and minerals. Additionally there are recent sulphur deposits from the volcanoes which are mined at great heights in Chile. Many mineral resources of the USA, notably copper, are concentrated in the Rocky Mountains. As hot water circulates through rocks in geothermal areas, various chemicals are dissolved in it, which are precipitated on the surface. Red colours show the presence of iron, yellow shows sulphur and green indicates the presence of copper. These are rarely deposited in commercial quantities, but they add to the attractiveness of thermal areas for tourists. The white and grey organ pipe terraces of Mammoth Springs, mainly formed by the precipitation of silicon, are just one of the tourist attractions of Yellowstone National Park (Figure 3.90). Bears and buffaloes may add to the park's attractions, but what really draws the tourists are the emissions of steam, hot water, sulphurous fumes and bubbling mud from geysers, hissing holes and fissures.

▲ **Figure 3.90** Mammoth Springs, Yellowstone Park

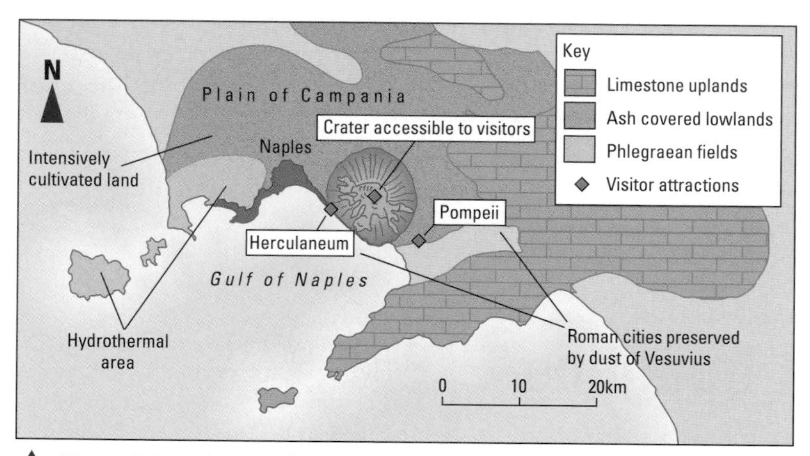

▲ **Figure 3.91** Vesuvius: the usefulness of volcanic activity

▲ **Figure 3.92** Vesuvius and the Plain of Campania

Large numbers of visitors are attracted to areas where there is hydrothermal activity (dependent upon hot water). In areas of active volcanoes, the risk is too great, except for the fissure eruptions in Hawaii. When operating, these do wonders for the islands' tourist trade. The hot water is frequently used for heating, and in areas where it is hot enough, for generating electricity from geothermal energy. This is a pollution-free alternative to fossil fuels. The top six countries for power production by this means are the USA, Philippines, Mexico, Italy, New Zealand and Japan.

Although the primary effects of most types of tectonic activity are disastrous, once the materials erupted from a volcano have had time to weather, they produce some of the world's most fertile soils because of the wealth and variety of their mineral content. So good are the opportunities for farming that some of the world's highest densities of rural population are located upon volcanic soils. There can be quite a contrast between population concentrations in areas of volcanic soils and those elsewhere. Below Vesuvius, the Plain of Campania around Naples is intensively farmed for wheat, maize, tomatoes, various vegetables and an immense variety of fruits including grapes, peaches, pears and plums. The fertility of the soils, weathered from the fine grade ash deposits of previous eruptions from Vesuvius, is legendary (Figure 3.92). Yields are well above the national average. In contrast, many of the surrounding areas, mainly composed of limestone which frequently outcrops as bare rock, are suited to nothing better than rough grazing by sheep and goats.

Iceland's use of geothermal sources

Case Study

Growing oranges in Iceland, more than 60° north of the Equator, does not seem natural (Figure 3.93). It is not. It is just one of the signs that Iceland makes good use of its geothermal sources. More than 70 per cent of the vegetables consumed are home grown in a country where the highest monthly temperature struggles to exceed 10°C. More than 85 per cent of homes are heated by natural hot water, available at about one quarter the cost of using oil or coal. The added bonus is no air pollution. The hot water for Reykjavik is drilled from boreholes and stored in the hot water distribution tanks on a hill in the city. The hot water is easier to use for the space heating – in greenhouses, homes, factories etc. – than for generating electricity which requires much higher temperatures. District heating plants for obtaining and distributing the hot water are concentrated near to all the main settlements, but are most concentrated east of Reykjavik where over the half the country's population lives (Figure 3.95). Electricity is mainly generated in the north and makes a 5 per cent contribution to the country's total output, the rest coming from HEP stations. The geothermal attractions are one of the main reasons behind the continuing growth of the tourist industry; despite the climate, visitors can bathe outdoors all year round in the thermal baths and see geysers, hot springs and mud pools (Figure 3.94).

▲ **Figure 3.93** Orange growing in Iceland

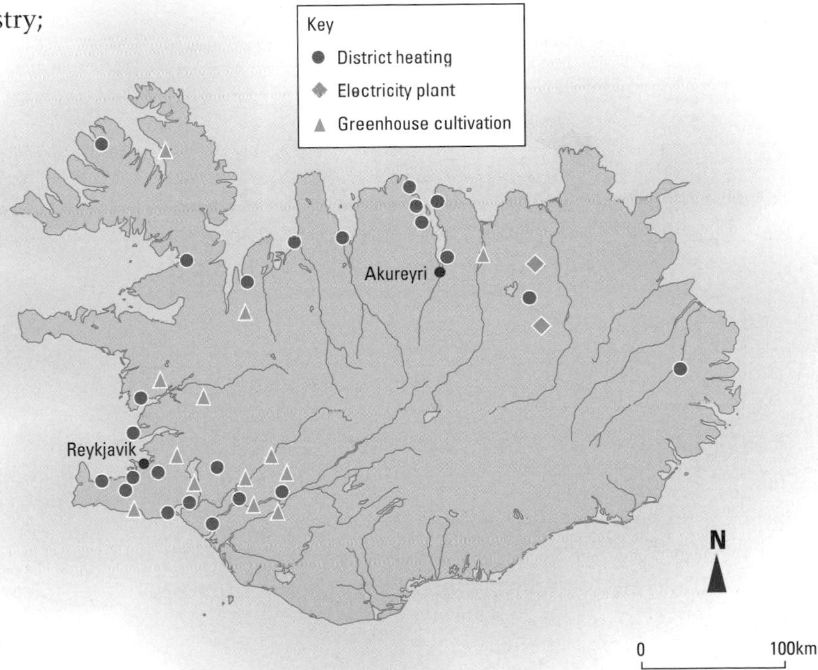

▲ **Figure 3.95** Use of geothermal sources

▼ **Figure 3.94** Tourists around Strokkur geyser

Questions

1 How does the theory of plate tectonics help us to understand that:
   a the risk of earthquakes is greater in Italy and Iceland than in the UK
   b physically Iceland is part of both Europe and North America.

2 a Make a case study of Iceland to show:
   i the features of tectonic activity along a constructive plate margin
   ii the usefulness of volcanic activity to people.
   b Draw a sketch map of the main features referred to in **a**.

Chapter 3 Questions

1 a Figure 1 shows the effect that the eruption of Mt Pinatubo in the Philippines in 1991 had upon world temperatures.

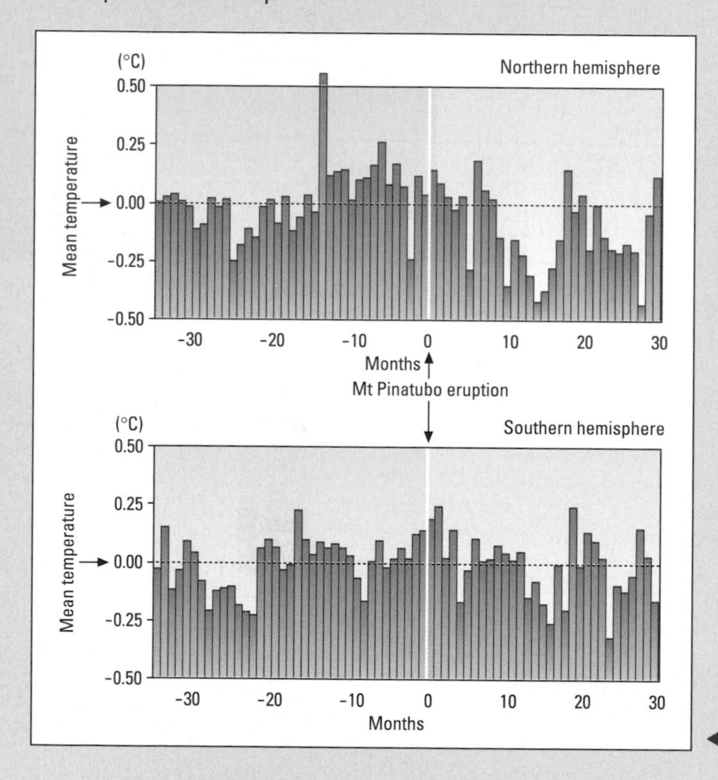

Figure 1

Comment on the main effects shown and suggest a reason for them. (3 marks)

b Examine the likely impact of a major volcanic eruption, such as that of Pinatubo, upon the ecology of the area around it. (3 marks)

c Explain where and why very destructive volcanic eruptions are most likely. (4 marks)

d Analyse the extent to which hot spots are different from any other forms of volcanic activity. (5 marks)

Total: 15 marks

2 Synoptic essay

Discuss the view that the later secondary effects of geomorphological hazards have greater impacts on landscapes and people than the immediate primary effects. (30 marks)

Chapter 4 Cold environments and human activity

igure 4.1
‹ing penguins, the main inhabitants of
his beach in summer on the sub-
ntarctic island of South Georgia. They
re supported by the massive food
esources of the Southern Ocean, not by
he meagre terrestrial food sources of this
old environment.

The location and characteristics of cold environments

A simple three-fold division of the world based upon latitude produces a tropical zone (within 30° of the Equator), a temperate zone (between 30 and 60° north and south of the Equator) and a polar zone (north and south of 60°). By using latitude as the basis for the division, a strong link with temperature is implied. Areas within the tropical zone are always hot and there are few, if any, temperature restrictions for plant and crop growth. Areas within the temperate zone do not regularly experience extremes of heat and cold, although seasonal differences between winter and summer can be quite pronounced. They are generally regarded as favourable areas for farming and living. Areas within the polar zone are cool or cold all year and intense winter coldness is a major limiting factor for any kind of productive human activity.

The focus for much of this chapter will be the polar regions of the world north and south of 60°. Latitude 60°N passes through the Shetland Islands, which means that the study area in the northern hemisphere is everywhere to the north of the British Isles. Although around and at the North Pole itself there are the frozen waters of the Arctic Ocean, there is a much greater amount of land in polar latitudes in the northern hemisphere, as the northern land masses of Eurasia and North America are at their maximum widths in these latitudes. In the southern hemisphere south of 60° there is only the occasional group of rocky islands until the land mass of Antarctica is reached. Continental drift and tectonic activity have currently placed the 'seventh' continent above the South Pole. Its landmass is large, larger than that of Europe, and the extent of the frozen sea water around it makes it appear even larger, especially in winter.

Two main types of land environment exist within these polar regions – ice cap and tundra.

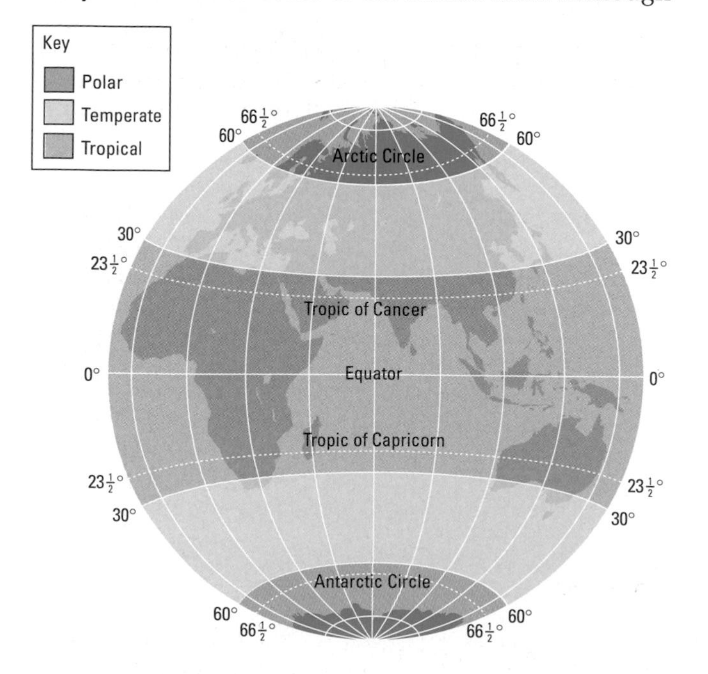

▲ **Figure 4.2** Three-fold division of the world. Note that in this simple division the tropical or hot zone extends outside the tropics and the polar or cold zones begin before the Arctic and Antarctic Circles are reached at $66\frac{1}{2}$°.

Ice cap

At present about one tenth of the Earth's surface is covered by ice. Of this, approximately 85 per cent is in Antarctica, 11 per cent in Greenland and the remaining 4 per cent in glaciers in mountainous areas located mainly in temperate latitudes. Therefore 96 per cent of the world's surface ice is in polar regions forming the continental ice sheets of Antarctica and Greenland. Antarctica is an upland plateau covered by ice that has an average thickness of over 2,000m. Rock is exposed in less than 0.5 per cent of its land surface, and mainly in that part known as the Antarctic Peninsula, which extends the continent northwards towards the tip of South America, the closest continent to Antarctica. Nevertheless Cape Horn is still some 1,000km away on the northern side of a notoriously rough area of ocean known as the Drake Passage. In Greenland the ice sheet which covers about four-fifths of the surface area is largely enclosed within a mountainous rim. It lies on a plateau about 500m above sea level, on top of which the ice is also more than 2,000m thick in places. This ice sheet feeds smaller, individual valley glaciers which lead down to the coast. In between these are the small patches of vegetation-covered rock, which gave the 'green land' that attracted settlement by the Viking, Erik the Red, in AD 985. Smaller ice caps cover significant proportions of the surface areas of Iceland and Spitzbergen.

Glacial terminology

- ***Ice*** *Snow which has been compacted so that the air passages between the individual crystals of snow become sealed which increases its density.*
- ***Glacier*** *A moving mass of ice on a land surface.*
- ***Ice sheet*** *Ice cover of all the land surface, over an extensive area. Occasional rock peaks, called nunataks, stick out through the otherwise continuous mass of ice. The ice sheet creeps with a slow massive movement towards its margins.*
- ***Ice cap*** *An ice sheet covering a plateau region, over an extensive area. Movement around the edges may be faster because of steeper gradients.*
- ***Cirque glacier*** *After snow has continued to accumulate in a hollow on a mountain side, ice forms and thickens with time. Ice fills the cirque (or corrie) hollow, which is deepened. The glacier may grow to the point where it spills out of its semi-circular hollow into the valley below.*
- ***Valley glacier*** *A glacier following the line of a pre-existing river valley, fed by cirque glaciers or ice caps, sometimes of great depth. The moving tongue of ice may extend for some distance down the valley until it reaches the lowlands or the sea.*
- ***Periglacial*** *Applied to land areas which lie around the margins of ice sheets. They are cold areas where permafrost exists either continuously (everywhere) or discontinuously (in patches).*
- ***Permafrost*** *Permanently frozen ground. Only the surface layer may thaw out briefly in summer; this is known as the active layer.*

▲ **Figure 4.3** Antarctica – continental ice sheet, occasional rock outcrops and surrounding icebergs

Tundra

According to the Concise Oxford Dictionary, the term 'tundra' is of Lappish origins and is defined as 'barren arctic regions where sub-soil is frozen'. This definition suggests two of the diagnostic characteristics of tundra regions, namely one, no trees and two, surface underlain by permafrost.

A third distinctive feature, clearly implied although not directly stated in the definition, is climate, which is commonly used to demarcate tundra from the other world natural environments. Mean temperatures during the three summer months remain below 10°C. Therefore the growing season is less than three months. Another distinctive climatic feature is that for at least seven months of the year temperatures remain below 0°C. Only when the length of the growing season increases with distance from the poles and allows coniferous trees to grow, does the tundra region end. In the northern hemisphere the southern margins of the tundra are typically further north on the western sides of continents (Figure 4.4) where polar conditions are more readily moderated by westerly winds crossing warm ocean currents and blowing onshore from relatively warm seas. Eastern parts of North America and Asia feel a stronger continental effect due to a combination of offshore prevailing winds and cold ocean currents, which together greatly reduce the winter warming effects of a position close to the sea.

The frozen sub-soil part of the dictionary definition for tundra refers to the presence of permafrost. Ground temperatures remain sub-zero permanently which keeps the soil frozen. Soil and pieces of loose rock are frozen rigid together; spaces in porous rocks such as chalk are filled by ice. The permafrost creates a solid, impervious mass, which has a great influence upon the

◀ **Figure 4.4** The distribution of cold environments in the northern hemisphere

geomorphological processes which operate above it. During the short summer, the upper layers of the ground are warmed from the surface downwards and thaw out. Depending on position, a ground layer anything from a few centimetres to a few metres in depth thaws out; it is known as the active layer. However, above the permanently frozen sub-soil, thawed water is trapped in the surface layer, saturating it and making it highly mobile even on quite gentle slopes. Solifluction (pages 145 – 146) is the most widespread process and leads to much mass movement of surface silts and clays. With the onset of winter surface layers are the first to be frozen; the cold gradually penetrates downwards towards the permafrost layer below. Since ice occupies a greater volume than water, the freezing of water trapped between a rigid frozen sub-soil below and a surface being frozen above increases the pressures on the surface leading to heaving upwards of the ground surface. This makes a major contribution to the formation of distinctive periglacial landforms such as patterned ground (Figure 4.5) and pingos, explained in more detail on page 147.

▲ **Figure 4.5a and b** Patterned ground on James Ross island in Antarctica

Climates in polar regions

Three climatic characteristics apply almost everywhere in high latitudes north and south of 60°:

- coldness
- low precipitation totals
- wind chill.

However, there are significant regional variations according to latitude, altitude, and position in relation to land and sea. Temperatures are coldest in the ice cap regions where mean monthly temperatures remain below freezing point all year. Their snowy appearance is misleading because they are also very dry regions. In most of the interior of the Antarctic continent it is estimated that less than 150mm (water equivalent) of snow falls in a year; average annual precipitation is as little as 50mm at the South Pole. This is why temperature values alone have been included in Figure 4.6. Average precipitation is only a little higher on the ice cap in Central Greenland. Therefore ice cap areas are examples of cold deserts.

Climatic conditions are more varied in the tundra regions around the ice cap edges, especially as some regions near to western coasts receive maritime influences. Precipitation levels, particularly in summer, tend to be higher and the winter cold is less extreme. Maritime influences show up strongly in the climatic data for Nuuk, the capital of Greenland, located on the south-west coast. They contrast markedly with the climatic data for Ruskoye Ust'ye in eastern Siberia (Figure 4.7).

South Pole 90°S Altitude 2956m												
	J	F	M	A	M	J	J	A	S	O	N	D
Temperature (°C)	-41	-49	-57	-57	-56	-58	-62	-59	-55	-45	-35	-39

Eismitte 70° 53'N 40° 42'W Altitude 3000m												
	J	F	M	A	M	J	J	A	S	O	N	D
Temperature (°C)	-36	-47	-40	-31	-21	-17	-12	-18	-22	-36	-43	-38
Precipitation (mm)	15	5	8	5	3	2	3	10	8	13	13	25

▲ **Figure 4.6** Ice cap climate, continental locations: Mean climatic data from weather recordings at the South Pole (where average annual precipitation is as little as 50mm) and at Eismitte in central Greenland

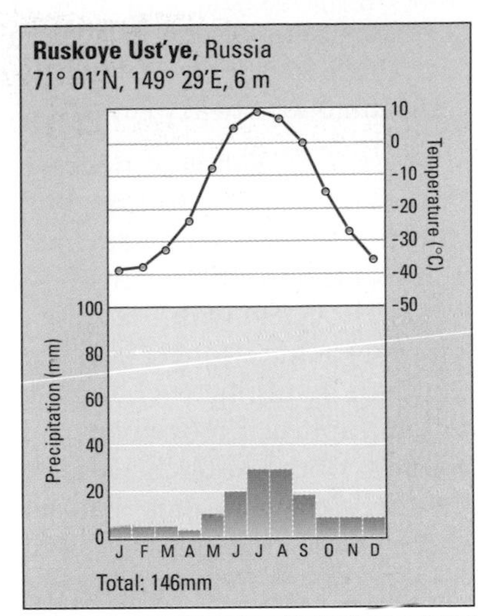

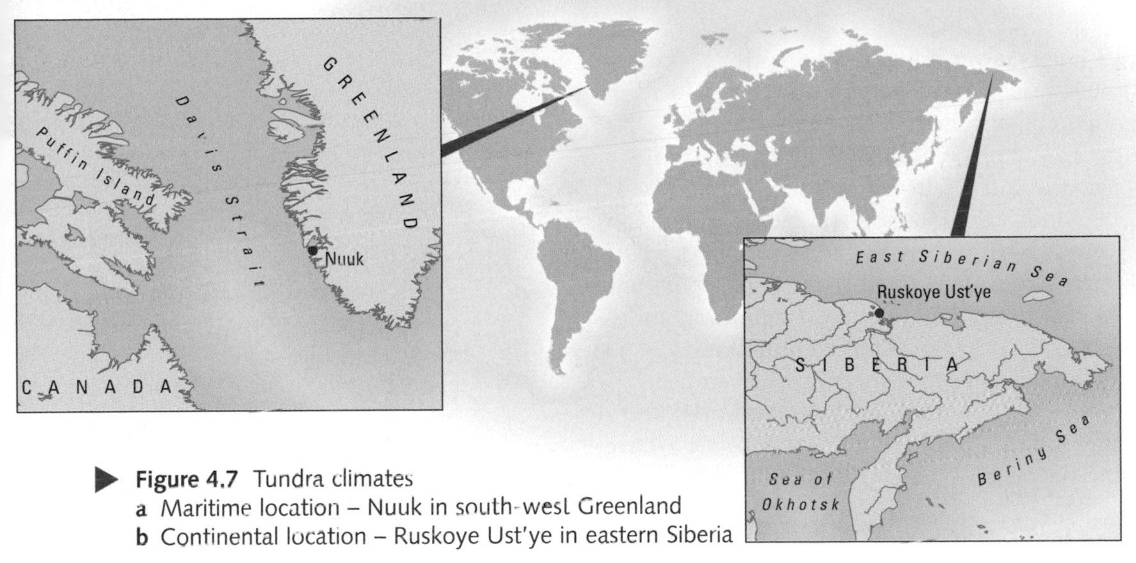

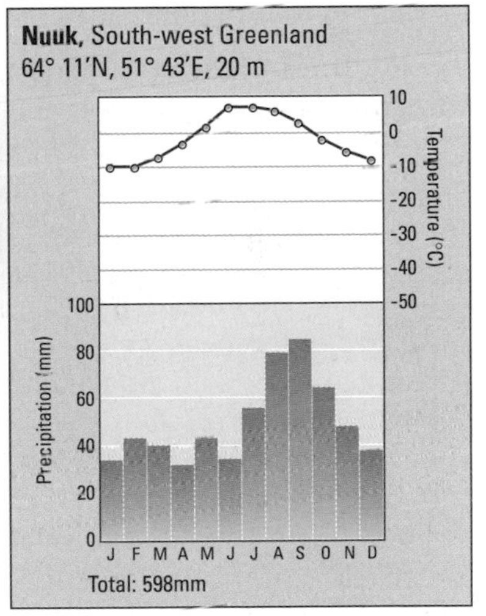

▶ **Figure 4.7** Tundra climates
a Maritime location – Nuuk in south-west Greenland
b Continental location – Ruskoye Ust'ye in eastern Siberia

Coldness is the result of low levels of insolation. Even in mid-summer the sun remains at a relatively low angle in the sky so that incoming rays strike the Earth's surface obliquely, leaving them with a wider surface area to heat up. A longer passage through the atmosphere means increased absorption, scattering and reflection. Nevertheless in mid-summer there is continuous (or almost continuous) insolation everywhere, because these are the 'lands of the midnight sun'. This causes a high daily input of solar radiation and a small diurnal temperature range. Some days feel pleasantly warm, but overall the heating power of the sun is only sufficient to raise temperatures in tundra lands above freezing point for between two and four months of the year. In winter the small amount, or total absence, of day light means that there is no incoming solar radiation to offset surface heat losses by radiation. Winter lasts for up to six months, during which time temperatures continue to fall creating a bitter cold. Average temperatures in Antarctica are some 10 to 30°C colder than for the same latitudes in the northern hemisphere. This is a result of it being a snow and ice-covered land surface with an average height of 2,300m above sea level. Snow surfaces have a high albedo (about 0.8) so that they reflect back much incoming solar energy. Also thinner air at high altitudes means that surface heat escapes more readily into the atmosphere.

Low precipitation totals are in large measure a reflection of the dominant influence of high pressure. As part of the global atmospheric circulation the polar highs reside over Arctic and Antarctic latitudes for most of the year. The cause of these high pressures is thermal. Hot air sucked up by the Equatorial Low is transferred by jet streams (high level atmospheric winds) towards the poles. Warm air forced to rise along the polar front in temperate latitudes contributes to the jet streams which descend near the poles at the northern (Arctic) and southern (Antarctic) ends of the polar cells. The high pressure is most persistent over Antarctica where the coldness of the air in the lower atmosphere resulting from contact with ice and snow-covered surfaces acts as further encouragement for air to sink. Only occasionally is the continent clipped by depressions moving from west to east which bring heavier snowfall almost exclusively to the edges of the continent. Over the frozen ocean surface in the Arctic the high pressure is less persistent and land areas just north of 60° do receive frontal precipitation, particularly where they are located on the western side of the land masses. However, there is another reason for low annual precipitation totals – the coldness of the air and the low amount of water vapour that it can hold. Cold air below 3°C is capable of holding so little moisture that, even when there is atmospheric instability and all the conditions needed for the occurrence of precipitation are present, often nothing more than flurries of dry, powdery snow emerge from a continuous and heavy cloud cover.

Strong winds leading to high wind chill levels form the third distinctive feature of the climates in polar latitudes. On the temperate margins of these regions is one of the world's strongest wind belts. Westerly winds associated with the zone of frontal depressions are stronger and more regular in the southern hemisphere where there are few land areas to interrupt their movement. Also the greater coldness of the Antarctic land mass compared with the Arctic Ocean means that steeper temperature and pressure gradients exist, which in turn generate stronger winds. The westerly winds encircle Antarctica making the oceans south of 50° the most feared by sailors.

▼ **Figure 4.8** How katabatic winds form

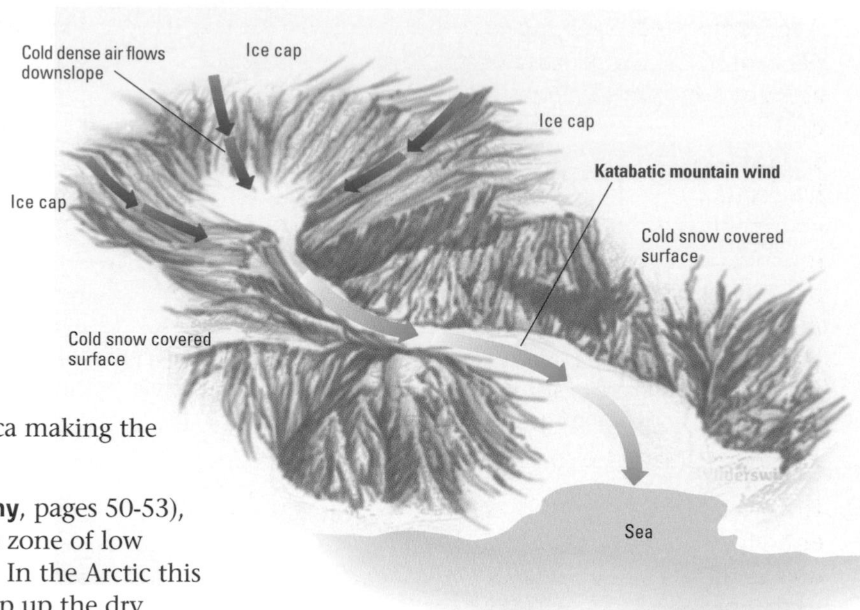

As part of the world's circulation (**AS level Geography**, pages 50-53), the surface air from the polar high flows towards the zone of low pressure along the polar front in temperate latitudes. In the Arctic this gives prevailing north-easterly winds. The winds whip up the dry powdery snow to create frequent blizzards and 'white-outs'. Polar regions also generate their own strong downslope winds called katabatic winds (Figure 4.8). The coldness of the surfaces and the serious loss of heat by radiation produces a surface inversion of temperature (Figure 4.9). At the surface there is a mass of dense, and therefore heavy, cold air, which flows down the valleys and off mountain and plateau slopes. It is felt as a very cold wind. In Antarctica the combination of a large land mass, mountainous terrain and extensive ice and snow-covered surfaces increases the scale of the differences between the interior of the continent and the surrounding oceans so that katabatic winds are frequent and exceedingly strong. Many reach hurricane force and some between 200 and 300kph have been recorded.

High wind speeds make temperatures feel even lower than those recorded by a thermometer. As the table in Figure 4.10 shows, wind can cause substantial reductions in temperature for the human body. While people welcome a breeze in hot climates, because it helps cooling and the maintenance of normal body temperature, in cold climates the effect of wind is to make the body work harder to stay warm. This is because wind carries the warm air away from around all exposed parts of the body. The faster the wind, the faster the heat escapes and the greater the risks from hypothermia and frostbite. Hypothermia leads to shivering, disorientation, unconsciousness and possibly death. If the skin becomes cold enough, it can actually freeze and ice crystals form, damaging tissue. This is frostbite. Ears, nose, hands and feet are at greatest risk, and in serious cases amputation is necessary.

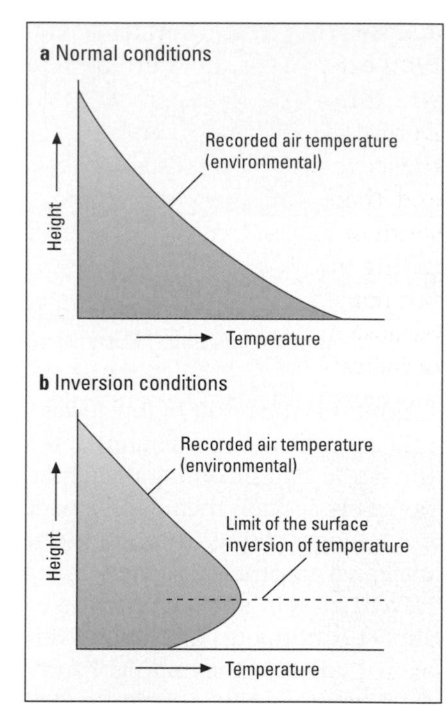

▲ **Figure 4.9**
Temperature–height graphs

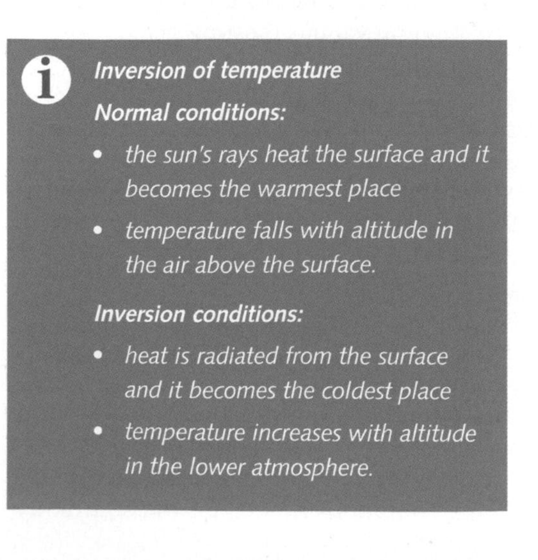

Inversion of temperature

Normal conditions:

- *the sun's rays heat the surface and it becomes the warmest place*
- *temperature falls with altitude in the air above the surface.*

Inversion conditions:

- *heat is radiated from the surface and it becomes the coldest place*
- *temperature increases with altitude in the lower atmosphere.*

The effects of wind speeds on exposed parts of the body. Example: with a wind blowing at 25kph (approx. 15 mph), when the thermometer was registering an air temperature of 0°C, it would feel more like -12°C.

Wind speed (kph)	Air temperature (°C)					
	0	-3	-6	-9	-12	-15
25	-12	-17	-20	-24	-30	-35
30	-14	-19	-23	-26	-32	-37
35	-15	-20	-24	-27	-33	-39
40	-16	-21	-25	-28	-34	-40
45	-17	-22	-26	-29	-35	-41
50	-18	-23	-27	-30	-36	-42

▶ **Figure 4.10**
Wind chill

Summary

As already mentioned, the polar ice sheets cover about 10 per cent of the surface area of the Earth. Tundra lands account for a further 25 per cent. Therefore present day cold environments cover about one third of the land surface. They are generally unattractive places in which to live. Antarctica is the coldest and most inhospitable continent on Earth and has no permanent human inhabitants. Greenland is almost nine times larger than the UK, but has a total population of less than 60,000, no more than the number of people living in a relatively small English town. Canada is the second largest country in the world in terms of area, but its total population is around thirty million, about half of that of the UK, largely due to the great area covered by its Northlands.

However, the area of study in this chapter is not confined entirely to polar regions. In the relatively recent past, during the Pleistocene glaciation, continental ice sheets invaded the northern parts of temperate latitudes in North America, Europe and Asia (Figure 4.11). At its maximum the ice front extended to the south of the Great Lakes and St Lawrence Valley in North America. During the Wolstonian glaciation in the UK the ice reached the line between the Severn and Thames estuaries, so that only the extreme south of England was never covered by ice during the Pleistocene. Even so this area could not remain unaffected by the ice advance, because melting ice released massive volumes of meltwater and climatic zones were pushed southwards so that southern England experienced a tundra climate. In Europe the ice halted across the North European plain at the level of present-day northern Germany. Valley glaciers in mountainous areas of temperate latitudes were deeper, longer and more numerous than they are today. These have left relict landforms formed by glacial processes, including some spectacular mountain scenery (pages 129). Although remaining valley glaciers are in retreat everywhere (Figure 4.12), glacial processes are still operating where glaciers have survived in young fold mountain ranges, notably the Himalayas, Alps, Rockies and Andes. Tundra-like environments occur above the tree line in mountainous areas. However, there are two significant differences between mountain and Arctic tundra. Sunlight is more powerful because the sun is at a higher angle in the sky and permafrost is generally absent.

The Pleistocene Ice Age

- *2 million years ago – onset of the Pleistocene glaciation.*
- *There were four major ice advances called glacials.*
- *These were separated by warmer periods, called inter-glacials, when the ice retreated.*
- *Anglian is the name given to the first glacial advance in Britain which occurred about 500,000 years ago.*
- *The maximum ice advance was during the third glacial advance, called the Wolstonian glaciation in Britain, which ended about 125,000 years ago.*
- *The Ipswichian or Eemian inter-glacial was particularly warm and ice retreat was great.*
- *The fourth and last ice advance was the Devensian glaciation, which ended about 25,000 years ago.*
- *Progressive warming of the Earth (but with some fluctuations) has occurred since this time and the end of the Pleistocene Ice Age is usually put at around 10,000 years ago.*
- *Many argue that we are living in a warm inter-glacial.*

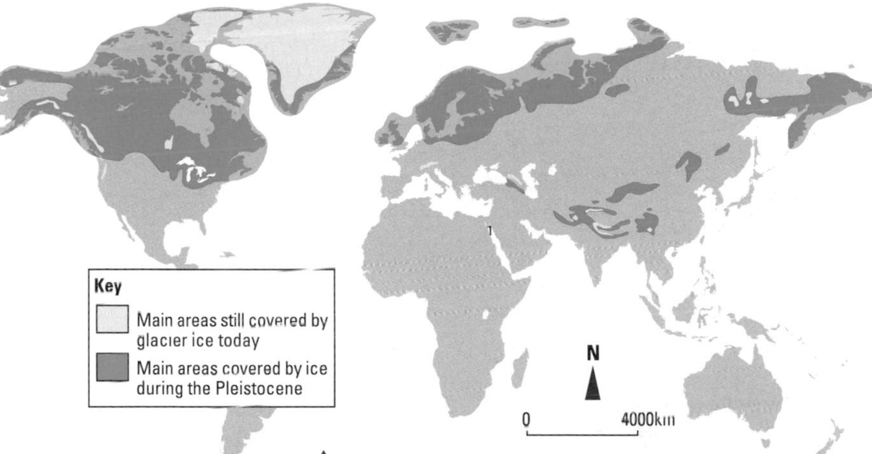

▲ **Figure 4.11a** The extent of ice in the northern hemisphere during the Pleistocene

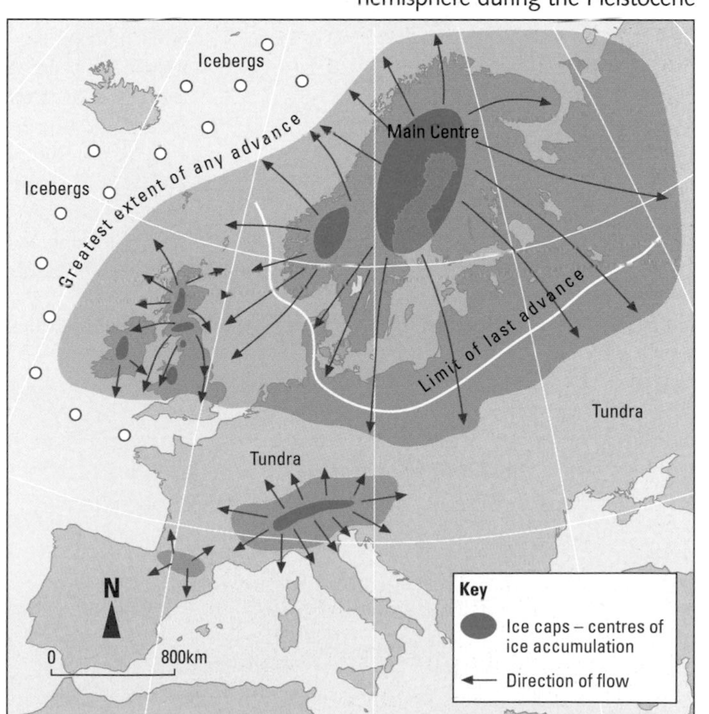

▲ **Figure 4.11b** The extent of ice during the Pleistocene Ice Age in Europe

Figure 4.12 Retreating glaciers

▲ **a** Glacier 'calving' into a lake in southern Argentina.

◀ **b** A closer view of the glacier in Figure 4.1. The two 'rock windows' have only appeared within the last ten years.

The next ice age

If you think the weather is getting warmer these days you should have been here 120,000 years ago. There were hippos wallowing in mud along the Thames, elephants and rhinos strutting through the Home Counties and lions roaming over the Midlands. It was so hot that the polar ice caps shrank and the meltwater forced sea levels up to 8 metres higher than today's levels.

Those were the glorious Eemian days and the world hasn't been as hot since. Why it was so hot has been taxing the brains of climate experts and although no one can be sure, there's a sneaking suspicion that carbon dioxide bumped up temperatures with a greenhouse effect.

Whatever the causes of the Eemian's balmy climate, it only lasted 20,000 years. In fact it was doomed before it began, a short breathing space between long deep freezes when the polar icecaps fanned out and crushed everything in their paths. Even more depressing, the Earth has been blowing hot and cold for the past 2 million years and it shows no sign of changing.

Strange as it may seem, we're living today in another brief break from the glaciers. It's not often you can forecast anything thousands of years ahead, but the bouts of cold are so regular we can predict another glaciation in about several thousand years' time – provided, of course, that the planet hasn't melted down with our own pollution-inspired global warming. So what, you might ask, drives the march of the glaciers backwards and forwards?

You'd think there would be some sort of metronome ticking away in the Earth itself, but the answer comes from space. All those school textbooks of the solar system showing the Earth orbiting round the sun in a nice, neat circle, spinning at a perfect 23.5 degrees on its axis aren't exactly correct. Thanks to the gravity of the Sun, the Moon and the other planets tugging away at the Earth, the Earth's orbit round the sun rocks and rolls like a drunken sailor with three different rhythms: a slightly egg-shaped orbit, a rocking and rolling in the orbit and a wobble in the tilt of the Earth. When you add all these three rhythms together, they make a slight change in how much of the Sun's heat reaches the Earth, just enough to explain the ebb and flow of the ice, although not everyone is convinced that a wobbly Earth entirely explains the glaciers. One other feature could be a belt of old dust lying around in space which we pass through every 100,000 years or so and which blots out a lot of sunlight, so cooling things down on Earth.

Whatever the explanation, what might the next glaciation be like? If it was anything like the last bout, we could expect London frozen in permafrost and blasted with howling cold winds at the edge of a glacier, Birmingham encased in ice and Edinburgh crushed under a three kilometre thick glacier. The south of England would just about be habitable, possibly hunting reindeer, seals and polar bears. Heating bills would go through the roof as winter temperatures plunged to around -20°C to -30°C. Sea levels would plummet and we would find ourselves re-connected to France by a land bridge. But let's look on the bright side – we'd have a few thousand years to prepare for it.

▲ **Figure 4.13** Adapted extract from *The Guardian*, 11 September 2000

Questions

1 Identify those factors which enable polar regions to be distinguished from others and comment upon the ways in which polar regions are different.

2 Compare ice cap and tundra regions using the headings
a location and extent
b climatic characteristics.

3 Explain the ways in which climatic hazards make polar regions inhospitable places for human settlement.

4 a Outline what happened in the British Isles during the Pleistocene.
b Read the extract in Figure 4.13.
i What are the possible causes of ice ages and inter-glacials?
ii Identify and comment on the physical changes which could occur in southern England and lands further south if glaciers advance to the point where ice covers most of the British Isles.

Glacial and periglacial processes and landforms

A glacier is a moving mass of ice on land. It forms where the amount of snow that falls during the year exceeds the amount which melts. It can only form above the permanent snow line. The origin for most glaciers is a snow patch in a hollow on a mountain side. Once the hollow is filled with snow it is enlarged by various types of weathering and the process of nivation. For example, frost action is likely to be an active type of weathering under periglacial conditions. The pieces of rock that have been loosened or broken off could be washed away by water from melting snow. Freshly fallen snow has a low density (under 0.5) because of the large amount of air trapped between the individual crystals; however, as more snow falls and the snow patch enlarges and thickens, old snow is compacted. Air is expelled by successive melting and refreezing; if snow survives at least one year, it is converted into higher density firn or neve (about 0.7). As annual snowfalls continue to accumulate, the firn becomes more compacted as air spaces are sealed. Crystals grow larger, increasing the density until it rises to the point where what was once snow has now become ice (density above 0.85). The change may take up to two hundred years in Antarctica where very low temperatures prevent melting and refreezing, which are needed to speed up the operation, compared with as little as five to ten years in the warmer more maritime environment of Alaska.

Key
Glacier ice
Snow
Input
Breakpoint (equilibrium point)
Zone of accumulation
Ice
The store
Seasonal accumulation
Zone of ablation
Meltwater
Seasonal ablation
Output

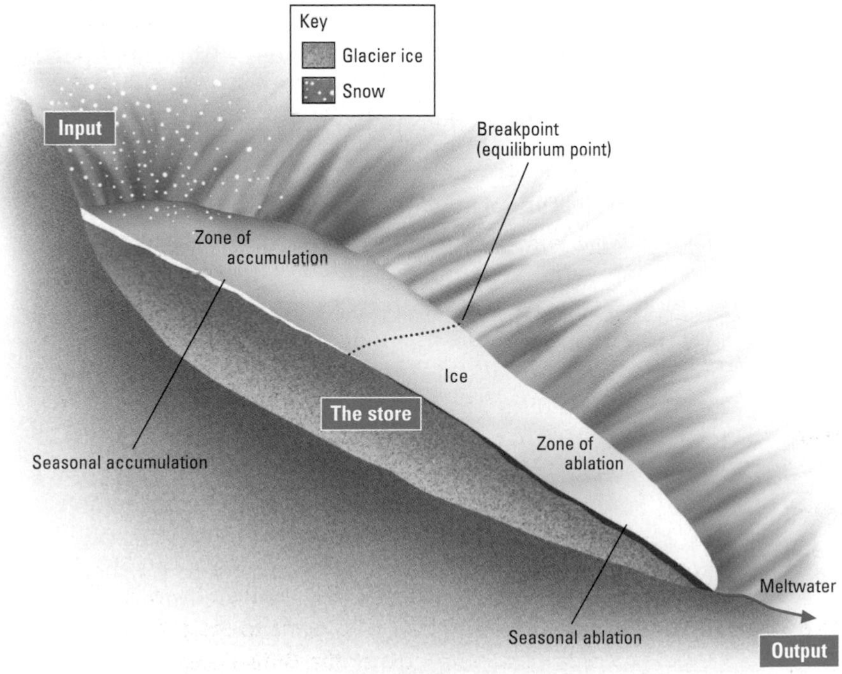

▲ **Figure 4.14** Model of the glacial system

Glaciers are examples of open systems. Their main input is snow either from direct snowfall or from avalanches. It accumulates in the upper part of a glacier, which looks white. The snow is stored in the system as glacier ice and is carried downslope by the glacier's movement. The main output is water. Although some water evaporates directly from the surface into the atmosphere, most water loss results from melting as lower altitudes, or latitudes with higher temperatures, are reached. There is melting on the surface of the glacier, particularly at the sides where it comes up against rock with a much lower albedo than the glacier ice; there is also internal and basal melting. Additionally there is calving where icebergs break off into streams, lakes and seas (see Figure 4.12b). A net loss of ice is known as ablation. Above the snowline accumulation is greater than ablation. However, at a certain point along the course of each glacier the zone of accumulation is replaced by the zone of ablation. This is the break point where outputs from the system begin to exceed inputs.

▲ **Figure 4.15**
Glacier flowing into a fiord in South Georgia, Antarctica. The white ice surfaces are in the zone of accumulation. The blue heavily crevassed ice surfaces indicate the zone of ablation, where ice density is highest (above 0.9). This is because deformation, extra pressures from movement, and much melting and refreezing have joined forces to reduce the size of air bubbles within it.

When the amount of new snow and ice is exactly balanced by the amount that has melted, a steady state is said to exist and the glacier remains stationary. However, often the position of the break point between the zones of accumulation and ablation changes from year to year or over a longer period of time. When the balance is lost the snout (front) of the glacier will either advance or retreat. Although the warming up of the Earth during the last 10,000 years has led to great retreat, colder interludes have led to local ice advances. One such interlude was the 'Little Ice Age', which lasted for about 500 years from 1350. It was at its worst in the late seventeenth century when it was nearly cold enough for the development again of the Laurentian ice sheet in North America. This was the time when the Thames in London famously kept freezing over. However, current global warming is encouraging glacial retreat everywhere (Figure 4.12) and calving great icebergs off the Antarctic ice mass, some the size of smaller European countries and Mediterranean islands.

Of great significance to the speed and effectiveness with which glacial processes operate is the size of a glacier's budget. Calculating the budget involves measuring the inputs in the zone of accumulation and outputs in the zone of ablation, as well as of any change in the volume of glacial ice in store. Glaciers in mountainous areas on the western sides of continents open to prevailing westerly winds and depressions, as in Norway, may have snow inputs above 2000mm in water equivalent. Lying on the southern edge of the polar region much melting also occurs. A high budget such as this, accompanied by the effects of gravity from the steep relief, encourages faster glacial flow than in continental ice sheets. In interior Greenland and Antarctica less than 50mm of new snow may be received during a year, although the intense cold means that little is lost from the system, which means that the ice budget is low.

Ice budget is one of the factors used in the two-fold classification of ice masses into ice sheets and valley glaciers. It supports the basic thermal division into cold glaciers and warm glaciers. Continental ice sheets are cold glaciers, so called because the temperature throughout the glacier ice remains below freezing point all year. The ice is frozen to the bedrock below, which slows down movement often to as little as only a few centimetres each year. Despite having great thickness and weight, lack of movement limits the amount of glacial erosion which takes place. Valley glaciers in contrast are warm glaciers. Many are located in temperate latitudes where meltwater is plentiful in summer; however, even on some days in winter surface ice will melt. This means that water is making its way down through the crevasses in the ice to the base of the glacier on many days of the year. Water can also be present at the base of the glacier even when the temperature is below freezing point as a result of the weight of the ice above and the friction of movement against the bedrock causing localized melting at the base. The presence of so much water is significant in easing movement and encouraging erosion.

Questions

1 Outline the differences between
   - a snow, firn and ice
   - b ice accumulation and ice ablation
   - c warm and cold glaciers.

2 Explain what is meant by the ice budget and comment on its importance.

3 Why is the glacial system an example of an open rather than a closed system?

Valley glaciers – processes and landforms

Valley glaciers are powerful agents of erosion. They have contributed greatly to the spectacular scenery found in many mountainous areas, being directly responsible for deepening pre-existing river valleys. By doing this, they have exaggerated, in quite a dramatic manner, the vertical differences between frost-shattered peaks above and flat valley floors below. These can best be seen in mountainous regions in temperate latitudes, large areas of which are clear of ice, but where the landforms were created relatively recently so that they have not been obliterated by further denudation. The Lauterbrunnen valley in central Switzerland is a classic example (Figure 4.16). The pre-glacial river valley was greatly straightened, widened and deepened by ice. The glacial trough that has resulted has a cross-sectional shape that is usually summarized as a deep U. The present river is lost within the cavernous spaces of the glacier-carved valley. Former interlocking spurs were planed off to give the valley a straight plan; their remnants are left as high points on the valley sides – truncated spurs. Streams left hanging from the top of the glacial trough cascade down as waterfalls to the floor deep below.

Although a smooth valley cross profile is created, the dominant feature of the long profile of a glaciated valley is its irregularity. A sudden drop at the head of the valley is the trough end. When the glacier was present, it ruthlessly exploited weaknesses within rocks, such as joints, and variations in resistance between one band of rock and another as it moved down the valley. Rock outcrops which resisted erosion for longer formed steps or rock bars, whereas those that did not were eroded into rock basins. Water on the land later filled up the basins to form ribbon lakes, some of which are of great depth and considerable extent. Exposed bedrock surfaces were scarred with fine grooves or more deeply scratched by striations on their upstream sides and quarried by plucking on their downstream sides which were made more jagged. These are roches moutonnées, another contributor towards the valley floor's uneven long profile.

▲ **Figure 4.16** The Lauterbrunnen valley above Interlaken in Switzerland which is testimony to a valley glacier's great erosive power

Rock that was eroded was transported, only to be deposited once the carrying capacity of the glacier was reduced due to melting. A ridge deposited across the valley floor at the maximum point reached by the ice forms a terminal moraine. This may be the last in a series of ridges, or recessional moraines, each one representing a point in the valley where the glacier remained stationary for some time. The floor of the glacial trough is littered with glacial debris which goes under the general heading of ground moraine. Where the ice was still moving freely, some of the mounds of boulder clay were shaped into egg-shaped hills called drumlins. However, in most places the hummocks and mounds are irregular heaps of glacial till. In general these landforms of deposition are more minor landscape features. They are small in scale compared with the landforms created by glacial erosion.

Glacial processes

Why are valley glaciers such powerful agents of erosion? Ice movement is needed for erosion to occur. In flow ice behaves plastically as stresses within it increase with movement; this takes place by a mixture of basal slippage and internal flow. At its base the ice creeps plastically around obstacles such as rocks. It also melts on the upstream side of the obstacle which aids movement, only to refreeze again after passing over or around the obstacle. Internally the force of gravity means that individual crystals of ice flow within the glacier. The pattern of crevasses tell us a great deal about the stresses and strains which are occurring within the glacier as it moves (Figure 4.17).

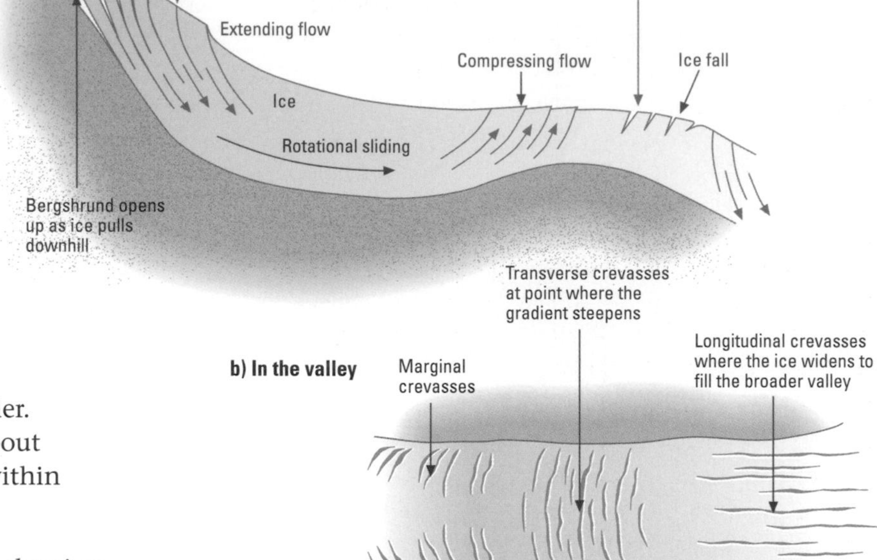

▲ **Figure 4.17** Crevasses and what they show
a in the cirque (corrie)
b in the valley

The two main processes of glacial erosion are abrasion and plucking. Certain characteristics of valley glaciers aid and speed up their operation.

Abrasion

Rock fragments embedded in the base of the glacier are forced, by the weight and pressure of the ice above, into the bedrock below as the ice moves. These pieces of rock are angular; their sharp edges are driven into the bedrock. Exposed bedrock surfaces are scarred with fine grooves or more deeply scratched by striations, which run in parallel lines and act as good indicators of the direction of ice movement (Figure 4.18). If smaller-sized debris is trapped in the bottom of the glacier, upstream rock surfaces are more likely to be polished. In all cases the height of the exposed rock is reduced and it is worn down.

The rate of abrasion is greatest when certain favourable conditions are present. One is a great thickness of ice, which will fill both the floor and sides of the previous river valley and exert great pressure on a wide area of exposed bedrock. A second condition is 'rapid' speed of flow. Not only is meltwater frequently present at the base of these warm glaciers, but by beginning in high mountains the glaciers are flowing down steep gradients as well. A large ice budget also helps. Much new accumulation is matched by much ablation meaning rapid ice through-flow. Being funnelled down an already existing valley is another contributory factor to rapid movement. Thirdly a great load of rocks is usually embedded in the ice which are used as tools for abrasion. Some is supplied by frost shattering on the valley sides and summits above; some comes from abrasion which has already taken place in the cirque glaciers above. Then it is added to by the valley glacier's own abrasion.

A fourth condition are the characteristics of the flow of valley glaciers. In a fast-moving glacier most of the ice flows at the same speed; however, there is a great reduction in speed as a result of friction against the bed

▶ **Figure 4.18** Striations on the hard rock outcrops in Central Park, New York. Hard rocks give the firm foundations needed by Manhattan's skyscrapers, but they were heavily eroded when Manhattan lay under ice.

and sides. This is confined to a zone close to the rock and is called Blockschollen Flow. The loose rocks in the glacier are dragged against the base and sides. The unevenness of the floor over which the glacier is moving produces sequences of extending and compressing flow. As the glacier flows into a hollow the effect of increased gradient is to speed up glacier movement and the ice becomes thinner. On leaving the hollow there is a reduction in gradient, which leads to the glacier slowing down and to the ice thickening. The greater pressure on the stones trapped in the base of the glacier from the increased weight of ice above leads to greater abrasion, which in turn increases the depth of the hollow, thereby emphasizing further the unevenness of the valley floor.

Clearly the characteristics of the rock over which the ice is flowing were of great importance to the rate of abrasion. Softness and plentiful jointing were great aids to abrasion. Also many of the river valleys down which glaciers passed had been affected by periglacial processes for a prolonged period before the glaciers arrived. Frost action preceded glacial action, leading to deep shattering of rock on the valley floors and sides, which made glacial abrasion easier and quicker and provided the tools with which to do more work.

Plucking

This is the pulling away of fragments of bedrock. From time to time glacier ice freezes and sticks to the bare rock below it. Later blocks of rock are pulled away by ice movement. Its effective operation relies upon alternate freezing and thawing taking place in the base, which is most likely to happen in two types of location where high rates of plucking are favoured. One location is where the ice passes over a rock step on the valley floor. At this point the glacier is likely to be thinner and heavily crevassed. Both water and warmer temperatures may be able to penetrate to the rock face more regularly to create the ideal conditions for plucking. The second is around an obstacle such as a hard rock outcrop. The increased weight of the ice upon the upstream side of such an obstacle often leads to pressure melting, even where the temperature is below freezing point. The water refreezes on the downstream side of the obstacle where pressure is reduced. In both locations the presence of weaknesses in the rock, especially joints, is of great importance. Water flowing into these is trapped there by refreezing, thereby helping to loosen pieces of rock over time. These are the chunks of rock plucked away by the forward thrust of glacier movement.

▼ **Figure 4.19** Flow characteristics of valley glaciers.
a Normal and Blockschollen flows
b Extending and compressing flow

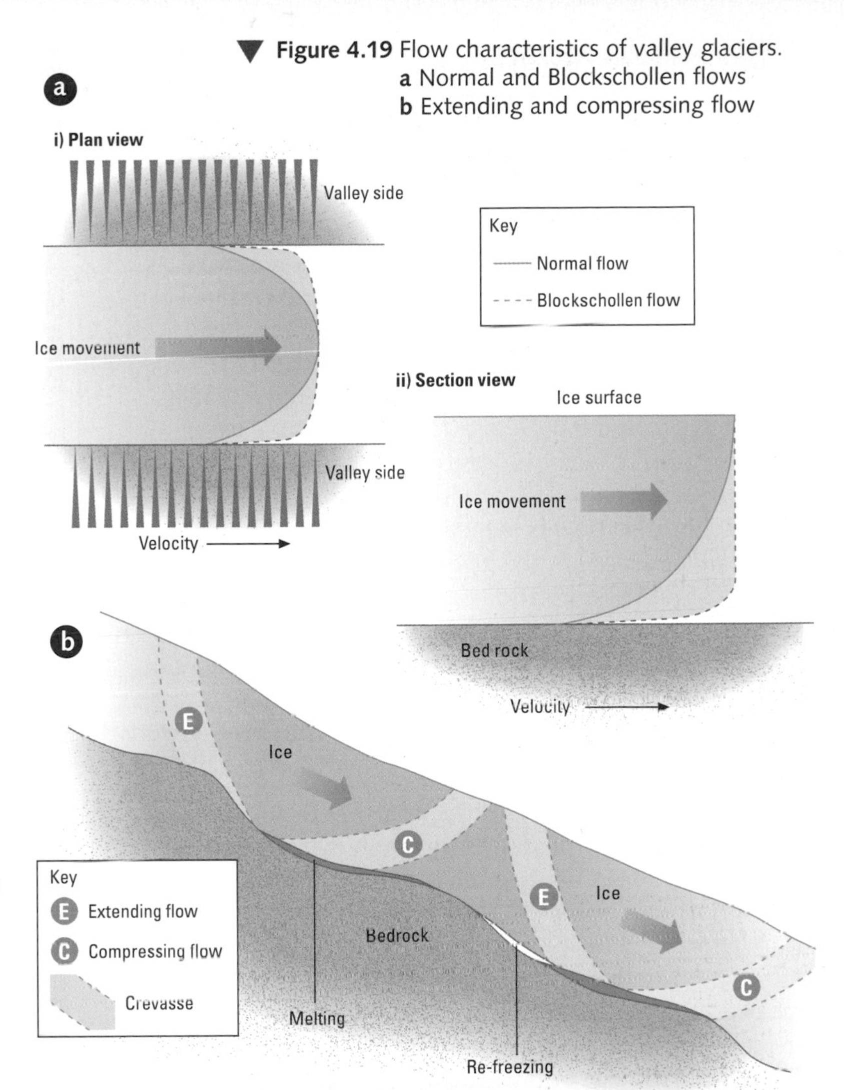

▲ **Figure 4.20** Roche moutonnée near Grantown-on-Spey, Scotland, with its jagged downstream edge, the result of glacial plucking

Other erosion factors

Frequent references have been made to freeze-thaw weathering, without which valley glacier erosion could not be so effective. Other factors are believed to help glacial erosion. One is pressure release. Ice has only one third of the density of rock. After ice erodes and removes rock, the weight of the ice is less than that of the rock removed. As pressure is released, rocks expand slightly and cracks develop running parallel to the surface. This is called sheeting. These are weaknesses into which water can penetrate, increasing the opportunities for freeze-thaw to occur and providing more shattered rock for the ice to remove. Another factor is erosion by sub-glacial meltwater streams. Meltwater works its way down through the ice into underwater streams, which flow under conditions of hydrostatic pressure in the glacier's base. The potent mixture of ice pressure and large amounts of water makes the streams perfectly capable of undertaking considerable fluvial erosion and cutting steep-sided V-shaped valleys under the ice. Some valleys are recognized by their uneven floors because, uniquely under hydrostatic pressure, streams can locally flow uphill.

There is lively debate about the relative effectiveness of abrasion and plucking. Some researchers have suggested that abrasion does no more than scrape, scratch and smooth off rock surfaces. They contend that plucking is more effective. Plucking undoubtedly operates most effectively where pre-existing rock fractures are present. It has been discovered that a joint giving blocks between one and seven metres in size seems to favour the maximum removal of bedrock by ice. Others argue that in the absence of jointing even soft rocks may be able to resist ice erosion by plucking. How could the many, very deep rock basins found on the floors of glaciated valleys be formed if not by ice abrasion? The dark colour of many rivers fed by melting glaciers is due to the ready availability of load materials at the glacier's snout (Figure 4.21). However, no one disputes the vital part played by freeze-thaw in the preparation of the rock for abrasion, plucking and transport by valley glaciers.

Frost action in regions where valley glaciers are present:

- *This is a type of mechanical (physical) weathering.*
- *It operates wherever changes in temperature above and below freezing point occur.*
- *The greater the frequency of these changes, the faster it operates.*
- *Diurnal changes between night freezing and daytime thaw are most frequent in early and late summer, at the change in seasons. The greater the frequency of these changes, the greater the speed of its operation.*
- *On rock outcrops protruding above the glacier it is the main process of denudation.*
- *Rocks on the bed and sides of the glacier are also attacked, especially if they are well jointed.*

▲ **Figure 4.21** Meltwater stream in the Alps heavily laden with glacial debris

Glacial transport

Greatest rates of valley glacier erosion occur in mountainous regions where thick glaciers, well nourished by new supplies of snow, are flowing down steep-sided slopes towards a free outlet, such as a large lowland area or the sea. Such conditions exist or existed in Norway, Greenland, British Columbia in Canada, southern Chile, South Island of New Zealand and western Scotland. Some of the pre-existing river valleys were enlarged into spectacular glacial troughs, the lower ends of which have been drowned by post glacial rises in sea level to form fiords and many of the world's most rugged coastlines and deepest natural harbours (pages 42–44).

The glacial debris removed by erosion or picked up for transport is an unsorted mass of sharp edged rocks and stones, boulders, clay and sand. Some debris is carried on the glacier's surface to produce two distinctive lateral moraines down each side. Frost shattering on rocky peaks above adds to that removed from the valley sides by ice erosion. Lateral moraines join together after tributary valleys have met and several lines of medial moraine may develop on wide glaciers. Close to their snouts many glaciers have a dirty appearance; the presence of surface debris gives the ice a lower albedo that speeds up melting. A lot of debris sinks down through crevasses, some of which is carried englacially (i.e. within the glacier), although much reaches the base either carried or moved further down by the meltwater. This is added to the sub-glacial material already present having been removed by abrasion and plucking. Movement reduces the size of the eroded pieces of rock and particles; the end product of the operation of the processes of erosion is rock flour, fine grained material carried away by meltwater streams. Under dry conditions, it is capable of being picked up and transported by strong winds.

▲ **Figure 4.22** Glacier near Zermatt. Some of the supra-glacial deposits have been organized into lines of moraine.

▲ **Figure 4.23** The ice at this glacier's snout is almost obscured by the amount of supra-glacial debris being transported.

Glacial transport

- *Some is on the surface – supra-glacial*

  Derived from frost shattering of peaks above and lateral moraines meeting after tributary glaciers join.

- *Some is within the ice – englacial*

  Debris falls down through cracks and crevasses in the ice.

- *Some is at the base – subglacial*

  This is a mixture of material scraped up from below the glacier and that which has made its way downwards through crevasses, with or without the help of meltwater streams within the ice.

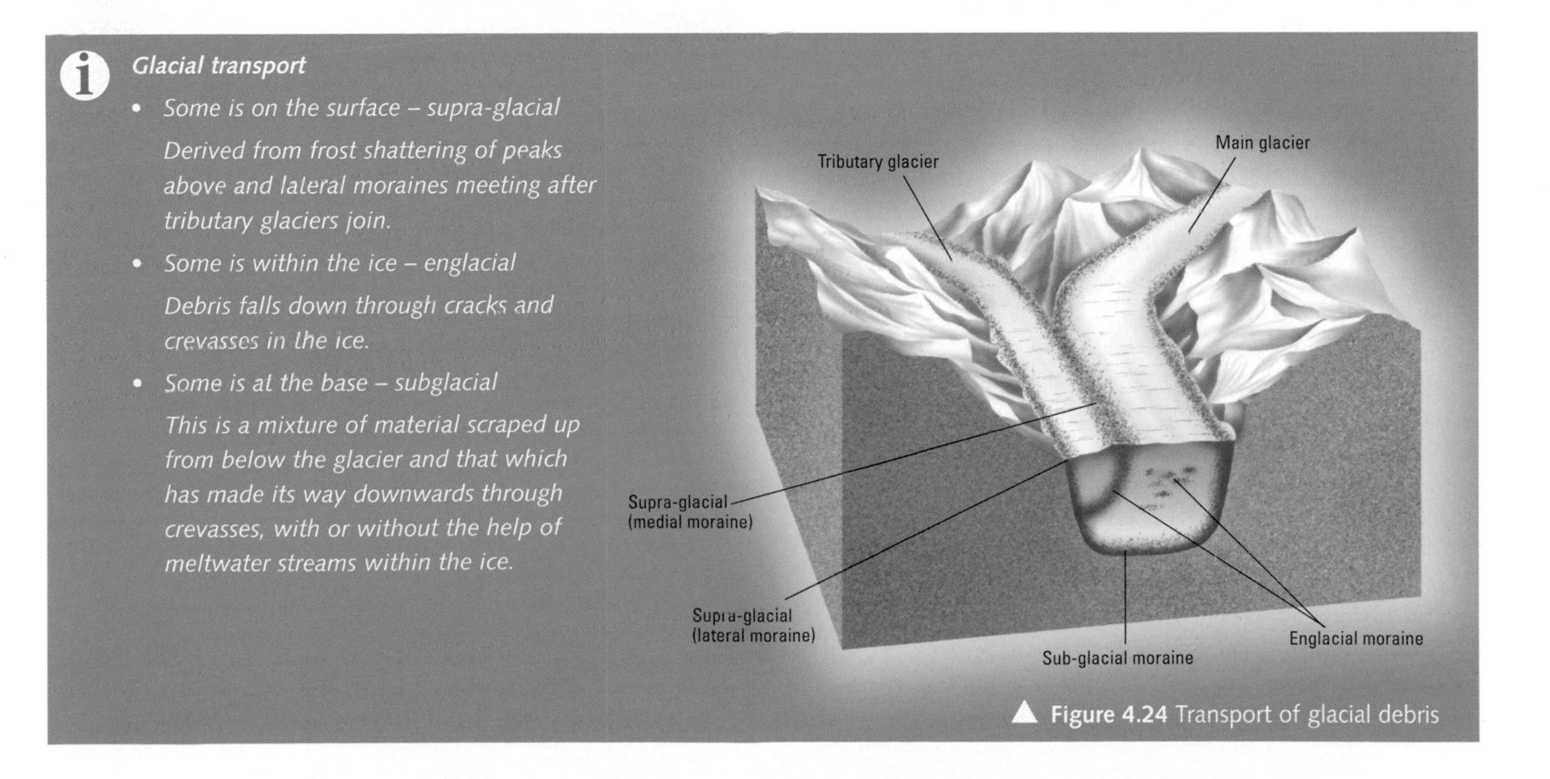

▲ **Figure 4.24** Transport of glacial debris

Formation of landforms

The obvious place to begin is with the cirque or corrie where ice first accumulates. Some cirque glaciers never leave their own basin, while others flow over their rock lips feeding into valley glaciers. As the cirque basin increases in size arêtes and horn (or pyramidal) peaks are formed on the ridge tops above. Below them valley glaciers carve the dramatic landforms highlighted at the beginning of this section.

Cirques, arêtes and horn peaks

A cirque (or corrie) is a deep, armchair-shaped hollow high up on the mountain side. The high, steep and rocky headwall, frequently 1000m or more high, extends around the back and sides of the cirque; the front, however, is open and often marked by a lip of hard rock. The hollow that is left after the ice has melted forms a natural catchment area that is usually occupied by a circular tarn lake. More cirques are located on the northern and north-eastern facing sides of mountains in temperate lands of the northern hemisphere where it is easier for the snow to accumulate away from direct sunlight.

Nivation hollows from which cirques begin are widespread features in mountainous areas. They form under snow patches which grow sufficiently to enable meltwater to penetrate cracks in the rock triggering off freeze-thaw action. The waste is removed by a mixture of flowing meltwater and solifluction so that newly exposed rock surfaces are subject to attack from frost action. As nivation hollows are deepened they become potential sites for ice accumulation and the formation of cirque glaciers. No one process can adequately explain the great depth and tremendous size of many cirques.

There is little doubt about the importance of freeze-thaw weathering. It weakens exposed rock surfaces before they are covered by ice. It continues to attack and sharpen up all rock outcrops above the ice. Wherever water seeping under the ice reaches the headwall, such as near the base of the bergschrund (the semi-circular tensional crevasse that is usually present near the top of the cirque glacier), there are opportunities for frost action to operate. There is also pressure release, which leads to sheet jointing parallel to rock surfaces. These joints are important in providing weaknesses for the plucking action of moving ice to pull pieces of rock away from the back wall. Both freeze-thaw and plucking provide the rock tools for abrasion (see pages 130–131). A rotational element in the movement of a cirque glacier is caused by the imbalance between great ice accumulation in the hollow and little wasting at the snout. The result is that the force of the glacier is concentrated on the back of the hollow. It is here at the base of the head wall that the great abrasive power of the ice is concentrated. Rotational slip not only helps to explain the great height of the back wall of the corrie, but also the presence of a rock lip on the open side where the erosional power of the cirque glacier is much less.

The cirque lip is made of bedrock and its origins are erosional. However, on some rock lips there is a capping of deposited glacial material. There are two explanations for this. One is that the moraine was deposited as the glacier retreated up valley to its last resting point within the cirque hollow. The second is that it represents the terminal moraine for those cirque glaciers which do not grow sufficiently large to flow out of the source hollow.

What happens in the cirque basin is the first stage in sharpening the rounded relief from pre-glacial times. As the head walls of two cirques cut back on either side of a ridge, impressively sharp knife-edged ridge tops are

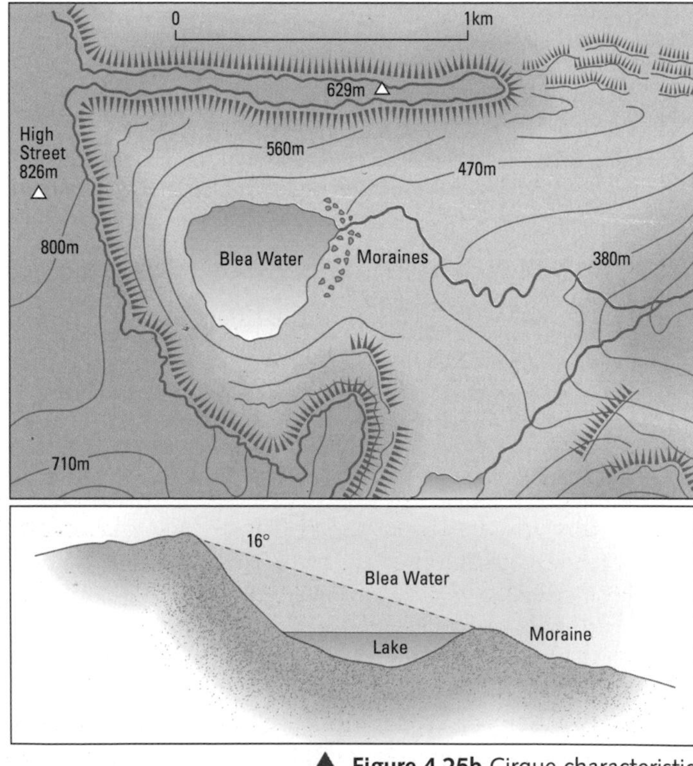

▲ **Figure 4.25b** Cirque characteristics

▲ **Figure 4.25a** Cirque formation

created. The arête is kept sharp by frost shattering. Where three or more head walls cut back, the original mountain mass is reduced to a three or many-sided slab of rock, of which the Matterhorn is the classic example.

▲ **Figure 4.27** The Matterhorn towering above valleys still subject to glacial activity.

▲ **Figure 4.26**
Cirque depression on South Georgia. The deepest part is filled by the tarn lake. Frost action is clearly an active process on the rock outcrops surrounding the depression.

Questions

1 Describe the features of the cirque in which Blea Water lies which make it a typical cirque (corrie) basin.

2 The size of many cirques suggest that no one process is responsible for their origins. Explain this statement.

3 Cirque (corrie) orientation in the Lake District and Snowdonia.

	Number of cirques							
	N	NE	E	SE	S	SW	W	NW
Lake District	8	13	7	5	4	0	0	0
Snowdonia	15	15	13	4	4	1	0	4

a Comment on the merits of the different graphical and diagrammatic techniques that can be used to display the data shown for cirques in this table.
b Display the cirque data using the method considered by you to be the most appropriate.
c Give reasons for the distribution of cirques in the Lake District and Snowdonia.
d Use the Chi squared test to determine whether or not there is a significant difference in the distribution of cirques according to their orientation.
i State the hypothesis.
ii Calculate the value of Chi squared.
iii Test its significance.
iv Comment upon what it shows.

Glaciated valleys

A valley glacier changes the cross profile, plan and long profile of a pre-existing river valley down which it moves. The underlying explanation for all three changes is that the glacier occupies and fills the whole of the valley floor. Ice erosion takes place wherever the ice is in contact with rock, whereas earlier direct erosion by the river took place only in the small part of the valley where the stream was flowing. When ice is present, meltwater streams are everywhere – within the ice, under it and along its sides; therefore, erosion is no longer concentrated in just one place. River water passes through the system quite quickly, but glacier ice is stored in the system for a much longer time. Ice movement is slow but it is inevitable and unyielding; although ice deforms plastically when it flows, its mass pushes it forward in a straight line whenever possible. Rivers naturally swing from side to side and flow around obstacles forming interlocking spurs. Rivers are less powerful than glaciers. However, the protruding spurs of higher land are cut off, or truncated, by the relentless down valley movement of the great mass of ice of a glacier. The ice takes away the edges of the valley floor and the lower slopes are eroded by glacier movement which creates the flat-

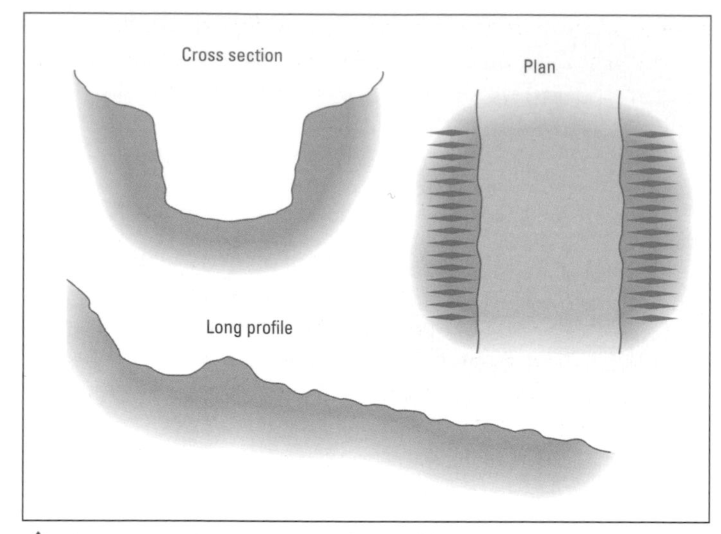

▲ **Figure 4.28** Cross section, plan and long profile of glaciated valleys

floored, steep-sided and straight valley – the hallmark features of a glaciated valley. The previous positions of the interlocking spurs are marked by higher tops to the valley sides. Today's tributary streams cut their small valleys between the truncated spurs before dropping down the steep valley sides as waterfalls. Above that part of the valley filled by ice, high level benches or shoulders of less steep land are sometimes present, especially in the Alps where they provide locations for farming settlements and ski resorts.

The irregular long profile of glaciated valleys demands separate explanation. The unevenness of the valley floor is partly a reflection of lithological variations, principally rock resistance and the degree of jointing. Soft and well-jointed rocks are vulnerable to severe abrasion and plucking. Once a rock basin begins to form, some of the characteristics of ice flow increase its size. For instance, extending flow increases ice thickness as it fills the hollow. This increases the weight for abrasion, and leads to more pressure melting at the base of the glacier which encourages plucking. Another reason for localized valley deepening is additions of ice. A steep drop in level often occurs towards the head of the valley after cirque glaciers and ice caps increase the size of the glacier in the main valley, thereby giving a sudden boost to its ability to erode. This is the trough end. Tributary glaciers joining the main glacier lower down the valley have a similar effect. Hard rock outcrops reduce the valley's width, constricting the glacier, but speeding up its rate of erosion as it forces its way through. Where the glacier has melted and can no longer erode, rock lips or rock bars form (rotational slip also contributes to their formation). Another example of rock bars is on the seaward edge of a fiord near to the maximum extent reached by the glacier (page 44).

▼ **Figure 4.29** Tourist panorama of the Jungfrau region

In comparison with the landforms of erosion, those formed by deposition are small and less impressive, although they can be quite extensive. Since the size and extent of most of these landforms of deposition are greater from ice sheets, their formation will be explained in greater detail under this heading (pages 139–140).

Questions

1 a Draw labelled illustrations to show how a valley glacier changes the cross profile, plan and long profile of a previous river valley.

b Explain why glaciated valleys are deeper, wider, straighter and more uneven than river valleys.

2 The Lauterbrunnen valley and Jungfrau region in Switzerland are an example of an area greatly affected by erosion from valley glaciers.

a Study Figure 4.16.

i Draw a labelled sketch of the landforms of valley glaciation shown.

ii How would you attempt to convince a non-geographer visiting this area that glaciers formed most of the landscape features of the area shown?

b Study Figure 4.29.

i Draw a sketch of the mountain peaks and glaciers from Eiger to Jungfrau. Annotate on it characteristics of the peaks and glaciers.

ii Give reasons for these characteristics.

iii Describe the features of the Lauterbrunnen valley shown in Figure 4.29.

iv Name the two different types of glacial lake present in this region and explain how and why their locations are different.

v Lakes Brienz and Thun, now separated by the town of Interlaken, were one lake at the end of the Ice Age. Why are they now two lakes?

vi Outline the distribution of settlement and suggest reasons for it.

Ice sheets – processes and landforms

Erosion often appears to be relatively less significant in areas previously covered by ice sheets. Depositional landforms are larger and cover wider areas than those formed by valley glaciers. Of course, without having eroded the land over which they passed first, ice sheets would not have had anything to deposit. However, what they do not do, despite their immense size and depth, is produce the same dramatic landscapes of erosion to rival those carved out by valley glaciers in mountain areas. Indeed some geomorphologists argue that ice sheets are agents of protection more than agents of erosion. By blanketing the surface with snow and ice, the bedrock is saved from more weathering and from being worn away by the other agents of erosion such as rivers. Very low temperatures and little meltwater mean that little freeze-thaw can take place around and under the ice. Without the help of frost action glacial erosion is less efficient. Interior Antarctica and Greenland are so cold that continental ice sheets are probably protecting the bed rocks beneath, giving them, despite all appearances, one of the lowest rates of denudation on the Earth's surface today.

Many of the favourable circumstances for erosion, present in those areas with valley glaciers, do not exist in areas covered with ice sheets. Ice sheets are cold glaciers. The ice base is firmly anchored to the bedrock below. Little meltwater is present. Movement tends to be by laminar (viscous) flow within the ice itself rather than by basal slippage. Consequently there is less erosion on the rock floor. Ice sheets have small ice budgets. In the cold deserts of Antarctica and Greenland there is little accumulation and little ablation so that there is no push through of ice for rapid movement. Located in the middle of a continent there is only the occasional rocky peak to supply frost-shattered rocks to use as tools for abrasion, whereas a valley glacier may be supplied from both sides throughout its entire length. Nor is the ice sheet in Antarctica being funnelled down pre-existing river valleys to increase its momentum. For all these reasons it flows by only a few metres per year. In Greenland it is noticeable how much faster the ice moves at the edges of the plateau towards the sea where it is channelled into valleys and where climatic conditions are many degrees warmer than in the centre.

Those continental ice sheets which covered North America and Europe in the Ice Age crossed over mainly lowland areas. Despite their slow movement, near to their source regions they scraped bare and reduced the height of the land. The Scandinavian and Laurentian ice sheets were of great thickness, with ice depths estimated at between 2000 to 4000 metres. There are not many prominent landscape features left on the Baltic and Canadian shields over which they crossed. By sheer weight and pressure, if nothing else, they removed all the surface rock and wore down these areas of old hard rock into peneplains (almost continuous areas of low ground). By abrasion they polished, striated and wore away rock. Plucking on the downstream side of rock outcrops contributed to this erosion. Minor differences in rock structure and resistance were exploited to leave innumerable ice-eroded hollows, many now filled by lakes. Look at atlas maps of Canada and Finland. North of the populated zone along the American border, Canada's surface is riddled with lakes of all different shapes and sizes. In Finland so many lakes are present that in some parts it is difficult to find the land! Post glacial processes have operated for 10,000 years, but what is mainly seen in today's landscapes is the work done by ice sheets.

A similar landscape, even if smaller in extent, exists in north-west Scotland (Figure 4.30). Part of it north of Lochinver is shown on the OS map in Figure 4.31. The landscape label for this is 'knock and lochan' (knobs of rock and small lakes). The bedrock is largely composed of well-jointed gneiss; it is also crossed by dykes (running north west to south east) and faults (running north east to south west), which created a rectangular pattern of major weaknesses. These increased rates of ice sheet erosion by creating more favourable conditions for the operation of plucking and abrasion. Almost all remaining rock outcrops are bare so that on many of the knobs of rock it is possible to see a smooth, abraded upstream slope and jagged, plucked leeward slope (Figure 4.20). In between the knobs of rock, rock basins were eroded along the joints to leave a multitude of small lakes. The integrated pre-glacial pattern of surface drainage was upset and replaced by today's confused pattern in which many small stream systems lead into and finish in lakes. Subsequent glacial deposition, as the ice sheets retreated, is indicated by the presence of many erratic blocks left perched on the rocky outcrops. In summary the landscape on the OS extract is the result of heavy glaciation by an ice sheet close to its source region.

▲ **Figure 4.30** A glaciated landscape south of Ullapool where an ice sheet scraped bare the surface and rounded off rock outcrops

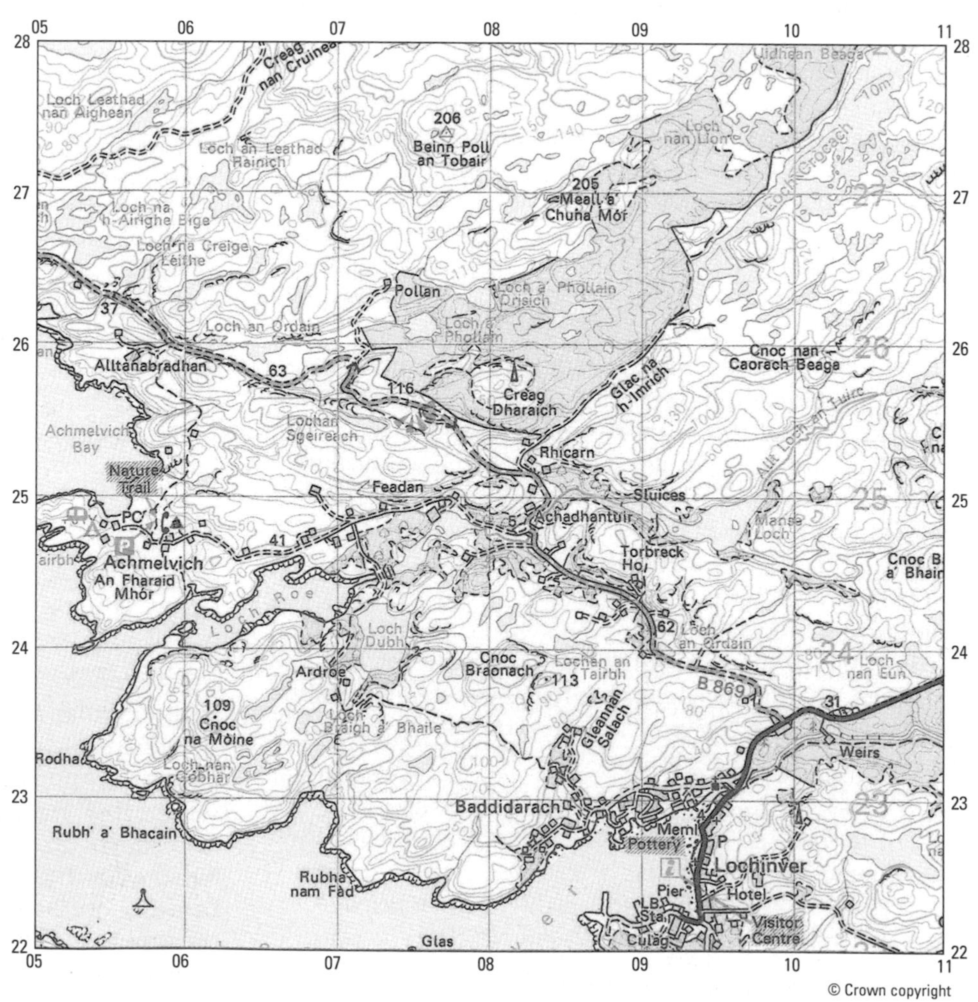

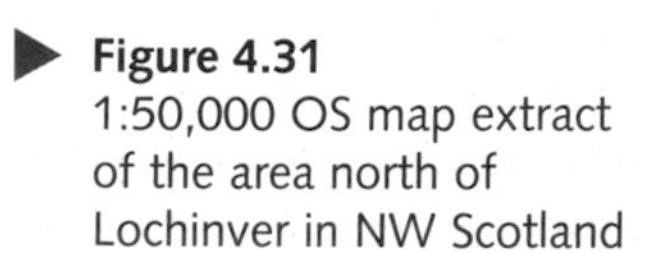

▶ **Figure 4.31**
1:50,000 OS map extract of the area north of Lochinver in NW Scotland

Ice sheet deposition

Deposited glacial material consists of a matrix of sand and clay around angular boulders of all different shapes and sizes. Everything from massive boulders to small particles of clay are present within it. The ingredients reflect the geological nature of the area over which the ice sheet flowed. From an examination of the contents it is possible to work out the source of the ice sheet and its route. The alignment of the stones within the deposits betrays the direction of flow of the ice. What distinguishes glacial from river deposits is that they are unsorted and unstratified, and boulders and stones are less rounded. Given the mixed nature of glacial deposits many geomorphologists prefer the term glacial till rather than boulder clay, because some glacial deposits are sandy and contain only smaller stones. However, the term boulder clay is still widely used, particularly when the nature of the deposited materials matches the label. Another name for deposited materials is unstratified glacial drift. There are also many individual large boulders among the drift. Large boulders dumped in obviously foreign locations are known as erratics (Figure 4.33). They act as a reminder that boulders of vast dimensions can be transported great distances by ice.

Much of the Midlands and East Anglia is covered by stony blue-grey boulder clay up to about 60m thick. It forms a hummocky but otherwise featureless landscape. Former river valleys have been filled in and the underlying geology has been masked by this deposition. This is ground moraine. In these regions the deposition occurred during the Wolstonian ice advance, when the ice sheet

▲ **Figure 4.33**
Erratics and perched blocks near Ingleborough in Yorkshire – the Norber blocks. Blocks of Silurian grit lie on top of Carboniferous limestone. The grit blocks seem to have protected the rock below from suffering the same rate of erosion as the rest of the limestone plateau. This would explain why many of the blocks are 'perched'. Is there another agent, other than ice, which could have transported blocks of rock of this size over and onto the top of a plateau?

▲ **Figure 4.32** Glacial till exposed by river erosion. Sand, clay and sharp-edged stones and pieces of rock are present.

was approaching its southern limit and was so overloaded that it was smearing debris over valley floors and simply dumping it anywhere. The surface material carried by the ice sheet was probably lighter than that in the base, and, where it was deposited, surfaces are covered by coarse sands. These deposits are usually referred to as the older drift.

Boulder clay deposits from the last major ice advance of the Ice Age, the Devensian, cover extensive lowland areas in 'Highland Britain', the area to the north and west of the Tees-Exe line. These form the newer drift. One of the most widespread depositional landforms in southern Scotland and north-west England is the drumlin. A drumlin is an elongated oval (or egg-shaped) hill; the steeper or blunt end faces into the ice flow, whereas the downstream end or lee slope is gentler and more pointed. Typically an individual drumlin is between 400 and 800m long and from 20 to 50m high. What makes drumlins easy to recognize is that they usually occur in swarms and form 'basket of eggs topography'. Even within a small area there is a lot of variation in drumlin size and shape; some are no more than rounded mounds. However, there is always uniformity in the alignment of the hills. Another landscape characteristic is chaotic surface drainage. Their presence greatly interferes with the pattern of surface drainage; streams are small and irregular in direction and there are many marshy hollows.

The key difference between boulder clay deposits and drumlins is that the drumlins are moulded into shape by the moving ice instead of just being dumped. Drumlins are formed when the lowest layers of the moving ice which are laden with mixed glacial till are obstructed. The cleaner ice in the layer above flows around the obstruction. This gives the drumlin its streamlined form. Quite specific ice conditions are needed for the formation of drumlins; they do not form where the ice is too thick or too thin, nor where ice movement is too fast or too slow. However, conditions for their formation were clearly ideal during the last ice advance judging by the great numbers of them and

Figure 4.34 Drumlins
a Section of an individual drumlin
b A drumlin swarm
c OS map extract of Gressingham, near Kendal, around the edge of the Lake District

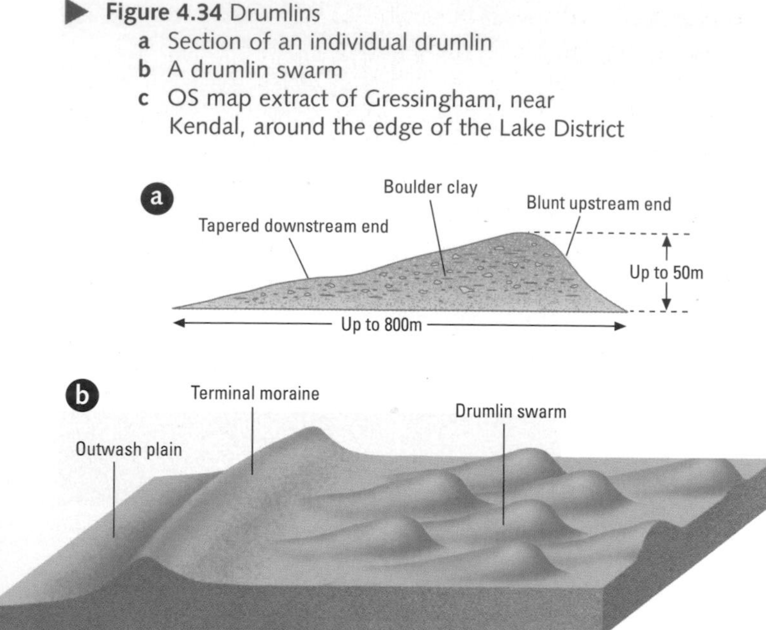

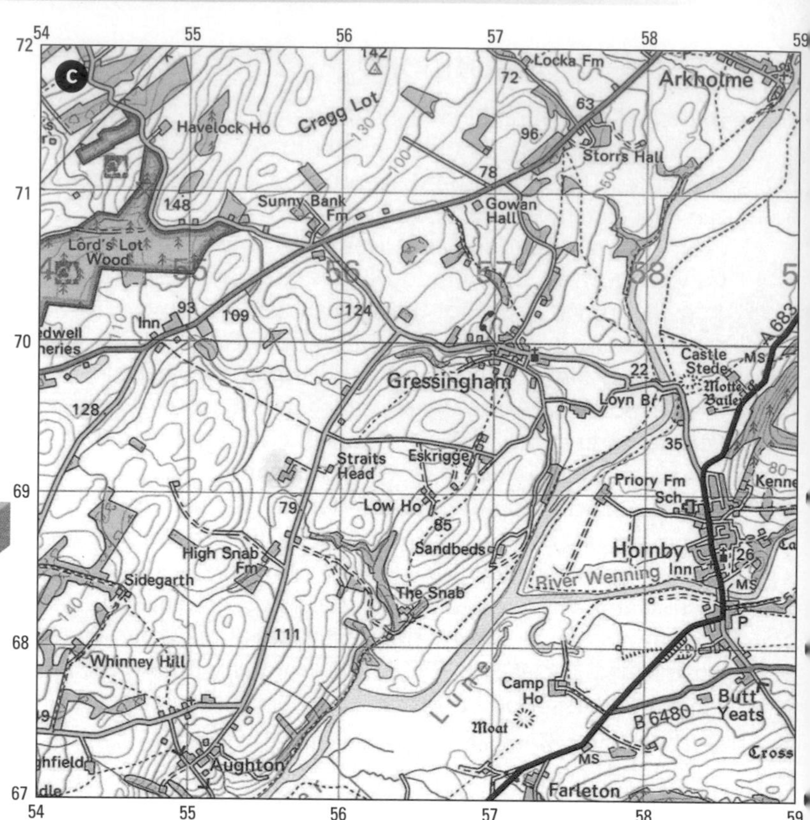

how they dominate the lowland landscapes around the edges of the Southern Uplands, Lake District and western Pennines. In the Scottish Borders in the Tweed valley near Coldstream and Kelso the drumlins have a rock base. The strike of the rock coincided with the direction of ice movement so that the deposits of drift were smoothed off around the pre-existing surface rock forms.

Terminal moraines mark the edges of former ice sheets. These are crescent-shaped ridges of glacial materials typically between 30 and 60m high. Final melting led to all the remaining glacial materials being dropped. In places terminal moraines form distinctive landscape features; some stretches across the North German Plain are about 200m high and stand out as prominent ridges within the otherwise low-lying landscape. Their exceptional height reflects the great size of the European ice sheets and their length of standstill. However, most terminal moraines form discontinuous landscape features. Some must have been destroyed almost as quickly as they formed by the massive amounts of meltwater present. Others are smaller recessional moraines formed during temporary halts by retreating ice sheets. A few are push moraines formed as a result of the ice front moving forward temporarily, bulldozing debris in front of it. Those lengths of terminal moraine that have survived erosion by streams, such as the Cromer moraine in Norfolk and the Tadcaster moraine in Yorkshire, stand out as slightly higher ridges. They are useful as dry point sites for settlements above the surrounding wet lowlands.

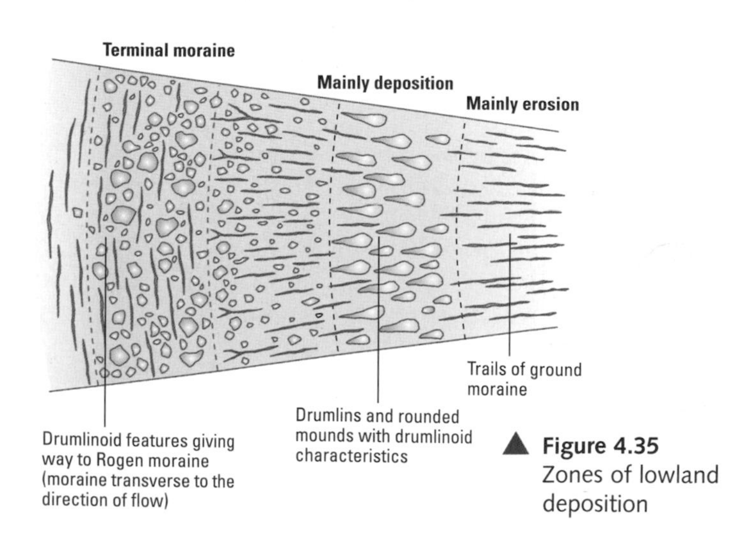

Figure 4.35 Zones of lowland deposition

Questions

1 Study the OS map in Figure 4.31.
   a Describe the relief and surface drainage of the area shown on the extract.
   b Explain how an ice sheet formed this landscape.

2 Study the OS map in Figure 4.34c.
   a Discuss the map evidence for the existence of a drumlin field west of the River Lune.
   b Suggest reasons for the great contrast in relief between this area and the valley of the Lune.
   c Comment on the similarities and differences in relief and drainage between the areas shown on the two OS map extracts.

3 a Identify the factors which favour deposition by glaciers.
   b i Study Figure 4.35 and describe what it shows.
   ii Suggest reasons for the change in alignment of deposited materials across glaciated lowlands.

4 **Essay**

'Ice sheets deposit. Valley glaciers erode.' How valid is this statement?

Meltwater and its effects upon the landscapes of glaciated areas

Whenever ice melts, whether during the day, or during the summer, or for most of the time as a result of climatic warming, there is water everywhere. Meltwater streams flow within the ice, along the sides, at the base and away from the ice front. The use of the term 'snout' to denote the end of the glacier suggests that there are holes or tunnels in the ice carved by meltwater streams. Streams that drain from glaciers have braided channels. The wide channel is an essential response to the need to remove vast quantities of water at peak times during summer. With the approach of winter, the reduction in water supply leads to lower stream capacity and competence. This forces the streams to deposit their loads filling their channel floors with great spreads of boulders. Stream loads are so great because of the plentiful availability of loose materials from glacial erosion and transport. In mid winter often only a trickle of water flows in tiny water channels, which weave in and out of the massive banks of boulders.

Streams everywhere erode, transport and deposit. It has already been shown (page 132) how streams flowing under ice are capable of cutting steep-sided valleys. This is because of the great volumes of water under the ice forced to flow under hydrostatic pressure in the base of the glacier. Beyond the ice edge, relict landforms show that meltwater streams cut deep, steep-sided spillways and overflow channels (page 144). In the periglacial zone, the presence of permafrost allows streams to flow across the surface even in areas of porous and permeable rocks such as chalk and limestone. After the return of post-glacial conditions, dry valleys are left here, dissecting the surface, as drainage underground resumes.

Fluvio-glacial landforms

Despite these important examples of erosion, the most widespread impact of meltwater streams upon the landscape is from deposition. All landforms created by meltwater streams are classified under the heading of fluvio-glacial. Glaciers supply the load and the water, but the deposition is undertaken by the streams which have transported the glacial debris. Rivers sort and grade materials so that what was unstratified glacial drift is re-deposited as stratified drift; boulders, gravel, sand and silt are dropped in separate locations. The sharp edges of frost-shattered and glacially-eroded rocks are broken off by river transport; they are changed into the smooth, more rounded boulders which fill river channels on the edge of glaciated regions.

Some fluvio-glacial landforms are formed by streams flowing within and under the glacier. These are kames, kame terraces and eskers, distinguished from each other mainly by form and position. Seasonal variations in water levels encourage deposition at certain times of the year, while the abundance of glacial debris means that the streams are overloaded as soon as water levels start to decrease. This deposition occurs within tunnels and holes in the ice.

In actively moving glaciers these tunnels keep closing up, but in the later stages of glaciation when the ice is stagnant, they are more likely to remain open. Deposition from one meltwater season is added to that from previous years. Eskers, which are long winding ridges of gravel, are built up to heights of 30m as a result of successive seasons of deposition from streams flowing through tunnels in the ice. They are aligned roughly parallel to the direction of ice movement. Apart from this, two characteristics of eskers strongly suggest their sub-glacial origins. First the ridges swing across the landscape with little reference to present day relief, which is a clear indication that the processes responsible for their formation are not operating today. Secondly some lines of stream-deposited gravels wind their way uphill over ridges on the present land surface. Only with the hydrostatic pressure that exists under ice can rivers flow uphill and leave depositional traces from having done so. Some eskers broaden out at intervals, forming small deltaic fans of gravel, for instance where meltwater streams met standing water under the ice; the name given to this feature is beaded esker. Eskers are common in both Finland and the Republic of Ireland. In Finland they are useful in providing narrow strips of land between the lake-pitted surfaces all around them; in Ireland they offer a strip of dry land between the peat bogs. As a broader issue, it is not clear why under hydrostatic pressure some streams should cut locally deep valleys while others deposit considerable amounts of gravel and form eskers.

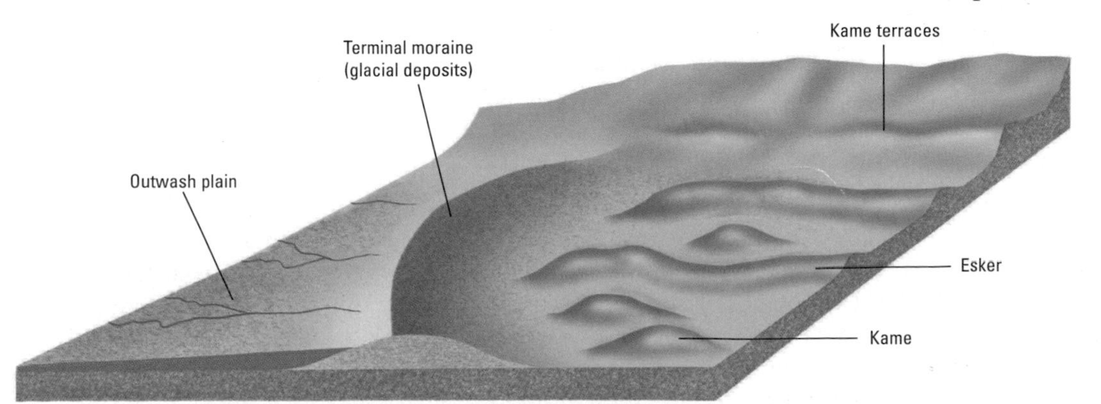

▲ **Figure 4.36** Fluvio-glacial landforms

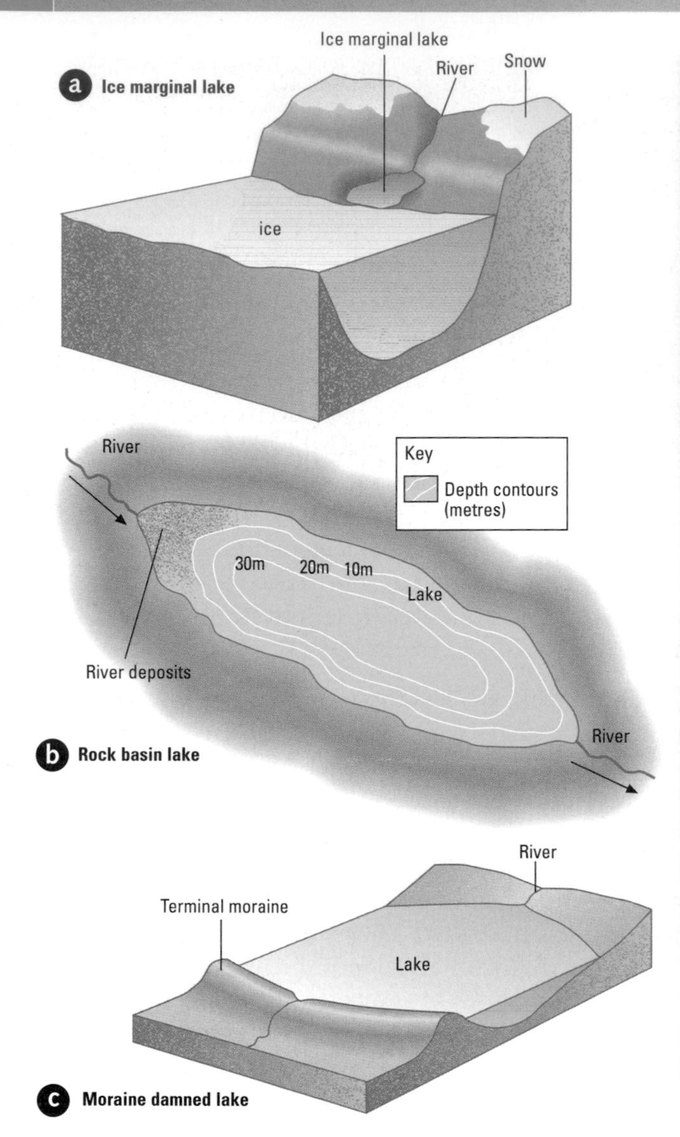

▲ **Figure 4.37** Ice marginal, rock basin and moraine-dammed lakes

Kames are mounds of sand and gravel. When isolated the mound is likely to be formed by glacial debris which becomes stuck in a large crevasse as it is being transported in a stream through the ice. More commonly kames are formed at the ice front. One suggestion is that a stream reaches a water body, such as an ice marginal lake, which encourages deposition and leads to mounds built up as alluvial fans or small deltas. Kame terraces are formed along the edges of a tongue of ice in valleys. Since heat radiated from the rock melts the edges of the ice, a stream commonly runs along the sides of an ablating glacier. In this position there is no shortage of load available to the stream. As the thickness of the ice continues to shrink sufficient gravel is deposited to build up and leave a terrace after the ice has completely melted. A line of kame terraces was formed along one side of Glen Roy (Figure 4.39) along the edge of the ice mass which filled the glen before it was replaced by a lake.

Glacial lakes

Glacial lakes are among the most common of all lakes.

However, all lakes are temporary (or ephemeral) landscape features.

Some lakes are present only when the glaciers themselves are present.

Lakes blocked by ice:

- *Ice marginal lake. The flow of a stream from a tributary valley is blocked by the glacier which is still present in the main valley.*
- *Proglacial lake. This lake lies in front of a glacier and is filled by meltwater, but is trapped between the glacier and higher relief (page 144).*

The water in these two types of lake soon drains away once the ice that was trapping it melts.

The majority of other glacial lakes are formed by glacial erosion.

Lakes of glacial erosion:

- *Tarn lake. Water fills a cirque hollow.*
- *Ribbon lake. Water fills a rock basin in a valley floor.*
- *Lochan. Water fills a rock hollow of irregular shape eroded by an ice sheet.*

Some lakes result from the presence of glacial deposits.

Lakes of glacial deposition:

- *Moraine-dammed ribbon lake. Water is retained by a ridge of terminal moraine across the valley floor.*
- *Kettle lakes and marshy ponds. Kettles form in depressions within the moraine. Ponds fill in badly drained depressions on hummocky boulder clay surfaces such as in a drumlin field.*

By far the largest fluvio-glacial landform is the outwash plain, which forms beyond the ice front. It is an extensive spread of boulders, gravel and sand that slopes gently away from the point where the ice front reached, built up by combined deposition from many small streams after emerging from the ice. Each stream produces its own small alluvial fan; with time the areas covered by individual depositions coalesce over a wide area forming the plain. Deposition fills up the floors of pre-existing valleys and masks other surface variations in relief. This is usually accompanied by the grading of deposits from coarse boulders near to the ice front to finer sand deposits on the edge of the plain. As the ice front moves back, the outwash streams flow over surfaces already plastered with glacial till. This adds to the complexity of surface features and makes the recognition of individual landforms of deposition difficult. The surface may be pitted with kettle lakes where trapped blocks of ice thawed out last leaving a depression soon filled by water. Therefore features of ice origin are mixed in amongst those formed by meltwater.

There is a fine example of an outwash plain across the North European Plain stretching from Western Jutland in Denmark across North Germany and into Poland. It was created south of the ice front from the last major advance in the Ice Age some 20,000 years ago. The surface deposits of sand and gravel lead to inherently infertile soils, such as podsols, which is why over large areas it remains a waste land of sandy heath, although there are some commercial coniferous plantations and pockets of reclaimed land for farming.

The finest grained fluvio-glacial deposits are laid down in lakes; so much meltwater is present during ice retreats that standing surface water is everywhere. There is evidence for many ice marginal and proglacial lakes during the Pleistocene era in which water was trapped until spillways and overflow channels were cut to enable some of it to drain away. Lakes were dammed in the Scottish glens (Glen Roy was an example). Lake Harrison covered much of the area between Nuneaton, Rugby and Stratford in the West Midlands, and Lake Pickering, at one time, drained into an even larger lake called Lake Fenland. There was a considerable difference in the carrying capacities of streams feeding into these lakes between summer and winter. With the approach of winter, sediments were the most fine grained of all. From the sediments on lake floors the annual pattern of sedimentation can be recognized in the layers called varves (Figure 4.40).

▼ **Figure 4.38a**
In the foreground are glacial deposits. These lie immediately ahead of a melting glacier in southern Iceland. Beyond is the zone of outwash.

▲ **Figure 4.38b**
Outwash plain on James Ross Island, Antarctica, built up from streams fed by melting ice caps in the mountains on the left. The deposits here are better sorted.

Loaded meltwater streams

Lake

Sediment accumulation in the lake bed

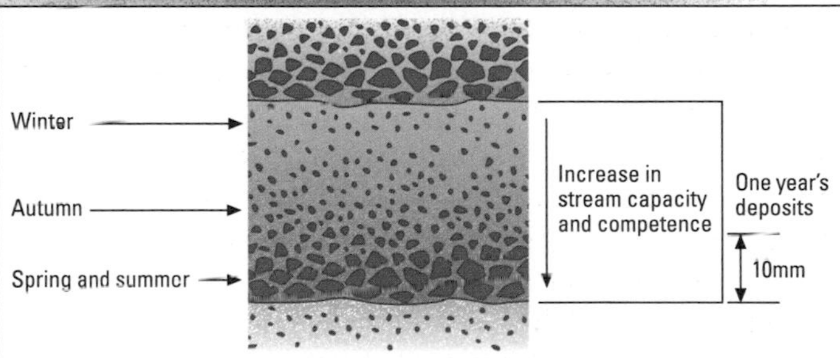

▲ **Figure 4.40** Varves in lake floor sediments deposited by meltwater streams

▲ **Figure 4.39**
The parallel roads of Glen Roy. These are shoreline deposits and terraces formed by the action of waves and currents when ice-dammed lakes were present. The two 'roads' at 350 and 325m can be seen most clearly on the photograph. These follow the contours around the side of the most prominent area of high ground in the background on the left side. There is also a lower terrace at 260m. The course of the road makes use of kame terraces, formed by meltwater deposition along the sides of the ice.

When trapped by ice, water rises until the lowest point on any of the other sides is reached, then it overflows, releasing large volumes of water capable of rapid erosion. As a result the form of the typical overflow channel is gorge-like with steep sides and narrow flat floor, as opposed to the usual gently sloping V-shaped profile. Because they are the product of different circumstances, these overflow channels rarely fit in with the established drainage pattern and frequently cut across watersheds and ridges.

East Yorkshire: overflow channels and proglacial lakes

Case Study

Events during the Devensian ice advance	Effects on the landscape
A During the Devensian the Cleveland Hills were too high to be covered by an ice sheet, and too flat to support growth of their own glaciers. The hills were drained by the River Esk and its tributaries.	The exit of the River Esk was blocked by North Sea ice. Lake Eskdale was one of several proglacial lakes which formed in the region.
B The water from Lake Eskdale found the lowest point to escape, Newtondale, and the water drained south away from the ice. At its peak the waters from Newtondale drained into the larger Lake Pickering.	Newtondale was eroded into a flat-floored and steep-sided valley with an abrupt change in angle where it met the flat-topped moorland above. A gravel delta upon which the town of Pickering is sited was formed where it met the still lake waters.
C The levels of Lake Eskdale fell as the North Sea ice retreated eastwards.	The River Esk was able to resume its easterly course which it still follows reaching the sea at Whitby.
D The waters of the River Derwent which used to reach the sea north of Scarborough were also blocked by ice.	This lake overflowed through the Forge Valley channel into the larger Lake Pickering, also blocked by North Sea ice.
E When the ice retreated the River Derwent did not resume its pre-glacial course.	Lake Pickering overflowed south through a sinuous gorge near to Kirkham Abbey into the even larger Lake Fenland.The River Derwent continues to follow this course to this day.

▼ **Figure 4.41a** An overflow channel – Forge Valley and the River Derwent

Field evidence for the existence of proglacial lakes and overflow channels in East Yorkshire

1 Deep and steep-sided water eroded valleys that are too large to have been eroded by the small streams which presently occupy them. Newtondale, for example, has only a small stream flowing for part of its length.

2 Overflow channels that go across ridge tops which do not match present-day patterns of drainage.

3 A diverted river, the River Derwent, which flows to within a few kilometres of the sea before bending inland and flowing southwards, taking the long route into the North Sea via the River Ouse and Humber Estuary.

4 A large level area, the Vale of Pickering, covered by lake sediments such as laminated clays.

5 A gravel delta under the town of Pickering supports the existence of a lake and powerful stream down Newtondale.

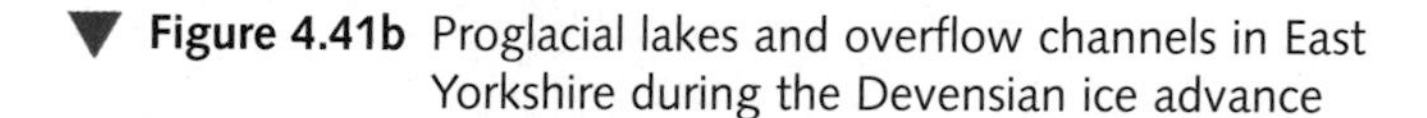

▼ **Figure 4.41b** Proglacial lakes and overflow channels in East Yorkshire during the Devensian ice advance

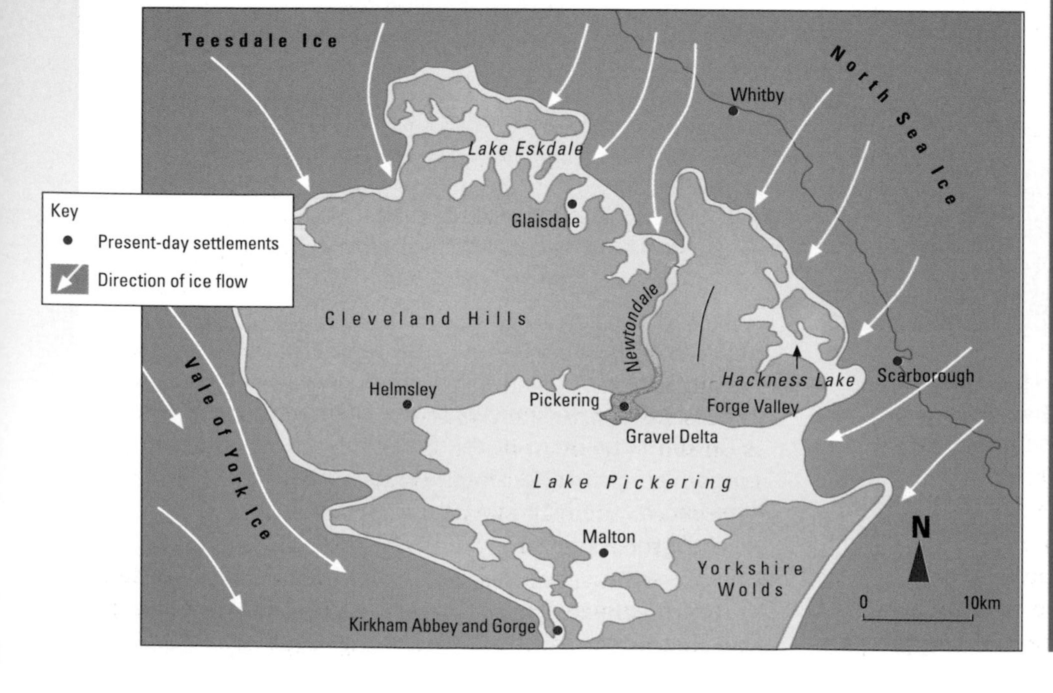

Questions

1 a In what ways can fluvio-glacial deposits be distinguished from those deposited by glaciers?
  b Why are fluvio-glacial deposits found in both glaciated and non-glaciated areas?

2 a Make classifications of fluvio-glacial landforms under the following headings:
    i location,
    ii origins.
  b Justify and explain one of the classifications.

3 State and explain the field evidence that suggests that during the Pleistocene era in the UK:
  a many more lakes were present
  b courses of surface streams were changed.

Periglacial processes and landforms

'Peri' comes from the Greek meaning round or about. Therefore periglacial is applied to those areas at and around the fringes of glaciers. These are areas of significant frost action – both freeze-thaw and frozen ground. Also they largely coincide with areas of tundra climate. The frequent and major ice advances and retreats during the last two million years means that the periglacial zone has had no fixed location. On occasions it included the whole of the British Isles, whereas during the maximum ice advance in the Wolstonian glaciation period it included only that part of England south of the Severn and Thames estuaries. During the last ice advance in the Devensian era the periglacial zone covered a larger area that included the East Midlands and East Anglia. It is in these southern and eastern parts of England that fossil landscape features formed by periglacial processes can more readily be recognized, because there have been no later ice advances to obliterate all signs of them. Today periglacial processes within the British Isles are restricted to the tops of the higher mountains. The world's main periglacial zone covers Alaska and the Arctic lands of Canada and Russia.

Permafrost

Although frost action is undoubtedly the most important process of denudation in the periglacial zone, the presence of permafrost is crucial to the operation of other processes. Permafrost itself is not a process; it is a ground condition. It means permanently frozen ground. As the result of low temperatures, bedrock, regolith and soil are all frozen. Any gaps within and between them are filled with ice. A porous rock such as chalk is turned into an impermeable mass by permafrost. Other loose materials such as weathered rock (regolith) and soil are cemented together and become solid. In those areas where winter temperatures are very cold and summers short, the permafrost is deep and continuous, in places up to 600m deep. Permafrost of great depth extends furthest south in Asia where the size of the landmass intensifies the winter cold. However, as warmer climates are reached in more southerly latitudes or maritime locations, the permafrost becomes thinner and less continuous. Its presence is greater on ridges and mountains than in river valleys. All important for what happens on the surface is the active layer formed by seasonal thawing of the top of the permafrost.

The active layer is the shallow surface zone which defrosts in summer. The low angle of the sun in high latitudes is partly offset by long hours of daylight. Temperature controls the depth of thawing, which ranges from a few centimetres to several metres. The surface always thaws first; during spring and summer melting of the ice continues downwards, usually quite slowly (Figure 4.42). However, water released is unable to drain away because the ground beneath is still frozen. The upper part of the soil becomes saturated and unstable and can move on slopes of as little as 2°. This is solifluction, one of the processes of mass movement. Rivers return, sometimes flooding wide areas despite the width of their braided channels, as most of their annual flow is concentrated into just a few weeks. When the land begins to cool down again in autumn, the procedure is reversed. Refreezing begins on the surface where heat is lost first; surface cold gradually penetrates downwards into the ground. As the width of the active layer narrows, expansion of water trapped by frozen ground above and below causes surface heaving and associated landforms such as patterned ground. What happens in the active layer has great implications for settlers, builders and engineers (page 159).

▼ **Figure 4.42** The active layer above permafrost

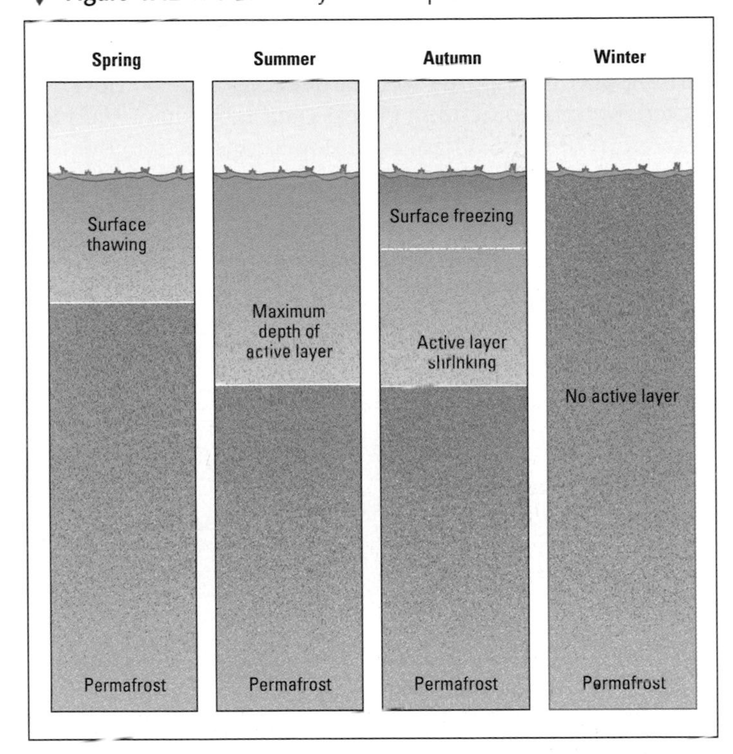

Mass movement and resulting landforms

Several factors combine to favour mass movement. The ground surface is seasonally disturbed by alternate thawing and freezing. Vegetation cover is very restricted. Waterlogged surfaces during summer thawing facilitate movement. Frozen ground below keeps soil moisture levels high in the active layer. The result is movement on even the gentlest of slopes. The main type is solifluction, which literally means soil flow. Its operation is most continuous in those localities where water is constantly present, such as on slopes below snow patches that are large enough to survive during most of the summer. Other types of mass movement include frost creep and rock slides (on for example scree slopes). Frost creep is similar to soil creep which is so widespread in temperate latitudes. It is caused by frost heaving which causes particles to rise to the surface and then move downslope according to gravity.

The great importance of solifluction as a periglacial process stems from its widespread occurrence rather than from any dramatic landforms that it is capable of producing. Indeed the general effect is to reduce and smooth out the relief as weathered and loose deposited materials are transferred from upper slope to downslope positions. Often these are no more than featureless accumulations at the foot of a slope (Figure 4.43a). However, in some places the formation of lobes, or terraces, gives greater form by producing a pattern of rounder and flatter areas on the lower slopes (Figure 4.43b). These lobes are of two types which are largely controlled by the amount of vegetation present. The first, without continuous vegetation cover, forms a stone-banked lobe or terrace (Figure 4.43c). Most are relatively small with lobes rising up to 5m and then extending up the slope to form a terrace between 10 and 30m long. The distinctive feature of each lobe is the stone wall behind which finer materials accumulate. Stones heaved to the surface travel more quickly downslope (by rolling and turning over in response to frost heaving) than do finer materials, until something checks their movement such as vegetation or minor changes in slope angle. Where the rolling stones stop, they build up as a small wall, which encourages finer materials to accumulate behind it, forming the terrace. The second type forms under a continuous vegetation cover where frost heaving is less effective at raising stones to the surface. Turf-banked lobes and terraces form instead, because it is the surface layers of turf and topsoil which are moved by solifluction (Figure 4.43d). The terraces are again created where a minor relief feature obstructs this movement, rolling up the turf flow backwards under the continued surface movement. This forms what is known as the riser below the lobe. When held together by the mat of vegetation and roots, the lobes are usually longer and cover larger areas on the lower slopes than the stone-banked ones. Fossil solifluction deposits are among the most widespread periglacial relict features in the British Isles. They go under different names. The general term is head deposits, which are widespread below outcrops of granite on Dartmoor and elsewhere in south-west England. Coombe rock is the name given to fans of chalk below escarpments and in dry valleys in downland regions of southern England. Lobes and terraces have been identified in the uplands of Scotland and Wales, which have been exposed to the action of solifluction for the longest time in the British Isles.

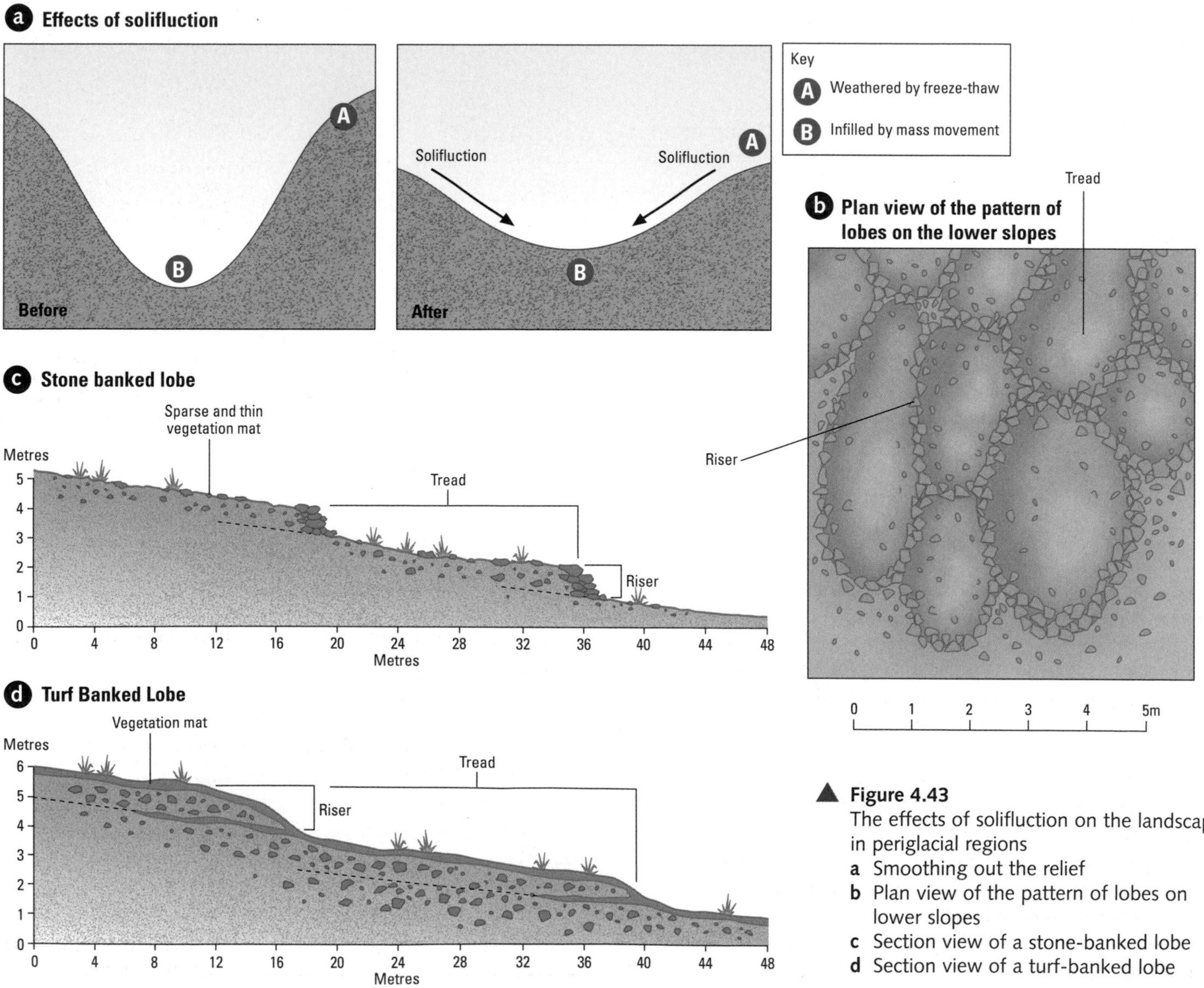

Figure 4.43
The effects of solifluction on the landscape in periglacial regions
- **a** Smoothing out the relief
- **b** Plan view of the pattern of lobes on lower slopes
- **c** Section view of a stone-banked lobe
- **d** Section view of a turf-banked lobe

Frost action and resulting landforms

As in all cold environments the most widespread weathering process in periglacial regions is freeze-thaw. In mountainous areas it is undoubtedly the main process breaking down rocks as the numerous scree slopes and blockfields below rock outcrops testify. Many of the distinctive periglacial landforms in lowland areas, which make up a high proportion of tundra land surfaces, result from freezing of the ground. It is the manner in which the active layer refreezes at the end of summer which is of particular importance (Figure 4.42).

Considerable pressures are created by the expansion of the water trapped in the shrinking active layer. Some deposits hold more water than others, so that freezing is an uneven process. A wet patch which freezes attracts water towards it, increasing its size, and forming a lump of ice. Lumps of ice form ice lenses. As separate pockets of ice with frozen sediments in between, they are an example of ice segregation. Solid lenses of ice grow by pushing up the ground above them, making the surface bulge, and causing frost heaving.

Frost heaving is responsible for several landscape features in periglacial regions:

a Thermokarst

This is the name given to very irregular surfaces of marshy hollows and small hummocks. These pitted surfaces resemble those formed by solution in some karst areas of limestone, which is how they came to have karst attached to their name without the presence of any limestone. Small domes that form on the surface due to frost heaving with the onset of winter are only temporary features. They then collapse with the arrival of next summer's thaw and leave a small surface depression. Some ice lenses grow and form larger surface hummocks, which last many years and sometimes become covered with grasses and sedges, until they begin to thaw. These domed surfaces eventually collapse either annually or after longer periods and form depressions which contribute to uneven surfaces. These are included within the general label of thermokarst.

b Pingos

Pingos are small circular hills up to about 50 or 60m high, occurring in groups, which add to the variety of thermokarst scenery. The presence of a central crater housing a pond makes some pingos look even more distinctive. The greatest numbers of them are found on the flat lands in and around the Mackenzie Delta on the Arctic coast of north-west Canada, where over a thousand have been counted. Within each pingo is a large ice core, which is responsible for the frost heaving which forms the conical hill. Their formation is explained in more detail in Figure 4.45b. After the lake forms, its ice core is no longer insulated against summer warmth. It gradually thaws away and the pingo form is lost.

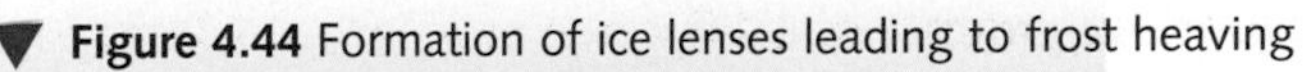

▼ **Figure 4.44** Formation of ice lenses leading to frost heaving

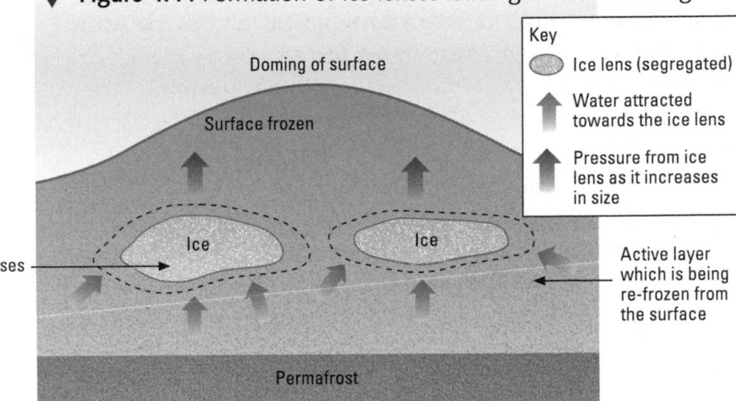

b

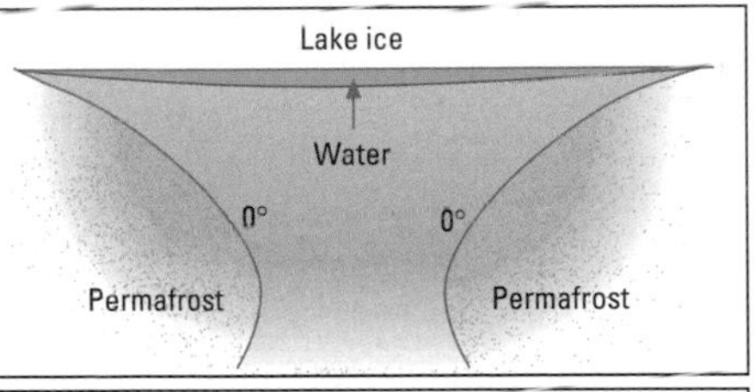

1) In the Mackenzie delta there are plentiful shallow lakes. The ground below them is insulated by the lake water and remains unfrozen.

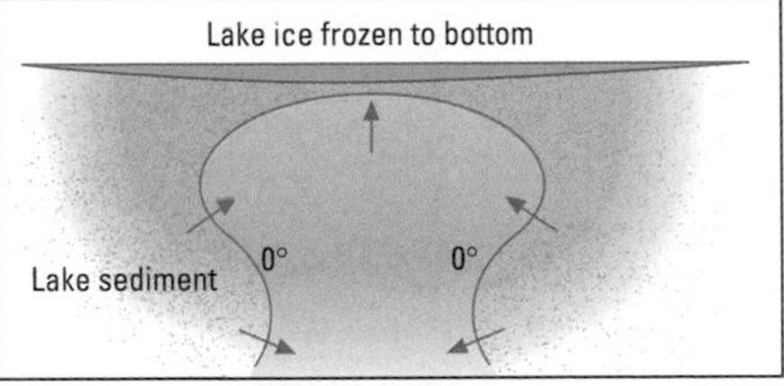

2) The lake is reduced in size by deposition from meltwater streams. Its insulating effect on the ground below is also reduced.

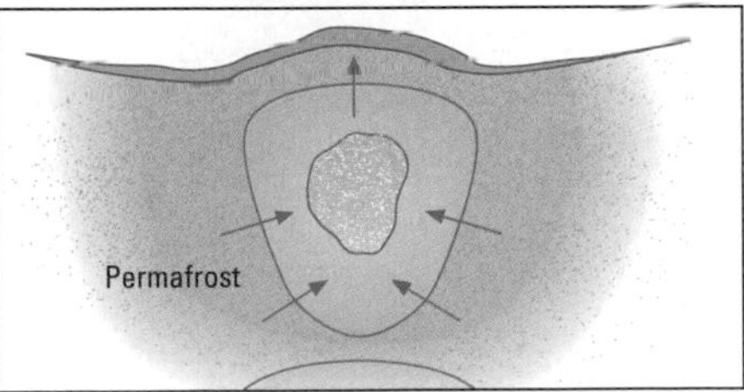

3) As the formerly unfrozen zone freezes, excess water is attracted towards it. An ice core forms and grows. Heaving pressure from the ice core forces up the sediments above it into a dome on the surface

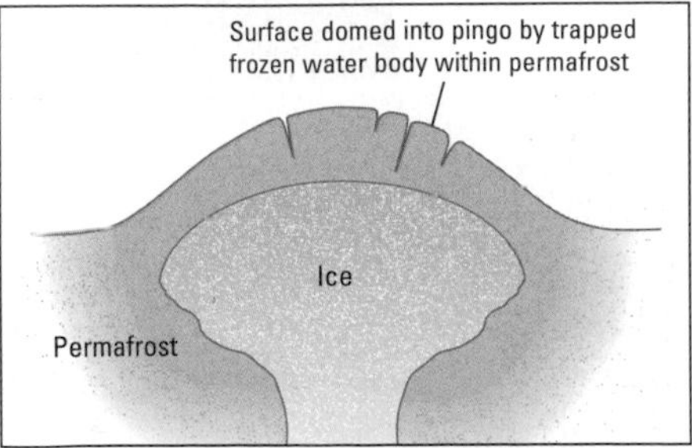

4) Pressure of doming from the ice core increases until eventually the cover of sediment splits. The ice core is subjected to summer melting which creates the pond.

▲ **Figure 4.45**
a Pingo in the Mackenzie delta
b Pingo Formation

c Patterned ground

The most widespread and readily visible landscape feature are the stones which have been sorted on the surface and organized into a variety of surface shapes – circles, polygons and stripes. Although individual circles are rarely more than five metres across, the sorting is often so complete that stones form the edges of circles and lie nowhere else on the surface. There is quite a contrast between stones all around the edge and the much finer, more sandy deposits in the middle. Stone circles meet each other and are either squashed by contact into polygons on gently sloping land or stretched into stripes on slopes.

Frost heaving is the process that brings stones to the surface. An ice lens forms below a stone; as the ice lens expands with winter freezing, the stone is pushed upwards. Thawing during the next summer takes place from the surface downwards, so that for a long time the stone is prevented from falling back down by the frozen ground below. When the ground below the stone is eventually ready to thaw, fine silts, already loose, fill up the spaces around and below the stone, stopping it from slipping back down. Freezing next winter lifts the stone a little higher in the ground. The finer sediments in the middle of circles tend to be domed upwards during winter freezing so that any stone reaching the surface by frost heaving wants to fall towards the edge of the circle under gravity.

▲ **Figure 4.46** Different types of patterned ground

Other periglacial processes and landforms

Although mechanical weathering by freeze-thaw is widespread in its occurrence, other types of weathering are of limited importance. Low temperatures, sparse vegetation cover and poorly developed soils reduce the likelihood of chemical and biological weathering taking place. The lack of vegetation cover, however, favours aeolian (wind) action. When and where the surface dries out, the widespread availability of rock flour (the finest grained glacial deposits), outwash sands and solifluction silts means that there is plenty for the wind to pick up and transport. Some further erosion occurs as wind-blown sand grains abrade rock outcrops producing grooved and polished surfaces. With time some sandy outwash material is re-worked into semi-circular dunes by wind action, as in the eastern heathlands of the Netherlands. However, the most widespread legacy of aeolian action is wind-blown loess. Extensive deposits were left behind in a well-defined belt across Central Europe and eastern Asia. Prevailing easterly winds across Europe at the end of the Ice Age extended the loess deposits as far west as

Figure 4.47 Frost shattering

◀ **a** Rock outcrop under attack

▼ **b** A nearby rock outcrop already shattered

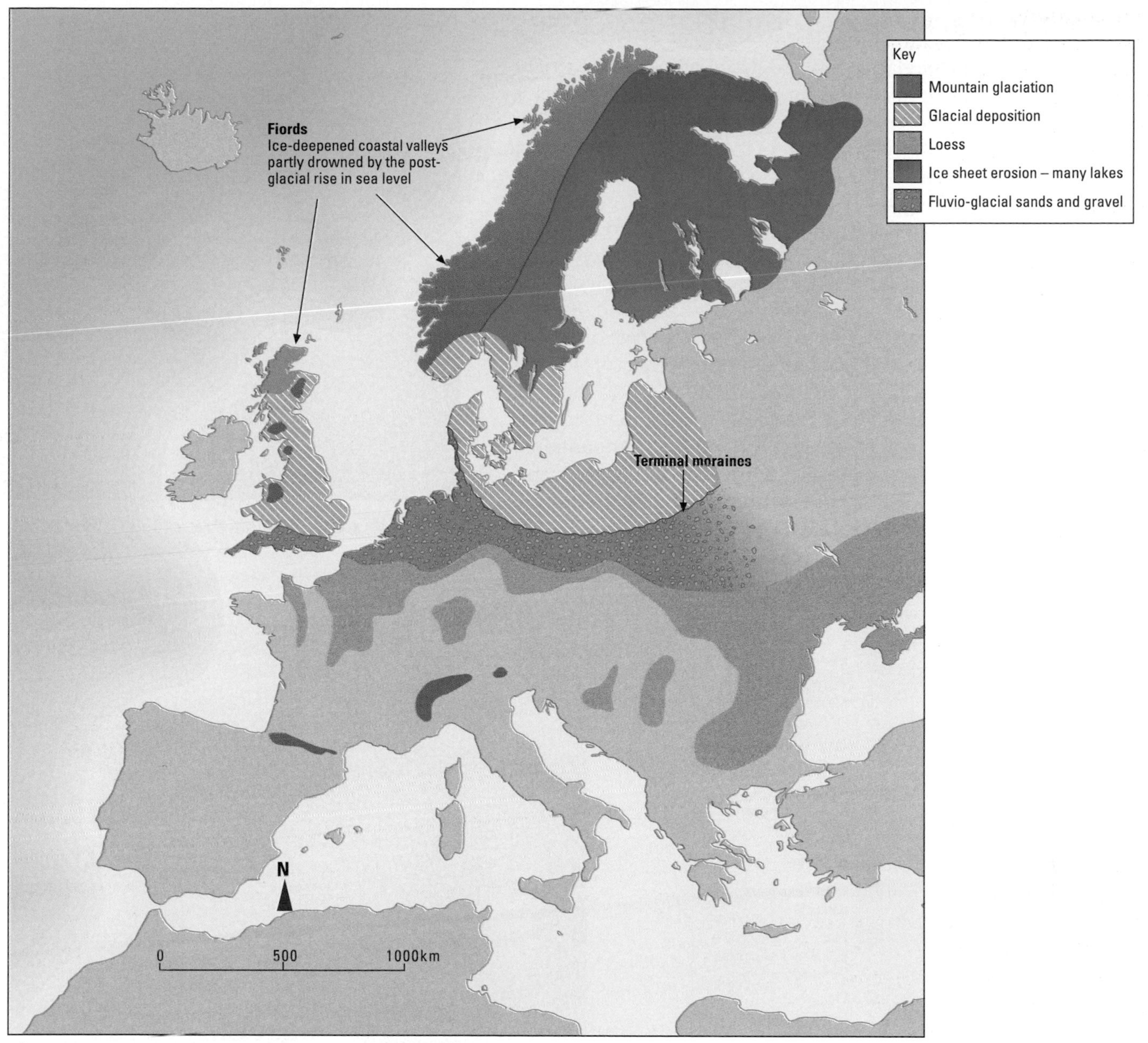

▲ **Figure 4.48** Summary of the effects of the Pleistocene period on north-west Europe

south-east England and the Paris Basin. The patches of loess found in England usually go under the heading of brickearth. Loess is a fertile and easy to work soil. As a result the loess belt of Europe is densely settled in sharp contrast to the outwash plains on its northern edge, which are almost empty. A covering of sterile sands underlain by acidic podsol soils is not attractive for farming or settlement.

References to the importance of meltwater have been made frequently already. In Arctic streams 80 per cent or more of the discharge is concentrated within one or two months of the year. Despite operating for a small proportion of the year, the amount of transport and erosion undertaken by them is enormous. The high load comes from flowing over areas liberally covered by loose debris from glaciers and solifluction. The high discharge comes from melting ice. The peak discharge is accentuated by the impermeable barrier of the permafrost beneath and low rates of evapo-transpiration above. Some surface streams are created in areas where they did not previously exist. Without the artificial presence of permafrost, the natural porosity of chalk favours low water tables, percolation, ground water storage and solution rather than erosion. However, chalk dry valleys and the coombe deposits on their lower slopes are some of the clearest indicators of the past existence of periglacial conditions in Britain. Geomorphologists have discovered examples of pingos and patterned ground in Britain, but these are small features and many other processes have affected the landscape since the time of their formation.

Summary for glacial and periglacial processes

The effects upon landscape of glacial and periglacial processes are easiest to observe and study in those (mainly polar) regions where they are still actively operating today. However, outside polar regions the legacy of the Pleistocene Ice Age remains strong. Figure 4.49 is a view looking across to the Cuillin Hills on the Isle of Skye from the Scottish mainland. It is easy to see that ice was a major force in shaping the landscapes. In the lowlands in the foreground the results of ice sheet erosion and deposition are on view. In the mountains of Skye the results of valley glacier erosion and frost shattering stand out. Figure 4.30 shows what might be described as the typical coastal landscape in much of north-west Scotland. Bare rock outcrops give way to raised beaches, which line the west coast of Scotland, formed by post-glacial isostatic readjustment after the weight of ice was removed from the land (pages 22 and 46). Here in the north of the British Isles near to the centres of ice dispersion ice sheets were thought to have been up to 2,000m thick at times. In the English and Welsh mountains, which formed local centres of ice dispersion during the Ice Age, evidence of glacial erosion remains strong and convincing even though more than 10,000 years have elapsed since the ice disappeared.

▲ **Figure 4.49** View from Pass of the Cattle south of Applecross, north-west Scotland

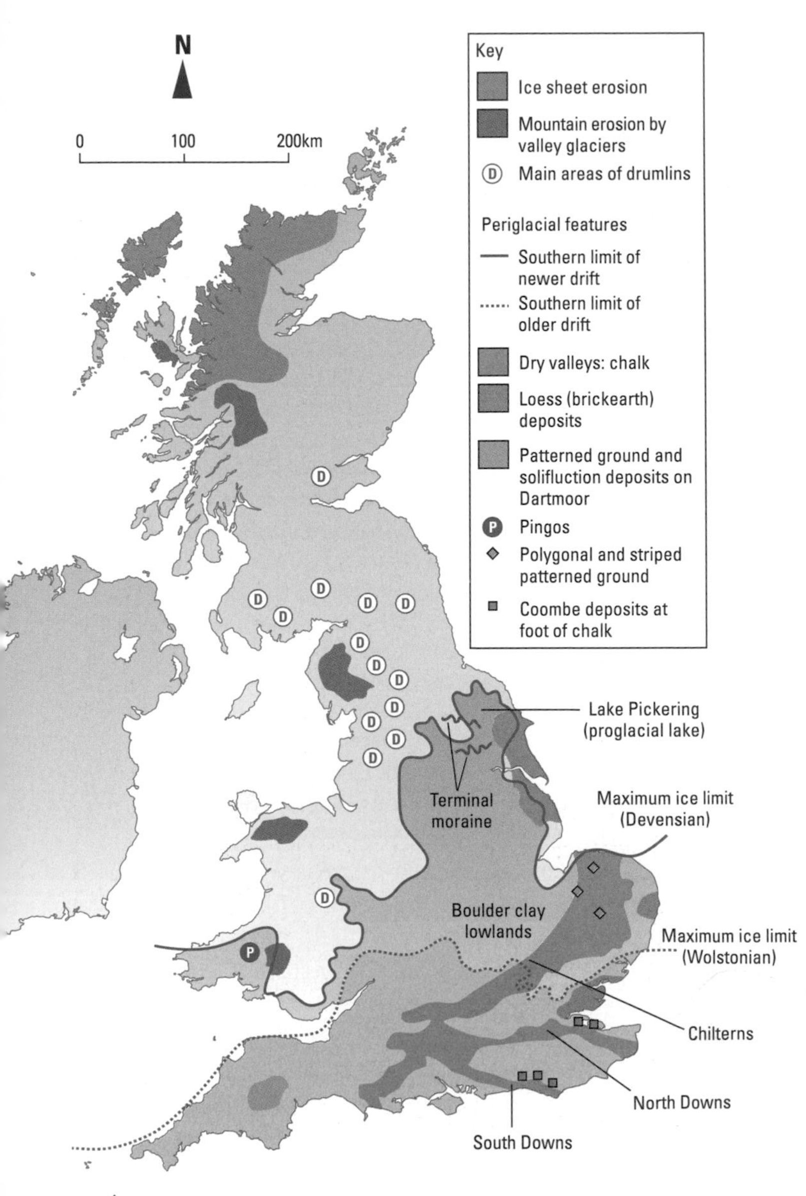

▲ **Figure 4.51** Summary of the effects of the Pleistocene era in Britain

▲ **Figure 4.50**
One of the typical Lake District views above 300m. What effects have previous glaciations had on this landscape?

Lowlands almost everywhere (as far south as the Severn–Thames line) are plastered with glacial till. Unlike erosion, the effects of glacial deposition is to mask rather than highlight landscape differences. Except in drumlin fields there are few distinctive landscape features. The repeated advance and retreat of the ice front and changes in position of the periglacial zone means that deposits are often a complex and confusing mixture of materials of glacial, outwash and periglacial origins. This makes distinguishing the separate landscape zones identified in Figure 4.52 difficult, if not impossible, in most lowland areas. Nevertheless what is shown in Figure 4.52 provides a framework for identifying processes and landforms in and around land areas covered by ice.

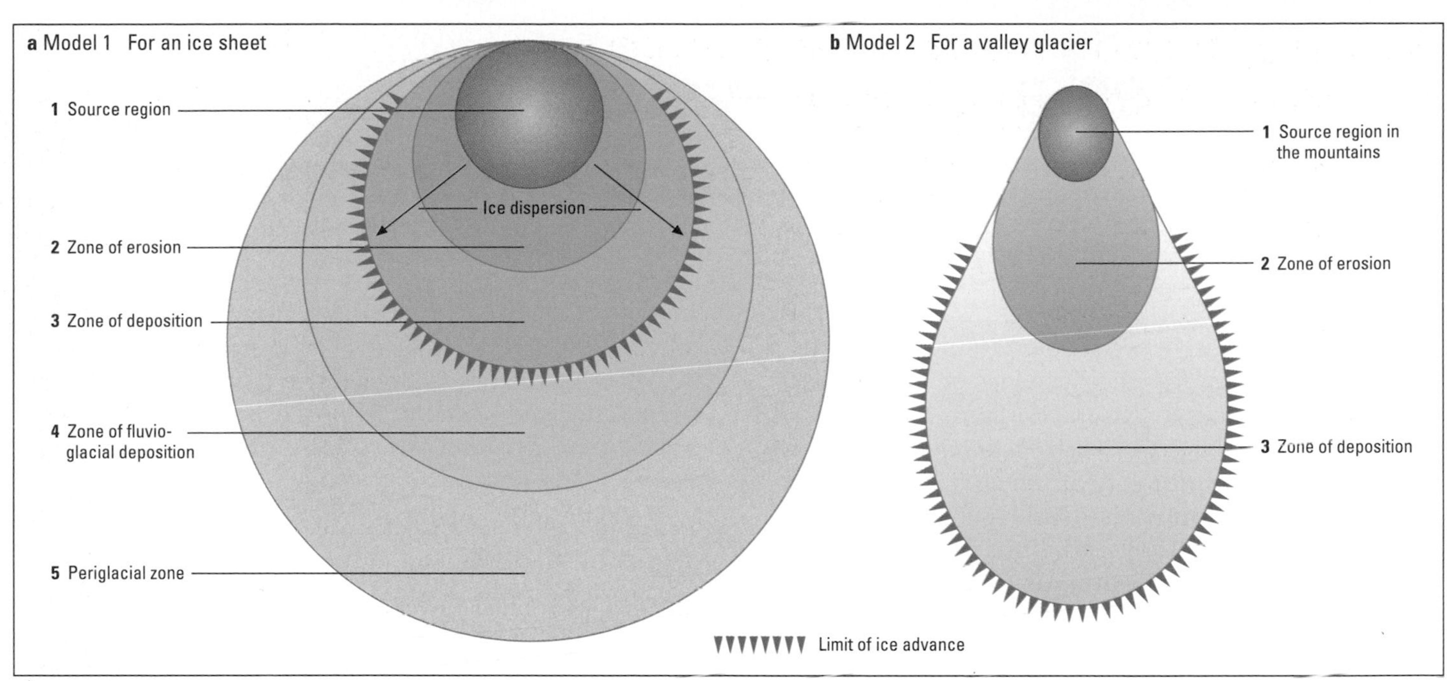

▲ **Figure 4.52** Models of spatial zones within and around land covered by ice

Questions

1 a In what ways is it possible to define the term periglacial?
b Outline the past and present distributions of periglacial regions.

2 a Describe the characteristics of permafrost which enable it to exert such a great effect on landforms in periglacial regions.
b Why is permafrost not a process?
c i Name the different processes which operate within periglacial regions.
ii Give reasons why such a variety of different processes operate here.

3 a What is frost heaving and why does it occur?
b Explain the formation of two landforms for which frost heaving is the main process responsible for their widespread occurrence in periglacial zones.

4 a Describe what Figure 4.51 shows about the impact of the Pleistocene era upon the landscapes of Britain.
b Assess the extent to which the particular effects of the Pleistocene era in Britain are concentrated within certain well-defined areas rather than being more widely distributed.

5 **Investigation**

Using Figure 4.48 as the starting point, research information from five different areas within north-west Europe (outside the British Isles) as examples of ice sheet erosion, mountain valley glacial erosion, ice sheet deposition of till (boulder clay), outwash of sands and gravels, and periglacial processes. Use the following headings:
a Effects on the landscape (with the support of references to named areas)
b Effects on human activities.

6 Below is a list of glacial, fluvio-glacial and periglacial landforms:

arête
cirque/corrie
coombe and head deposits
drumlin
esker
ground moraine/till deposits
hanging valley
horn/pyramidal peak
kame
kame terrace
knock and lochan
lateral moraine
overflow channel/spillway
patterned ground
pingo
proglacial lake floor deposits
roche moutonnée
rock basin
solifluction lobe
tarn lake
terminal moraine
trough end
truncated spur
U-shaped valley

a Draw good-sized versions of the two models in Figure 4.52 and distribute these landforms in the zones where they belong, noting that some occur in zones on both models.
b i Explain why it is possible to identify these different zones in and around glaciated regions.
ii Discuss the advantages and disadvantages of using these two models as an aid to understanding the distribution of landforms in and around areas covered by ice.

7 **Essay**

Discuss the role and relative importance of the presence of water within and around glaciated land areas.

Biomes and ecosystems in cold environments

Although interaction between abiotic and biotic elements is essential for all ecosystems, climate is the most influential element. In the northern hemisphere the tundra biome covers extensive land areas (Figure 4.4 page 122). In the southern hemisphere it is restricted to the rocky fringes of sub-polar islands such as South Georgia and South Orkney, and to the tiny parts of Antarctica that are ice free in summer. This is because the inhabited continents taper and there is only a small amount of land south of 40°. This land is still in warm temperate latitudes, the latitudinal and climatic equivalent of the Mediterranean region in the northern hemisphere. Only South America extends south of 50°. Rocky Cape Horn and the ocean waters around it have fearsome reputations among sailors, despite lying at the same latitude south of the Equator as southern Scotland is north of it. In the southern hemisphere the sea-based ecosystem in the cold waters of the Southern Ocean is of much greater significance than those based on the land.

The tundra biome

Climate is the restricting factor. Only in scrub-covered deserts and semi-deserts is the net primary productivity of a biome as low as or lower than that of the tundra. Average productivity levels are between 50 and 200 grammes/m^2 /year, with the upper end of the range confined either to tundra alpine environments in temperate latitudes, or to milder maritime locations within and near the margins of polar latitudes. Since one of the definitions for a tundra climate is a mean temperature under 10°C during the three warmest months, climate never favours rapid or continuous plant growth. The growing season is less than three months everywhere and in many places considerably less. Climatic data for the Tundra is displayed in Figure 4.7 (page 123).

The characteristic, which distinguishes tundra from most of the other biomes, is the absence of trees. An area where coniferous trees, such as the larch that can withstand bitterly cold winters, cannot grow successfully because of the shortness of the growing season, is tundra. Temperature may be the main controlling factor for being treeless, but two other factors contribute. One is the frequency of strong winds. Vegetation that is not covered by snow (as trees would be) suffers frost damage in winter from strong winds blowing at a time when temperatures are very low. Another factor is the presence of waterlogged soils above the permafrost; over wide areas the depth of free-draining soil needed by the tree roots is insufficient. On mountainsides both in temperate and tropical latitudes similar treeless types of vegetation are found at altitudes above the tree line.

The tundra biome is also characterized by low biological diversity. It is species poor. All plants are slow growing and must complete their life cycles within 30 to 60 days. Few plants reach more than half a metre above the surface. These are ground-huggers spreading low along the surface and making a tight cushion as protection against the wind. Below the surface plants are shallow-rooted to avoid the permafrost. Species of mosses and lichens are plentiful and form a well-defined ground layer. On rock outcrops and boulder-strewn surfaces, where they are the only vegetation able to grow, they represent the first community in a lithosere. Large areas are covered by hardy grasses, sedges and rushes. Heath communities, consisting of low woody shrubs, are restricted to relatively well-drained sites. Common plants are heathers and the Arctic blueberry. Well-drained sites with a favoured aspect (southerly in Arctic regions) are dominated by flowering herbs which form bloom mats creating a mass of colour during the height of summer.

▲ **Figure 4.53** Bloom mats in the tundra

Most flowering plants are perennials; by coming year after year they do not need to start life all over again in spring as annuals must do. They have hardy seeds, armoured in a thick seed case. Well-established shrubs also adopt a low or creeping habit instead of growing upwards to avoid the cold, desiccating winds. Precipitation is low and irregular and water may not be readily available in well-drained locations and under icy conditions. Plants need to protect themselves against physiological drought (no water availability) by reducing their exposure to strong winds. Another way they do this is by having small leaves. In areas where dwarf trees such as birch and willow are present, it suggests that physical conditions, whether local or regional, are more favourable than those found elsewhere. However, the fact that tree tops are shaped by the wind and have only stunted growth suggests that nowhere in the tundra can conditions be described as easy for plant growth.

Another noticeable feature of the tundra biome is how rapidly the vegetation cover changes from place to place. In areas of great physical adversity for plant growth minor local variations in relief, drainage and soils assume great importance (see Information box).

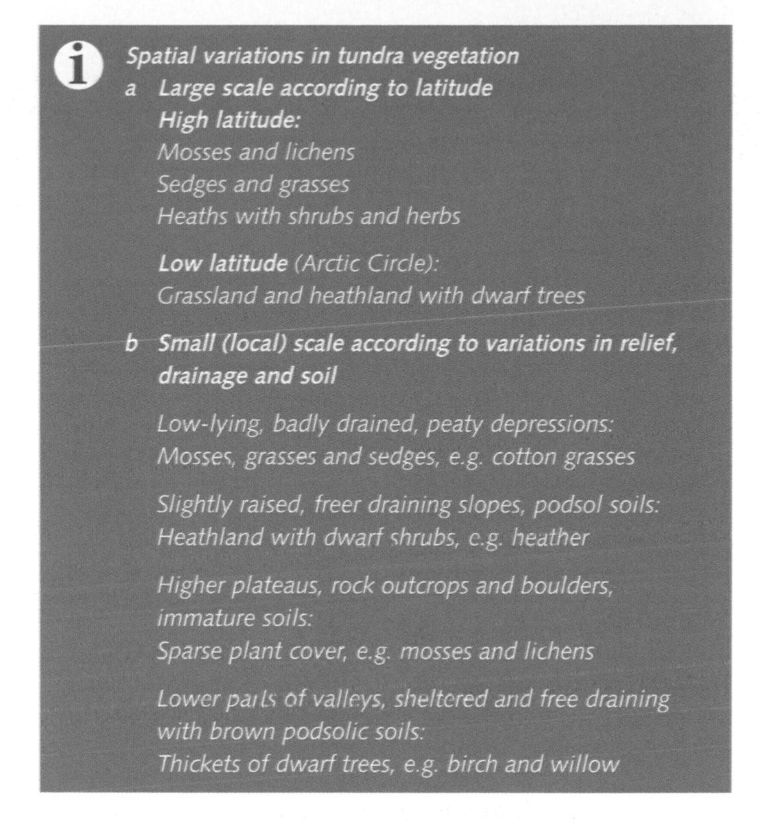

Spatial variations in tundra vegetation

a Large scale according to latitude

High latitude:
Mosses and lichens
Sedges and grasses
Heaths with shrubs and herbs

Low latitude (Arctic Circle):
Grassland and heathland with dwarf trees

b Small (local) scale according to variations in relief, drainage and soil

Low-lying, badly drained, peaty depressions:
Mosses, grasses and sedges, e.g. cotton grasses

Slightly raised, freer draining slopes, podsol soils:
Heathland with dwarf shrubs, e.g. heather

Higher plateaus, rock outcrops and boulders, immature soils:
Sparse plant cover, e.g. mosses and lichens

Lower parts of valleys, sheltered and free draining with brown podsolic soils:
Thickets of dwarf trees, e.g. birch and willow

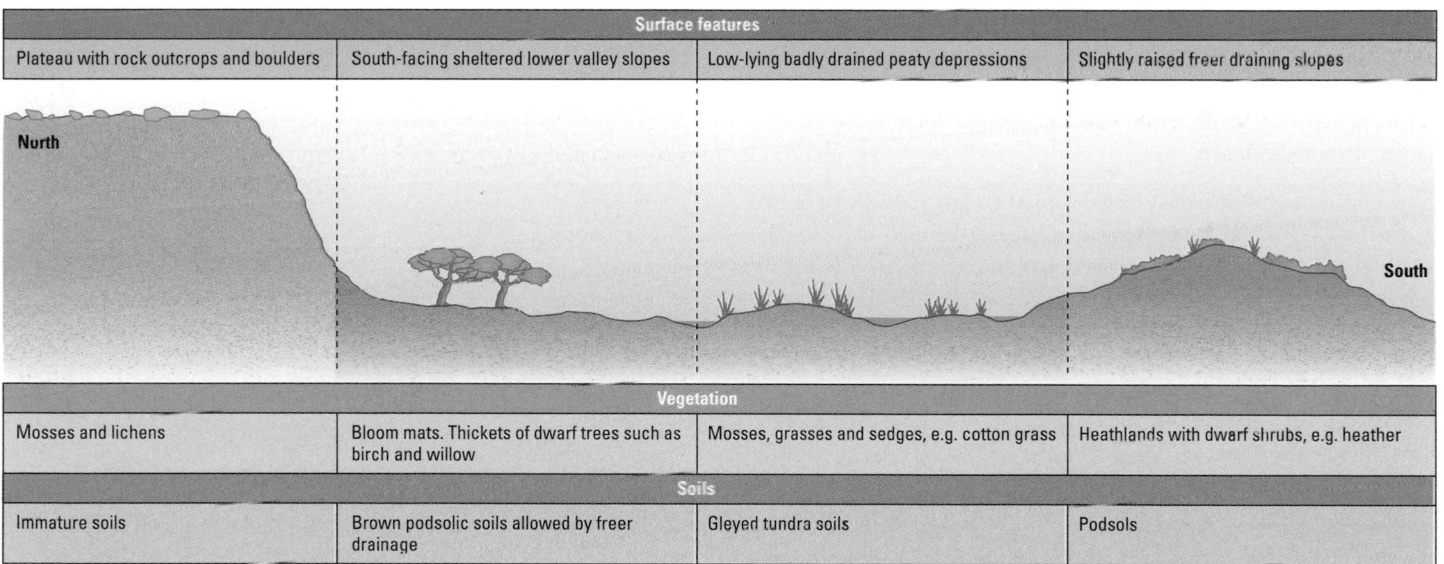

▲ **Figure 4.54** Small scale variations in tundra vegetation

Tundra soils

Most tundra soils are gleyed due to waterlogging. Under waterlogged conditions iron compounds are reduced to their ferrous form (FeO). This is the process of gleying. Ferrous oxides are grey in colour (as opposed to the ferric oxides present in tropical soils which are reddish brown). The main reason why tundra soils are waterlogged is the presence of permafrost. In summer the water released in the active layer cannot drain downwards through the impermeable frozen layer beneath. In addition, evaporation rates are low. Organic matter is limited in amount and what there is decays slowly. Few soil biota (which decompose organic matter) and few soil organisms (which act as mixing agents) can survive the cold and wet soil conditions. As a result the thin surface organic layer consists mainly of acidic peat, which accumulates because the breakdown of plant remains is so slow. Below it, if there is a little free drainage at the top of the profile, the beginnings of horizons of silt loam can be recognized (Figure 4.55). Otherwise the soil is a uniform grey-blue colour as a result of the gleying without any developed horizons until the permafrost is reached. In waterlogged locations it is continuous from the organic layers downwards. The cold and the wet inhibit processes of decomposition that turn dead matter into nutrients. This is a severe limitation for plant growth in the tundra.

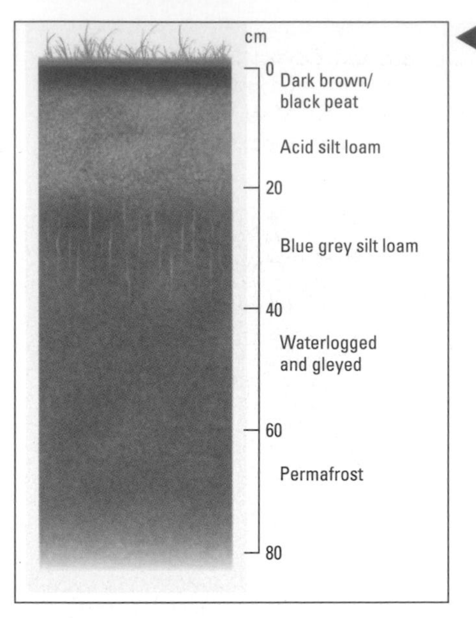

Figure 4.55 Profile of a gleyed tundra soil

The depth at which permafrost begins is a strong factor influencing tundra soils, and in those valleys where the permafrost level is lower and drainage better some horizons in the soil may begin to develop. If water is allowed to drain downwards, minerals and iron compounds are redeposited at a lower level and the soil takes on more of the characteristics of a podsol. On rocky outcrops and boulders, where lichens and mosses are the only pioneering colonizers, soil formation has not proceeded very far. A typical lithosol has a thin organic A horizon resting directly upon the rock below.

The biome's low primary production in turn supports a low number of animal species. The combination of bitter cold and snow-covered surfaces prevents many animals from living and feeding in tundra lands in winter so that there are marked seasonal variations in animal numbers. In summer the large herbivores such as reindeer, caribou and moose return to the tundra from the boreal forests following the thawing snow and reappearance of surface vegetation northwards. The larger herbivores occupy different niches; for example in North America the more numerous caribou feed on lichens and assorted plants and shrubs, whereas the moose are browsers on the bushy areas and branches. Many of the tundra plants, such as the reindeer mosses, have high sugar contents and these large herbivores enjoy summer feasts to increase body weight and build themselves up for survival during the next cold winter. The smaller herbivores, such as hares, lemmings and shrews, remain in the tundra all year, adapting by staying in burrows insulated by the snow cover above them.

Food chains are usually short. The plants make insect and animal life possible. The small herbivores that live closest to the plants themselves are the most numerous. They are the food supply for the small carnivores such as Arctic foxes, wolves, hawks and owls, whose numbers fluctuate greatly from year to year in line with the numbers of lemmings and hares. Top of the food chain in the Arctic are the bears. Polar bears and the great brown bears are the largest flesh-eating animals on Earth. The great brown bears are famous for their sumptuous summer feasts of salmon, taken when the salmon are returning up Alaska's rivers. Previous to this they eat roots and berries showing that the brown bear is a true omnivore.

The Southern Ocean

In broadest terms the Southern Ocean consists of the southern parts of the Atlantic, Indian and Pacific Oceans between latitude 40° south and the continent of Antarctica, where there is little land. The ocean is noted for its westerly gales and strong surface currents. The Antarctic Convergence (between latitudes 50° and 55° south) is the natural boundary between the relatively warm sub-Antarctic surface water to the north and the cold Antarctic surface water to the south. Sea temperatures drop by anything from 3°C in summer to as much as 10°C in winter (Figure 4.56). The sudden meeting of waters of two different temperatures incapacitates or kills much of the plankton and brings it to the surface. Sea birds flock along the convergence for this reason. South of the convergence, there is a dramatic rise in the number of birds.

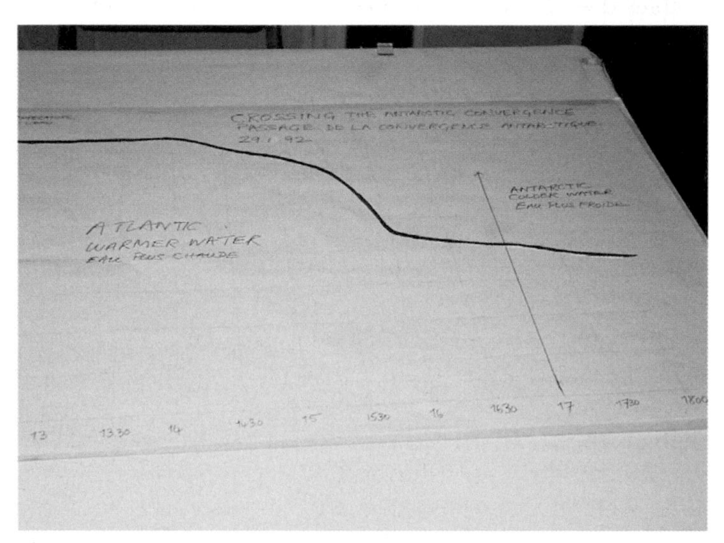

Figure 4.56a Plot of sea temperature changes taken by a cruise ship as it crossed the Antarctic Convergence in late December (mid-summer).

Figure 4.56b The chances of seeing icebergs and whales increase south of the convergence.

Life abounds in the Southern Ocean south of the convergence for three reasons. First the sea water is cold; cold water holds dissolved gases, such as carbon dioxide and oxygen, much better than warm water. Secondly, the sea waters are turbulent; currents upwell from the depths, surface currents are strong and regular storms make the sea surface rough, all of which keep nutrients and minerals in suspension where they can be utilized by the phytoplankton. Thirdly, there is almost continual photosynthesis during the long daylight hours in summer; this cultivates the huge algal blooms which are at the base in the Antarctic food chain. As a result the biological productivity of coastal Antarctic waters, based upon measures of the size of the standing crop of phytoplankton and its yield, is the highest of any waters in the world. Antarctic phytoplankton blooms from October onwards after the surface ice has started to break up and when the sun is permanently above the horizon. It is the primary producer in the Southern Ocean. The second stage in the food chain is the zooplankton of Antarctica. This is relatively diverse in species, but is dominated by the 5cm long shrimp-like krill, which feed directly upon the phytoplankton. Krill often form dense swarms just below the surface, so dense that on occasions the ocean looks pink. This enables their predators to catch them with the minimum of effort. Krill is the major link in the Southern Ocean and Antarctic food chain. It is the direct food supply for millions of fishes, penguins, albatrosses, some seals and the large baleen whales. It is the indirect food supply for all the other aquatic birds and mammals present here. Krill is also the main food supply for squid which are abundant in Antarctic waters. Most of the species of squid are small, under 40cm in length, but these form another link in the food chain as they are extremely important in the diets of the larger fishes and sea birds, seals and the toothed whales.

Figure 4.57
The food chain in the Southern Ocean. Since the destruction of the great whale populations and a reduction in their consumption of krill, the numbers of seabirds and seals have greatly increased. This shows the pivotal position of krill in the food chain.

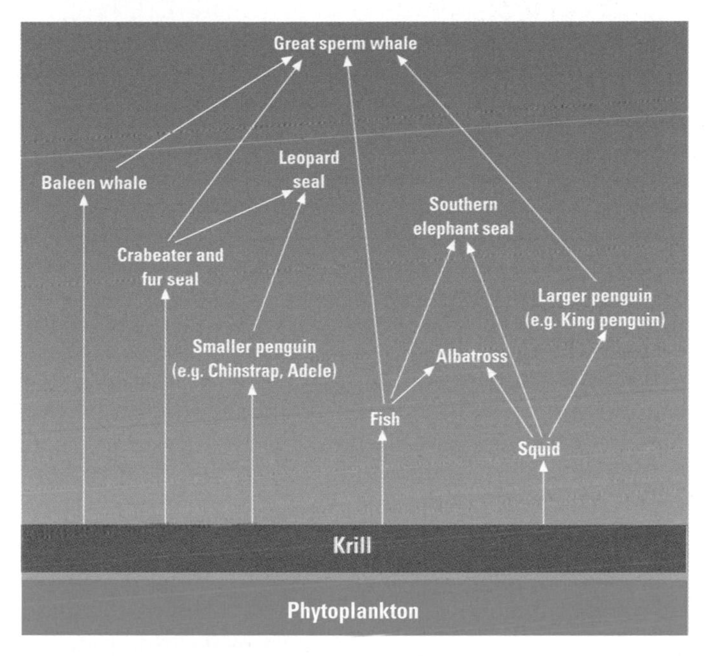

Figure 4.58
The Great Right Whale – or the part of it which most people on cruises see. It was given this name because it was the 'right' whale to hunt – right, because it was a slow-moving species, which made it easy to catch; right, because its body is so rich in oil that it floats even after death.

Whales

Whales are air-breathing mammals which have perfected the ability to live in water over the past 50 to 60 million years. There are two basic types:

a ***Those without teeth (baleen whales)***

Examples: Great right, blue, fin and minke whales.

- *Rows of horny baleen (whalebone) hang down from the roof of the mouth on both sides. As the whale moves through the water it opens its huge jaws and takes in a large quantity of water. The water is squeezed through the rows of baleen plates thereby trapping any small prey animals such as krill or shoals of tiny fish.*
- *These whales feed in the upper layers of the water because their food source, the zooplankton, is dependent on the phytoplankton, which in turn is dependent upon sunlight.*
- *They feed in cold Antarctic waters in summer and breed in warmer temperate waters in winter.*

b ***Those with teeth***

Examples: Great sperm and killer whales

- *They eat the larger creatures – squid, fish, birds, seals and other whales.*
- *They dive to great depths and use sonar systems which help them to locate and capture their prey. The killer whale is the most predaceous favouring warm-blooded prey, even including other whales when attacking in a group.*
- *This is the less numerous group in the Southern Ocean.*

Birds are the most famous animal inhabitants of Antarctica. Species diversity is very low; out of well over 8,000 bird species in the world, only 43 are regularly present south of the Convergence. However, in summer they breed in their millions on the Antarctic peninsula and islands such as South Georgia (Figure 4.1). Penguins, albatrosses and petrels are dominant among the different species present. Penguins spend most of their lives at sea until they come ashore to nest in enormous colonies (Figure 4.57). Total numbers nesting in the Antarctic region are estimated at 100 million. The smaller species such as Chinstrap and Adele penguins feed mostly on krill. The larger species such as King penguins feed primarily on squid. Albatrosses are perfect flying machines and spend most of their lives in the air; they mostly feed on squid, small fishes and krill, which they catch by landing on the surface and dipping their heads underwater. The Antarctic fur seal is the smallest of the region's seals and is only found south of the convergence because it feeds almost exclusively on krill. The largest is the southern elephant seal; the male grows up to six metres long and can weigh as much as four tonnes (Figure 4.65, page 162). Squid accounts for about three-quarters of their food intake, the rest being made up of mainly fish. The seal with the most misleading name is the one which is most abundant, the crabeater seal, which lives entirely on krill. However, the leopard seal does live up to its name. It is a great predator and the only species of Antarctic seal that regularly eats warm-blooded prey. Penguins are its favourite menu choice.

Summary

The Southern Ocean is biologically at its most productive where it interfaces with the world's least biologically productive land surface, Antarctica. The contrast is not as dramatic in the Arctic because greater plant cover supports more terrestrial life. The cold waters of the Arctic are also rich in plankton, especially where ocean currents are present; a varied marine life of fish, seals and whales is supported, of which the shoals of cod are the most commercially valuable. However, there is no northern equivalent to the krill which supports such vast numbers of aquatic creatures in the Southern Ocean.

Both the Arctic tundra and Antarctica are examples of fragile environments. Plants in the tundra and zooplankton and fish in Antarctic waters grow slowly because of the cold. Even in June in the Arctic a sudden frost can injure or kill many seed-producing flowers. Some varieties of lichen upon which caribou feed grow at a rate of under 2mm per year. They obviously cannot tolerate heavy grazing; after being grazed it takes them between 50 and 100 years to regenerate. The caribou have adapted to this by their ceaseless migration. In the few places where rocks outcrop in Antarctica, the combined effects of low temperatures, frost action (which all the time produces more rock debris), strong winds and surface meltwater streams make it difficult for an immature soil to become stabilized. As a result much of the soil remains poor and without humus, discouraging attempts by the simplest plants to colonize it. Even in the most favoured areas on the Antarctic peninsula no truly mature organic soils have developed and nothing more than algae, lichens and mosses grow. These struggle to grow, so much so that a human foot on a lichen-covered rock may undo the progress achieved by a hundred years or more of growth. The upper biological limit of vegetation development in Antarctica is two species of flowering plant. The sparsity, small biomass and slow growth of plants preclude the existence of herbaceous animals. The only terrestrial herbivores to be found are tiny insects and mites which mainly feed on algae, fungi and rotting plant material.

Questions

1 a Describe the main characteristics of a tundra climate from Figure 4.7.
b Explain the relationships in the tundra between natural vegetation and
i climate
ii soils
iii local variations in relief and drainage.
c i Draw a food chain for Arctic tundra.
ii Why is it an example of a short food chain?

2 a Explain the main features of the Southern Ocean's food chain.
b Give reasons why aquatic life is plentiful and terrestrial life almost non-existent in the polar lands of the southern hemisphere.

3 a What do you understand by the concept of a fragile environment?
b What makes polar environments a good example?
c Investigation

Investigate another example of a fragile environment and discuss why it is classified in this way.

4 a Define what is meant by the snow line and the tree line.
b In what ways is each one significant for
i the operation of geomorphological processes
ii vegetation characteristics.

The nature and impact of human activities

Comparison of polar regions

Arctic	*Antarctic*
• *Ocean surrounded by land*	• *Continent surrounded by ocean*
• *Life forms:*	• *Life forms:*
2,000 species of lichens	*400 species of lichens*
500 species of mosses	*75 species of mosses*
900 species of flowering plants.	*2 species of flowering plants*
• *More than 2 million people live north of the Arctic Circle*	• *No permanent residents*

Figure 4.59
Port Lockroy, Antarctica, a natural harbour set amidst scenic beauty

The Arctic region

Arctic lands had land links to the inhabited world, although there was still the ocean divide between 'Old' and 'New' Worlds, which was probably first bridged by the Vikings. The indigenous populations developed in separate but similar ways. Both the Inuit in North America and the Lapps in Europe were hunters and fishers, but the Inuit lived mainly in or near the coast, depending on seals, while the Lapps in northern Europe followed the annual pattern of migration of the great herds of wild reindeer.

The Inuit survived the rigours of the Arctic by using the animal resources to the utmost. Their main activity was hunting seals, which provided meat, oil and skins. They lived in scattered groups along the Arctic coast. They needed to be mobile to ensure adequate food supplies at all times of the year. Sledges pulled by dog teams were used over the pack ice; kayaks or large boats were used over water. Larger groups occasionally hunted polar bears and whales. Tents, used in summer, were made of animal skins; clothes were made out of animal fur and skins. They were totally dependent upon what the environment provided. Numbers were always small in relation to the size of land area available to each group so that the environment was little disturbed. While the Inuit had less interest in caribou, the Lapps depended upon its 'Old World' equivalent, the reindeer. The Lapp families followed the seasonal movements of the herds of wild reindeer that provided them with all the food and materials they needed, living in tents. Fishing was used to supplement and vary the diet. The deer spent the winter in the coniferous forests living on mosses and tree bark. In spring they migrated north into the treeless lands of the tundra.

Total self-sufficiency for many centuries meant that both Inuits and Lapps could only survive by being in tune with their environments. Nature was the provider of all that they had and needed. Both groups of people developed sustainable ways of living. They were skilled operators who had adapted to survival in one of the world's most difficult natural environments. To ensure continued survival the skills of hunting and fishing needed to be passed down from one generation to the next.

In broader terms, however, indigenous groups are usually placed within stage one in the demographic transition model. High birth rates are needed to allow for low life expectancies and the occasional devastating effects of natural hazards. Death rates fluctuate in response to hunting successes and availability of food supplies. The group only continues to thrive provided that the balance between number of people and availability of food is maintained; otherwise overpopulation occurs accompanied by Malthusian consequences. Being cut off from the outside world meant that knowledge of new inventions and new techniques never reached them. They lived sustainably but according to historical traditions, which meant that any changes were slow, if indeed any occurred. Contacts from outside, at first occasional and then regular, progressively reduced the chances for survival of the traditional ways. The issue today is how much of the traditional culture can be saved before it is destroyed forever. The majority of Lapps, for example, are now townsfolk with urban jobs. Only a few thousand retain the connection with the reindeer, although many of these live in permanent settlements and some undertake paid work in farming, forestry, fishing and occasionally in related manufacturing industries.

Contact with some Inuit groups had already begun by 1700. The Hudson Bay Company had been founded and was trading (as its name suggests) in the Arctic areas of eastern Canada. The fur trade was the attraction. Contacts with Inuits gradually increased as more trading posts were established in the Canadian Northland; during the twentieth century the pace of change speeded up.

Resource exploitation by outsiders

Continuous settlement in an area is usually agriculturally inspired. In most areas within polar environments agriculture is not a feasible option. All of the world's sparsely populated natural environments are characterized by nucleated settlement. In between the vast areas of nothingness occasional pockets or concentrations of people exist – for example around mineral deposits, along routes or at strategic locations. Here, the factor responsible for an area's unattractiveness to people, whether too cold, too dry, too steep or too rocky, is immaterial; something with people-pulling power must exist. Discover gold, as happened in the Klondike in the 1890s, and people flock there in their thousands. How difficult it is to get there, or how unpleasant it is living and working there, are irrelevant. The chance of 'getting rich quick' seems to supersede all other considerations.

Exploitation of natural resources is one prime reason why settlers have been and are still drawn into cold polar environments. Nineteenth-century gold rushes brought in haphazard prospectors. In the twentieth century planned investments by large companies and governments both seeking to exploit the great mineral wealth of Arctic regions were more important. The old hard rocks of the Canadian, Baltic and Siberian shields are locally heavily mineralized. There are significant deposits of iron-ore, nickel, copper, lead, zinc and uranium, many of them commercially viable despite remote locations and the harsh operating conditions. The mineral with greatest pulling power today is oil; it has been called 'black gold'. Discover petroleum in commercial quantities and the trans-national oil companies will develop the technology (if it does not already exist) and come up with the money to extract it.

The classic illustration of this was the discovery in 1968 of great quantities of oil and gas beneath Alaska's North Slope overlooking Prudhoe Bay. The problem for the oil companies was that the deposits were on the wrong side of Alaska – north of the Arctic Circle and over 1,000km away from the ice-free coasts on the southern side of Alaska. Another problem for them was the strength of the environmental lobby, which by the 1960s had become quite a substantial force in the United States. Conservationists argued that the tundra regions should be left alone. (Some protesters travelled from California to Alaska in private jets to place their objections, apparently unaware of the hypocrisy involved in doing this.) The delay until 1974 in beginning construction did reflect real concerns and uncertainties about the pipeline's design, route and ecological impact, which led to a wide-ranging debate about environmental and social costs of major developments in relation to potential damage to the environment. The usual oil industry construction technique of burying the pipeline in a trench was not possible as hot oil and a buried pipe would melt the permafrost. The overriding argument that was always going to win the day was that USA oil demand was great and increasing. It would supply west coast states such as California where it was much needed in the car-orientated society, and it would reduce dependence upon supplies from the politically unstable Middle East. After all the Alaskan oilfield is the biggest that the USA possesses. The conservation debate ensured that the oil companies consulted an army of engineers and scientists and that they were not allowed to take the cheapest option. As in the Shetland Islands in the UK, royalty revenues given to the Alaskan State government have boosted service provision and general development in a remote state.

In some polar regions maritime resources are the main attraction. Economic activity in the Southern Ocean has been entirely maritime (pages 161–163, the Antarctic region). In countries such as Iceland and Norway although only a small percentage of the workforce is employed in fishing, fish make an enormous contribution to their national economies, to the point where there is some concern about over-dependence on one commodity in Iceland (see the case study page 167). Salmon fisheries line the west coast of North America from Alaska south to

British Columbia. Although outside the polar regions, one of the world's great fishing grounds on the Grand Banks off Newfoundland, noted for its cod and herring, depends for its continued existence upon the cold water and plankton supplies transported from the Arctic by the Labrador ocean current.

The other powerful, not to say unstoppable, factor favouring occupation of otherwise empty polar lands is strategic. Alaska was in the vanguard for this as well. During the Second World War Japanese troops landed on the outermost Aleutian Islands, which almost form a land bridge to Asia. The invasion of the mainland of North America seemed possible. The hasty response was for the United States army to build the Alaska Highway running north west from Dawson Creek in Canada to Fairbanks in Alaska. It was used to carry heavy weapons to protect Alaska against the threat of invasion. After the war, the rise of the Soviet Union as a military power and the Cold War so increased the strategic significance of Alaska that directly employed military personnel made up one quarter of Alaska's population (not including supporting civilians). This is a prime example of settlement being affected by a geo-political consideration. The most obvious geographical (spatial) expressions of this are the transport links (roads and airports), radar stations and early warning systems. The

Alaska: construction of the oil pipeline

Case Study

Problems which needed to be taken into account in construction:

- permafrost – thick and continuous in the north; discontinuous and isolated in the south. A pipe laid on or above the surface would cause melting, movement of the surface layer, pipe fracture and oil spillage.
- fragile tundra ecosystems – vulnerable to disruption. Any oil spillage could not seep away because of the permafrost and would cause immediate and long-term damage to the fauna and flora. Even the tracks of construction vehicles are visible for many years across tundra vegetation.
- active faults and a real earthquake risk – Alaska has already experienced some of the world's strongest earthquakes, notably the 8.5 at Anchorage in 1964.

Special construction features:

- when on the surface, the oil pipeline is kept above the ground by deep supports that are frozen into the permafrost. The steel pipe is insulated to keep the oil warm and flowing inside but also to prevent any heat from escaping. It is only fixed to the ground at intervals to allow adjustments for ground heaving. It follows a zig-zag line which allows the pipe to expand and contract to adjust to wide temperature ranges between summer and winter and to seismic shocks.
- when underground (mainly in places where it would have blocked the caribou migration routes), the pipe is insulated in a jacket and refrigerated brine is pumped through smaller pipes in the trench to maintain the permafrost.

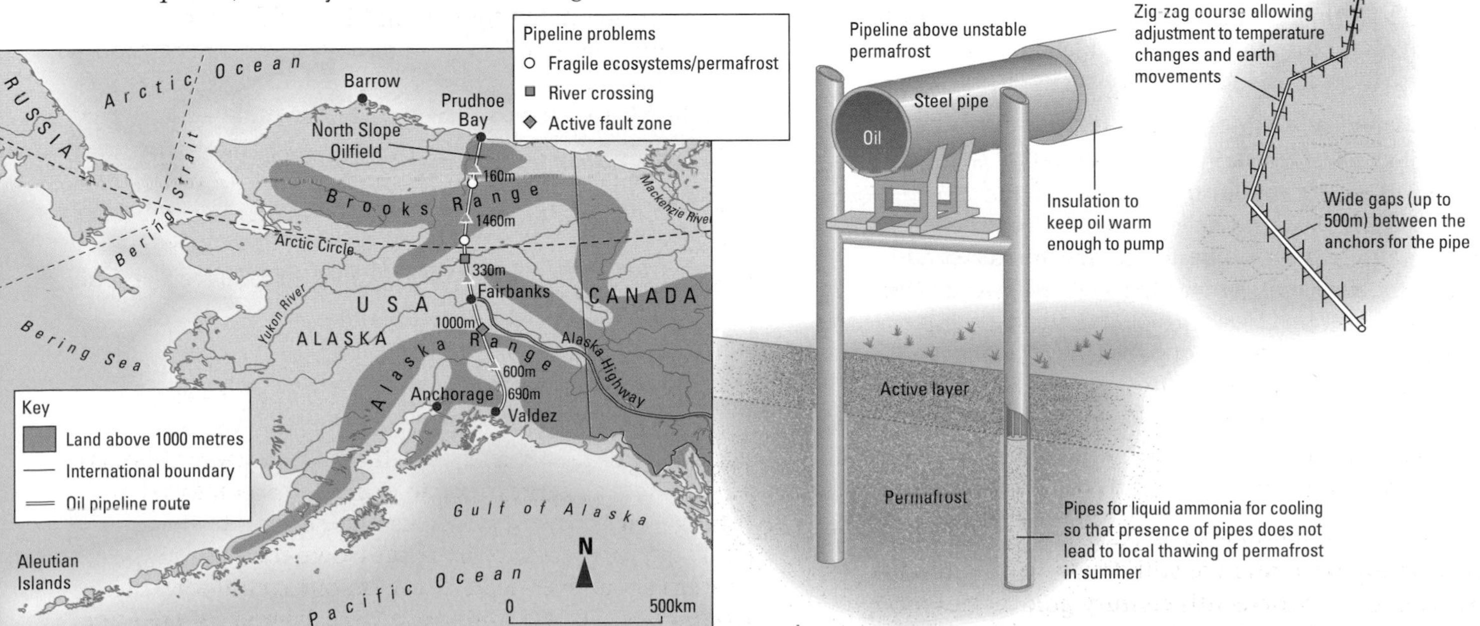

▲ **Figure 4.60** The Alaskan pipeline

▲ **Figure 4.61** Construction problems and their solutions for building the pipeline stations were built to look out over the eastern back door of the USSR. Yet when Alaska was bought from the Russians in 1867 for just over seven million dollars the deal was highly criticized in the USA. What was at that time considered a lot to pay for bare mountains, glaciers and permafrost turned out to be one of the bargain buys of all time. Despite the end of the Cold War, the surveillance of the Arctic Ocean continues. There are facilities in Canada and Europe. NATO maintains a large base at Keflavik airport in Iceland, which is a significant source of invisible income for a country of less than 300,000 people. It seems amazing that strategic considerations should have affected the almost empty south of the world, but conflicting territorial claims around the edges of the region led to the Falklands conflict and subsequent increased military presence.

Exploiting natural resources tends to create work opportunities only in the primary sector. The minimum amount of processing is undertaken before the natural products are taken to be refined and processed in areas or countries where they are to be consumed. In the case of many minerals, such as the oil from Alaska, local processing is nil. The cheapest and easiest option is to transport the minerals in a crude state by rail, ship or pipeline. In some of the more maritime land locations, such as in Norway and Iceland, a proportion of the great HEP potential has been realized, but the electricity is rarely consumed at source. Instead it is sent by wire to populated areas. In contrast, the seals and whales that were once caught in the Southern Ocean were perishable and because of distance separation between source and markets in Europe and North America, local processing was essential. This led to whaling stations in South Georgia and on the Antarctic peninsula (page 162). In military inspired settlements it is largely tertiary sector work, which leads to greater urban living. Life at home in warmer latitudes is replicated as closely as possible in polar lands. Military considerations have certainly opened up access to Alaska and the Canadian Northlands, but they have led to little permanent settlement outside the major bases. They are sustained from outside and not by the resources of the local area.

Thus there is a key difference. The indigenous peoples survived and lived sustainably because they adapted their economies to the environment, whereas outsiders impose their style of living and needs upon the environment. This creates particular difficulties in environments where permafrost is present. As was highlighted by the construction of the Alaskan pipeline, there are major problems with permafrost engineering. Placing even a small unheated building on permafrost changes the radiation balance at the surface (Figure 4.61). Heated buildings cause worse problems leading to tilt and sometimes collapse. Roads are subject to heaving during freezing and collapse during thawing breaking up the surface. The Alaska Highway was built under wartime pressures without proper site surveys; also permafrost engineering was not as well understood in the 1940s. Maintenance costs have been high ever since its construction.

Tourism

The Arctic is surrounded by the inhabited, and in places, densely populated continents. It is an important source of food from the sea, petroleum and minerals. Another activity is also increasing – tourism. As personal wealth and length of leisure time increase, people are seeking out new, more exotic locations; the wild places in polar lands are being considered more and more seriously as tourist destinations. Many visitors to Alaska, Greenland and northern Norway and Spitzbergen are ship based. Coastal areas have a share of the spectacular scenery, as well as some of the largest concentrations of wildlife, and cruising is a more comfortable and luxurious way to visit polar regions than overland travel. Land tourism is significant in some areas, for example in Iceland, where geothermal and volcanic attractions add to the wilderness attractions of the tundra, mountains and glaciers (page 117).

▲ **Figure 4.62**
The Trans-Alaskan oil pipeline

Questions

1 Give reasons why indigenous cultures are soon destroyed after the settlement and establishment of commercial activities by people from outside.

2 a Describe the primary activities undertaken in the polar zone around the Arctic.
  b Account for their dominance in this zone.
  c Explain some of the advantages and disadvantages of primary activities as the basis for settlement and development in polar regions.

The Antarctic region

During his second voyage of discovery (1772–75) Captain Cook discovered not only South Georgia and neighbouring islands, but also the wealth of fur seals and seals. News of this wealth spurred the new era of exploration into Antarctic waters, in which sealers became the explorers of the far south. Within a few years of discovery, 30 sealing vessels of British, American and Russian origins were operating in and around South Georgia, taking more than one million skins a year. By 1800 the fur seals of South Georgia were wiped out and sealers began their search for new islands harbouring colonies of fur seals. When the South Shetland Islands were discovered by chance in 1819, boats pounced upon them. In the first year there were 40 vessels; in the second season this had risen to 90 boats working there. By the end of the third season, more than 320,000 seal skins and 940 tons of seal oil had been taken from the South Shetland Islands. For all practical purposes, the fur seal populations had been worked out there. This was an example of exploitation without any thought for the future. It set the precedent for the predatory exploitation of the southern polar region, which has occurred ever since.

After 1840 sealers were replaced by whalers. Whales and elephant seals were taken primarily for their oil. Right whales were killed only for their oil and baleen (whale bone); the larger blue whales provided not only oil, but also great quantities of meat, bone meal and other by-products. In the next one hundred years whale populations were reduced to a tiny proportion of their original numbers. Although some people had begun to protest against the slaughtering of whales in the early twentieth century, there was no real control or means of implementing conservation measures until the International Whaling Convention was set up in 1946. The international regulation came too late and the whale populations in Antarctica remain severely depleted, especially those of the larger blue and fin whales, which were of greatest commercial importance. At its peak whaling was a hugely profitable business. Grytviken on South Georgia was the first shore-based whaling station to be established in the Antarctic region in 1904. It was set up by Norwegians. In its heyday one large fin whale was being processed each hour of the 24 hours in the day in summer when 300 men worked there. The range of products increased as regulations insisted that more of the carcass was used and these included oil, meat meal, bone meal, meat extract and, in later years, frozen whale meat. Whaling ended at Grytviken in 1965 simply because whale stocks had become exhausted and it was no longer commercially viable.

As in isolated locations everywhere, as soon as activity ceases everything is abandoned. The huge profits are never used in clearing up. Grytviken and the two other whaling stations on South Georgia – Stromness and Leith (whose names betray the origins of the people working there) are outdoor museums to a discontinued

▲ **Figure 4.63**
The location of Grytviken whaler's station. The rotting tanks are where the whale oil was stored. The non-military resident population in 2000 is about five. Up to 100 tourists (in the red coats) per ship can do no more than breathe temporary life back into the place for a few hours.

▲ **Figure 4.64** Decaying buildings in Stromness

primary activity and its associated processing, which once employed up to 1,000 men on land each summer and many more in whalers at sea. The buildings are left to fall into rack and ruin, just as in ghost towns abandoned by miners in deserts. In Stromness new inhabitants are taking over, mainly seals (Figure 4.65). Only a handful (literally) of civilians live in Grytviken today. As a consequence of the Falklands conflict the British military garrison was strengthened; it is serviced from the Falkland Islands, although these are two days' sailing time away. Some tourist cruise ships call in each summer, and landing charges have contributed towards renovation work.

▲ **Figure 4.65** Male elephant seal, one of today's locals in Stromness. Fancy your chances of entry? It only weighs about three tonnes.

The exploitation of natural resources in the region did not end with whaling. Fish were the next target. In 1967 the Soviet fishing fleet began commercial operations for fin fish around the Antarctic peninsula and sub-Antarctic islands. In the early years massive quantities of Antarctic rock cod were caught, but now catches are low and the focus has had to switch to other commercially less attractive types of fish. What soon became obvious was that the large catches represented the removal of accumulated stocks when, in fact, only a relatively small catch was sustainable. The long line hooks used in fishing often snare albatrosses (Figure 4.67). Recently both Russia and Japan have begun large-scale krill fishing. Krill has a high protein content, but needs immediate processing. In Russia the krill harvest is used primarily for animal feed and for mixing with other meats to produce sausages and fish balls. In Japan it is sold as flavouring, soup mixes, paste and a drink.

▲ **Figure 4.66** The garrison building behind the landing area at the entrance to Grytviken harbour

However, there is a clear need to determine how much krill can safely be taken by humans without causing adverse effects on the fragile ecosystem that it supports.

▲ **Figure 4.67** Russian trawler fishing south of the Antarctic Convergence, surrounded by albatrosses. So high is the mortality rate on fish hooks that albatrosses may soon become an endangered species.

▲ **Figure 4.68a** Cruise ships are the main means of access for tourists to both Antarctica and Alaska

The most recent Antarctic 'invaders' are tourists. The first organized tourist cruise was in 1964 and now about 10,000 people visit this ultimate tourist destination each year. Landings are made by inflatable Zodiacs and visitor movements among the penguin colonies are closely controlled. The ship operators abide by a code drawn up by IAATO (International Association of Antarctic Tour Operators) with its strict bylaws and codes of conduct with the purpose of ensuring safe, responsible and environmentally sensitive tourism in the fragile ecosystem of Antarctica. The enormous penguin colonies are the prime attraction, although on clear days the scenery is stunning.

▲ **Figure 4.68b** View from the base in the opposite direction. The whale bone is a reminder of a past human activity.

Questions

1. Draw a timeline, or make a time chart, summarizing changing human activities in the Antarctic region.
2. Evaluate the extent to which human activities have become less predatory with time.

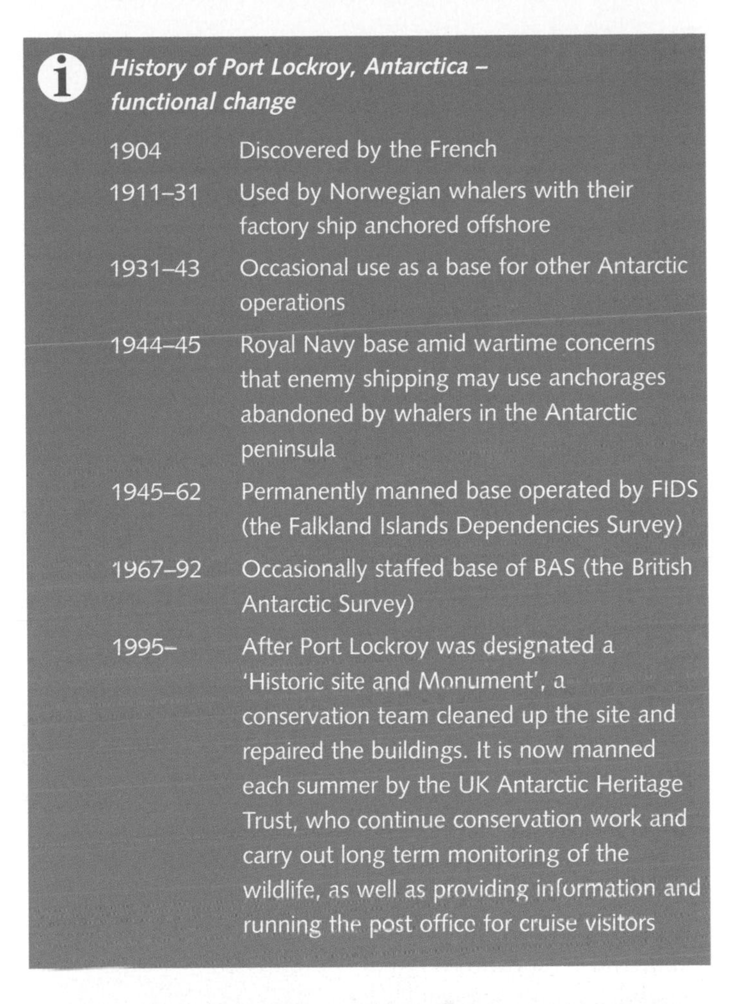

History of Port Lockroy, Antarctica – functional change

1904	Discovered by the French
1911–31	Used by Norwegian whalers with their factory ship anchored offshore
1931–43	Occasional use as a base for other Antarctic operations
1944–45	Royal Navy base amid wartime concerns that enemy shipping may use anchorages abandoned by whalers in the Antarctic peninsula
1945–62	Permanently manned base operated by FIDS (the Falkland Islands Dependencies Survey)
1967–92	Occasionally staffed base of BAS (the British Antarctic Survey)
1995–	After Port Lockroy was designated a 'Historic site and Monument', a conservation team cleaned up the site and repaired the buildings. It is now manned each summer by the UK Antarctic Heritage Trust, who continue conservation work and carry out long term monitoring of the wildlife, as well as providing information and running the post office for cruise visitors

▲ **Figure 4.68c** The now repaired former British base, with tourists (who stay for about two hours) and Gentoo penguins (who stay for breeding in summer)

The Alpine regions

For human activities in the Alpine regions of Europe, physical factors are more benign than those in polar regions. Although altitude and continental effect give cold winters, the height of the sun and continental effect give warm and locally hot summers. Even the cold winters, however, are an asset for the many centres of winter sports in France, Switzerland, Austria and Italy. Hot summers, on the other hand, with mean temperatures up to 20°C on valley floors and south-facing slopes, allow a wide variety of temperate crops to be grown, not only cereals and roots, but also many types of fruits, including vines. However, traditional farming practices throughout Alpine regions are dominated by pastoral farming, with a particular emphasis upon dairy cattle. Tradition had it that the animals from the villages were driven up with some ceremony in early summer to high pastures on the alps (high level benches and flatter areas) to use the rich pastures exposed by the retreating snow line. Freed from grazing animals, the lowland pastures were used for hay, stored for feeding animals indoors on farms in the valleys during the cold winter. Like long-established traditions everywhere, this seasonal migration of animals, known as transhumance, is in decline as the more remote of the high alpine pastures are abandoned and younger generations show less interest in farming and become more urbanized.

Farming led to a substantial processing industry. Nestlé, the chocolate and milk products multi-national, is a Swiss company. Cheeses such as Gruyere are marketed outside their Alpine areas of origin. Plentiful opportunities for generating HEP from the glacially created lakes and fast-flowing rivers have been harnessed to supply power to factories, homes and railways. Tourism has replaced farming as a more profitable and more reliable source of income for many Alpine communities. The infrastructure of mountain railways, cable cars and chair lifts used by skiers in winter also allows summer visitors to reach into the mountains, so that in many Alpine areas tourism is a year-round activity. The Alps are surrounded by well populated and affluent countries without the same natural conditions for winter sports. This leads us into another factor, which helps to explain the wealth of Alpine countries such as Switzerland and Austria – position. Alpine countries lie in a cockpit position in the middle of Europe on through routes between Mediterranean lands and northern Europe, along which ideas and goods have passed for thousands of years stimulating new development and changes. As elsewhere, not everyone is happy with the loss of old traditions; new developments bring new problems such as air pollution from industry and traffic and erosion of mountainsides from skiing. Increased income and wealth, however, are powerful palliatives.

▲ **Figure 4.69** Summer pastures on the high alps

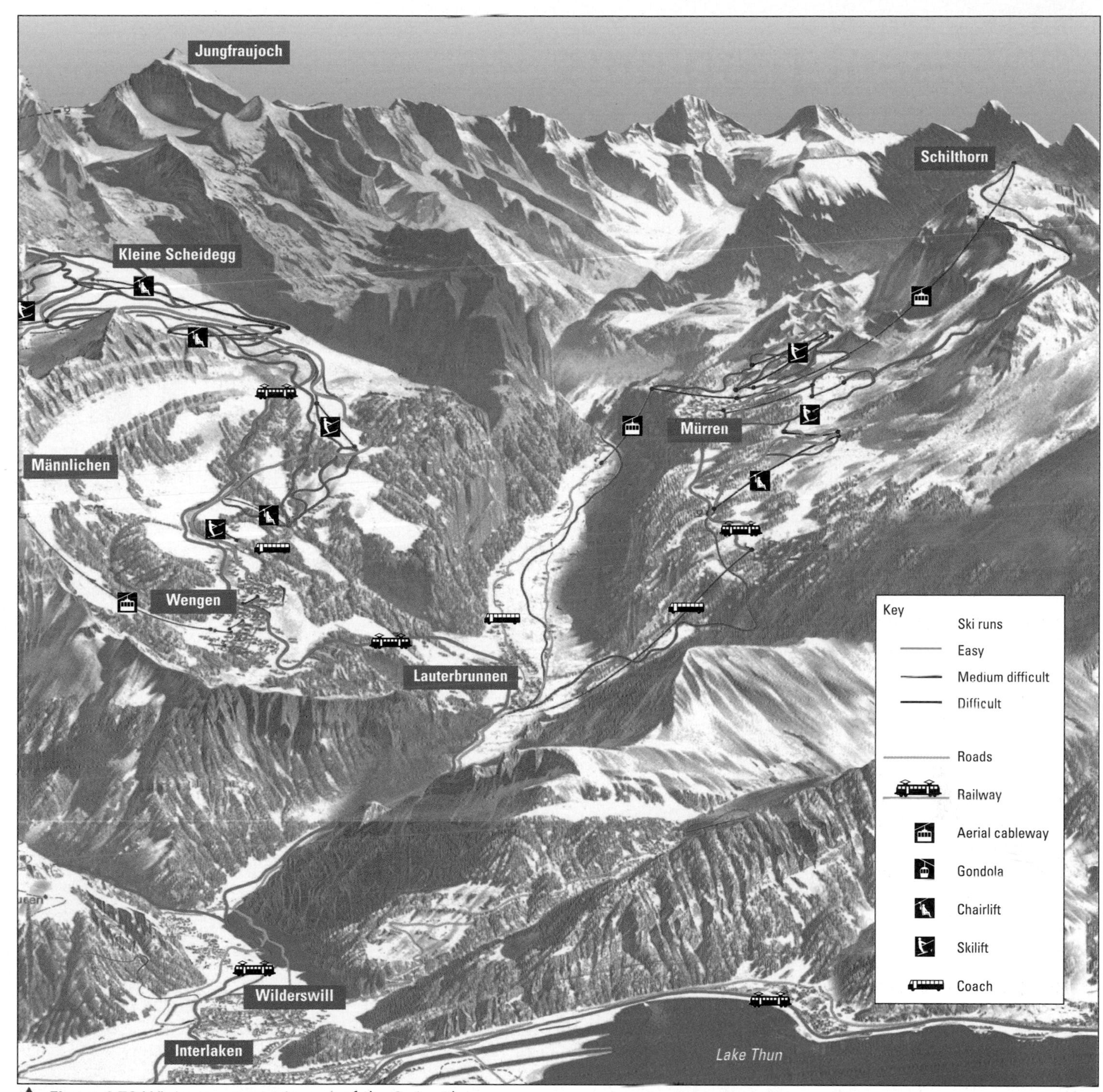

▲ **Figure 4.70** Winter panorama in part of the Swiss Alps

Questions

1 Study Figure 4.70.

- **a** State the locations for the two main areas with ski runs and describe what is similar about them.
- **b** Outline the nature of the infrastructure which is supporting the skiing.
- **c** Explain the ways in which physical conditions are favourable for the provision of
  - **i** large numbers of ski runs of varying degrees of difficulty
  - **ii** transport links to the ski resorts.

2 Investigation

Country	Location	GDP per head (US$ mid-1990s)	Estimated population (m.) 1960	2000
Switzerland	The Alps	24,967	5	7
Nepal	The Himalayas	1,137	10	25

Why is there such an enormous difference in wealth between two mountainous countries with cold environments?

Present problems and future issues

Much of the Arctic region remains a wilderness; the wilderness zones of Canada and Russia, some of the world's largest, are mainly polar lands. Virtually the whole of Greenland and Antarctica are wilderness. Wilderness is defined as undeveloped land still primarily shaped by the forces of nature. It is land without permanent human settlement. Only about one third of the world's land surface can now be classified as being free from domination by people. Outside polar regions other wilderness regions are mainly desert, mountain and rainforest.

The issues for conservation and development are somewhat different between Arctic and Antarctic regions. The remoteness and inhospitability of Antarctica has allowed a pristine environment and very fragile ecosystem to endure to this day. The hope is that the incredible wilderness that is Antarctica may be saved from humankind's relentless encroachment, which has already changed certain places within the Arctic where the threat to the environment from human activities is more keenly felt. There is also the issue of change and damage to local cultures (Figure 4.72). This, of course, does not apply in southern polar lands.

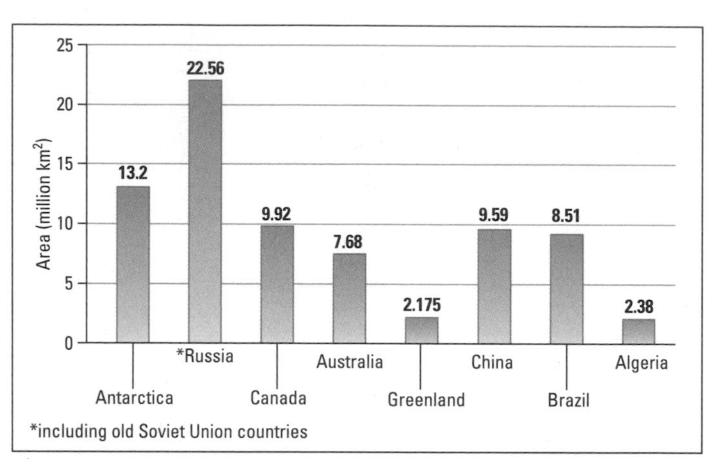

▲ **Figure 4.71** Countries with the largest areas of wilderness

▲ **Figure 4.73** Nunavut, the new Canadian Territory

Canada – homeland for the Inuit

A huge self-governing Arctic Inuit territory came into being in 1999. Now begins the tricky job of getting it to work.

It is an unavoidable truth these days that ethnic self-determination can stir violent passions. The deal for self-government took more than twenty years to negotiate and ended in a compromise. Inuit leaders surrendered rights to some of their traditional land in exchange for a degree of autonomy no greater than that of the other Canadian territories from which Nunavut split. The gains are notable. The first subdivision of Canada's map in 50 years. The first experiment in native self-government in Canada.

The architects of the new territory are striving to make a break with the past. It needs doing: the territory's 22,000 Inuit residents are burdened with Canada's highest levels of youth unemployment and imprisonment. Suicide rates are six times the national average. "What will make the new administration different will be the people occupying the positions of power," says John Amagoalik, one of the long time agitators for self-government. "They are from our own culture. They understand our language and history." His greatest fear now that Nunavut was a reality? "That none of the social indicators will change."

Ethnic identity is the soul of the new regime. Fifteen of the nineteen legislators are Inuit and decisions will be reached in the traditional Inuit way by consensus. Hunting, which is still a cherished activity, is to be permitted without a licence. The government is likely to challenge a new federal gun control law requiring registration of all shotguns – known locally as the Inuit shopping cart. The biggest target of reform is the justice system. Most Inuit tell stories of abuse at the hands of white courts and police officers. They want less emphasis on jails and more on remedial programmes, sending prisoners out to hunt and fish.

Most funding will still come from Ottawa and the budget is limited. Inuit leaders point to the vast untapped mineral potential, as well as to arts and crafts (soapstone carving and sealskin mittens) and tourism as possible money spinners. But even they admit that self-sufficiency is a distant dream. Moreover education levels are appallingly low. Office jobs are going a begging in Iqaluit, the largest town with 4,000 people, for lack of qualified candidates, while the cafés are filled with unemployed young men.

▲ **Figure 4.72** Adapted extract from *Time* magazine, 3 May 1999

Issues in Iceland (in 2000)

Case Study

Iceland is a country with one of the highest standards of the living in the world, despite being a small volcanic creation battered by the waves of the North Atlantic. As in other polar regions, the economy is heavily dependent upon primary resources, in this case fish. There are issues about the sustainability of fish stocks. The country has in place a far-sighted management system which aims to avoid the catastrophic over-fishing which has destroyed stocks in other parts of the world. However, a larger than expected cut in the fish catch quota for the year beginning July 2000 acted as a reminder of the continued dependence upon nature. Other issues exist about activities being promoted in the interests of diversification and maintenance of living standards. Having to be cautious and flexible is nothing new to Icelanders who have learnt to live with the tectonic dangers of exploding volcanoes and shuddering earthquakes.

a Fishing

New system promises brisk trade

The dramatic depletion of cod stocks has forced Iceland to overhaul its quota system

Cod harvested from the rich fishing grounds of the North Atlantic are the mainstay of Icelandic fisheries and are of central importance in a country where the industry accounts for about 13 per cent of the GDP and up to 70 per cent of the merchandized exports. While the fishing industry in most European countries is struggling to cope with diminishing stocks and poor profitability, the industry in Iceland is confident about its future.

This has not always been the case. Before Iceland battled for and then established its 200-mile exclusive fishing zone in 1976 it is estimated that in some years more than 500,000 tonnes of cod were being caught. Even with foreign vessels excluded by the mid-1980s the symptoms of over-fishing were apparent with an expanded fleet delivering lower catches. Attempts to limit the amount of time boats could fish were unsuccessful in protecting stocks and cod levels. In 1995 the catch fell to less than 170,000 tonnes.

A new fixed catch system was imposed based on a fixed formula to stop haggling between the industry and politicians. The independent Marine Research Institute estimates the size of the fishable stock, cod four years and over, and the industry is allowed to take 25 per cent. Over the past few years the quota has steadily risen to 250,000 tonnes for 1999–2000.

But this June the system received a setback. The MRI dramatically cut back its estimates of the size of the cod stock. Automatically the fishing quota was cut back from an expected 260,000 tonnes to 203,000 tonnes. In response the Minister of Fisheries sought a review of the quota rules. This led to a modification which limits the absolute change in a yearly quota to 30,000 tonnes. The effect has been that the 2000–2001 quota at 220,000 tonnes will be higher than originally proposed, a move which has been criticized as showing evidence that the government has fudged on taking the tough measures necessary to protect stocks.

Figure 4.74 Adapted extract from a survey on Iceland in *The Financial Times*, 19 September 2000

b Whaling

Iceland stopped whaling in 1989, but as whale stocks have improved in recent years the government has come under increasing pressure to lift the ban. Opinion polls show about 80 per cent of the population are in favour of whaling. One line of argument is that Iceland needs to start whaling in order to protect its fishing industry. Whales not only eat fish but also take food upon which fish feed. The Icelandic view is that they would be managing their natural resources and maintaining the balance. They claim that by catching 200 fin whales and 250 minke whales there would be no significant effect upon whale stocks. Greenpeace sees it differently warning that a resumption of commercial whaling would soon put the whales' survival under threat. The government of Iceland is concerned about international reaction. There is a real fear that the country's image abroad would suffer, which could have a big impact on the tourist trade. Also international boycotts of Icelandic products could have a big impact on the economy.

c Aluminium industry

The presence of aluminium production has nothing to do with home demand. Rather it is the result of Iceland's attempts to harness its enormous potential for hydro and geothermal energy by attracting power intensive industries. Less than 20 per cent of the estimated power potential is used. There has been an aluminium smelter near Reykjavik since the mid 1960s. Construction of another larger plant began in 1997. With untapped supplies of renewable energy and plenty of greenfield sites next to deep water anchorages, some see this as one way of expanding and diversifying the economy. Others are less convinced of the wisdom of attracting more energy intensive industries, mainly on environmental grounds. Although hydro-electric is clean power, the associated flooding of Iceland's unique wilderness is a real issue. Norsk Hydro has put forward plans to build an even larger new smelter in the east of the country, which is firmly supported by Iceland's Energy marketing unit and by some in government. Environmentalists, however, are questioning whether the electricity potential is that unlimited. They wonder whether it is right to build one of the world's biggest aluminium plants in a part of the island where only about 10,000 people live and ask 'Would it really benefit the local economy?'

Issues in Antarctica

In Antarctica some issues are more current than others. Sovereignty is not an active issue. Although seven countries still maintain official claims upon the continent (Argentina, Australia, Chile, France, New Zealand, Norway and the UK), and an atlas map shows overlapping territorial claims, the Antarctic Treaty that proposed that the continent be left open to all nations for the pursuit of scientific and other peaceful activities was re-ratified in 1991. Nor is the use of known and unknown mineral resources a current issue. The Environmental Protocol signed in 1991 bans all mineral resource activity in Antarctica, including oil exploration on the continental shelf. Nevertheless one can never be certain when an issue's status will change from inactive to active.

However, fishing in the Southern Ocean is a big issue. Fishing south of the Antarctic Convergence is regulated by CCAMLR (Convention on the Conservation of Antarctic Marine Living Resources), set up in 1982 after over-fishing had already taken place. As over-fishing extends to more of the world's ocean and seas, more nations are investigating commercial fishing opportunities in the Antarctic zone. Since most species are bottom dwellers and are too small to be commercially important, attention is being focused upon about a dozen species that are the most common large fish and also upon catching krill. What needs to be taken into account is that most Antarctic fish tend to be very slow growing, take a relatively long time to reach sexual maturity, and they seem to have low levels of fertility.

▲ **Figure 4.75** Notices on the Falkland Islands. Hunting whales is an emotive issue outside Japan and Norway, the two countries which still capture whales in the interests of 'science'

> **i** ***A conservationist's recommendations***
>
> *Before fisheries are developed on too large a scale it is important to:*
>
> - *evaluate the gross potential of fish resources*
> - *study their population dynamics*
> - *develop systems to monitor fish stocks which are being exploited*
> - *evaluate the effects of these fish exploitations on other elements of the ecosystem*

Tourism may be more of an issue in the near future if numbers of visitors double in the first decade of the new century as some have predicted – with the possibility of larger ships, helicopters and demand for air strips. How much of an ecological disaster will it be if one of the cruise ships sink? Most of the present tour operators obey IAATO guidelines and instil responsibility into their passengers. All waste is removed from Antarctica on the cruise ships, unlike the debris left by earlier human visitors (Figure 4.76). Comparative surveys among breeding penguins between colonies within reach of cruise visitors and those never visited have yielded no measurable differences in numbers of chicks successfully reared. The IAATO guidelines not to feed, touch or handle birds or seals, or approach them in ways that cause them to alter their behaviour, are largely being obeyed. Penguins in the nesting colonies are much more interested in stealing stones, which appear to be the penguin equivalent of gold, from neighbours' nests than in worrying about red coated human visitors taking photographs.

▲ **Figure 4.76**
Debris left from earlier human activity on Deception Island. The amount and nature of it may surprise. The natural harbour occupies a caldera with an open side to the left. From 1910–31 it was a whaler's station. Later British and Chilean research stations were set up. All was abandoned to the mass of black ash, which is everywhere, after eruptions in 1967, 1969 and 1970.

▲ **Figure 4.77** Antarctic wilderness in Hope Bay

Questions

1. Describe the traditional way of life of the Inuit and explain its sustainability.
2. Why was the new Territory of Nunavut created?
3. To what extent is it a solution to the issue of indigenous people in the Arctic?
4. Study Figure 4.77. Describe and comment upon the features which indicate that the area shown is a wilderness.
5. **a** Discuss the differences between past and present attitudes to human exploitation of the Antarctic region.
   b Are the same differences evident in the Arctic region? Explain your answer.

The Lake District:

Case Study

glacial features, problems and issues

Closer to home, the great popularity of the Lake District is largely due to past glaciation. As an unglaciated upland area of old hard rocks, such as the Borrowdale volcanics, it would no doubt have attracted its share of fell walkers, mountaineers and rock climbers. However, the height of the domed structure, which concentrated the highest land in its centre, made it the source of a local ice cap during the Ice Age. Valley glaciers flowed out in all directions, sharpening the relief, increasing the amount of lowland in the valley floors, eroding rock basins within the glacial troughs and creating the basis for today's circular arrangement of ribbon lakes. The lakes offer a variety of human activities and 'mass market' visitor attractions.

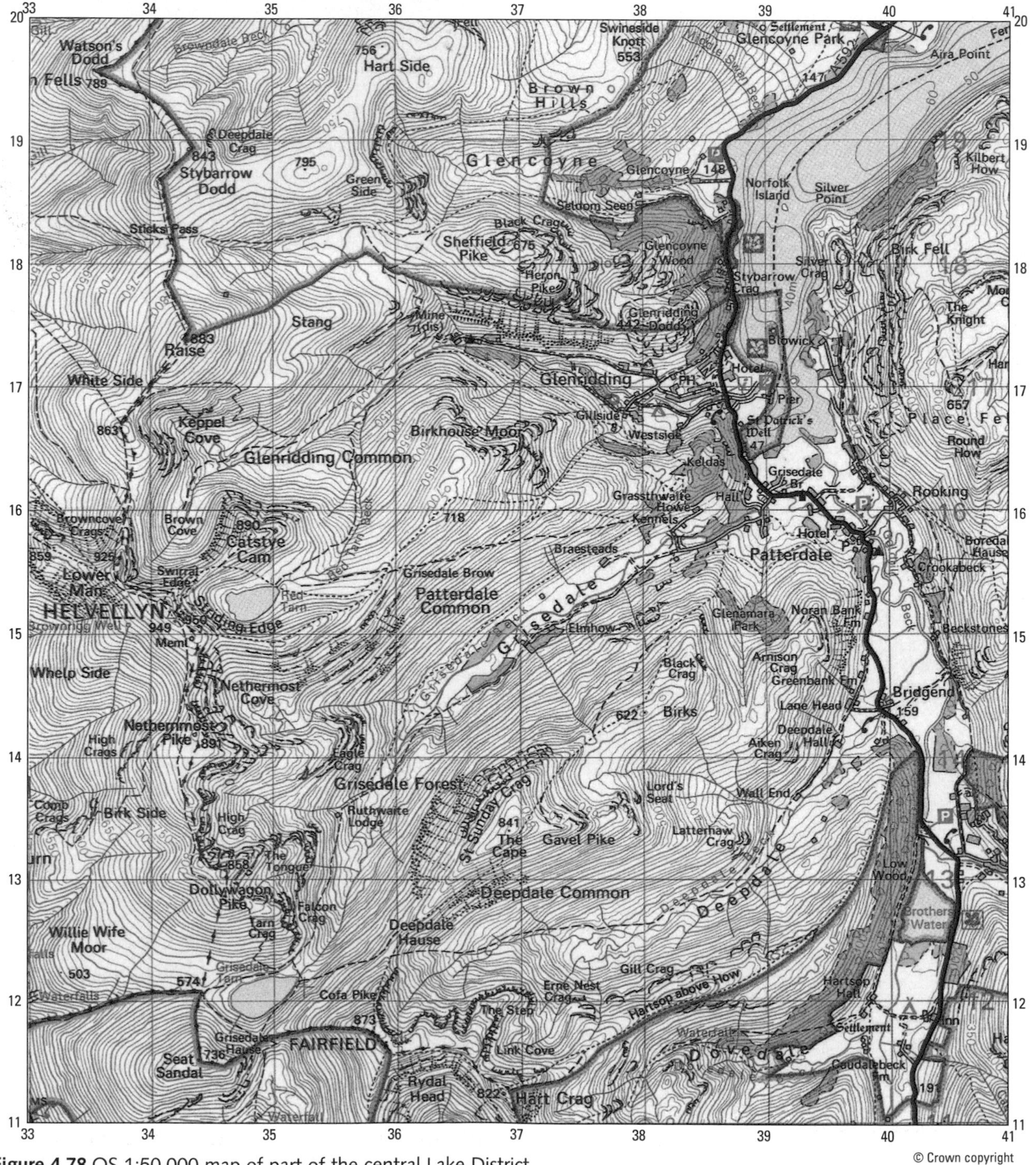

▲ **Figure 4.78** OS 1:50,000 map of part of the central Lake District, including the southern end of Lake Ullswater

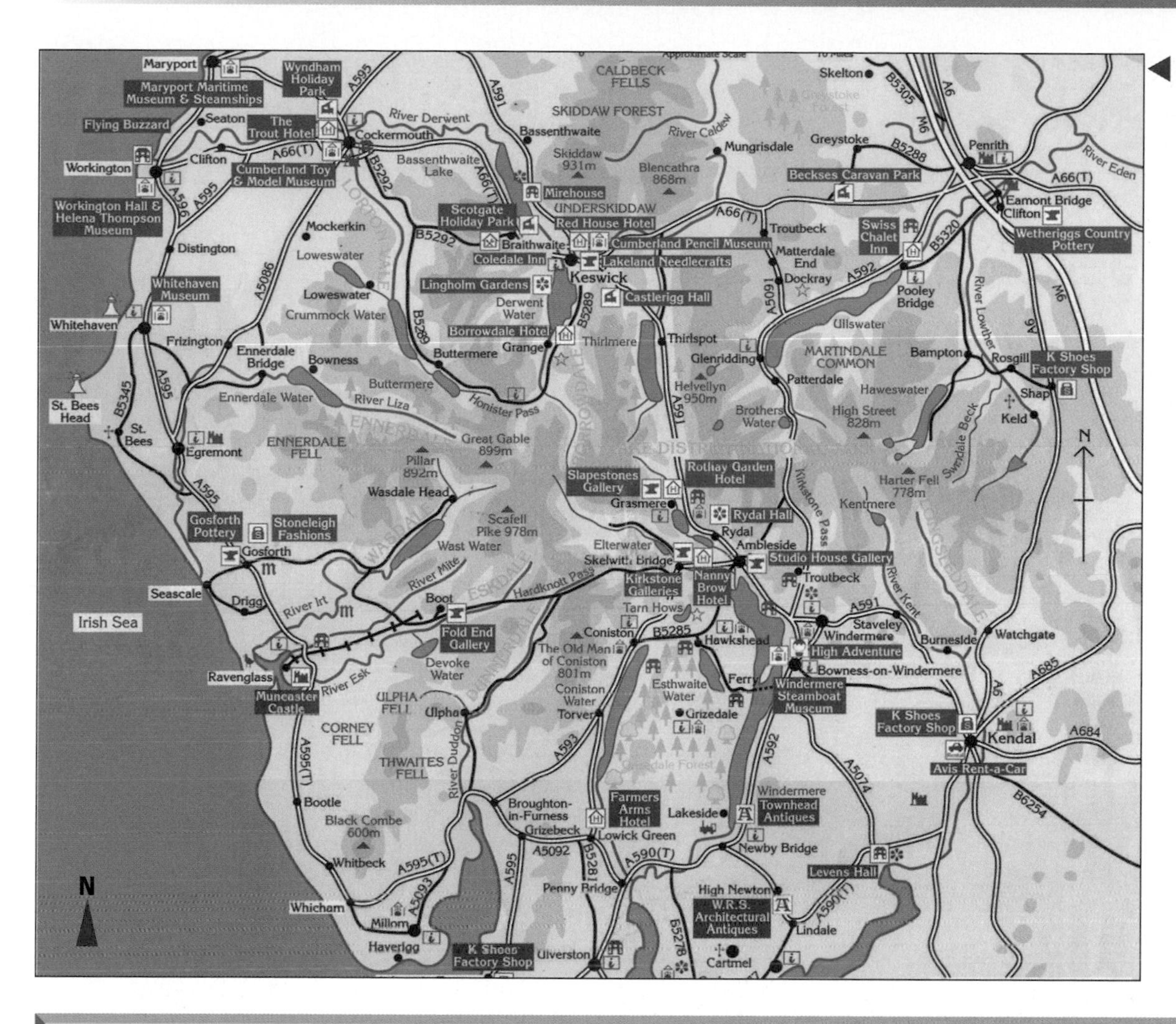

Figure 4.79 The Discovery Tourist Map for the Lake District

Questions

1 Study Figure 4.78.

a Draw a frame the same size as that of the OS extract. On it show and annotate the distributions of **i** scree slopes, **ii** main arête ridges, **iii** corries (with and without tarns), and **iv** glaciated valleys.

b **i** Sketch the long profile of Grisedale Beck.

ii Explain its shape.

c **i** What does a study of the submarine contours in Lake Ullswater suggest about its glacial origins?

ii How do post-glacial changes to Lake Ullswater support the statement that 'Rivers are the enemies of lakes'?

2 Study Figure 4.79.

a **i** Describe the pattern of lakes (both tarn and ribbon) shown.

ii Explain this pattern in relation to the physical background of the Lake District and the work of glaciers.

b **i** Identify the corridors of greatest visitor movement and likely areas of greatest tourist pressure.

ii Suggest reasons for the uneven spatial distribution of visitors.

Further individual investigation from other sources.

3 Farming and tourism

a Outline the main features of Lake District farming.

b Why are farm incomes in the Lake District low and declining?

c Identify the potential conflicts between visitors and farmers and suggest ways in which they may be reduced.

d **i** In what ways may Lake District farmers supplement their incomes from tourists?

ii Why are opportunities for doing this unequally available?

4 Visitor pressure and management in a National Park

a When, where and why do visitor peaks occur in the Lake District?

b Identify the environmental and human problems which result from visitor pressure.

c Suggest ways in which they can be managed.

5 Zoning of the Lake District National Park to reduce conflicts of use

a Identify and explain the locations of 'quiet areas' in the Lake District.

b What restrictions are in place on larger lakes such as Windermere?

Chapter 4 Questions

1 Figure 1 shows landforms in an area of lowland after an ice sheet has advanced and retreated across it.

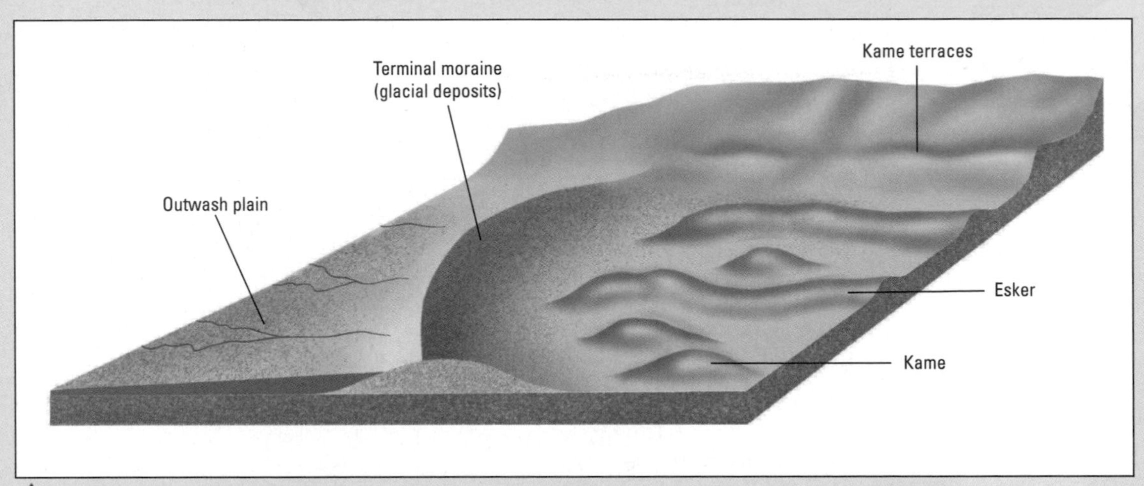

▲ **Figure 1**

a If you were undertaking fieldwork in an area similar to the one shown, what evidence would you seek for each of the following?

i To distinguish between glacial and fluvio-glacial deposits. (3 marks)

ii To determine direction of ice movement. (3 marks)

b Why are drumlins common in some areas of glacial deposition and absent from others? (4 marks)

c With the aid of an example, examine the effects on the landscape of meltwater streams flowing beyond the ice front. (5 marks)

Total: 15 marks

2 Synoptic essay

Choose two different polar environments. Discuss the extent to which the problems and issues associated with human activities in difficult physical environments are similar. (30 marks)

Chapter 5 Population pressure and resource management

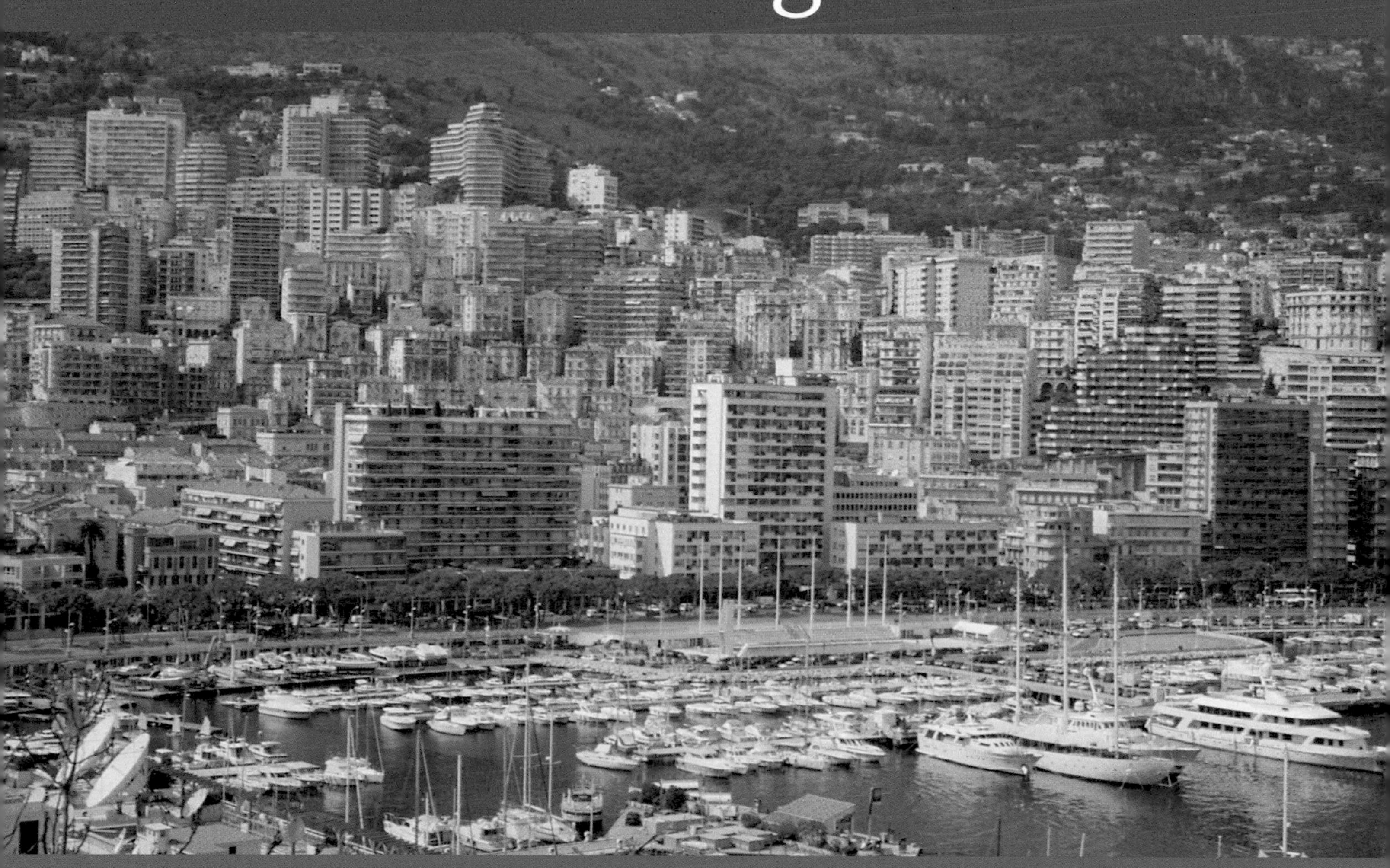

Figure 5.1 The Principality of Monaco, an increasingly attractive home for wealthy people. It is surrounded by EU countries, but it is outside the EU's tax system. Is it densely populated, or overpopulated or both?

Patterns, trends and concepts

The Earth's human population total has moved in just one direction during the last few centuries – upwards. 12 October 1999 was the day that the world population was adjudged to have reached 6 billion. After thousands of years of slow but persistent growth, world population had reached one billion by about 1830. Whatever graphical technique is used to show population change since that date, the message is the same (Figure 5.2). During the last two centuries there has been a world population explosion. Having taken almost 100 years to increase by one billion from 1830 to 1927, successive one billion increases took fewer and fewer years. Doubling from two to four billion and from three to six billion each took under 50 years. Gradients on line graphs showing total world population steepen significantly from about 1950. This exploding population growth is described as exponential.

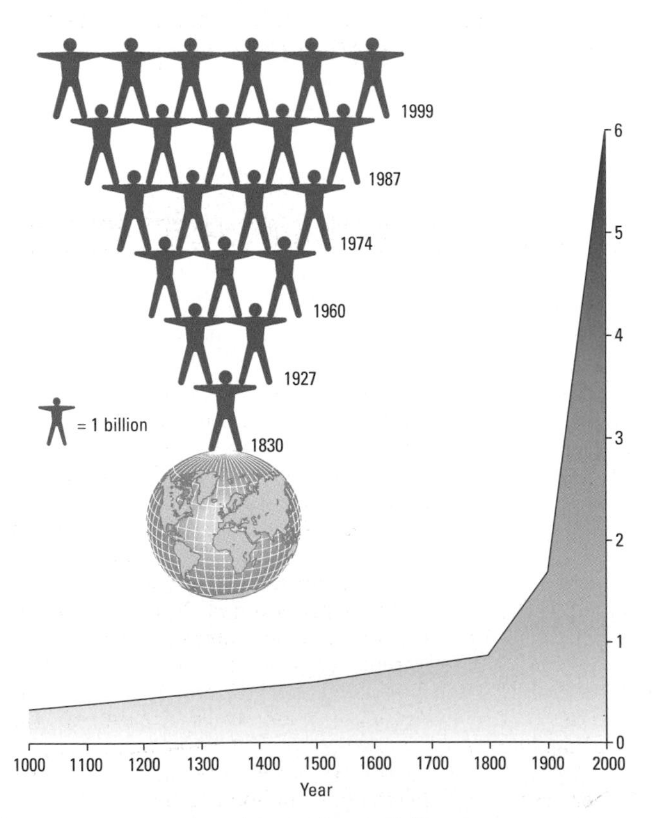

▲ **Figure 5.2** Total world population (billions)

> ***The meaning of exponential***
>
> - *Exponential – an increase which is more and more rapid.*
> - *Exponential growth – growth whose rate becomes ever more rapid in proportion to the growing numbers or size.*

Such rapid population growth is a relatively recent phenomenon. Humans are thought to have existed on Earth for about two million years. For most of this time our ancestors were hunter-gatherers using little more than hand axes made of stone. Life was precarious. However, about 10,000 years ago human existence was made more secure by the dawning of the age of agriculture. Planting seeds and cultivating crops happened first in the fertile crescent between the Tigris and Euphrates in present-day Iraq. Eight thousand years ago this area was at the forefront of human invention. By planting seeds and growing crops food supply became more assured than it ever could be by collecting wild plants. For the first time agriculture allowed humans to settle in one place. This promoted opportunities for further human invention. Use of bronze and iron replaced stone; brick and pottery took over from reeds and skins. Ways to transfer water onto crops in fields were invented. The ancient Egyptians pioneered methods of irrigation that allowed crop cultivation to be extended into the desert. Greater and more assured food supplies allowed for population increase and the growth of towns and cities.

▲ **Figure 5.3** A satellite image of the Nile Valley, one of the most densely populated strips of land in the world, despite the hot desert climate. The narrow dark area along the river is fertile and populated land. Either side of the river it is desert.

Although long-term population numbers continued to grow, made possible by more technological advances increasing human control over the natural environment, they did fall from time to time. The very fact of more people living closer together meant that plagues and infectious epidemics could spread. Also human control over the natural environment was fragile and the early farmers were highly vulnerable to natural disasters and the spread of famine. These acted as checks on population growth. This is why in Stage 1 of the demographic transition model periods of natural decrease are shown to alternate with times of increase. One example: the years up to 1300 were a time of warmer and generally kinder climatic conditions in north-west Europe, which gave many years of favourable harvests. It was a time of population increase in Europe based upon rising food supplies. However, the Black Death halted and reversed what might have been an incipient population crisis as Europe's climate reverted to a cooler and wetter period. Between 1346 and 1351 about a third of Europe's population was wiped out by an epidemic of bubonic plague that arrived from Asia. The Black Death killed 30 million people in Europe during the fourteenth century and it took roughly two hundred years for Europe's population to regain its 1340 level.

The Industrial Revolution, which increased in pace from 1800 onwards, brought even more fundamental changes in its wake. Inventors discovered ways of using more of the Earth's natural resources. Revolutionary improvements in transport allowed almost empty lands in the Prairies of Canada, the Great Plains of the USA, the Pampas of Argentina and the interior lowlands of Australia to be opened up to supply food to the growing populations in Europe, who were increasingly living in towns and working in factories not on farms. Scientists were beginning to understand why diseases took life and how they could be prevented, for example by clean water supply and sanitation. Medicines were developed to contain and to cure diseases. For a long time birth rates did not change, but survival rates did. This set world population into its exponential growth in Stage 2 of the demographic transition model.

What is clear is that world population will continue to grow for some considerable time into the future (Figure 5.4). There are too many population increases already in the pipeline. Population structures in many LEDCs will not allow for an immediate decrease. Young people make up a high percentage of total populations in most LEDCs. Even if they practise birth control to levels beyond those of their parents, and there is some evidence that many will, there will still be an increase until the large youthful element works its way through the population structure. For example, this is the situation in Ghana, one of the countries of sub-Saharan Africa (Figure 5.6)

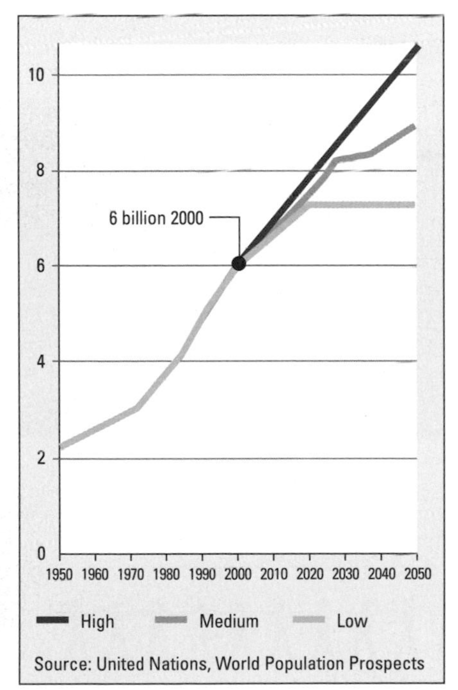

▲ **Figure 5.4** Different projections for world population growth until 2050

UN trims population estimate

The United Nations yesterday announced that it had scaled back its expectations of world population growth to reflect a decline in global fertility rates. It now expects the world's population to be about 8.9 billion in 2050, rather than the 9.4 billion predicted in 1996.

The revision largely reflects improved health care and greater access to contraception for women. But a third of the reduction in the prediction is due to the impact of Aids in sub-Saharan Africa and parts of the Indian subcontinent.

More than 95 per cent of population growth is in developing countries. The USA is the only industrial country where large population increases are projected, largely through immigration. The study highlights significant differences between the poorest countries and other developing countries. Fertility has declined most rapidly in the last 50 years in Latin America and Asia, from 5.9 to about 2.7 children per woman. Most population growth is taking place in the world's poorest and least prepared countries. In 62 countries in Africa, Asia and Latin America, over 40 per cent of the population are under age 15. In many of these countries the use of family planning is less than 15 per cent, a level the average developing country had reached by 1969.

▲ **Figure 5.5** Adapted news report from *The Financial Times*, 23 September 1999

Ghana: country of the young

Case Study

▼ **Figure 5.6** Adapted extract from *The Guardian*, 22 September 1999

The rising tide that nobody can hold back

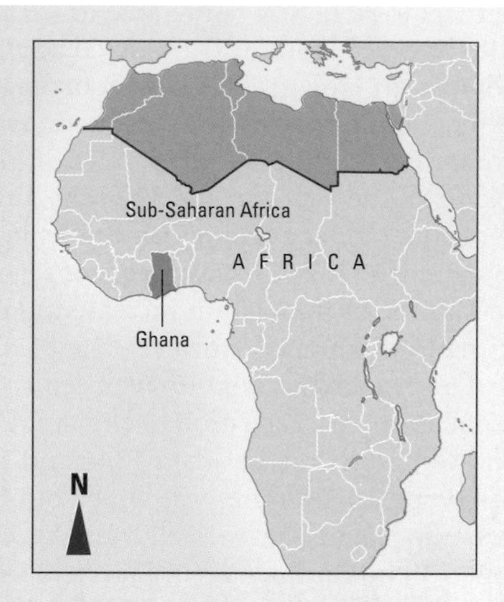

Philip Mensab is a civil servant and his wife Rhoda has just given birth to twins, their first children, without any family history of twins. Their grandparents had seven and eight children respectively; their parents five and four. They intend to have one more child. 'That's enough' says Rhoda. The crude birth rate is falling, but so is the mortality rate of children and Ghanaian mums bear 4.4 children on average. It's far less than nearby Nigeria, but there is nothing anyone can do about the next stage of the population explosion.

Almost one in five Ghanaians are now under 5, half are under 15 and almost two thirds are under 25. The momentum in this country of the young is unstoppable. At best government policies can reduce the long-term numbers. The national plan is to reduce the fertility rate to 4.0 by 2003 and then bring it down, as fast as possible, to 3.5. This represents a herculean task in educating people and providing contraception. The culture in the countryside, where 70 per cent of the people live, is still to see children as assets, conferring status, wealth and recognition. Despite the government family planning association working with churches, schools, hospitals, villages and chiefs, birth control is only practised by 15 per cent of couples.

A member of the Ghanaian family planning association said that 'There is no problem with the growing numbers, if the economy and environment on which people depend keep up with the needs'. It's a big if. The country needs to invest in infrastructure, education, health and agriculture now to avoid massive problems later. It can't. Ghana may be one of Africa's most economically successful and peaceful countries, but the average wage is just over £600 per year, and it depends heavily on US and Japanese aid for help with population control.

Accra, the capital city, is now bursting out of its boundaries, ten times the size it was 40 years ago. Even in its poor quarters there is singing and dancing at ceremonies where babies are named, because birth in Ghana is celebrated as a gift. 'But no more children, no more please' is a plea being made by an increasing number of mothers.

The cost of children

- *Estimates of the cost of children in the average family budget in the UK in 2001.*
- *For food, clothing and other essentials, cost per week:*

  1 child – £87

  2 children – £117

  3 children – £169.

▼ **Figure 5.7**
Population increase in Ghana (known and projected)

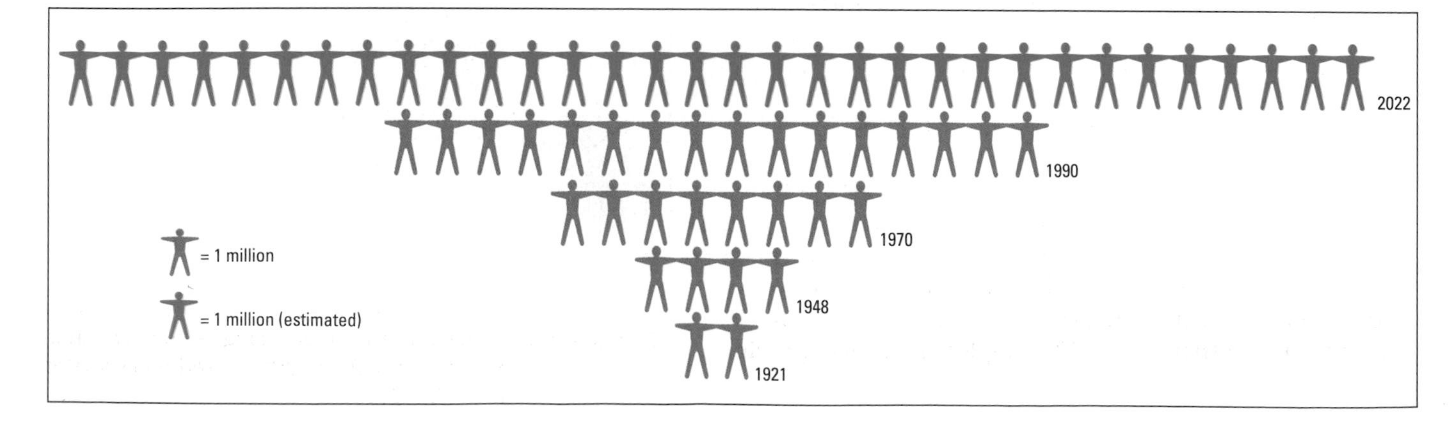

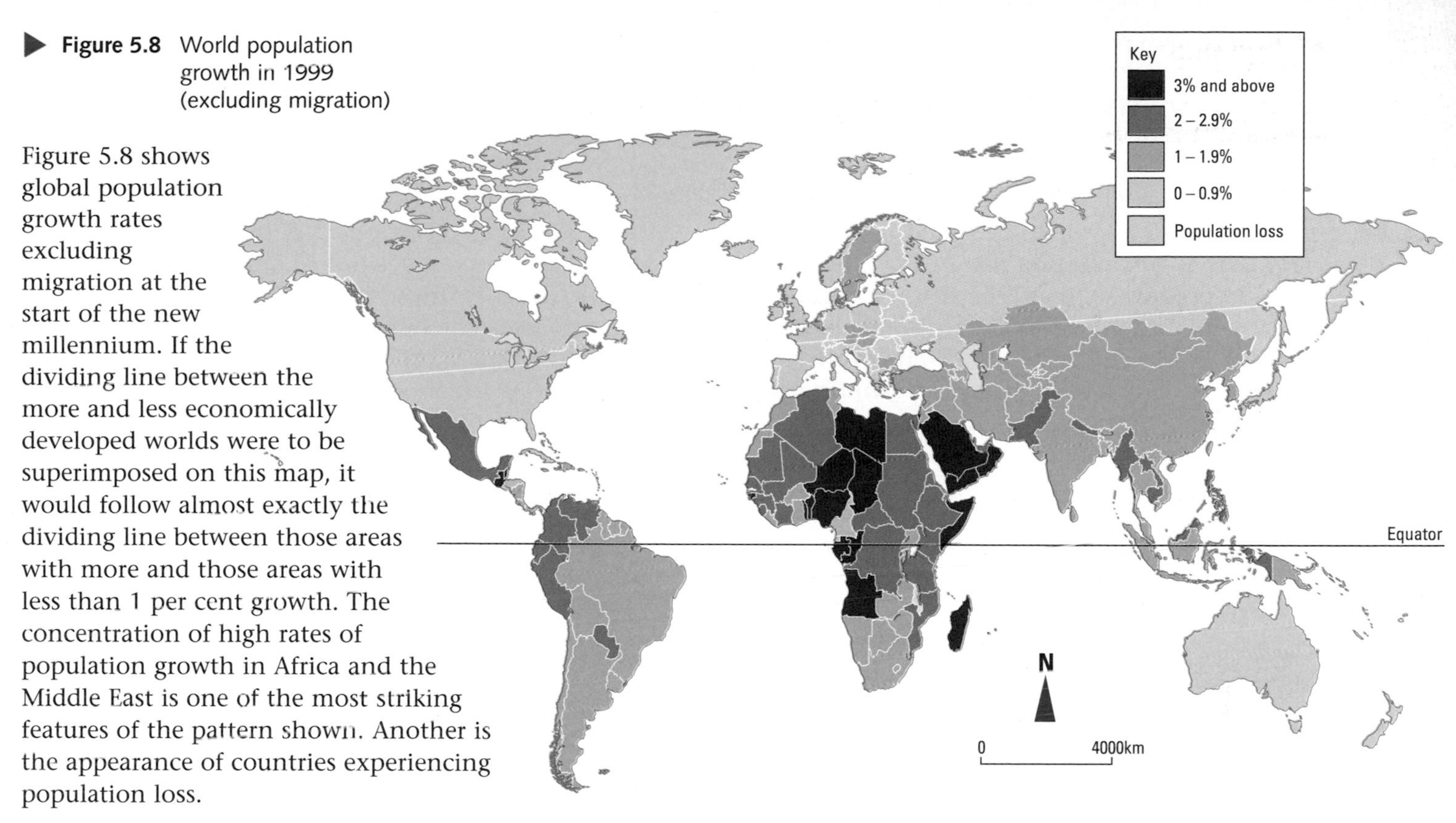

▶ **Figure 5.8** World population growth in 1999 (excluding migration)

Figure 5.8 shows global population growth rates excluding migration at the start of the new millennium. If the dividing line between the more and less economically developed worlds were to be superimposed on this map, it would follow almost exactly the dividing line between those areas with more and those areas with less than 1 per cent growth. The concentration of high rates of population growth in Africa and the Middle East is one of the most striking features of the pattern shown. Another is the appearance of countries experiencing population loss.

Differences in rates of population growth between the more and less economically developed worlds are becoming increasingly polarized. Some countries are approaching, or have already reached, zero population growth and even a natural decrease in a few cases. These countries are mainly in Europe. They were among the first to begin the passage through the various stages of the demographic transition model. When first conceived, the model was constructed in four stages. A stage 5 was later added to accommodate the new phenomenon of natural decline. In other countries the population explosion is continuing out of control, as if family planning had never been invented. There are strong associations between poverty, lack of education and the emancipation of women, and religious teaching on the one hand, and large average family sizes on the other. In between the two extremes are many countries in Latin America and Asia, referred to in Figure 5.5 and shown in Figure 5.8. Declining rates of demographic growth are synonymous with increasing rates of economic growth. Individuals gain economically from limiting family sizes and having more money released for spending, saving and investing. Governments can take more in tax, some of which is available for welfare and improved public services.

The turn around in Italy has been nothing short of remarkable. Italy is the most Catholic of countries and Italians still pack the churches on Sundays, but they are flouting the Pope's teaching on contraception as never before. The fertility rate of 1.2 per woman is one of the world's lowest, far below the 2.1 children needed for population replacement in a country. The average age for the first-time mother is over 27. Couples are delaying their first child by an average of 2.5 years after marriage. Pleas from the Catholic church to desist from the evil of contraception have left 90 per cent of couples unmoved according to surveys. Abortion was made legal in the 1980s. The projection is that the population of Italy will drop from the current figure of just over 57 million to a little over 51 million by 2025.

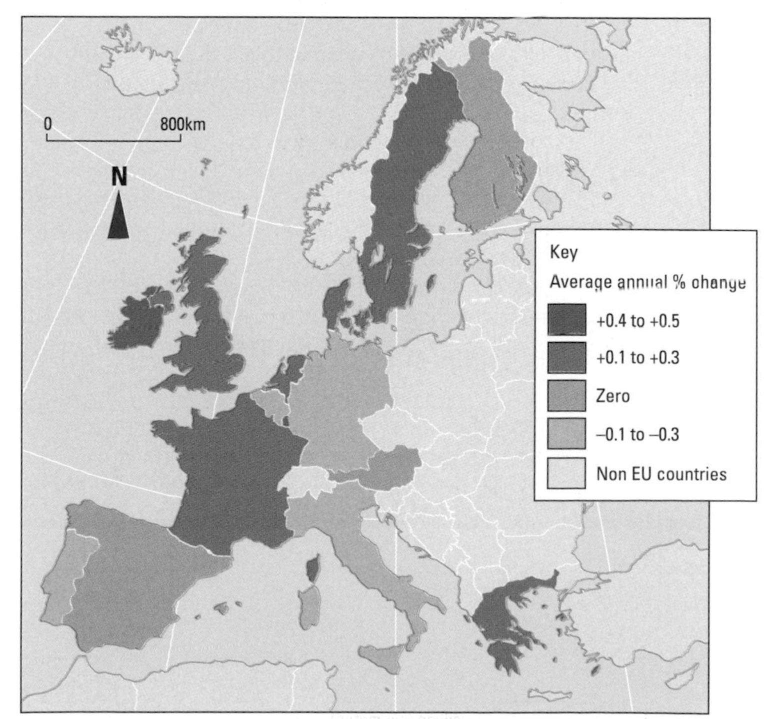

▲ **Figure 5.9** Predicted percentage change in population in EU countries (2000–2010 based on estimates made in 1999)

Another country with population decline is Russia, although for totally different reasons. Deaths continue to outpace births. Since 1985 the birth rate has almost halved; analysts believe that it continues to fall mainly because Russian women do not want to bring children into a country in such difficult circumstances. There are twice as many abortions as live births. In the three years after the ending of communism in 1991 male life expectancy dropped by six years, the sharpest decline known in any industrial society. The rocketing death rate and diving life expectancy were blamed on poverty, political upheaval, loss of guaranteed state employment and 'binge-drinking'. Widening divisions between the rich, who were able to profit from the new capitalist system, and the poor, who lost the guaranteed employment and stable fixed prices of the communist system, were coupled with extreme psychological stress caused by the political upheaval. People could not survive; many lost jobs they had expected to keep for life. Life expectancy only began to rise again in 1995, largely because the weakest two million people, who could not adapt to the changes, had died. Much of the excess mortality, especially among men of working age, was put down to alcohol poisoning and to alcohol-related problems such as accidents, heart disease and suicides. Life expectancy is just 61 years for men, 14 years below that for men in the UK. As the country attempts to make the traumatic change to the system from communism to capitalism, economic decline shows no immediate signs of being reversed. Lack of resources for the state part of the new healthcare system means that it is bordering on the edge of collapse; its real funding was halved between 1998 and 2001 because of inflation. Deaths from TB and Aids are soaring.

Questions

1 Study Figure 5.10.

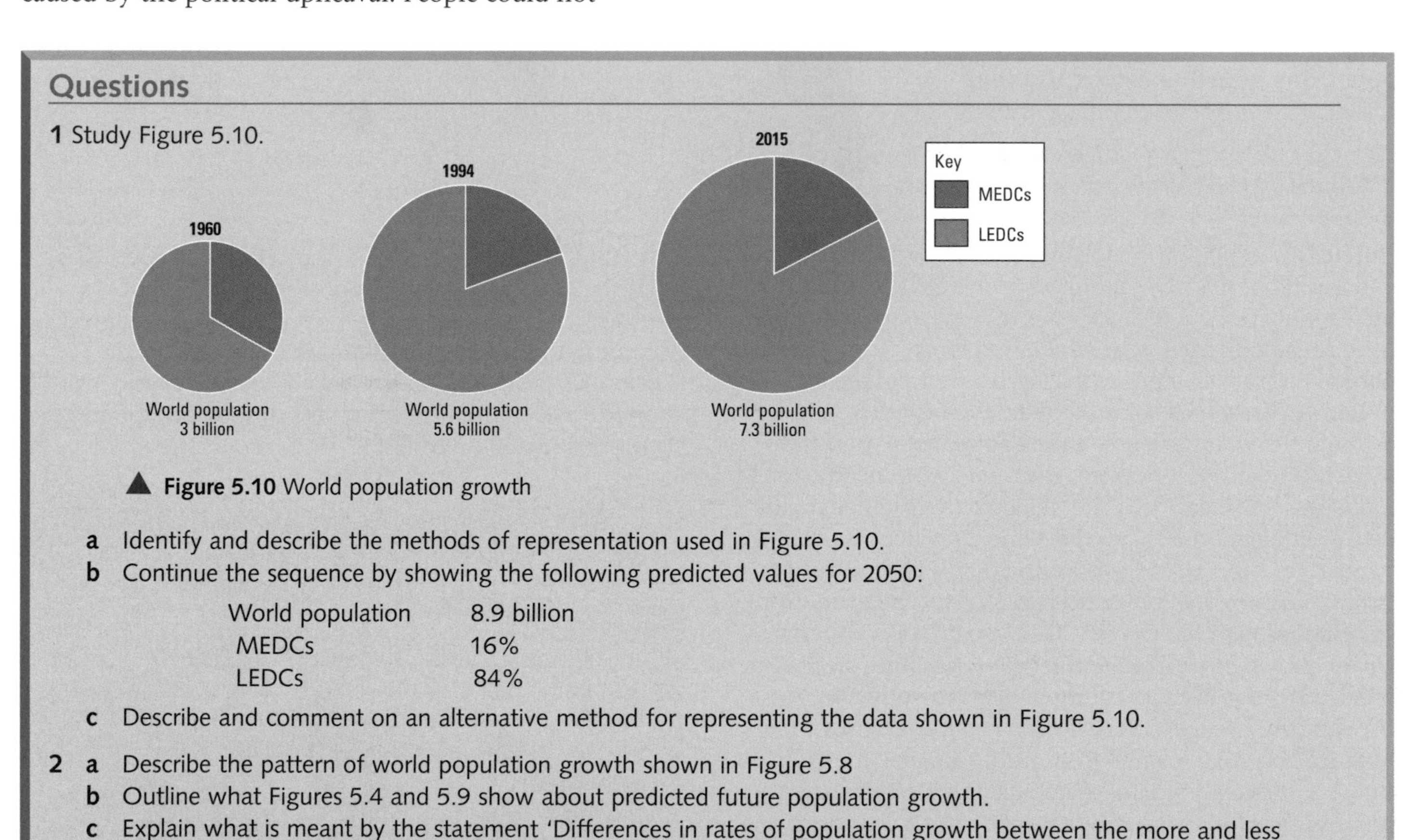

▲ **Figure 5.10** World population growth

a Identify and describe the methods of representation used in Figure 5.10.

b Continue the sequence by showing the following predicted values for 2050:

World population	8.9 billion
MEDCs	16%
LEDCs	84%

c Describe and comment on an alternative method for representing the data shown in Figure 5.10.

2 a Describe the pattern of world population growth shown in Figure 5.8

b Outline what Figures 5.4 and 5.9 show about predicted future population growth.

c Explain what is meant by the statement 'Differences in rates of population growth between the more and less economically developed worlds are becoming increasingly polarized'.

3 Essay

With reference to examples, explain why there are wide differences in rates of population change between countries.

Optimum, under and overpopulation

It might be reasonable to expect there to be an ideal population size for the wealth of a country and the quality of life for its inhabitants. This is the concept of optimum population. If achieved, income per head and quality of life are at maximum levels for that country's resources. It is a time-sensitive concept because today's optimum population is not necessarily the same as yesterday's or tomorrow's. The most efficient use of resources today may lead to shortages tomorrow, unless new resources are discovered. In practice, optimum population is a difficult concept to apply, because of the dynamic nature of human activities. In addition, as with all other theoretical concepts and models, certain assumptions are made. One assumption usually made for optimum population is that each country is a closed unit, whereas in practice countries trade and exchange resources. Human enterprise can be a more significant factor than a country's natural resource base. However, applying the concept loosely, it could be argued that optimum population applies to MEDCs in general. In MEDCs the majority population enjoy high standards of living and a good quality of life, even if the uneven distribution of income within countries means that the poverty of a few has not been exterminated.

▼ **Figure 5.11** The world's ten largest countries (by area)

Country	Land area (thousands km²)	Total population (millions in 2000)	GDP per head (US$ mid-1990s)	Density of pop. (km²)
1 Russia	17,075	147	4,800	8.6
2 Canada	9,976	30	21,500	3.0
3 China	9,597	1,237	2,600	128.9
4 USA	9,373	280	26,400	29.9
5 Brazil	8,512	170	5,400	20.0
6 Australia	7,867	19	19,300	2.4
7 India	3,288	1,000	1,400	304.1
8 Argentina	2,767	37	8,900	13.4
9 Sudan	2,506	30	1,100	12.0
10 Algeria	2,382	32	5,500	13.4

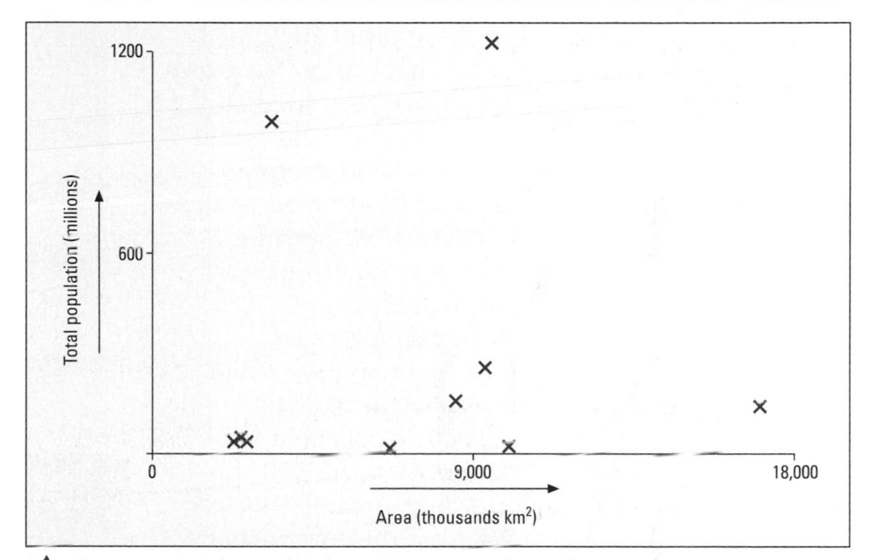

▲ **Figure 5.12** Relationship between area and population

Underpopulation indicates that a country has fewer people than could be supported by its resources. In this era of exploding world populations, countries with surplus resources of food, minerals and other raw materials above the needs of their inhabitants might no longer be expected to exist. However, there is a very uneven spatial distribution of population in the world (see **AS Level Geography**, page 138). Some areas were little settled until recent times. Countries like Canada and Australia had small indigenous populations, at low levels of technological capability and without the population pressure to occupy all the territory. These countries continue to have low total populations in relation to the sizes of their land areas (Figure 5.11) During the nineteenth century, and through most of the twentieth as well, the USA, Canada, Australia, New Zealand and Argentina welcomed immigrants. Immigrants, at first mainly from Europe, were the ones responsible for exploiting natural resources and developing the countries economically. Although each country contains areas physically unattractive to human settlement, pressure on space and resources is frequently at levels below those in the countries of the 'old world' in Asia and Europe. New Zealand and the UK cover similar areas, but the UK houses more than fifteen times as many people (Information box). Therefore is New Zealand underpopulated, or is the UK overpopulated or is it a combination of both?

UK and New Zealand compared

	UK	NZ
Area (thousands km²)	*245*	*269*
Total population (m)	*58.6*	*3.7*
Density of population (km²)	*240*	*13*
Latitude (°)	*50-60N*	*34-47S*
Climate	*maritime*	*maritime*
Physical	*islands*	*islands*
GDP per head ($US)	*18,620*	*16,851*

Is it easier to apply the concept of overpopulation? A country is said to be overpopulated when its population exceeds the optimum level for its resources. There are both human and physical consequences when this happens. Human consequences are both social and economic, such as malnutrition and starvation, underemployment and unemployment, overcrowding and poverty, wars and racism. Environmental consequences include land degradation, soil erosion and desertification, along with the loss of wildlife habitats and air, land and water pollution. Of course not all of these are consequences unique to over-population. Within a country there may in fact be no overall shortage of resources; instead problems may arise from their mal-distribution either among people or between regions or both. When a country or region is overpopulated, there is certainly nothing left in reserve should a climatic hazard or other natural disaster occur. People who are only able to survive at unsatisfactory levels under normal circumstances depend upon outside aid when disaster strikes. Sometimes migration is their sole option, swelling the world's growing numbers of refugees.

The *caatinga*, the dry zone in the rural interior of North East of Brazil, can be used as an example of an overpopulated region. The region's population has grown to a level where peasant farmers, given their level of technology and the uneven distribution of land (in the absence of an effective programme of land reform in Brazil), cannot accumulate surpluses in wet years to allow them to survive the periodic dry years. Malnutrition, rising levels of disease, loss of life and rural–urban migration are the visible consequences of overpopulation. Bangladesh is an example of an overpopulated country. There are no empty areas and untapped natural resources to absorb the national population which has grown rapidly from about 50 million in 1960 to well over 120 million by 2000. Flooding during the monsoon season and after tropical cyclones are known annual risks, but the government and people do not have the resources needed for effective preparation and total protection. Bangladesh is one of the world's poorest countries and the quality of life for the average Bangladeshi is one of the worst in Asia. The application of the green revolution helped in the 1970s, but other ways of increasing food production are urgently needed.

The Netherlands (MEDC) and Bangladesh (LEDC) compared

	NL	BG
Area (thousands km²)	37	143
Total population (m)	15.5	120
Density of population (km²)	457	899
Physical	delta	delta
GDP ($US)	19238	1331
Daily calories (kilocalories)	3222	2019

Although the concepts of optimum, over and underpopulation are often subjective, one thing is definite. They are unrelated to a country or region's density of population. The Netherlands is the most densely populated country in the EU, but this has not stopped it from becoming one of the top twenty richest countries in the world. It occupies the equivalent physical position in western Europe to Bangladesh in western Asia, at the mouth of major rivers – the Rhine and Maas compared with the Ganges and Brahmaputra. Deltas everywhere are challenging, but potentially very productive, environments. One factor that helps to explain the economic gap between the two countries is global position. The Dutch control the routeways and trade routes into the wealthy industrial heart of Europe, whereas Bangladesh is at the mercy of upstream countries such as India and Nepal; the Himalayas block rather than encourage routes into the interior of Asia.

▼ **Figure 5.13a** The *caatinga* in North East Brazil, overpopulated with an average of two per square kilometre

▲ **Figure 5.13b** A street scene in Dhaka, the capital of Bangladesh, the world's most densely populated country

▶ **Figure 5.14** The Netherlands – cubes and flats, modern high density living in Rotterdam

Questions

1 Study Figures 5.1, 5.13 and 5.14.
  a Describe the main features shown on each photograph.
  b To what extent is it possible to determine whether or not the areas shown are overpopulated?

2 a Describe what Figure 5.12 shows about the relationship between the size of the world's ten largest countries and population totals.
  b **i** Using the data in Figure 5.11, calculate the Rs value for the relationship between land area and GDP per head.
  ii Test and comment on the strength of the relationship between land area and GDP.
  c Suggest geographical explanations for the answers given in parts **a** and **b**.

3 Investigation
  a Undertake research to investigate ways in which New Zealand is different from the UK with respect to **i** its relief and structure and **ii** its global position.
  b Evaluate the extent to which these explain the great differences in total population and population density between the two countries.
  c State and justify your opinion about whether or not the UK has an optimum population.

4 Why is overpopulation more likely to be a problem associated with LEDCs than MEDCs?

Theories for the relationship between population and resources

The starting point for all theoretical studies between population and resources is Thomas Malthus, who lived from 1766 to 1834, at a time when the Industrial Revolution was in its infancy. His essay on 'The Principle of Population' was published in 1798. It is often summarized in a graph (Figure 5.15). He predicted a gloomy view for the human race. Population would grow until it reached the limit of food supply, after which there would be poverty and widespread famines.

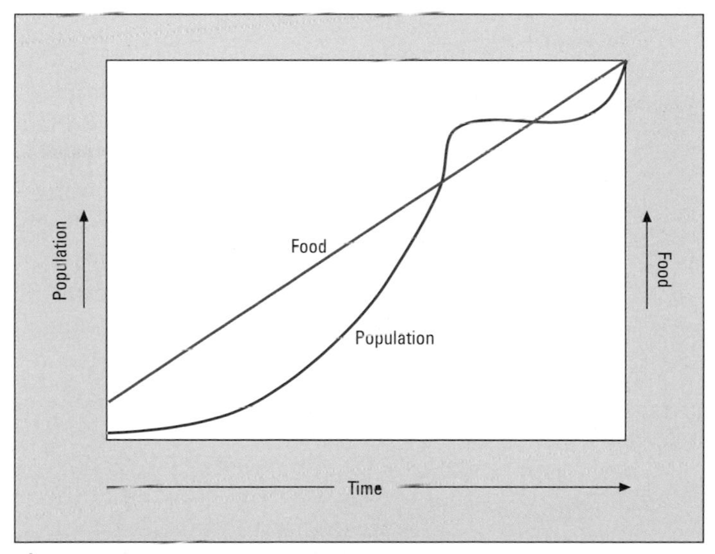

▲ **Figure 5.15** The theory of Malthus

Malthus's view was based upon the belief that people, like other animals, increase geometrically by multiplication (1, 2, 4, 8, 16, 32 etc.) whereas food supplies increase arithmetically (1, 2, 3, 4, 5, 6, etc.). Eventually a gap opens up that widens. Although Malthus recognized that fertile land could be made more productive by improved organization and increased investment, he insisted that there was still a point when the 'law of diminishing returns' clicked in. As a result of greater inputs and by bringing more land that was marginal into cultivation, farmers would reach the point of maximum output, after which time any extra amount that could be produced would no longer justify the additional effort expended in producing it. Malthus identified certain 'checks' on population growth once numbers of people exceeded food supply, which meant that a country's population could never increase beyond the food necessary to support it. The checks are of two kinds. One group is 'positive checks', such as inadequate food, famine, disease and war leading to poor nutrition. The other group is 'preventative checks', such as delayed marriages and abstaining from sexual relationships leading to a reduction in the fertility rate. In other words, the checks to growth will be achieved by death rates increasing (positive checks) and birth rates decreasing (negative checks).

Accelerated population growth in LEDCs since 1950 renewed Malthusian fears. Malthus still has many supporters; they argue that the day of reckoning has only been delayed. This has been because of technological improvements, the like of which Malthus writing at the end of the eighteenth century could not have foreseen. They believe that there are already twice as many people on Earth as can be supported in the middle-class comfort experienced by many people in MEDCs. They point out that the world is running out of new arable land and supplies of fresh water, that repeated famines in Africa are examples of Malthusian checks, as also are wars, food crises, environmental degradation, destruction of natural vegetation, disastrous floods, soil erosion and crop failure.

Opponents of Malthus say that he did not make sufficient allowance for new technology, the opening up of land to cultivation in the New World and the spread of cropland by use of irrigation. He also failed to predict the reduced population growth as countries develop economically and progress through the later stages of the demographic transition model.

Easter Island: the theory of Malthus in action

Case Study

Easter Island is the world's most isolated piece of inhabited land (Figure 5.16). The island was settled by Polynesians in about 400AD. Landing on Easter Island was difficult because of steep cliffs, strong winds and high surf. There is only one small harbour site. Once there, the natural resources available to the new settlers included fertile volcanic soils, wood from subtropical forests and palm trees, fresh water in volcanic craters, at least 25 species of nesting birds and volcanic rocks for making cutting tools. With time, the settlers clearly prospered. They had the time, human power and organization to cut giant statues in the quarry on the sides of one of the three volcanic peaks, drag them to coastal sites in other parts of the island and erect them on platforms in honour of their ancestors. These gigantic statues, carved from volcanic rock, averaging 5-7 metres in height and weighing up to 90 tonnes, are what Easter Island is best known for. At its peak, between 1400 and 1500, the population was estimated at between 7,000 and 20,000. The different clans had their own altar sites; competition between clans led them to erect larger and more impressive statues.

▲ **Figure 5.17** The stone statues, or moai, standing again on the platform Ahu Tongariki, close to the quarry where they were made

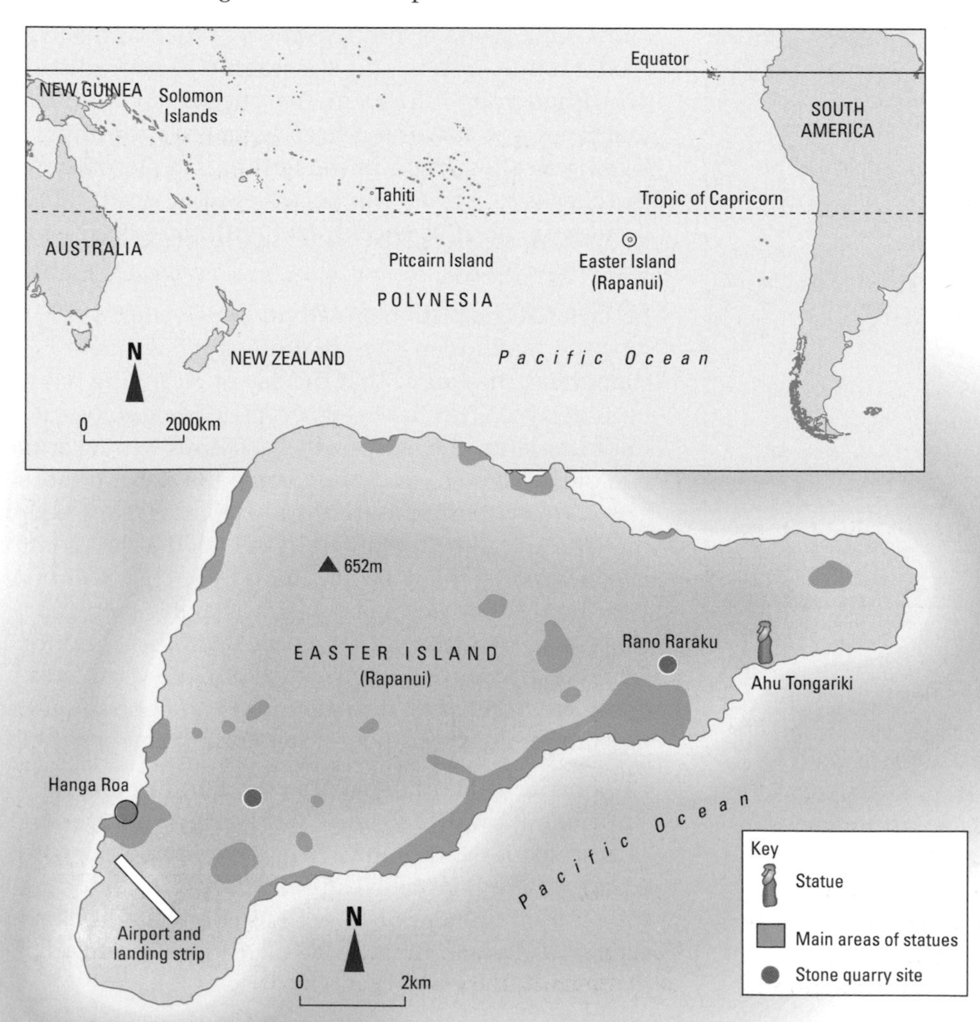

◀ **Figure 5.16** Easter Island and its location

Yet when Captain Cook visited Easter Island in 1774 he found the islanders in poor condition, describing them as 'small, lean, timid and miserable' and noting that 'nature had been exceedingly sparing of her favours to this spot'. By this time some of the statues were no longer standing. The population was estimated at about 2,000. In the absence of anything written, no one can be absolutely certain what went wrong, but it is known that there were inter-clan wars. The statue-building period ended in about 1500 and is likely to have coincided with the disappearance of the key resources – forests and palm trees. Rising populations had finally led to all the forests being cleared for farmland, housing, canoes, firewood and increasingly for moving the statues. Statues were abandoned as human survival became the number one priority (Figure 5.18).

Easter Island was a closed system. For 1300 years there was no known contact with the outside world. Resources were finite. Potentially renewable resources such as forests were over-exploited by the growing population to the point of removal. Once they could no longer build sea-going vessels, they had no means of obtaining resources from elsewhere. Conflicts ensued, population growth was checked and over time it declined to a new level that the remaining natural resources could sustain.

Figure 5.18 Moai left abandoned on the sides of the quarry. They are the same size as those on the platforms, but have been half buried by mass movement since 1500.

Figure 5.19 Hanga Roa is growing and more of the land is being farmed productively again.

The modern post-script is that the population is rising again. Over the last decade it has risen from about 2,000 to 3,000. The island is no longer a closed system. There is a twice-weekly flight from Santiago in Chile and a supply boat several times a year. Tourism now provides the income. The one settlement of Hanga Roa is expanding and more food is now grown on the island than for several hundred years (Figure 5.19).

The Club of Rome and other theories

Malthusian ideas formed the basis for 'The Limits to Growth' model published by the Club of Rome in 1972. The club was formed from a group of thirty interested individuals, including industrialists, scientists, economists and statesmen, from ten countries. Their basic conclusion ran along the following lines:

- If present growth trends in world population continue, and if associated industrialization, pollution, food production and resource depletion continue unchanged, the limits to growth on this planet will be reached some time within the next one hundred years.
- The most probable result will be a rather sudden and uncontrollable decline in both population and industrial capacity.

The club used a computer model. The results are shown in Figure 5.20. Historical values from 1900 to 1970, for population growth, food per head, industrial output per head, resources and pollution, were fed into the computer model. They were then projected forward into the future to model how the different variables might inter-relate and affect one another. Exponential population growth was projected to continue for longest. There was a time lag between the reduction in natural resources affecting food production and industrial output and its effect on population growth. Due to decreased food supply and a rapidly deteriorating resource base, death rates increase to the point where the total world population begins a sharp decline.

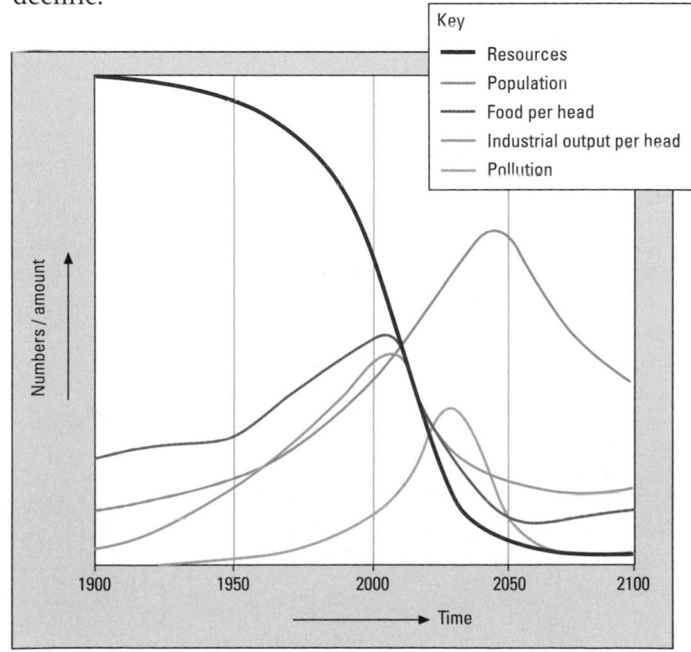

Figure 5.20 The Club of Rome model

However, as with every computer model, all sorts of assumptions are made when entering the data. The reliability of the outcome is heavily dependent upon the quality and certainty of the data entered. A slight change in one assumption can produce results that are greatly different. The assumptions about world resources are fundamental to this model. If the world's resource base does not collapse during the first half of the twenty-first century, the time scale for predicted events will be pushed further into the future. There is now more evidence of the slow down in world population increase than was available to the members of the club in 1972 (Figure 5.23).

The main criticism of the 'Limits to Growth' model is its failure to take the human dimension sufficiently into account. It is too much like Malthus with a computer. Human history has shown the adaptability of the human race and its immense capacity for technological innovation. This is what has allowed world population to increase from about 900,000 in the time of Malthus to the current six billion. As circumstances change, such as the need for additional food supplies or for alternatives to dwindling natural resources, so too do human responses. The development of high yielding seeds which fostered the green revolution in some LEDCs has prevented many of the predicted famines from accelerated population growth. Many complain about the slow progress being made towards replacing fossil fuels with renewable alternative energy sources, but others argue that the need has not yet been strong enough to make this the number one human priority.

Will Malthus be right?

It is how humans fit into the natural world that will settle whether Malthus was right or wrong. He was wrong in 1798. But if he had been writing 10,000 years earlier, before agriculture, he would have been right. And were his book published today on the brink of the third millennium, he would be more right than wrong. Let me explain.

The human species is an unusual one. With the invention of agriculture 10,000 years ago, we became the first species in the 3.7 billion-year history of life not to be living as small populations off the natural fat of the land. Taking food production into our own hands, we stepped outside the local ecosystem. As hunter-gatherers humans occupied niches in the local ecosystem; population numbers were limited by the resources available. Agriculture liberated people from the confines of the local ecosystem and removed the Malthusian lid in one fell swoop.

So, when he wrote 200 years ago, Malthus was wrong. He did not see that nations are not like ecosystems, that people could expand into new regions and, with the burgeoning technology of the Industrial Revolution, became vastly more efficient at producing food and wresting raw materials from Earth.

But the position of humans within the natural world is once again undergoing a great change. The system in which we are living, extracting our energy and other supplies, is global. We have converted woodlands and grasslands into farmland virtually all over the globe. Our cities have paved over natural communities. Pollution and overfishing are rapidly destroying our rivers, lakes and oceans. As these ecosystems go down, we are losing perhaps 30,000 species of plants and animals a year, out of perhaps 10 million total species, even though we still deeply rely on at least 40,000 species for food, shelter, clothing and fuel.

The tide is turning back towards Malthus. We are emerging from a 10,000 year vacation with nature still not fully realising that our own survival hinges on reducing the damage we do to Earth's natural systems. We may not drive ourselves to biological extinction, but I fear that the Malthusian spectres of famine, warfare and disease will rise in the next few centuries, coupled with an accelerating loss of human cultural diversity and quality of life.

▲ **Figure 5.21** Adapted extract from *Time* magazine, 8 November 1999

The main challenge to Malthusian views came from Ester Boserup, who in 1965 published *The Conditions of Agricultural Growth*. She started from the viewpoint that the widespread misery predicted by Malthus had not occurred. Rather than being a hindrance to development, population growth and its pressures had been the driving forces for human innovation. They had provided the incentive for increasing agricultural output and for supporting agricultural improvement and change. Boserup's theory was based upon technological change, which is why it is so different from those of Malthus and neo-Malthusians such as the Club of Rome. Boserup recognized that most human invention was a response to human needs, confirming the old adage that 'Necessity is the mother of invention'. Technology developed in one place can be transmitted and taken up elsewhere, until it achieves a global spread. Growing populations gradually exhaust certain types of natural resources, such as timber, virgin land, game, fish and fresh water supplies. Boserup's view was that the ingenuity of people, driven by need, develops substitutes for natural resources as they become scarce and either improves agricultural technology or opens up new land to farming as the demand for food increases.

Another contributor to the population–resources debate was Julian Simon, who published *The Ultimate Resource* in 1981. His general view was that in certain situations moderate population growth may have a positive effect because it is good for development. He viewed the various sudden increases in world population as a result of major improvements or inventions. Growth of population is gradually moderated as the changes are assimilated. Figure 5.22 illustrates this. One million years ago the increase was as a result of making and using tools. Ten thousand years ago it developed from cultivating crops and domesticating animals. The spurt within the last 200 years had its origins in the Industrial Revolution. If some of the medium and low predictions for future population growth prove to be accurate (Figure 5.4), we may be on the edge of entering an era of more moderate growth as the massive economic changes since 1800 are assimilated.

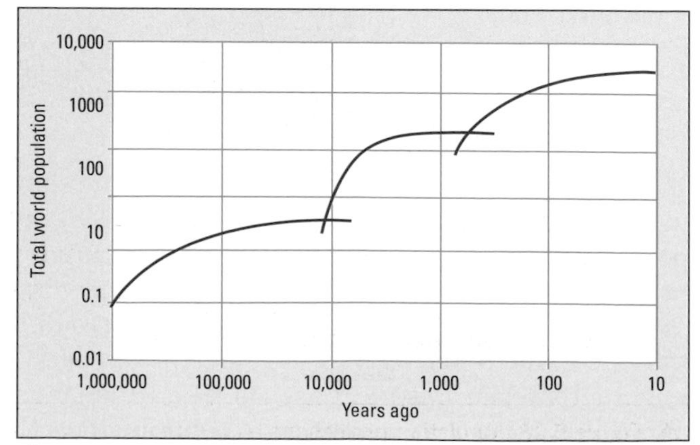

▲ **Figure 5.22** The model according to Julian Simon

Therefore on certain key issues Julian Simon's views are different from those of Malthus. He does not agree that population growth is limited by the availability of resources; human skill and labour create value from natural resources. This value is constantly being re-appraised in line with new technology or new discoveries. A shortage of a natural resource creates its own remedy as the impetus to recycle or substitute rises. Nor does he agree that population growth is geometric; there are periods when it appears to be, but these are followed by periods during which it naturally slows down. Larger populations do not necessarily lead to famine and disease. A larger population can achieve higher levels of productivity, more specialization and more varied skills. Standards of living have in fact increased with population growth. In the short term all resources are limited, but in the longer term availability can be increased.

Summary

Although twentieth century population growth has been exponential and projected increases through the twenty-first century remain formidably large, there are signs of a real slowing down in the rates of increase in many countries of the world. If present trends continue world population will stabilize at some time in the next century, even though this will be at much higher levels than at present in most LEDCs (Figure 5.23), since the global average conceals many regional variations. Also there is nothing permanent or fixed about a trend. However, it is encouraging that many poor countries have recorded sharp falls in average family sizes after adopting successful birth control policies, which lessen some of the gloomy predictions of Neo-Malthusians. No one, however, is complacent because population growth already in the pipeline will continue to place severe pressures on natural resources and the environment for many years to come.

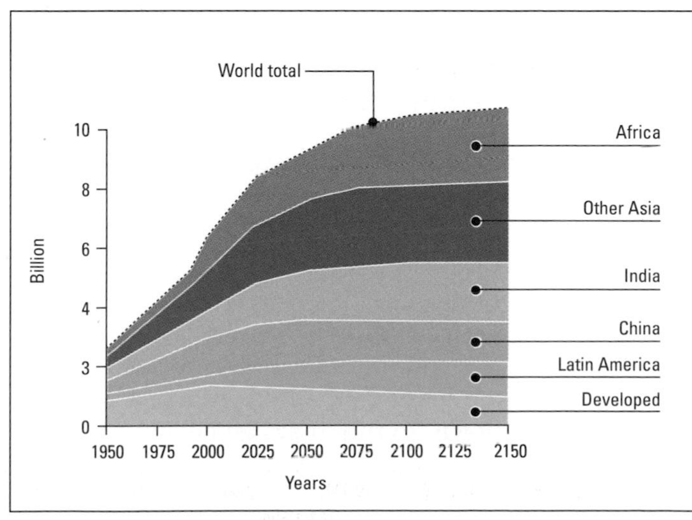

▲ **Figure 5.23** Population projections by region based on the medium variant

The world region of greatest concern is sub-Saharan Africa, where fertility rates of six children per woman remain commonplace and populations continue to increase in the manner predicted by Malthusians. Poverty is widespread showing that population and resources are not in balance (page 215). The best developed of the MEDCs have another fear, that of an unprecedented influx of immigrants from poorer countries. Already more than one million illegal immigrants are believed to enter North America and Europe each year. With their ageing populations, governments may need to contemplate the politically unpopular and legalize immigration from LEDCs, which has its potential socio-economic consequences. The UN has made estimates for the number of new migrants who may be needed to maintain the size of the working-age population (Figure 5.24). Do these confirm that these more economically developed countries are underpopulated?

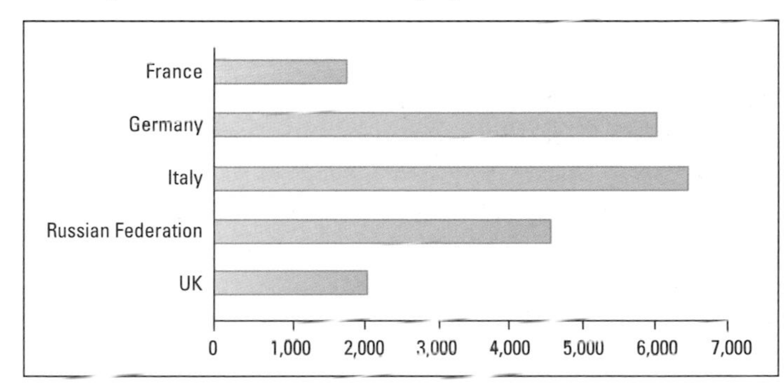

▲ **Figure 5.24** Migrants needed to maintain the size of the working-age population per year between 2000 and 2050 (per million inhabitants in 2000)

Questions

1 a Draw large versions of the graphs in Figures 5.15, 5.20 and 5.22. Add labels to describe what each one shows about the relationship between population and resources.
  b Explain the main strands of Malthusian and neo-Malthusian theories about population growth and resources.

2 With respect to Easter Island,
  a quote distances to amplify the statement that it is 'the world's most isolated inhabited piece of land',
  b explain how and why it can be used to exemplify the theory of Malthus.

3 Evaluate, with supporting detail, the extent to which you consider Malthus
  a was right between 1798 and the present day,
  b is likely to be right during the next century.

4 Suggest reasons why
  a there are different predictions for total world population during the next 100–150 years,
  b there is more than one theory for the relationship between population and resources.

Resource exploitation and management

The Concise Oxford Dictionary's first definition of resource is 'means of supplying a want, stock that can be drawn on; country's collective means for support and defence'. This gives us a guide to the general use of resource in Geography, as something that is useful to, and can be used by, people and countries. Solar energy is basic to all life on Earth, human and otherwise, as also is fresh water from rain. Natural resources on the land surface include trees, plants, animals, soil and minerals. Fish stocks and some minerals, notably oil and natural gas, are natural resources on continental shelves, the areas covered by shallow water which fringe coastlines, especially in areas of enclosed seas such as the North Sea.

Lower down in the same dictionary entry is 'skill in devising expedients, practical ingenuity, quick wit' in the context of describing a person as being full of resourcefulness. This suggests another use of resource in a geographical context. People are included in a country's resource base, not only for their human skills but also for what they have already built. Therefore one classification of resources is divided into natural and human, although in reality they are inter-linked because natural resources cannot be developed without people. The extent to which natural resources are developed depends upon the demand and level of technology.

The commonest classification of natural resources is into renewable and non-renewable. The most renewable of natural resources are solar energy, precipitation and wind power from the atmosphere and tide and wave power from the sea. They are naturally renewable as they will always exist and they occur independently of any human presence or use. The most non-renewable are fossil fuels and certain other minerals. They took millions of years to form and the amount of each mineral available on Earth for human use is strictly limited. Once consumed, they cannot be directly replaced within a known human time scale. The distinction seems clear cut. However, in reality there are many resources that can normally be considered renewable, such as clean fresh water, plants, forests, animals, fish and soil, but which may become non-renewable as a result of excessive amounts of human use and abuse. Some of the Earth's natural biological resources need to be more carefully conserved and managed in the future if they are going to regenerate naturally to continue to provide new supplies for human use and hence maintain their status as renewable resources. This is the issue at the heart of the debate about sustainable development. Its basic tenet is that the needs of the present generation should be met while leaving a resource base that is the same or improved for the next and future generations.

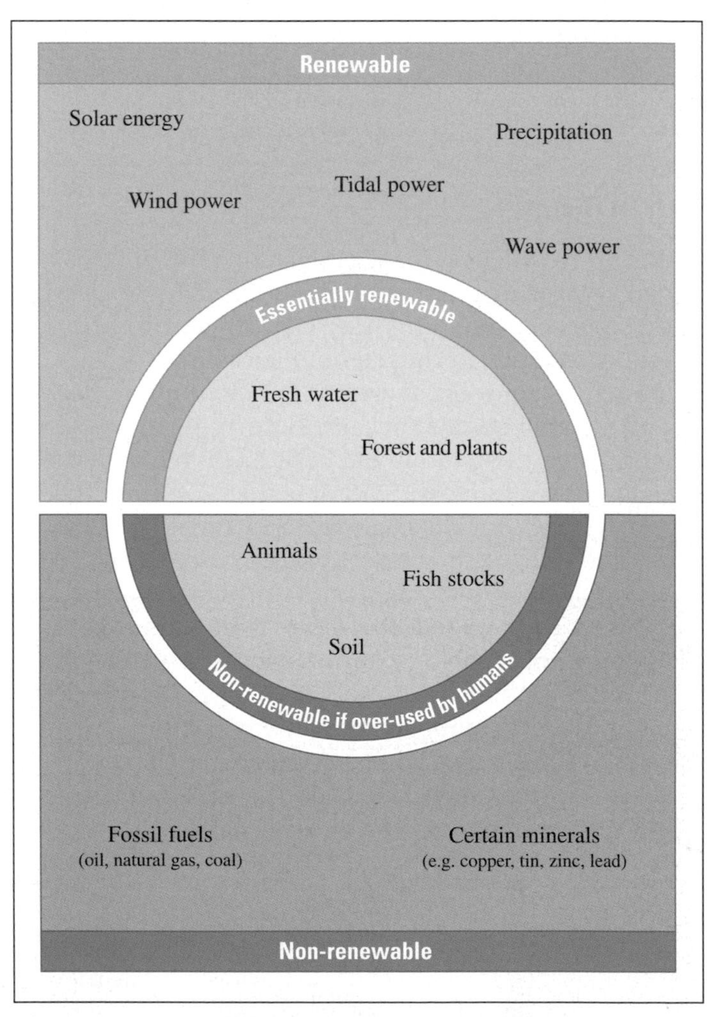

▲ **Figure 5.25** The continuum between renewable and non-renewable resources

There is a further sub-classification of resources between those in stock and those held in reserve. Some resources that have already been obtained from land or sea have been stockpiled ready for future use. Others have been left where they are; these are the reserves. Their existence and extent are known, so that they can be obtained when future demand arises. Other quantities of natural resources are known or thought to exist; but without having been fully explored yet. Their potential size can only be guessed at. They may be located in politically unstable countries or in some of the more remote and wilder places on Earth, none more so than the mineral resources which are believed to exist in and around Antarctica (see Chapter 4, pages 161–163).

A variety of factors control which resources are used first and where (Figure 5.26). It would be expected that a high quality resource, available in large amounts, cheap and easy to obtain and close to point of need would be exploited first; however, it is never possible to rule out obstacles such as political hostility, war or overwhelming environmental opposition. Factors such as improvements in technology, changes in economic climate and increasing demand may lead to the re-appraisal of a potential resource leading to its exploitation and use. All three factors were needed before the oil and natural gas resources in the North Sea, long known to exist, began to be exploited commercially (Figure 5.27). The big rise in world oil prices in the 1970s justified the high costs of exploration and extraction, which new technology allowed. There was also no shortage of demand as oil consumption in Europe greatly exceeded production. For how long a resource is exploited is influenced by complex inter-relationships between supply and demand; rarely does exploitation cease for the sole reason that all the deposits have been physically exhausted. Costs of mining tend to increase as the deposit becomes smaller and a point is reached where it is more commercially viable for a company to invest elsewhere or in substitutes. Only very significant increases in price or scarcity lead to mines being re-opened.

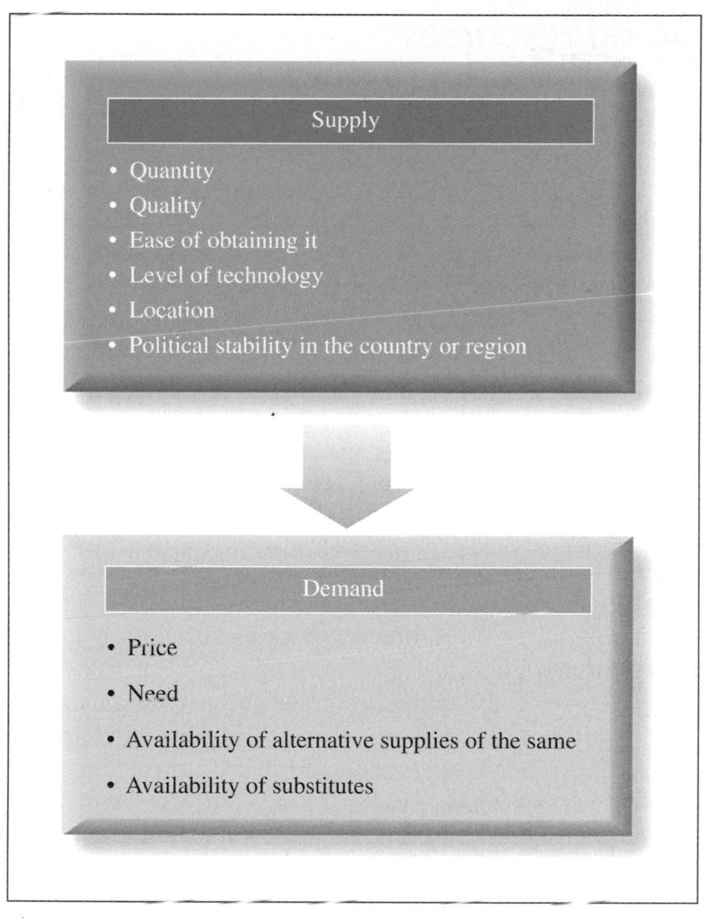

▲ **Figure 5.26** Factors which affect whether or not a resource is used

▲ **Figure 5.27** North Sea drilling platform. The oil companies were not short of experience of working offshore, but had never previously drilled for oil in a place where weather and sea conditions were so persistently rough.

World resources

Will there be enough natural resources available to satisfy the needs of a world population predicted to continue to grow until at least 2100? When other animal populations are studied, the natural environments upon which they must depend have resource limits usually referred to as their 'carrying capacity'. If carrying capacity is exceeded, nature takes its course. Breeding is reduced and fewer young survive because of food shortages. Total population is quickly brought back into balance with the resources available. However, humans are unique among animals because they can increase carrying capacity by technological advance. They are also able to swap resources from resource-rich to resource-poor parts of the world.

Despite the uniqueness of humans within the living world, the Earth is nonetheless a closed system. There are finite limits to global stocks and reserves of non-renewable mineral resources. Life expectancies for selected minerals shown in Figure 5.28a are calculated on the basis of current known reserves and use. It is merely a 'snap-shot' because new discoveries are being made all the time, while amounts used go up and down. The fossil fuel estimates are made by BP-Amoco and the other mineral estimates are from the US Geological Survey. They are not necessarily the same as you will see quoted in other sources, but they are responsible estimates. Estimates for some minerals have changed little over the last 50 years. Oil is the classic example. Its life expectancy has remained at around 40 years, despite phenomenal increases in world consumption. Increased consumption has been matched by new finds and by improvements in technology which allow a higher proportion of the oil present in each well to be extracted. The life expectancy of natural gas has actually increased. Previously oil companies had little use for it and it was burnt off as a by-product from obtaining crude oil. It is now recognized as an increasingly valuable fuel because of its combination of low emissions of pollutant gases and high heating power.

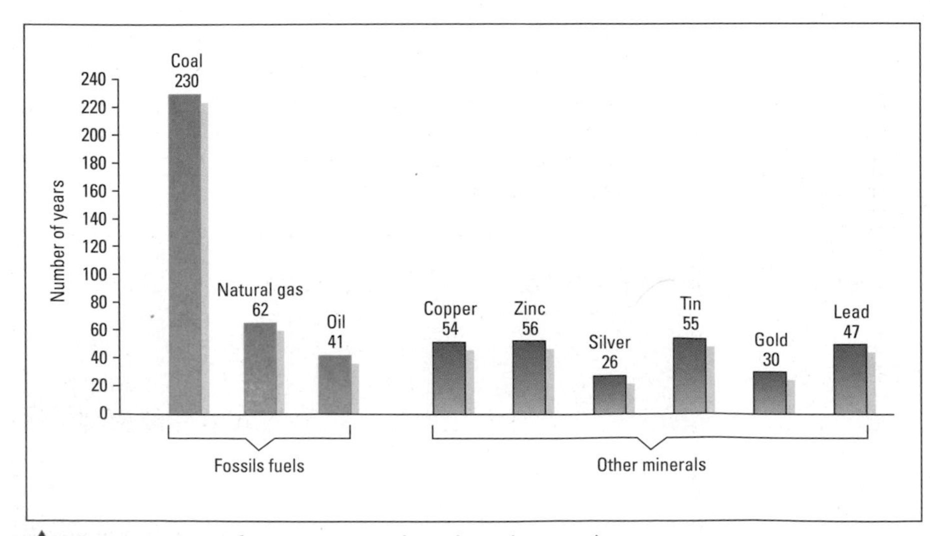

▲ **Figure 5.28a** Life expectancies for selected minerals

▲ **Figure 5.28b** Bingham copper mine in Utah, USA. It is one of the world's largest and deepest open pits.

Reduce, Re-use, Recycle

Although finite, there are ways in which the life expectancies of minerals can be extended even in a time of rising populations. The three Rs for resources are Reduce, Re-use, Recycle. Reduced consumption is achieved by individuals switching off lights and machines when not in use and by companies installing energy efficient lighting, heating and air conditioning systems. Roof insulation, double glazing and cavity wall infilling are included as standard in new homes and grants are available in the UK for older properties. An example of re-use is water cleaned in sewage works; another is containers and plastic bags. Recycling is not new. Some industries have recycled for many years; scrap iron has been used for decades in making steel and has reduced the amount of new iron ore needed. Collecting metal and textiles for recycling is a profitable business. Scrap men touring residential areas in the UK with carts and wagons cannot afford to look rich, but not many are poor. Awareness among the public in MEDCs about the need to recycle is increasing. Bins for glass, cans and newspapers are sited in frequently visited places. The government-imposed landfill tax is forcing a change in attitude; many local authorities in the UK now organize house-to-house collections and encourage separation of different types of waste to facilitate re-cycling. Even so, the UK still lags behind many of its EU partners in the percentage of waste recycled (see Chapter 6, pages 253–256).

▲ **Figure 5.29** The three Rs for resources

In most LEDCs there is no such thing as organized recycling, but it happens spontaneously since a rich person's waste is a poor person's income. Municipal rubbish dumps, and waste bins in wealthy urban neighbourhoods, are meticulously scoured by an army of workers of all ages; anything capable of being recycled or re-used is rescued. 'There's money in muck' is an old saying that remains true and it is the incentive that people need to allow the life of some of the world's finite resources to be extended.

▲ **Figure 5.30** 'Workers' on the municipal rubbish dump in Manila, the Philippines. An example of unofficial yet highly efficient resource conservation

Questions

1 **a** Outline two classifications of resources.
b Discuss the problems of making a classification of resources.

2 **a** Explain what is meant by 'The Earth is a closed system'.
b Evaluate the relative merits of two strategies for conserving natural resources that are known to be finite.

3 Investigation
a Research the policies of your local authority towards resource conservation.
b Investigate the spatial effects.

4 Read the newspaper article below from February 1998.

▼ **Figure 5.31** Adapted extract from *The Financial Times*, 6 February 1998

Cornish tin mine to close after rescue bid rejected

A £6m rescue package for the South Crofty tin mine in Cornwall was rejected by the government as 'clearly not viable'. The chairman of South Crofty and a senior partner of Crew Group, the Canadian owner, blamed low tin prices and competition from South America and the Far East, where low wages and easier mining make operations cheaper. 'The reality is the price and exchange rates and low grades we are operating means mining comes to an end'. The announcement of closure ended months of speculation over the future of Europe's last working tin mine, which employed 275 workers.

The local MP said that she would press to keep the South Crofty mine dry so it could be re-opened if the price of tin rose again, but it is widely expected that it will be flooded, ruling out ever working the mine again. Crew Group, which has minerals, metals and coal mining interests in South America, southern Africa and Thailand, has invested £6m in South Crofty in the last four years.

a To what extent were global factors responsible for the closure of South Crofty?
b Make a justification (even though you may not agree with it) for the government paying out the rescue package to keep this mine open in local, national and global terms.

Oil as an example of a non-renewable resource

Coal was already well established as the fuel of the Industrial Revolution by the time oil was discovered in Pennsylvania, USA, in the mid-nineteenth century and it took some time for its potential to be appreciated. However, by the second half of the twentieth century it had overtaken coal and become the fuel of the modern era. This happened for a variety of reasons, many of them related to the fact that oil is a liquid and coal is a solid. Oil is easier and cheaper to obtain from underground, to transport long distances by tanker across water and by pipeline across the land, and to use in transport, homes and factories. An added bonus is that useful by-products are recovered in the refinery.

Commercial exploitation of oil occurs in about 50 countries; it is therefore a mineral with a reasonably wide distribution. However, from many countries amounts produced are quite small and half of world production is in the hands of just seven countries (Figure 5.32). It is purely a matter of geological chance whether gently folded anticlines of sedimentary rocks, in which oil-bearing porous rocks are trapped between impermeable rocks above and below, have remained undisturbed. Within countries of production, oil-bearing rocks are often highly concentrated spatially, sometimes in inhospitable locations such as Alaska in the USA and under the North Sea in the UK and Norway.

There is a poor match between the big producers and consumers of oil. The top ten consumers are listed in Figure 5.33; only two produce more than they consume. Half of them do not have any significant oil production of their own. One key feature is that the USA alone accounts for one quarter of total world consumption. Despite being the world's second largest producer, it is still the world's largest importer. In fact in 1999 the USA imported 427 million tonnes of crude oil – almost as much as was imported into the whole of Europe and double the amount imported by Japan (Figure 5.34). The Middle East is the source region for half the crude oil that enters international trade. This is easy to understand. The Middle East is a sparsely populated desert region with low consumption demands, yet it is responsible for one third of the world's annual crude oil output. The dominant oil state is Saudi Arabia; 11.9 per cent of world production compared with only 1.8 per cent of world consumption leaves it with a massive 10 per cent of world oil production available for sale to other countries. It is no surprise that the economic, political and strategic importance of Saudi Arabia is immense.

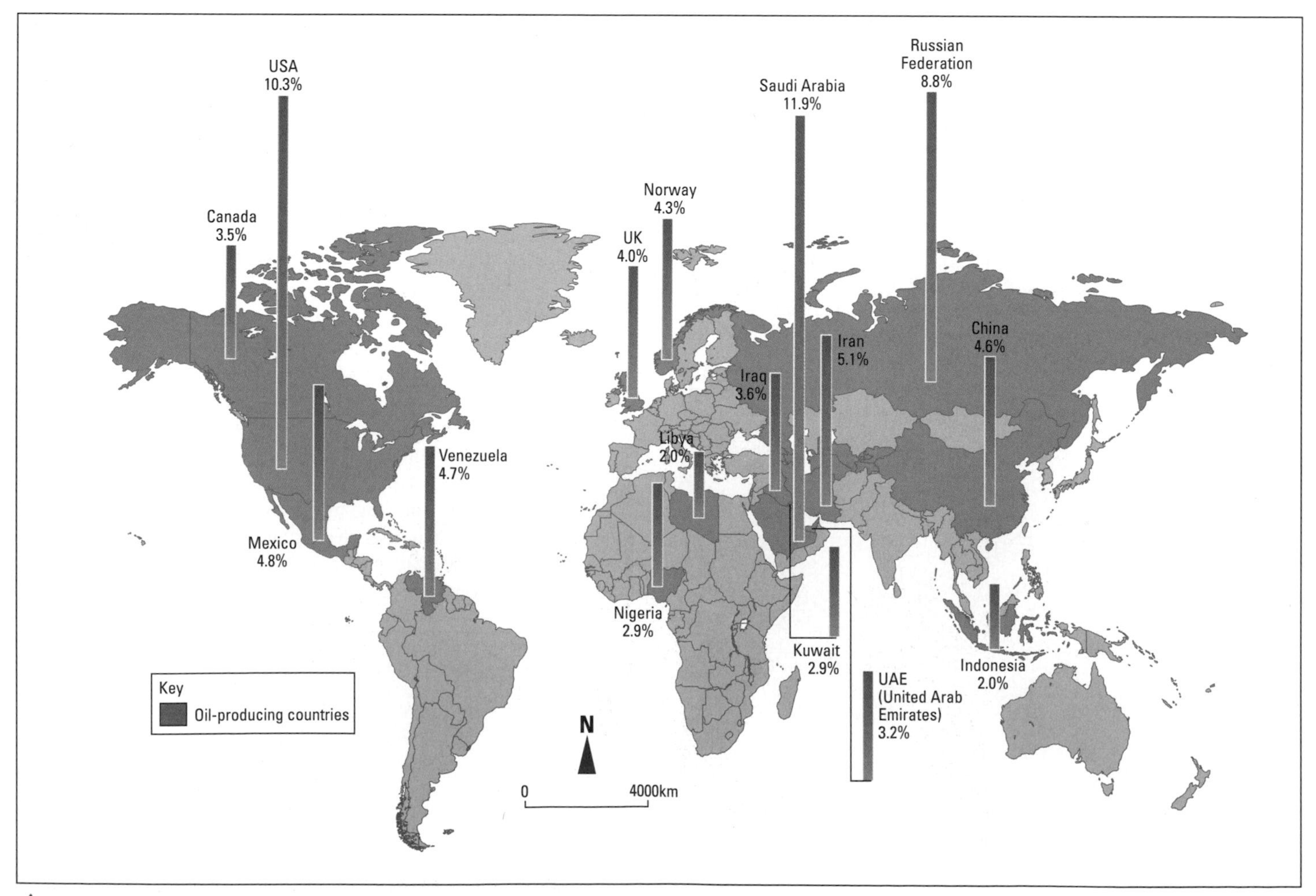

▲ **Figure 5.32** Countries responsible for 2 per cent or more of world crude oil output in 1999

▼ **Figure 5.33** The ten countries which consumed most oil in 1999

	World consumption (%)	World production (%)
1 USA	25.5	10.3
2 Japan	7.5	-
3 China	5.8	4.6
4 Germany	3.8	-
5 Russian Federation	3.6	8.8
6 South Korea	2.9	-
7 France	2.8	-
8 India	2.7	1.0
9 Italy	2.7	0.2
10 Canada	2.4	3.5

As Figure 5.34 shows, oil from the Middle East supplies every world region. The greatest amount to a single country in 1999 went to Japan (207.4 million tonnes), highly developed but without any of its own oil deposits. The greatest amount to a region went to Asia (excluding Japan and China), with 292 million tonnes exported in 1999. Southern and eastern Asia is the most highly populated world region and many countries within it are developing economically; oil fields in the Middle East are its closest source of crude oil. Much of the remainder goes to more economically developed countries in Europe, a continent in which consumption far exceeds production. The USA sucks in the oil surpluses from other countries in the Americas, notably Canada, Mexico and Venezuela because of proximity. It reduces American reliance upon Middle Eastern imports to less than 25 per cent of national needs.

The other significant aspect to consider in any study of oil as a resource is world reserves (Figure 5.35). Geological and engineering information indicates with reasonable certainty that these are the quantities that can be recovered in the future from reservoirs under existing economic and operating conditions. These are even more highly concentrated spatially than is current production. The Middle East, a politically volatile region, has almost two thirds (and Saudi Arabia alone has one quarter) of world reserves, compared with just over 5 per cent in the USA. More than 6 per cent are in the Russian Federation and other former Soviet republics, countries which have yet to settle down fully politically and economically after the end of communism. The rest are in LEDCs. Therefore the separation between the big producing and consuming countries, already large, is set to widen in the future.

▶ **Figure 5.35** Proved reserves of crude oil at the end of 1999

Top 10 countries for oil reserves	
Country	**World total (%)**
1 Saudi Arabia	25.5
2 Iraq	10.9
3 UAE	9.4
4 Kuwait	9.3
5 Iran	8.7
6 Venezuela	7.0
7 Russian Federation	4.7
8 Libya	2.9
9 USA	2.8
10 Mexico	2.7

Key

USA	South & Central America	Middle East
Canada	Europe	Africa
Mexico	Former Soviet Union	Asia Pacific

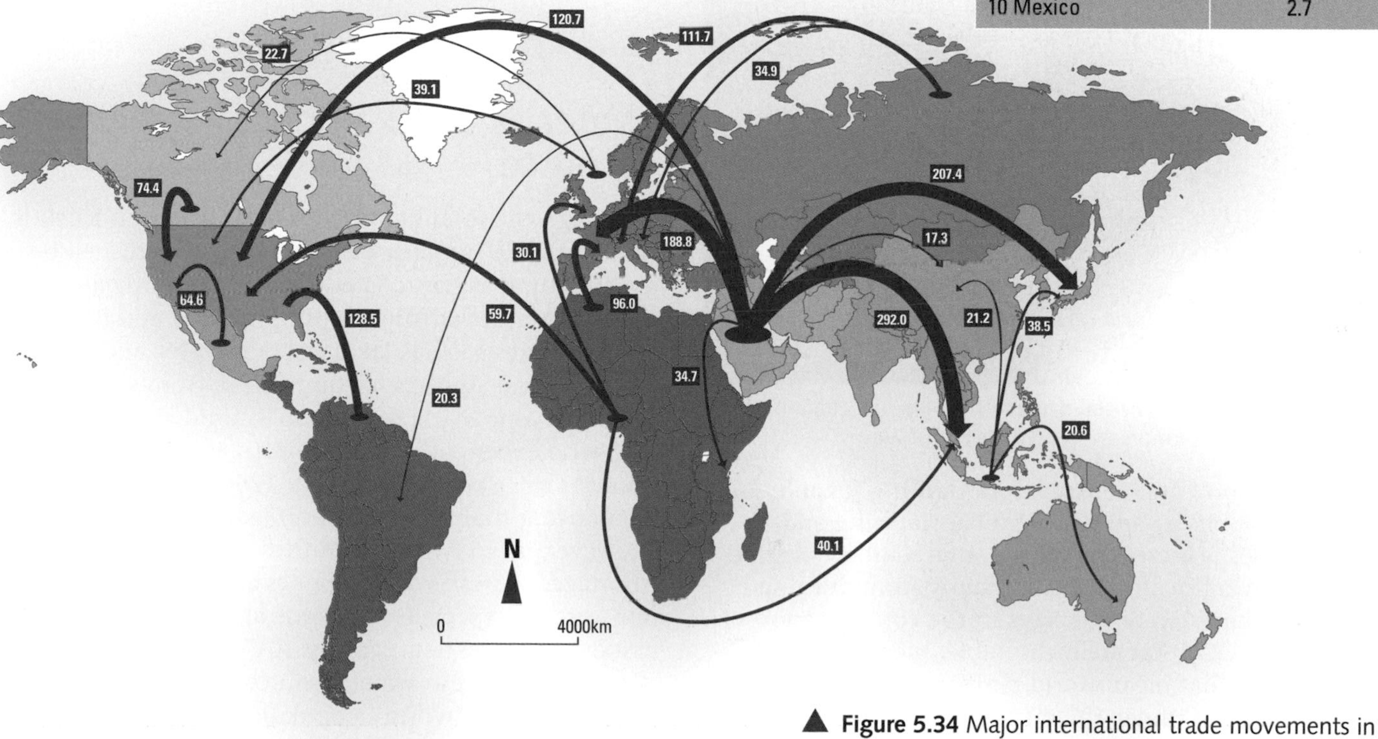

▲ **Figure 5.34** Major international trade movements in crude oil in 1999 (million tonnes)

The current low life expectancy of oil among the world's minerals (Figure 5.28a) and the spatial concentration of world reserves outside areas of greatest use in the more economically developed world might be expected to be factors encouraging research into alternative energy sources. The drawback is that oil is a cheap fuel, convenient to use, and without an obvious replacement for some of its uses such as for transport and petro-chemical products. Another factor that should be supporting the search for alternatives is environmental damage. Exploitation, transport and use of oil cause considerable environmental problems. Some are short term. Oil spills from tanker accidents devastate local ecosystems, but in coastal locations nature repairs the damage in the medium term and the ecoystem frequently returns to what it was before. However, there is public disgust at television pictures showing damage to bird and other marine life. Sometimes particular events stick in the public's memory, such as the wrecking of the Exxon Valdez in the fragile tundra environment of Alaska. After the oil companies had been forced into taking expensive precautions when building the trans-Alaskan pipeline (chapter 4 page 159), their reputation was sullied when the Exxon Valdez left an extensive oil slick in Prince William Sound, one of the most environmentally sensitive places on earth.

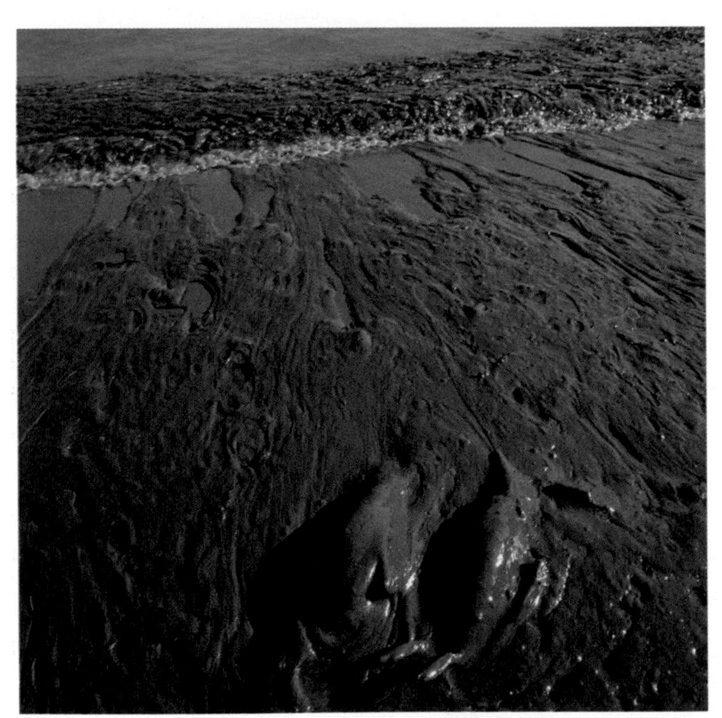

▲ **Figure 5.36** Environmental damage from the wrecking of the Sea Empress, Milford Haven, Wales

Other environmental damage from burning fossil fuels is long term. Public awareness of global warming and its consequences is increasing all the time. Carbon dioxide emissions into the atmosphere, mainly from burning fossil fuels, have led to increases in the concentration of atmospheric CO_2 that are measurable. Meteorological records show that mean world temperatures have increased by just under 1°C during the last 150 years. The Rio Earth Summit in 1992 was seen by many as a turning point since this was the first time that the issue of global warming had been discussed at an international forum. The next meeting in Kyoto created targets for carbon dioxide reductions, which are currently being 'worked towards' with widely varying rates of commitment and enthusiasm by governments. At least the principle has been established that global issues require international solutions, even if concrete results remain elusive.

Questions

1 a Study Figure 5.34.

i How many million tonnes of oil did the USA import in 1999?

ii The total amount of oil traded in 1999 was 2,025.7 million tonnes. What percentage of traded oil was imported into the USA?

iii Draw a pie graph to show the relative importance of regions and countries supplying oil to the USA in 1999.

b Give reasons for **i** the amount and **ii** the pattern of oil imports into the USA.

2 a Outline the reasons why oil remains a vital world resource.

b Explain the global importance of **i** Saudi Arabia and **ii** the USA in connection with oil as a resource.

3 **Investigation**

With the support of short case studies, examine the environmental effects of the exploitation, transport and use of oil.

Water as an example of a renewable resource

Although the total quantity of fresh water on Earth is finite, surface supplies keep on being replenished by precipitation as part of the water cycle. Rainwater supplies surface streams, tops up natural and human surface stores such as lakes and reservoirs, and fills underground aquifers for human use from springs and wells. Anyone living in the cool humid climate of the UK, who experienced in 2000-2001 its wettest twelve months since records began in 1766, may need some convincing that there is a shortage of fresh water! However, up to twenty countries are highly vulnerable to shortages of fresh water supplies and the world's thirst for water is expected to become an increasingly pressing issue during the new century. A United Nations assessment of fresh water resources in 1997 found that one third of the world's population lives in countries experiencing medium to high water stress (Figure 5.37).

Figure 5.37 World water scarcity. The map shows the vulnerability of countries to water scarcity using a composite index based on available water resources versus current use, reliability of water supply, and national income.

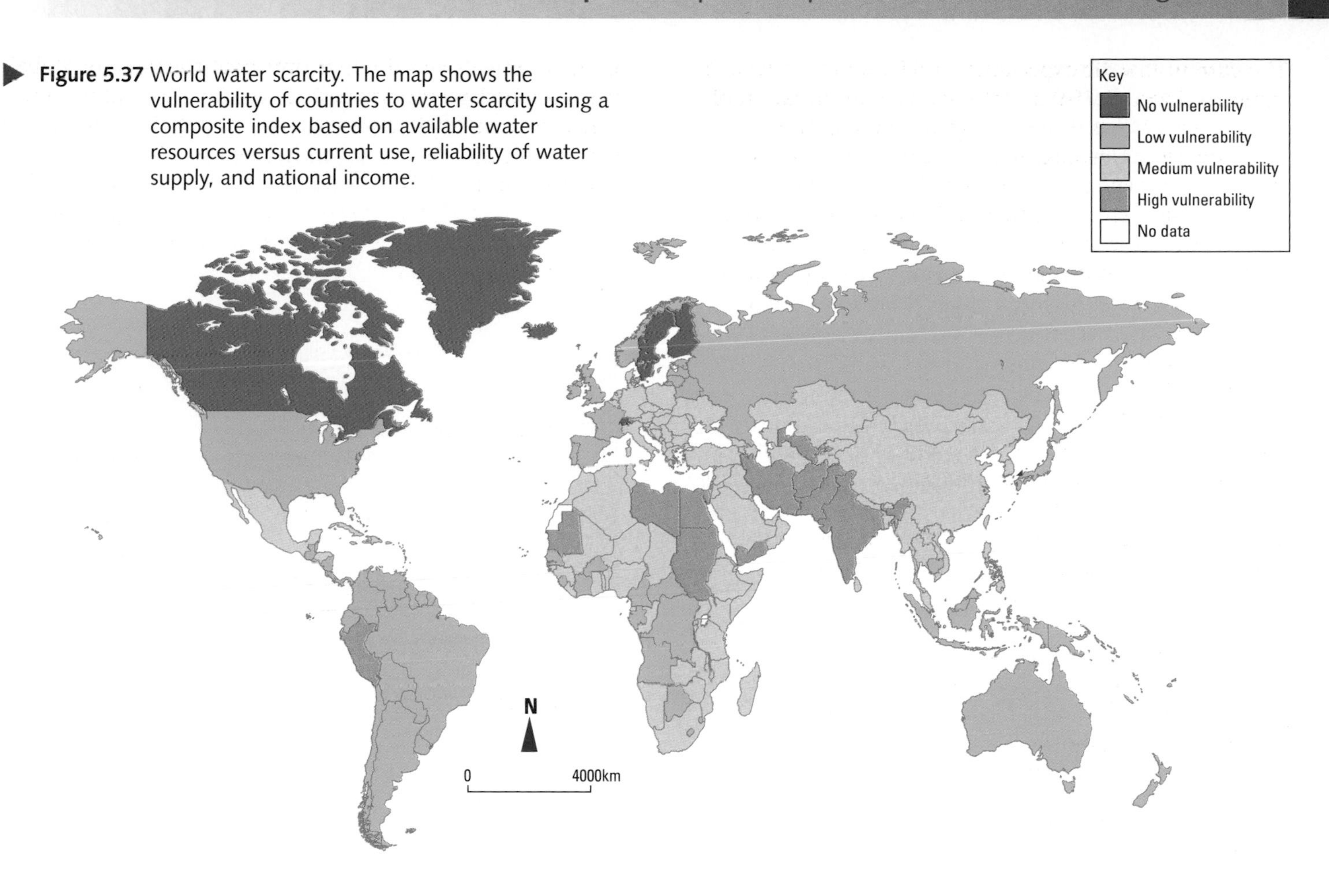

The background to the water issue, and why water resources in many countries will require more careful management in the future, is threefold.

First, global water consumption is increasing rapidly, well ahead of population growth. During the twentieth century, water consumption increased sevenfold. Figure 5.38 shows that two thirds of world water goes to agriculture and that the proportion tends to be higher in the LEDW. More water used for irrigation is itself a sign of the need to grow more food to feed the world's growing numbers of people by increasing yields and extending the area under cultivation. Population is going to continue to grow and so too is the demand for food. A significant increase in water use in the household and industrial sectors from population growth and new economic development is also forecast. Although consumption per head continues to rise in industrialized countries such as the UK, the greater increase in water use will be in LEDCs in line with their faster rates of population growth.

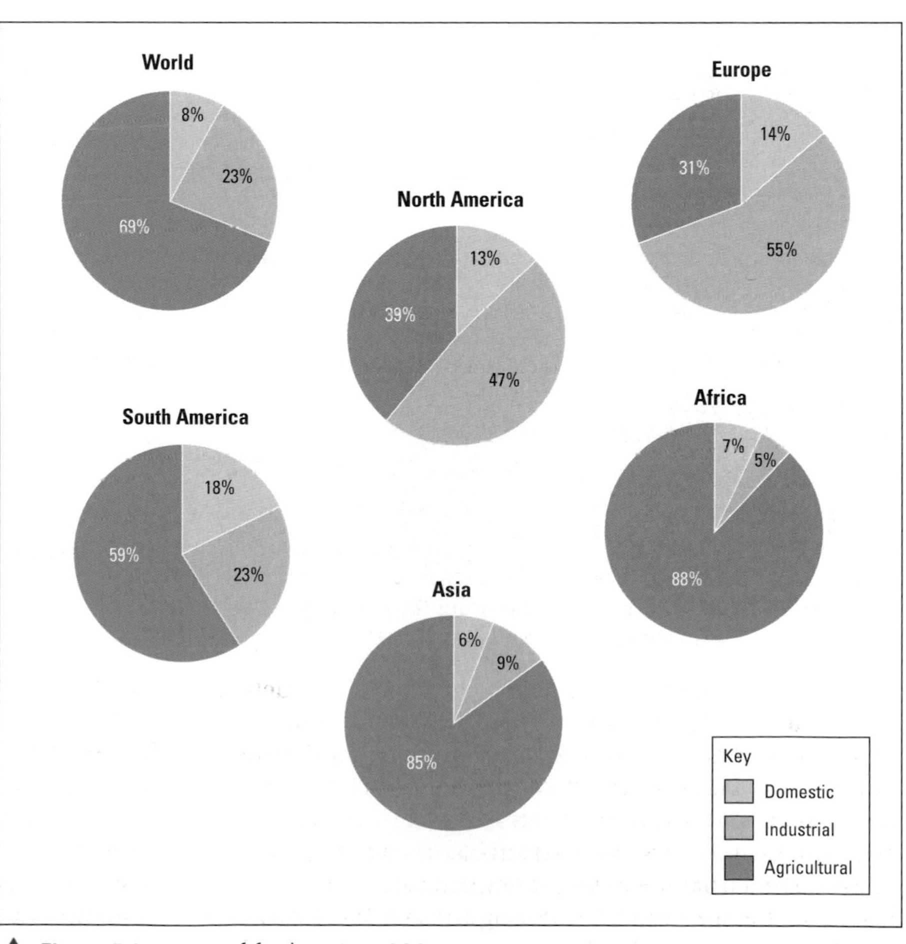

Figure 5.38 Users of fresh water 1998

Second, fresh water supplies have an uneven spatial distribution. The world average is over 7,000 m^3 per person per year; if this were evenly spread across the globe, water supply would not be an issue, because in global terms water supplies are abundant. Figure 5.39 shows the extremes of water wealth between countries. The data is for the annual internal renewable water resources per head of population (in cubic metres). The very water rich (at least ten times more than the world average) are located either in the hot, wet tropics or in humid temperate latitudes; the very water poor (under 5 per cent of the world average) are predominantly located in the Middle East and North Africa. Gulf countries such as Saudi Arabia and Kuwait overcome their lack of internal fresh water by operating desalination plants. The great input of energy required to change sea water into fresh water is usually a major hurdle to desalination as a source of fresh water, but it is not a problem in countries that are oil rich. This is why they are not shown in Figure 5.37 as having high vulnerability. Singapore imports water from Malaysia, its water-rich northern neighbour (21,259m^3 per head). Egypt is a populous country; its low value serves to emphasize the country's total dependence upon Nile water obtained from wetter lands to the south and water management after the construction of the Aswan High Dam. Some countries are living in an unsustainable manner by depleting their groundwater reserves faster than they can be replenished by precipitation. Water is a bulky resource with a low money value, which makes transfers from water-rich places to those that are water poor difficult if not impossible.

▼ **Figure 5.39** Extremes of national water wealth (from a study of 150 countries)

Water rich (cubic metres per head per year)		Water poor (cubic metres per head per year)	
1 Iceland	606,498	150 Kuwait	11
2 Suriname	452,489	149 Egypt	43
3 Guyana	281,542	148 U.A.E.	64
4 Papua New Guinea	174,055	147 Libya	100
5 Gabon	140,171	146 Jordan	114
6 Canada	94,373	145 Saudi Arabia	119
7 New Zealand	88,859	144 Mauritania	163
8 Norway	87,691	143 Singapore	172
9 Congo Republic	78, 668	142 Yemen	243
10 Liberia	72,780	141 Israel	289

Third, water pollution is increasing, which means that large volumes of surface water are no longer available for human uses. In many MEDCs, since there have been investments in infrastructure, stronger legislation, closer monitoring and improved management, water quality has steadily improved in recent years. In the majority of LEDCs undergoing rapid industrialization and experiencing an urban explosion, populations are faced by accelerated contamination of surface water supplies by untreated human and industrial wastes. The pollution threat is even more serious when mining and manufacturing pollute groundwater supplies, where contamination is difficult to control and slow to dilute.

▲ **Figure 5.40** The northern end of Lake Nasser viewed from the top of the Aswan High Dam. The lake stretches the length of England into Sudan.

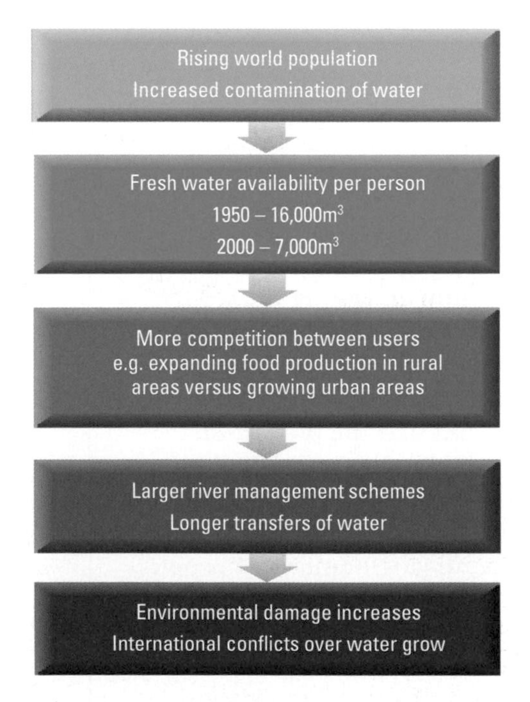

▲ **Figure 5.41** Fresh water is a decreasing resource

Some of the consequences of water becoming a scarcer resource are summarized in Figure 5.41. The Chinese government, already building the controversial Three Gorges Dam on the Yangtse River, is likely to go ahead with an even larger scheme to transfer water from central China into the less water-rich north east. However, many argue that, instead of building more and larger dams, the key to reducing water worries is better management of the water resources already available. Most irrigation projects are badly managed, judging from the estimate that about two thirds of irrigation water is lost to evaporation, run off and seepage rather than reaching the crop for which it is intended. The open channel method of irrigation, the one most widely used due to cheapness, is wasteful of water. The drip or trickle irrigation method, currently used on less than one per cent of the world's irrigated land, is much more water efficient; it has the added advantage that, by keeping moisture more permanently in the root zone, the accumulation of salts and resulting soil salinization are prevented. Given the high percentage of water used for irrigation in LEDCs, a lot of water could be saved and released to other users. More water could be re-cycled, especially in areas which lack waste water systems at present; municipal waste water after treatment is a potential source of new irrigation water in arid regions.

Fresh water supply is a growing international issue. Water shortages are heightening political tensions in those areas where surface rivers or underground aquifers cross borders. The problem is widespread (Figure 5.42). Watersheds and drainage basins are shared by countries for at least 70 of the world's major rivers. To be sound and effective, water management must be undertaken at the level of the whole basin; in practice most decisions are taken at national or local levels. The number of countries drained by one river and its tributaries can be high. In Europe, it is 13 for the Danube and 8 for the Rhine-Maas; in Africa it is 10 for the Nile and 9 for the Congo. In Asia, the Ganges and Brahmaputra each pass through three other countries, leaving Bangladesh, the country at the mouth of both rivers, at the mercy of decisions made in the other nations' interests. The drainage basins of the Tigris and Euphrates are in four countries, but Turkey controls the headwaters in both. Its ambitious water management schemes have met with the wrath of its Arab neighbours to the south. Of all the world regions, the Middle East is the one most sensitive to water supply issues.

▼ **Figure 5.42** Major watersheds and drainage basins which cross national borders

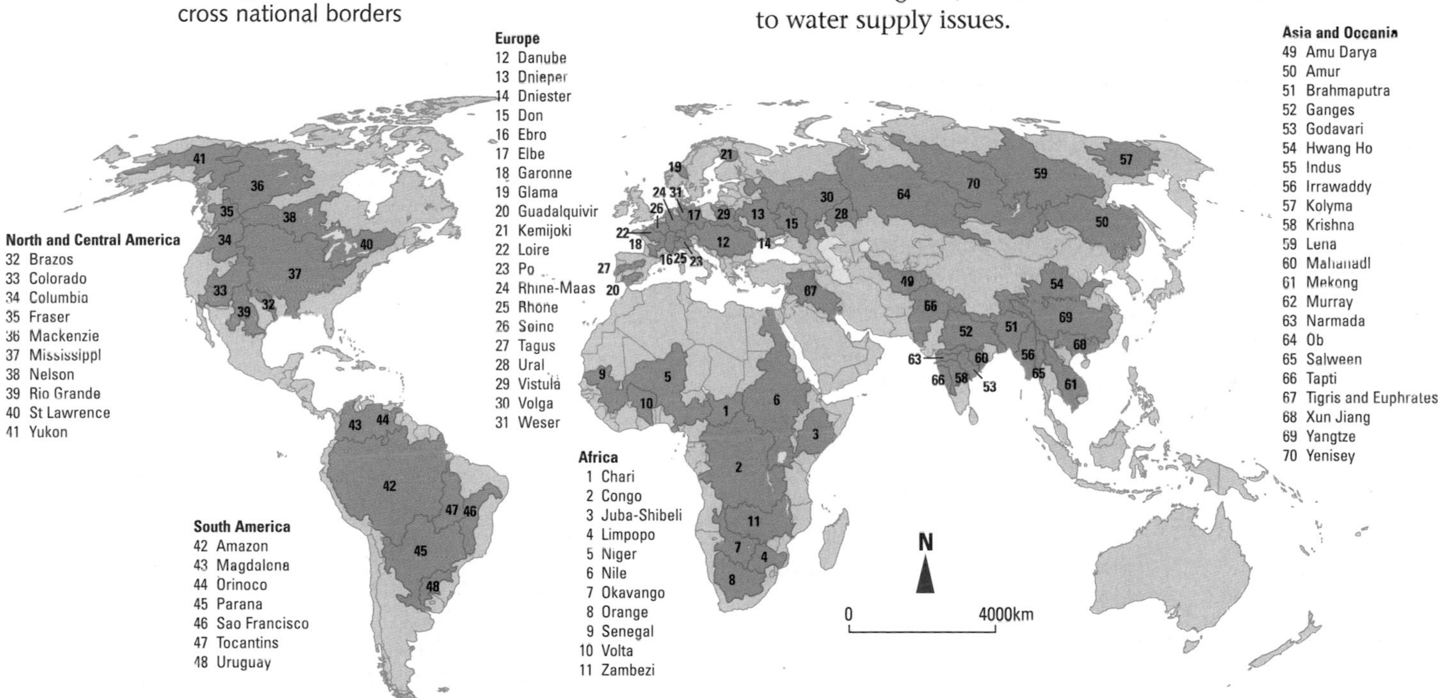

Questions

1 'Water is a renewable resource'.
'Some countries are short of fresh water'.
 a Elaborate upon each statement.
 b Discuss the extent to which they conflict.

2 **Investigation**
 a Find a map in another source which shows the world pattern of precipitation. Describe the main features.
 b Where and for what reasons is it different from the pattern of world vulnerability to water shortage shown in Figure 5.37?

3 **a** Describe what Figure 5.38 shows about the ways in which the world's fresh water supplies are used.
 b Explain why there is great potential for improved management of them.

4 Annual renewable water resources in the UK are 1,219 cubic metres per head. Comment on whether the UK is water rich or water poor in global terms.

5 **a** Give reasons why 'fresh water supply is a growing international issue'.
 b **Investigation**
 Choose one region/area (see Figure 5.42) where water supply is an international issue. Examine the causes, consequences and likelihood of finding solutions.

Summary

The world seems unlikely to run out of resources as quickly as neo-Malthusians and the most gloomy of environmentalists are predicting. Although according to one estimate there is enough oil in the world to last for another ninety years, perhaps the most urgent challenge is to develop alternatives to fossil fuels to the point where they are price competitive. At one time nuclear power was seen as the big hope, and some scientists still believe that it is, but since Chernobyl and other incidents this has become an increasingly unpopular option with the public. In countries where the Green lobby is strong, as in Germany, it is no longer being considered as a future option. The UK government is wrestling with its target from Kyoto that by 2010 at least 10 per cent of energy needs will be met from renewables (Figure 5.43). To raise this from the 2001 level is going to be a major challenge. Wind power is seen as a big hope since the UK's climate, island nature and position on the western edge of Europe give it a high potential. After improvements in turbine technology, inland wind farms in the UK are now cost competitive with coal and gas-fired power stations. In April 2001 the locations of the 18 offshore windfarms were announced, each with as many as 30 turbines, which together will generate the equivalent of 1 per cent of electricity supply. Some of the other options for renewables in the UK are given in Figure 5.45. Globally the UK contribution can only be small; the major world player is USA. The Kyoto Protocol for the USA to make a cut of 5 per cent by 2010 was not officially ratified by the Clinton administration and was torn up by President Bush as too costly for American business.

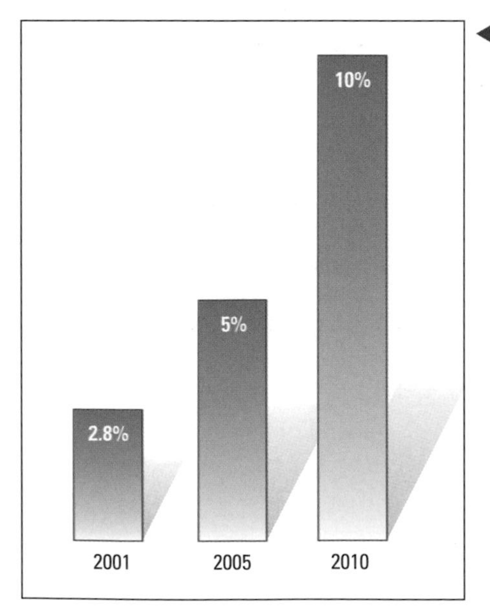

◀ **Figure 5.43** Targets for the use of renewable sources of energy in the UK

▲ **Figure 5.44** A coastal wind farm near Workington in Cumbria, which has won general approval from the local community soon to be added to by offshore wind farms using larger turbines

Much resource exploitation causes environmental damage, often to avoid higher costs, and sometimes because of bad management methods. It is likely to remain unsustainable in the medium and long terms, unless resource management receives a higher level of commitment and financial support. Management is needed as much for resources usually considered renewable, such as fresh water, forests, soil and fish stocks, as for non-renewable minerals. The evidence for the unsustainable use of the Earth's resources is everywhere.

▼ **Figure 5.45** Renewables in the UK – actual, probable for 2010 and estimated potential

Technologies	Now (%)	2010 (%)	Potential (%)
Large-scale hydro	1.4	1.4	1.4
Landfill gas	0.6	0.75	0.5
Wind power	0.3	5	45
Other biofuels	0.4	3	10
Solar power	0.001	0.5	85
Tidal power	0	1	25
Wave power	0	0.5	18
Total	2.8	10 plus	More than 100

Questions

1 Describe and comment on the relationship between the forecast for world resources made by the Club of Rome in 1972 and more recent estimates of world resources.

2 **Investigation**

'People hold widely differing opinions about future relationships between world population and world resources'. Elaborate upon this statement and discuss the reasons why opinions of people are so different.

3 Study Figure 5.46 below, which shows water pollution.

▼ **Figure 5.46** Water pollution

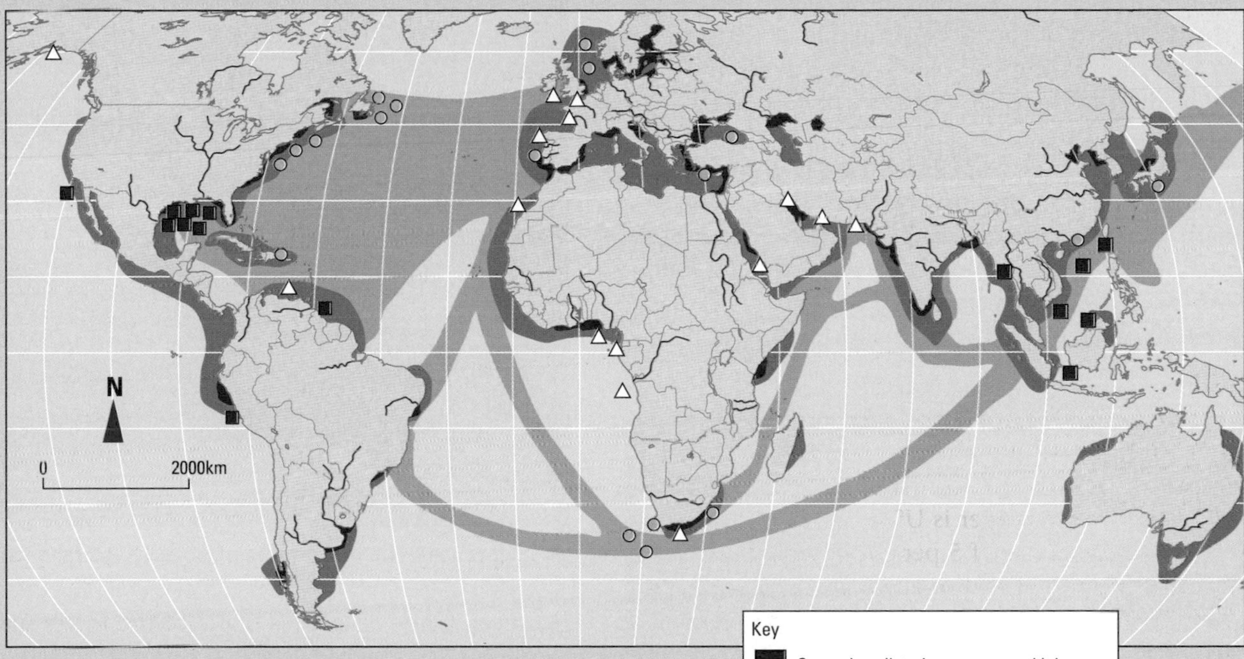

a Describe the main features of the distribution of water pollution in the world.

b Explain why:
i water pollution is a global problem
ii the problem is greater in parts of the world than others.

Demographic response

Figure 5.47 shows that there are many global signs of human-induced unsustainability. Take the top box headed 'Altered biogeochemistry'. Global average temperatures are rising and extreme weather events seem to be increasing in frequency and severity. The amount of ultra-violet radiation reaching the surface is increasing due to the depletion of the layer of high level ozone. Nitrogen is accumulating and overloading rivers and lakes and acidifying them. Toxic heavy metals and chemicals are building up steadily in organisms and ecosystems. Water tables are falling in every continent and some rivers are running dry. Nuclear waste, which will remain radioactive and a danger to life for thousands of years, continues to accumulate. It can be argued that the countries of the more economically developed world, with about 20 per cent of the total world population, are chiefly responsible.

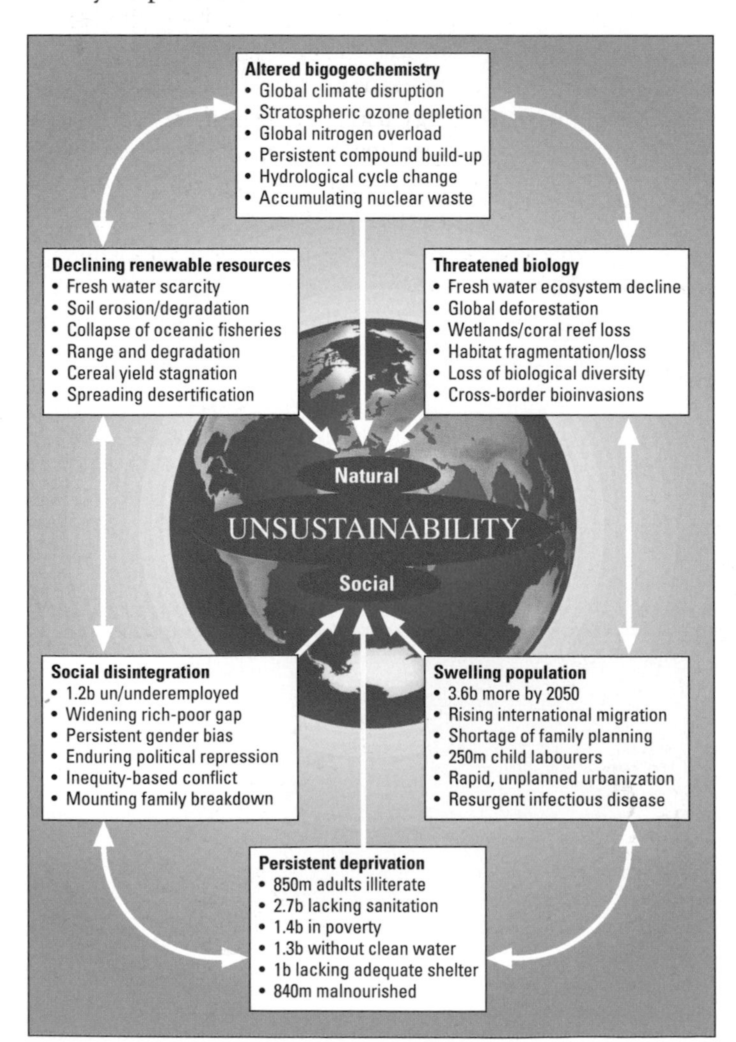

▲ **Figure 5.47** Global signs of human-induced unsustainability

▲ **Figure 5.48** The many faces of poverty. Accra in Ghana

However, when a study is made of the lower half of Figure 5.47, many of the social signs of unsustainability are more applicable to countries in the less economically developed world. Rapid population growth in the recent past, at the present and into the future is an LEDW phenomenon. Already the economic and social indicators are less favourable for the poor South than for the rich North. If rapid population growth continues, the outlook is bleak for many LEDCs. Returning to the example of Ghana, the government there is already finding it hard enough to service a population of 20 million, let alone another 18 million during the next 20 to 30 years. Today a third of the population of working age is unemployed. A clear majority of the total population still live in rural areas. Many perceive leaving the villages for the cities as their only hope. Accra is already the magnet for thousands of illiterate people. Unplanned urbanization and its range of associated socio-economic problems are the inevitable results. In many LEDCs resources and populations are out of balance with little likelihood of an early correction to the problems associated with overpopulation.

Poverty has many faces. The most obvious one is economic – low income. Its social faces include poor health, lack of knowledge and education, strained personal relationships, frequent family breakdown and low status for women. A political dimension is frequently present as well with limited freedom and few rights, and in some countries outright government repression. On top of these, there is environmental impoverishment for squatter settlement residents living in urban squalor or for villagers trying to scratch a living from land affected by soil erosion and water shortages. Some people are living desperate lives in abject poverty without choices. In the box headed 'Social disintegration' in Figure 5.47 there is reference to the widening gap between rich and poor. At one level this refers to MEDCs becoming richer while LEDCs remain poor. At another level it refers to the widening gap between one LEDC and another. Some LEDCs have enjoyed substantial economic development, especially the NICs, mostly concentrated in the Far East, whereas others, many located in sub-Saharan Africa, have made minimal progress. The least economically developed form a group of very poor nations, suffering from the 'Persistent deprivation' referred to in Figure 5.47.

Questions

1 a Briefly outline how the signs listed in Figure 5.47 show 'human-induced unsustainability'.

b Give further details about the human causes of two signs from each box that are related to the natural world.

2 To what extent is the MEDW responsible for the natural and social signs of unsustainability highlighted in Figure 5.47?

Indicators of development and welfare

Some elements of wealth and welfare are capable of being measured. However, a health warning has to be attached to all national statistics that are going to be used for international comparisons. How reliable are they? The most widely used economic measure is GDP. This is always likely to under-estimate income per head in those countries with large subsistence and informal sectors, the full output from which is unlikely to enter official statistics. On the other hand by taking into account population size and converting local currency into US dollars, the GDP provides the best comparative statistic available. It acts as a quick and easy guide to a country's level of wealth. For some countries GNP records a truer picture of total national income; examples include those MEDCs that derive a substantial income from overseas investments, and those LEDCs that have large numbers of their nationals working abroad. Examples of the latter are North African, Middle Eastern and south-west Asian countries that are close to the oil rich, but lowly populated, Gulf States. Employment structure and energy consumption can be viewed as reliable indicators of different levels of economic development; with only enough exceptions to prove the rule. The following statement holds true that, as the economy of a country grows, the percentage working in agriculture decreases and the amount of energy used per head increases. When calculating energy use per head traditional fuels, such as firewood and dried animal manure, although used in substantial amounts in some LEDCs, are not taken into account because reliable and comprehensive data is not available for them.

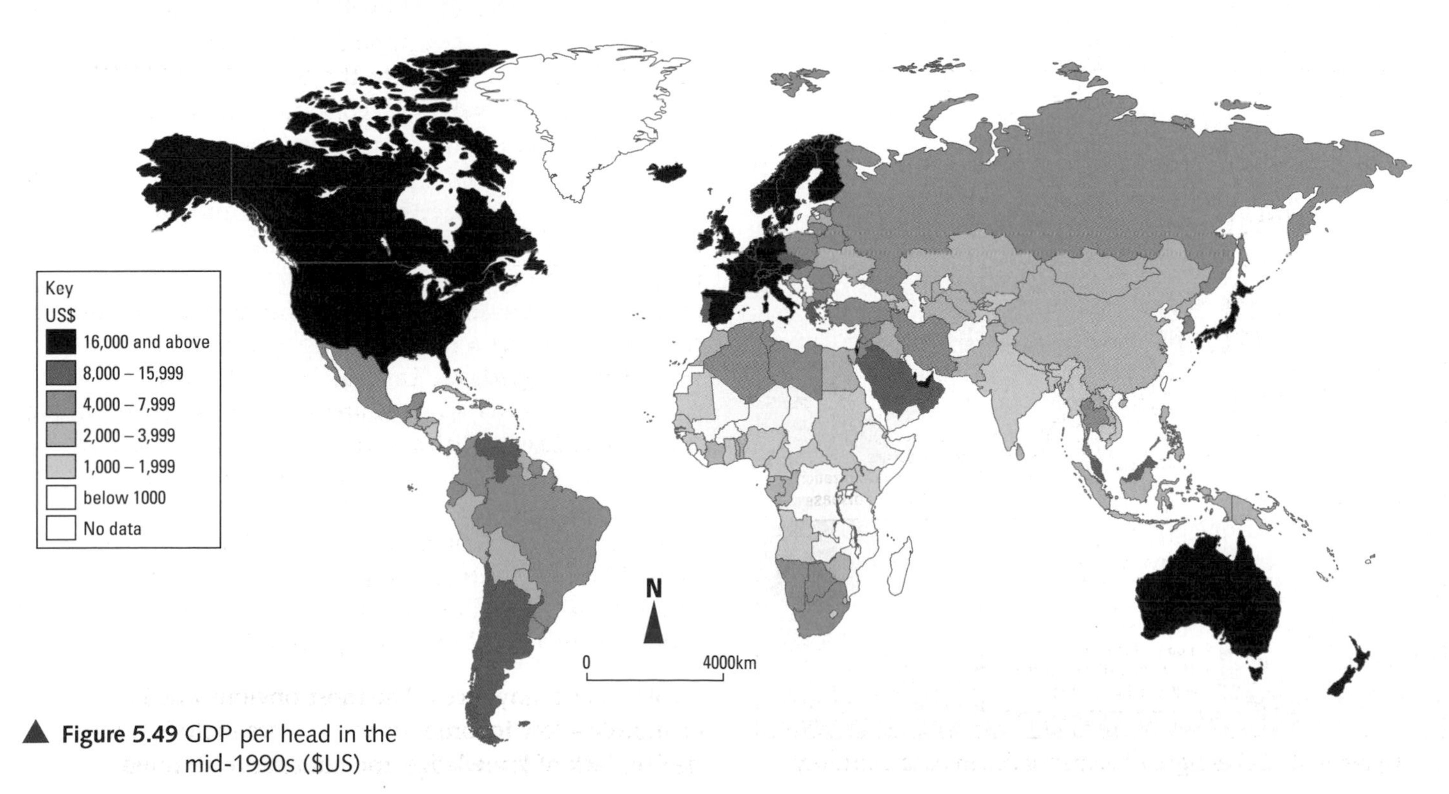

▲ **Figure 5.49** GDP per head in the mid-1990s ($US)

▼ **Figure 5.50** Total fertility rates (mid-1990s)

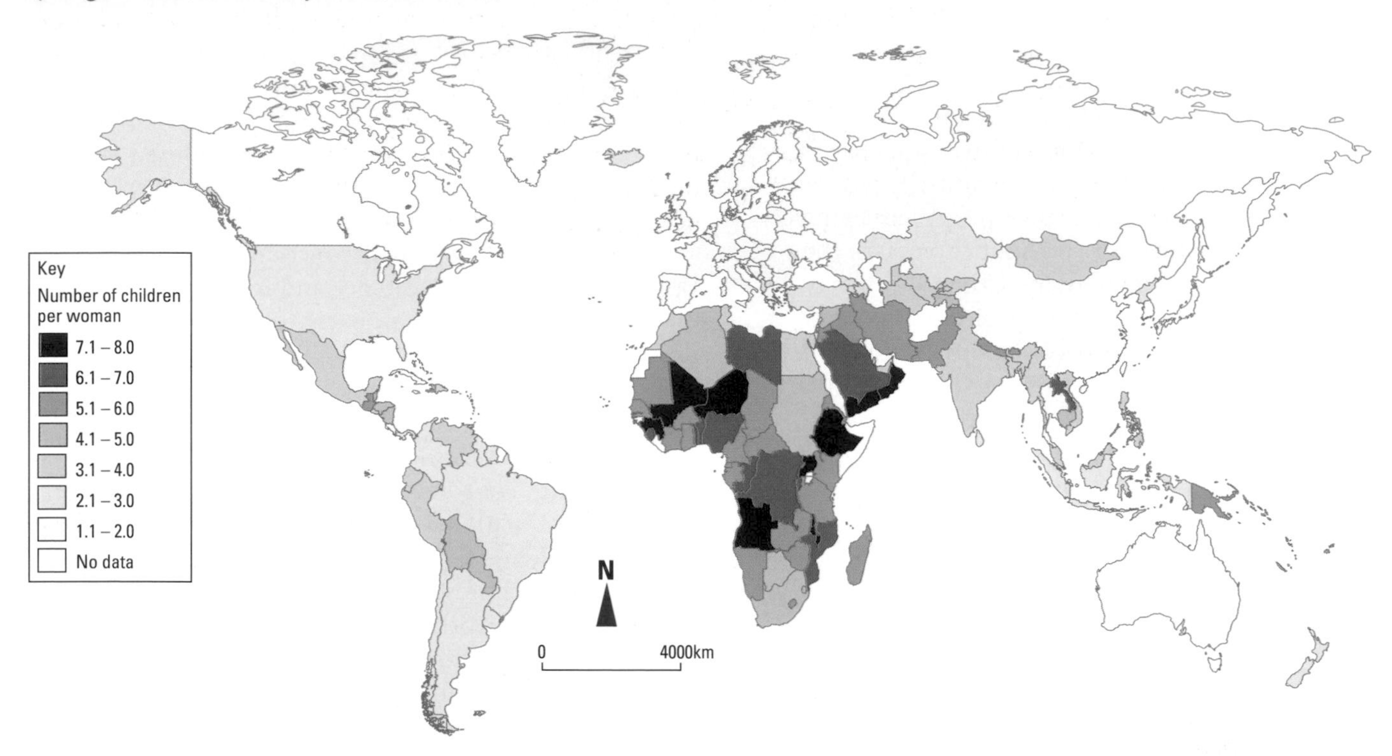

Definitions for measures of development and welfare

• Economic

Commercial Energy Consumption *– the amount of fuel used per head of the population in a year, obtained from both home sources and imports*

Employment structure *– the percentages of the working population distributed between agriculture, industry and services*

GDP (Gross Domestic Product) *per head – total output of goods and services produced in a country in a year per head of its population stated in $US*

GNP (Gross National Product) *per head – the total output of goods and services produced in a country in a year plus any net income from abroad, per head of its population stated in $US. For example, net income from nationals working abroad would be included in GNP but not in GDP.*

• Social

a *Demographic*

Crude birth rate – annual number of births per thousand population

Crude death rate – annual number of deaths per thousand population

Fertility rate (total) – average number of children born alive to a woman during her lifetime

Natural increase – annual difference between numbers of births and deaths per thousand population

b *Health and welfare*

Access to safe water – percentage with reasonable access to safe water, including treated surface water and uncontaminated underground sources

Infant mortality rate – annual number of deaths of infants under one year of age per thousand live births

Life expectancy at birth – number of years a newly born infant can expect to live.

Population per doctor – number of people per physician (who has graduated from any faculty or school of medicine)

c *Education*

Adult literacy rate – percentage of people aged 15 and above who can, with understanding, both read and write a short, simple statement on their everyday life

Many other social measures are used to indicate imbalances between countries. Those related to health and education are prominent because they are fundamental in indicating levels of welfare and opportunity for individuals. Some give a direct measure of the healthcare available to people, such as population per doctor, whereas life expectancy indicates levels of health care in a more general way. Children under one year old need extra help; the infant mortality rate of a country is a reflection of health care, food supply and availability of safe water in a country. The critical importance of access to safe water in disease prevention and primary health care cannot be over-emphasized. Repeated bouts of diarrhoea kill infants and weaken adults, while water-borne diseases such as cholera and typhoid can cause death, particularly to the vulnerable members of society such as the very young and the elderly. Access to

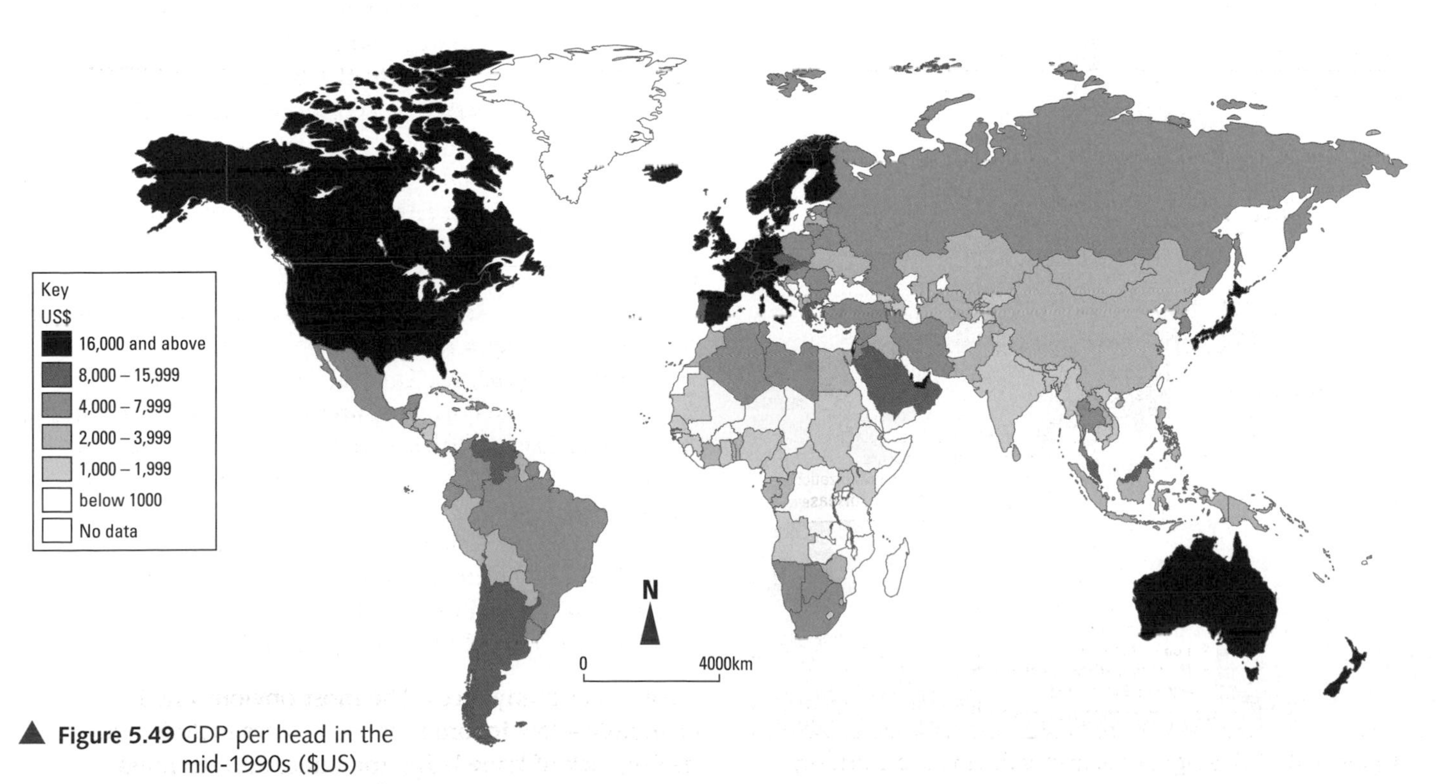

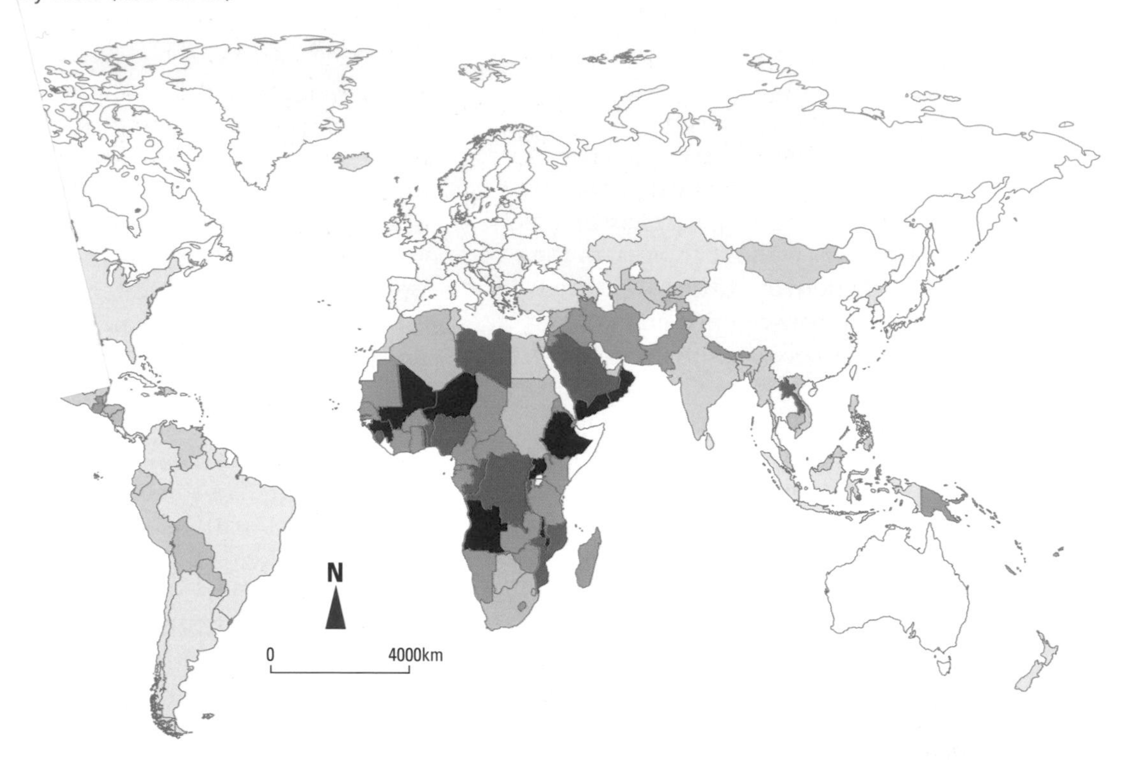

safe water is taken for granted in MEDCs, as also is its availability through the tap in homes. In LEDCs collecting water may involve much time and effort each day without any guarantee that supplies will be clean to drink. Reliable data about percentages of people with access to safe water are difficult to obtain in many LEDCs. However, one of the lowest percentages is in Ethiopia where in the late 1990s it was estimated that only 25 per cent of the population had access, although this is still a significant improvement on the estimate of 8 per cent for the late 1970s.

▲ **Figure 5.51** A stream in Bangladesh used for water supply and sanitation, an unhealthy cocktail

The adult literacy rate gives a good overall picture of a country's education provision. It tells a lot about the effectiveness of a country's education system and the proportion of children who are able to participate in it. In MEDCs, where state-provided primary and secondary education is taken for granted as a right for all, literacy rates are between 99 and 100 per cent. Among well developed LEDCs educational provision is often a high priority both for governments and parents; in the Asian 'tigers' such as Singapore and South Korea literacy levels are on a par with those in MEDCs. In the majority of South American countries primary level education has been universally available for such a long time that, even in rural areas, literacy rates are frequently between 80 and 90 per cent. In sub-Saharan Africa, however, the picture is very different; adult literacy rates rarely reach 50 per cent and this general figure hides the major gender bias against the education of females. Without literacy, opportunities for improvement are very limited. Inadequate education is a real impediment to development.

International agencies such as the United Nations prefer to use an index composed of several different measures. Using a combination of measures reduces the disadvantages of individual indicators and increases reliability. One index is the HDI (Human Development Index). It measures average achievements in a country in terms of three basic areas of human development – longevity, knowledge and a decent standard of living. It is calculated by creating a scale of values between 0 (the minimum) and 1 (the maximum) for each of the three variables for a common form of measurement. Values are aggregated and divided by three to give the index value. The top country was Canada (index value of 0.960), the bottom was Sierra Leone (0.176). The value for the UK was 0.931.

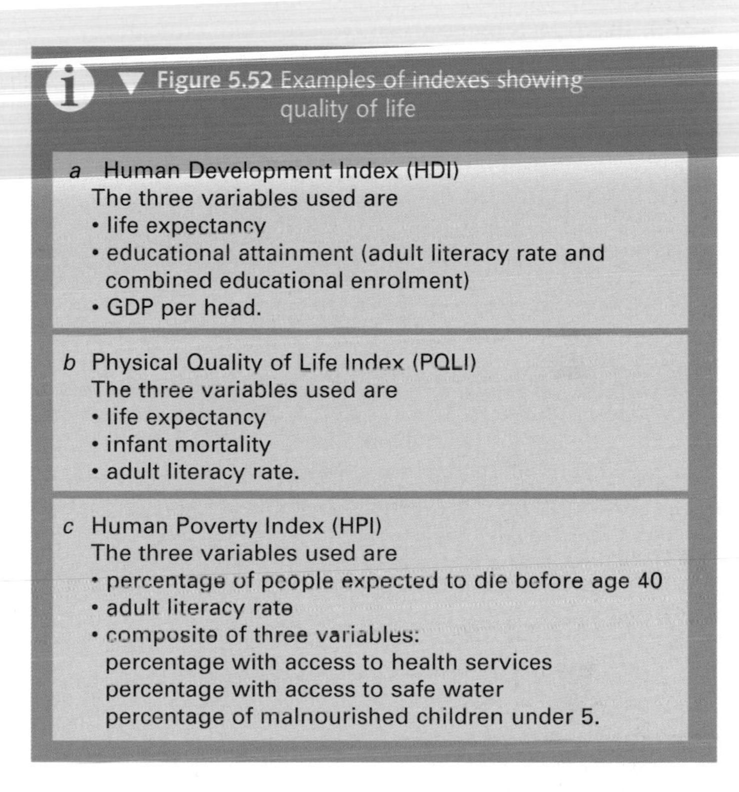

▼ **Figure 5.52** Examples of indexes showing quality of life

a Human Development Index (HDI)
The three variables used are
- life expectancy
- educational attainment (adult literacy rate and combined educational enrolment)
- GDP per head.

b Physical Quality of Life Index (PQLI)
The three variables used are
- life expectancy
- infant mortality
- adult literacy rate.

c Human Poverty Index (HPI)
The three variables used are
- percentage of people expected to die before age 40
- adult literacy rate
- composite of three variables:
  percentage with access to health services
  percentage with access to safe water
  percentage of malnourished children under 5.

By including the GDP and by taking economic as well as social factors into account the HDI is different from many other indexes, which are more tightly focused upon quality of life and the well being of people. The HPI (Human Poverty Index), for example, concentrates upon what needs to be provided for a decent standard of living, namely health care, safe water and plentiful food. It is not used for MEDCs where these are taken as standard; its main use is for showing variations in quality of life between one LEDC and another. Countries with many people suffering from severe deprivation and poverty can be identified. The manner of calculation means that a high value indicates the greatest poverty. The bottom eight countries with HPI values in excess of 50 per cent are Niger, Sierra Leone, Burkina Faso, Ethiopia, Mali, Cambodia, Mozambique and Guinea; poverty affects 50 per cent or more of the population in these countries. All are in sub-Saharan Africa apart from Cambodia. Some of the anomalies associated with only taking the GDP, such as the way it inflates the position of mineral-rich countries with small total populations, are avoided by using the HDI index. Oil-rich Gulf States, such as Kuwait, Oman and Qatar, are classic examples of these anomalies.

How valid is it to measure wealth and poverty in these ways? Poverty depends on the context. In LEDCs issues of poverty revolve around hunger, illiteracy, limited health services and lack of access to safe water, which is why they are used in the HPI. Examples of LEDCs which have moved up towards the top of the HPI, such as Singapore and Chile, have reduced poverty to the point where only a small percentage of their population is affected. This reminds us that there is a development continuum, that there are many intermediate levels of development between the highest and lowest in the world. In MEDCs by contrast, where food, education, health care and safe water are either universally provided or not an issue, poverty means something different. It concentrates more on social exclusion, such as for minority groups, or spatial segregation, such as in inner-city areas and on run-down council estates in the UK.

Questions

1 a Describe how Figure 5.49 shows that there is a major imbalance in the distribution of wealth in the world.
b Outline the ways in which Figures 5.50 and 5.52 help demonstrate the imbalances in wealth.

2 Using the photographs in Figures 5.48 and 5.51, describe how they show the economic, social and environmental faces of poverty.

3 Discuss the relative merits of using an index in preference to individual measures of development and welfare.

4 Assemble the evidence from the text and figures so far in this chapter that clearly show that sub-Saharan Africa is the poorest world region.

Population policies

On the one hand, people count as part of a country's resource base, and without people a country's natural resources would be left untapped. On the other hand, the greater the number of people living in a country, the greater the number of portions into which the national resource cake must be split. Many governments in LEDCs have woken up to this, but by no means all of them. The majority have population policies in place that aim to reduce birth and fertility rates, although the vigour with which they are pursued and financed varies greatly from one country to another. It was not always thus. While today China is best known in a population context for its 'one child policy' begun in the 1970s, the relatively new communist government in the 1950s promoted the idea that a populous nation was a strong nation. China's strength was in its numbers; with one quarter of the world's population China obtained an international status far beyond that justified by its level of economic development. The government of Nigeria maintained its love of population growth for even longer, until 1988 (Figure 5.53). Most countries shown in Figure 5.50 as having high fertility rates above 5.0 are still without national population policies.

Anti-natalist and natalist population policies

***Anti-natalist** = against birth*

Types of policies

a Prevention of births

- *setting up family planning clinics*
- *dispensing free contraceptives*
- *instigating sex education in schools*
- *using advertising and the media*
- *encouraging later marriages*
- *financial inducements for couples keeping below the specified number of children*

b Termination of births

- *promoting sterilization*
- *legalizing abortion*
- *financial penalties for couples going above the specified number of children*

***Pro-natalist** = for birth*

Types of policies

- *birth bonuses, both cash and goods*
- *lower tax rates with increasing numbers of children*
- *favoured treatment for housing and welfare benefits*

Many of the most successful long-term population policies have two important ingredients. One is government attitude. Commitment to the cause and a willingness to fund the policy are vital. The second is working closely with the people, getting them involved and operating at village or neighbourhood level. Coercive policies work only in the short term; they work for longest in countries where governments are non-elected and everything is centrally planned, as in China. They are more difficult to operate in a democracy, as the government of Sanjay Ghandi in India found when it lost at the polls after putting its weight behind a desperately unpopular policy of compulsory sterilization. However, each country's situation is unique (Figures 5.53 and 5.54). Further brief studies of India and Singapore show this as well.

The main criticisms of family planning programmes in India is that they have emphasized sterilization, which largely restricts their impact to couples who have already reached desired levels of fertility. Younger couples' needs for family planning and for spacing and delaying having children are partly neglected. Since most Indian families hope for more than one son to survive into adulthood, family sizes can be large before sterilization is sought. This still leads to considerable population growth.

▼ **Figure 5.53** Adapted extract about Nigeria from *The Financial Times*, 2 September 1994

Falling prosperity hurts family planning

In a continent where population growth outstrips economic growth, Nigeria with well over 100 million people is by far the biggest nation in Africa. Until Nigeria's health minister launched a national population policy in 1988, Nigerians had been so proud of their self-styled tag as the 'giant of Africa' that, as long as the oil money rolled in, they regarded high population growth as healthy, and saw little point in controlling the rate of growth. Since the mid-1980s, because of lower income from oil, economic decline had set in. An average population growth rate of 3.1 per cent per annum meant a doubling in size within 30 years. Population policy strategies included limiting each woman to four children and reducing by 50 per cent the number of women who marry before they are 18 years old.

Generalizing about Nigeria, a country of over 200 ethnic groups and very diverse cultures, is often deceptive. In the mainly Christian south, female education and literacy are far higher than in the predominantly Moslem north, where even the discussion of birth control is not widely accepted. Declining oil revenues in the early 1990s halted the progress towards family planning clinics and universal primary education, especially in the north, bolstering the influence of the Koranic schools. Even nationally, a UN review painted a bleak picture. 'The status of women in Nigeria has improved little over the last decade. In general, they are considered second class citizens not by law but because of the social and cultural climate. Although some women have made considerable progress in the academic and business world, Nigerian women, particularly rural, are clearly underprivileged.'

The fertility rate is 6.1 per woman. The literacy rate for woman is 31 per cent (54 per cent for men) and more than half of all Nigerian women are married at the age of 15. The problem of education lies not just with women. As a prominent woman's group in Nigeria points out, there may be a target of four children per woman, but in a polygamous society many men far exceed that figure. However, if the prospect of curtailing population growth is limited, the outlook for economic growth has become bleak. Strikes, shortages and a dearth of foreign exchange have taken the economy further downhill.

▼ **Figure 5.54** Adapted extract about Egypt from *The Financial Times*, 2 September 1994

Egypt boasts a decade of progress

'I am convinced that Islam is not against family planning' said a 30-year-old woman attending one of Cairo Family Planning Association's clinics, swathed in the black robe and veil, the badge of Islamic piety. 'My brother-in-law is a religious man and he ordered his wife not to use contraception. He tried to deter me, but I didn't listen. I encouraged all my friends to come to the clinic. Now all of them blossom like fresh jasmine'. The strictures of Islam have so far done little to put a brake on a decade of progress in population control, which Egypt's policy makers and aid workers consider little short of remarkable.

In ten years the population growth rate plunged from 3 per cent to 2.1 per cent. A fertility rate of 5.3 was reduced to an average of 3.9 births per woman and only 2.9 in urban areas. Knowledge of family planning among married couples is almost universal, while 47 per cent of women use contraceptives in Egypt, predominantly IUD devices and the pill, against 24 per cent ten years ago. Behind such results lie 20 years of concerted government policy, backed by foreign aid, of which USAID has provided 75 per cent of all family planning assistance, a total of about $170m. Enough to fill the media with birth control information and stock and staff hundreds of clinics, and for 96 per cent of all Egyptian women to be within 5km of a family planning centre.

Cheered as they are by the results, they haven't reached their ambition of creating population growth which Egypt can comfortably sustain. The 60 million plus population grows by another million in 10 months. Constraints on the country's most basic resources are severe enough. All but 4 per cent of the country is desert. Egypt is already consuming 95 per cent of its available water sources. However, population experts tend to agree that cutting the growth rate further is unlikely to come by providing more pills, coils or publicity campaigns alone. 'There is something missing,' says the clinic's doctor. 'It is the status of women in this country. We need to work hard on this'. A guide to the task ahead is that 66 per cent of Egyptian women are illiterate. It will need not only teachers and schools, but a change in ingrained attitudes. An improved economic climate would help. All that before the air can thicken with the scent of jasmine.

Nevertheless with economic improvement birth rates have fallen everywhere in India, as usual more in the cities than the countryside. There are, however, some pronounced regional differences. In the more socio-economically backward states in northern India, such as Uttar Pradesh, traditional attitudes persist and a woman's status is low so that the fertility rate has fallen less than in southern states, such as Kerala. The more favourable position of women in society in Kerala is considered to be the key factor. Historically women have enjoyed a high social status and are recognized as the heads of families. They have a more equal place in society and take a leading role in family decisions. The female literacy rate is almost 90 per cent, comfortably the highest in any Indian state. It is significant that Kerala is the only Indian state in which the fertility level is now below replacement level, despite it not being an economically advanced state.

Singapore introduced one of the world's most successful family planning policies in the late 1960s with the slogan 'stop at two'. However, the country has seen such economic success as the leading 'Asian Tiger' that by the early 1990s there were not sufficient young people to fill all the job vacancies. The present policy is pro-natalist, although targeted at its better qualified inhabitants, who are offered large tax exemptions and other benefits if they have three or more children. The discussion taking place in Singapore about the necessity of using foreign workers (Figure 5.55) may be an advance copy of what is likely to follow in some Europe countries as ageing populations bite into the numbers of nationals of working age (page 185).

▼ **Figure 5.55** Adapted extract about Singapore from *The Financial Times*, 11 April 2001

Courting the workforce of the future

Singapore has a problem: it does not have enough talented, young workers to drive its expansion into the new economy. The government has been playing Cupid by promoting dating agencies and encouraging Singaporean women to have more children.

The workforce is steadily growing greyer while the economy is changing shape. The demand for higher skilled workers has grown. The government is making a major effort to recruit more foreign talent. However, Singapore's newspapers have also been running a series of articles about how local people are feeling angry that their own careers are being stunted by the recruitment of foreign managers. One quarter of the island's 4m residents are now foreigners. This has led to a lot of concern and unhappiness, and fear about the future.

Questions

1 Explain with the aid of examples, the differences between:

a anti-natalist and pro-natalist population policies

b anti-natalist policies based on prevention and termination.

2 a Outline the reasons why fertility rates have fallen more quickly in Egypt than in Nigeria.

b Identify the main characteristics of successful population policies to control growth and comment on their relative importance.

3 Total fertility in different states of India was correlated with certain other variables. The results from calculating the correlation coefficients for three variables are shown in Figure 5.56.

▼ **Figure 5.56** Effects of social factors on fertility

Variable	R value
Primary health centres (per 1,000 people)	-0.24
Female health visitors (per 1,000 people)	- 0.09
Female literacy (%)	- 0.84

a Comment on the nature and strength of the relationships between total fertility and the other variables.

b Suggest explanations for them.

Migration policies

No matter how good a population policy to reduce growth is, there is a lag time before the full aim of low or zero growth can be achieved. Death rates continue their inexorable decline and this offsets early gains from falling birth rates. For a considerable period of time there are still more mouths to feed and provide with the essentials of life. When European countries were in a similar demographic situation during the nineteenth century to that of LEDCs today, they were fortunate. The 'New World' was in the process of being opened up; North America was full of empty spaces and undeveloped natural resources. There was somewhere for Europe's overspill population to go.

LEDCs progressing through Stages 2 and 3 in the demographic transition model today are less fortunate. Most international borders are sealed for legal immigrants. By the 1980s unemployment was a growing problem in many MEDCs, caused largely by mechanization and de-industrialization. Only people with shortage skills continued to be officially welcomed. Illegal immigration has grown, leading to significant movements across the North-South divide where the wealth gradient across the line is great, notably from Mexico, Central America and the Caribbean into the USA, and from North Africa into Spain, France and Italy.

▲ **Figure 5.57** Illegal immigrants are deported back to Mexico from the USA.

Most migration movements are internal. In the past migrants moved into empty areas containing undeveloped natural resources. However, the main movement is now in the opposite direction. As the ubiquitous problems in rural areas in LEDCs, such as landlessness, lack of water supply, and soil erosion, have been worsened by population growth, migration to the cities has become the universal movement, leading if anything to greater spatial concentration rather than dispersal. One country which did have empty land suitable for development, at least in the eyes of its government, was Indonesia. Java and Bali are very crowded islands; larger outer islands, such as Sumatra and Kalimantan (the Indonesian part of Borneo) have much lower levels of settlement. However, this is for a good reason; instead of recent volcanic soils of legendary fertility, their soils are derived from older and more weathered rocks and are less fertile. Large areas were left forested. The government began the policy of 'transmigration' in 1950; it was a programme of voluntary assisted migration to give poor people the chance to farm land of their own in hitherto unsettled areas. Movement was at its peak in the 1980s when up to three million people migrated. The policy has been very controversial. It has led to considerable deforestation (see **AS Level Geography**, pages 112-115) and many conflicts (see Figure 5.58).

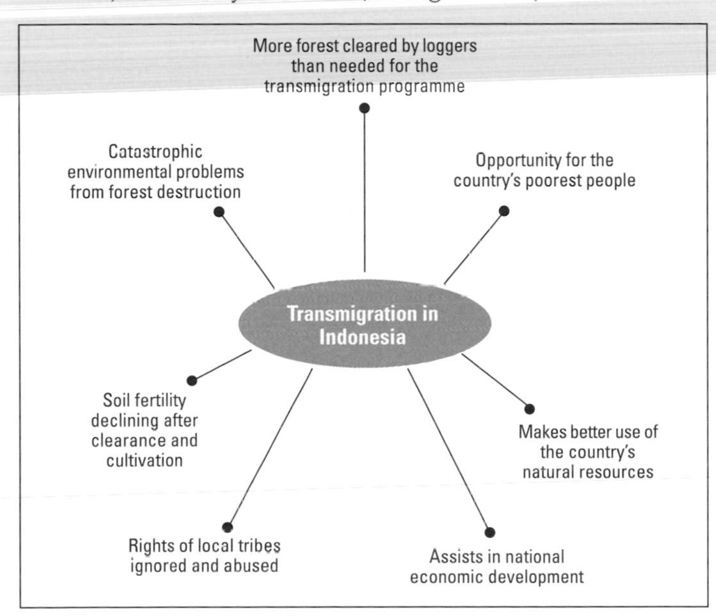

Figure 5.58 Issues and conflicts associated with the policy of transmigration in Indonesia

Equally controversial has been Brazil's 'march to the west'. Serious attempts to open up and develop the natural resources of its vast interior began after the symbolic re-location of the capital city in 1960 from Rio de Janeiro to the planned new city of Brasilia, founded on the eastern edge of the plateau as the gateway into the interior. Building roads was the key to the opening up of the interior physically. The government encouraged the migration of landless people from overpopulated regions, such as the *caatinga* of the North East, by promises of plots of land with legal titles, basic aid and infrastructure provision. The promised government help rarely materialized (as in Indonesia). Peasant farmers left to themselves did not have the resources to make a success of farming in the wet tropical environment. Instead, clearing the vegetation and opening up the interior was handed over to large logging and mining companies and to large farmers and organizations with financial support from the banks. This speeded up the rate of forest removal and it is still increasing as roads are paved and access into the interior is improved. Cynics suggest that government policy is driven by the need to divert attention from problems in the east – notably the very unequal distribution of land in which the poorest half of the rural population own just two per cent of the land and also the problems in the big cities. However, the economy of Brazil is benefiting from the exploitation of the Centre's mineral resources.

Figure 5.59 Climatic climax forest in the Amazon Basin. An untapped resource?

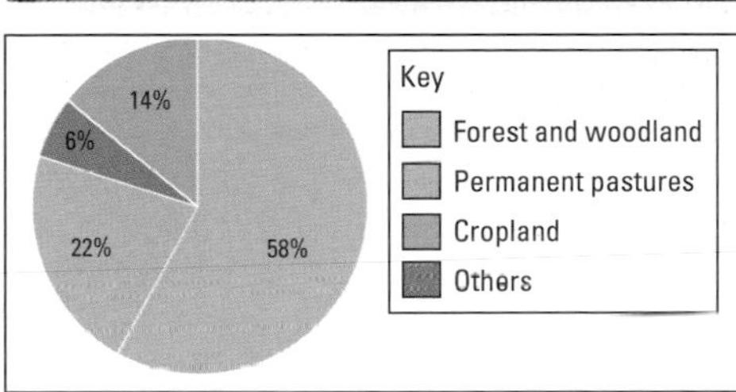

Figure 5.60 Land uses in Brazil (in 2000)

Questions

1 a Why is legal international migration for economic reasons (for work) on a smaller scale today than at any time during the last 200 years?

b Where and for what reasons is illegal economic international migration currently taking place?

c Why might legal migration from LEDCs to MEDCs increase within the next 50 years?

2 Investigation

a Draw a sketch map to show the pattern of roads in Brazil west and north from Brasilia.

b Outline, with named examples, the variety of economic activities in the area of Brazil covered by your sketch map.

c Taking a Brazilian viewpoint, draw up a table for the costs and benefits of continuing to open up the interior.

d **i** Why might the viewpoint of people living outside Brazil be different?
ii To what extent do you feel that the views of people living in MEDCs are valid about what happens in Brazil?

Resource response: food surplus in MEDCs

At the beginning of the new millennium the gap between the rich and poor worlds is wider than it has ever been. In North America and Europe obesity is the problem, not malnutrition. In the EU agricultural problems are to do with surpluses not shortages. Crop land is being set aside not extended. How countries in Africa would welcome having the same 'problems' as the EU and North America! Until the late 1980s, however, both MEDCs and LEDCs were pushing in the same direction, seeking to intensify farming and increase food production. The three ways to increase food production are summarized in Figure 5.61. Converting land from extensive to intensive uses is largely a matter of intention, planning and investment, although technological innovation has increased the number and extent of areas in which it can happen.

Figure 5.61 Ways to increase food production

a Increase output from land already being farmed by:
- using new seeds and improved breeds of animals
- using new crops not previously grown in the area
- changing from livestock rearing to crop growing
- improving disease control with pesticides and insecticides
- using inorganic (chemical) fertilizers
- education about good practice, e.g. rotation, soil conservation
- improving water control (both supply and drainage).

b Extend farming to land thought to be 'marginal' by:
- developing new strains of seeds more tolerant to 'difficult' physical conditions,
  e.g. in cold areas, seeds that can tolerate a shorter growing season
  e.g. in dry areas, seeds that are more drought resistant
- offsetting the effects of problematic physical factor, e.g. in areas of unreliable rainfall supply irrigation water.

c Open up virgin land to farming by:
- clearing the natural vegetation cover and replacing a natural ecosystem with an agricultural system
- extending irrigation to land that was previously desert beyond the margins of settlement.

Intensive farming and intensification

Intensive farming
Large inputs to gain as high an output as possible from the land.
Examples:
MEDCs – commercial market gardening close to urban markets in which high amounts of capital, technology, labour and fertilizers are invested per unit of land. Often farm units are small which allows for concentrated investment.
LEDCs – subsistence rice farming on the floodplains and deltas of rivers in Asia, where labour is the main investment on small plots.

Intensification of farming
Making the land produce more by increased inputs and efficiency. Some of the ways of achieving this are outlined in Figure 5.61

Extensive farming
Output per unit area of land is low. The lower income per hectare is balanced by spending less on inputs. Usually the available land area is large so that production and profitability from the whole area is all that matters. This may need to change if demand increases.

Figure 5.62 Intensive market gardening in Holland

Causes of the intensification of farming

Most changes in agriculture in MEDCs during the twentieth century led to intensification and increased output. What has happened in the UK is mirrored to a greater or lesser degree in other MEDCs. Farms have steadily increased in size through amalgamation enabling 'economies of scale'. Large farmers, banks, organizations and companies with interests in food products such as the Co-op, Findus and Birds Eye bought up fields and farms as they came on the market. Farming became a business, hence the term agri-business, especially in productive farming lowlands dominated by arable farming such as the Fens and East Anglia. Manpower has steadily declined, from about two million farm workers in 1800, to one million in 1900 and down to a quarter of a million in 2000. Machinery has taken over. Much large farm machinery is no longer farmer owned, but hired from contractors, thereby following business practices common in other industries.

▲ **Figure 5.63** An abandoned farm in Virginia, USA. Farmers and farm workers have deserted the land in all MEDCs, not just the UK.

The major effect on the landscape is that hedgerows are no longer a major feature of the countryside in prime arable regions such as East Yorkshire, Lincolnshire and East Anglia. Few grazing animals are ever seen grazing. For centuries British agriculture was dominated by mixed farming with crops grown and livestock kept on every farm. Now farmers specialize; the eastern half of the UK is more predominantly arable than it has ever been. On many farms a maximum of four or five types of crop are grown. The top seven crops planted in 1999 (in terms of total hectares) were wheat as number one, followed by barley, oilseed rape, linseed, peas, sugar beet and potatoes.

Agro-scientists developed new varieties of seeds suited to British conditions. Today much of the wheat and barley grown in England is winter wheat, which is ready to be harvested earlier and gives a higher yield per hectare than many of the old summer varieties. Friesian cows (the black and whites) give higher milk yields per animal than any other breed. Aided by selective breeding from the best stock, they are the only breed kept by the great majority of dairy farmers in the UK. Research by scientists employed by agro-chemical companies has led to the development of chemical fertilizers and pesticides for particular needs, so that crop yields keep on reaching new peaks while crop losses to diseases and pests keep falling to new lows.

All of the above were encouraged by the political and economic climate within the EU and the way in which the CAP (Common Agricultural Policy) was formulated and operated. The CAP was set out in the Treaty of Rome (1957) at a time when high agricultural productivity was considered essential to securing plentiful food supplies. One of the prime beliefs underpinning agricultural policy was that Europe should become as self-sufficient as possible in food, almost at any cost. Crops that saved on imports, such as sugar beet for tropical sugar cane and oil-seed rape for tropical oil palms, were given financial support. A complicated set of mechanisms were put in place to encourage farmers to produce more. Surpluses were bought up to maintain market prices and stored by the EU, which led to the infamous cereal, beef and butter mountains, and milk and wine lakes. Land improvements such as drainage and reclamation were supported, as also was the amalgamation of farms. Small holders were encouraged to retire early or give up farming to allow more efficient larger scale operators to take over.

▲ **Figure 5.64** A splash of yellow in North Yorkshire. Parts of British countryside turn yellow every spring as oilseed rape flowers, but this did not happen the CAP began to support its growth.

Other economic forces were pushing farming output in the same upward direction. Farmers working in the rural–urban fringe felt the market forces for intensification strongest. Market gardening (or horticulture), with or without the aid of greenhouse cultivation, has the highest inputs of labour and capital of any type of farming. Two or three crops of vegetables, flowers and fruit might be expected from each piece of land during a calendar year. These are the most perishable of fresh agricultural products; a quick consumption ensures maximum taste, greatest nutritional value and least waste. Taste and freshness are factors of increasing importance to a breed of consumers who are not totally ruled by price, as also is food grown organically without having seen or felt any type of agro-chemicals. One of the greatest UK concentrations of glasshouses is in the Lea Valley in East London, serving the UK's largest and wealthiest market (Figure 5.71). Fields growing green vegetables, such as sprouts, cabbages and peas within a radius of about 50km from the edge of London's built-up area, are also market driven (Figure 5.65).

◀ **Figure 5.65** A field of cabbages near Maidstone in Kent, the county referred to as the 'Garden of England'. It is a major supplier to London's fruit and vegetable market in the 'new Covent Garden'

▶ **Figure 5.66** The 'Pick Your Own' plastic strawberry dragged out each June on to the sides of a main road

Farmers in the rural–urban fringe are the most responsive to changes in urban demand. These make ripples in the countryside as fashions of city folk change. During the 1990s it became fashionable for townspeople to go and pick their own fruit, strawberries most of all, but also other soft fruit such as raspberries and blackcurrants. The number of garden centres has mushroomed! Many go well beyond plants and seeds and have become places for a family outing with cafes and play places; they represent an extension of urban retailing into the rural fringe. For farmers located close to urban areas providing for other recreational activities, such as horse riding, represents opportunities for diversification out of farming.

Governments in Europe were supporting schemes to increase agricultural land long before the CAP was invented. The enterprising Dutch, driven by population pressure and land shortage began reclaiming the shallow coastal inlet of the Zuider Zee into five large polders (units of reclaimed land at or below sea level) in the 1930s (Figure 5.67). The prime motive was new agricultural land and almost 90 per cent of the land in the first two polders reclaimed is used for farming, mainly arable. However, priorities change during the lifetime of major schemes such as this. The need for land for urban overspill and recreation increased as that for food production decreased so that land uses in polders number three and four, East and South Flevoland, are different. The final twist is that the intended fifth polder, Markerwaard, has been left unreclaimed largely on environmental grounds.

▼ **Figure 5.67** Zuider Zee scheme in the Netherlands

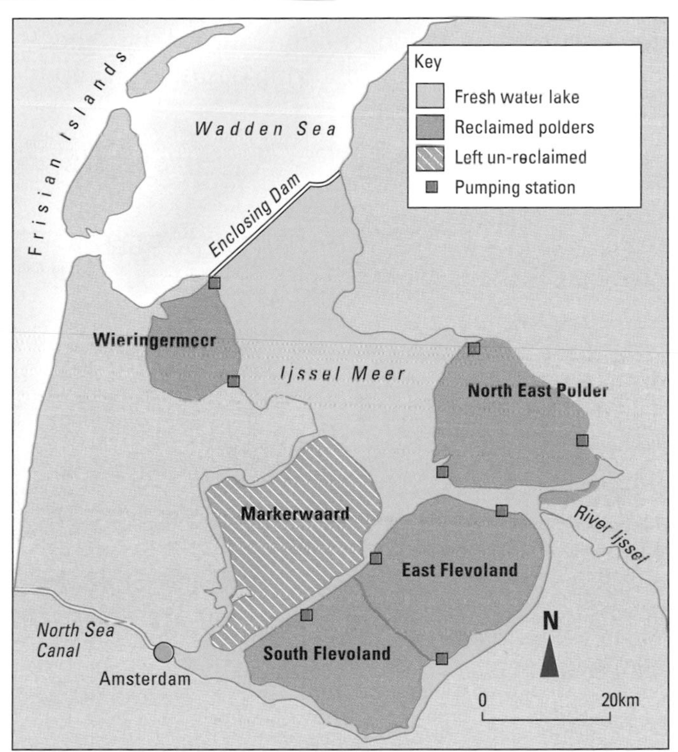

Polders	W	NE	EF	SF	M
Total area (ha)	20,000	48,000	54,000	43,000	41,000
Period of reclamation	1930–40	1942–58	1957 70	1968–83	-

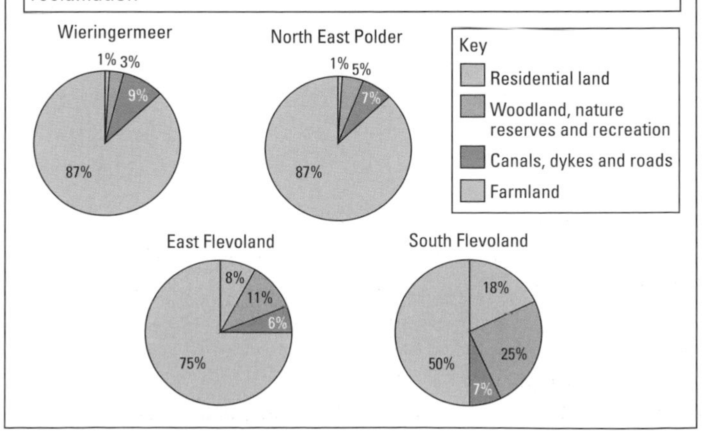

The Mezzogiorno in Southern Italy: increasing food production

Case Study

The Mezzogiorno is the 'land of the noon-day sun' south of Rome. While there were good physical reasons for limited agricultural output in many areas (mountains, rugged relief with bare rock outcrops, thin and dry limestone soils, torrid summer heat and drought), only extensive farming was practised on the potentially fertile coastal plains. Two human factors were responsible – fear of invasion and the system of land tenure. A history of invasions led to settlement in tightly packed hilltop villages for defence away from the lowlands (Figure 5.68). Absentee landlords owned large estates (*latifundia*) on the plains. They were more interested in holding the land for prestige than income. Monoculture of wheat alternated with fallow meant that the region's physical and human resources on the good land were under-utilized. Whereas on the poorer land on the slopes population pressure led to the subdivision of holdings into *minifundia* that were being overcropped leading to severe erosion.

▲ **Figure 5.68** Ravello, a typical hilltop settlement in the southern Apennines. Agricultural terraces visible below the settlement show that it was once intensively farmed despite the rugged terrain.

Piecemeal attempts at reform had been made, but post-1945 poverty persuaded the Italian government that more co-ordinated reform was essential. For this purpose the Cassa per il Mezzogiorno (Fund for the South) was set up in 1950 to implement a development plan, at first mainly for agriculture. One element of the plan was land reform. Land was expropriated from large and inefficiently run *latifundia* into which no money had been invested and redistributed to landless people. Over 200,000ha were taken away from about 1,500 landlords and given to over 30,000 families. The second element was to provide the infrastructure so that farming could be modernized and output increased. New roads, farmhouses, villages and service centres were laid out across the plains and connected up to power and water supplies. Large lowland areas such as the Metapontino west of Taranto were provided with irrigation water. A complete landscape transformation was achieved, as carefully cultivated plots of oranges and other citrus fruits, peaches and pears, salad vegetables and tomatoes replaced little cared for wheat fields, sheep pastures and olive groves.

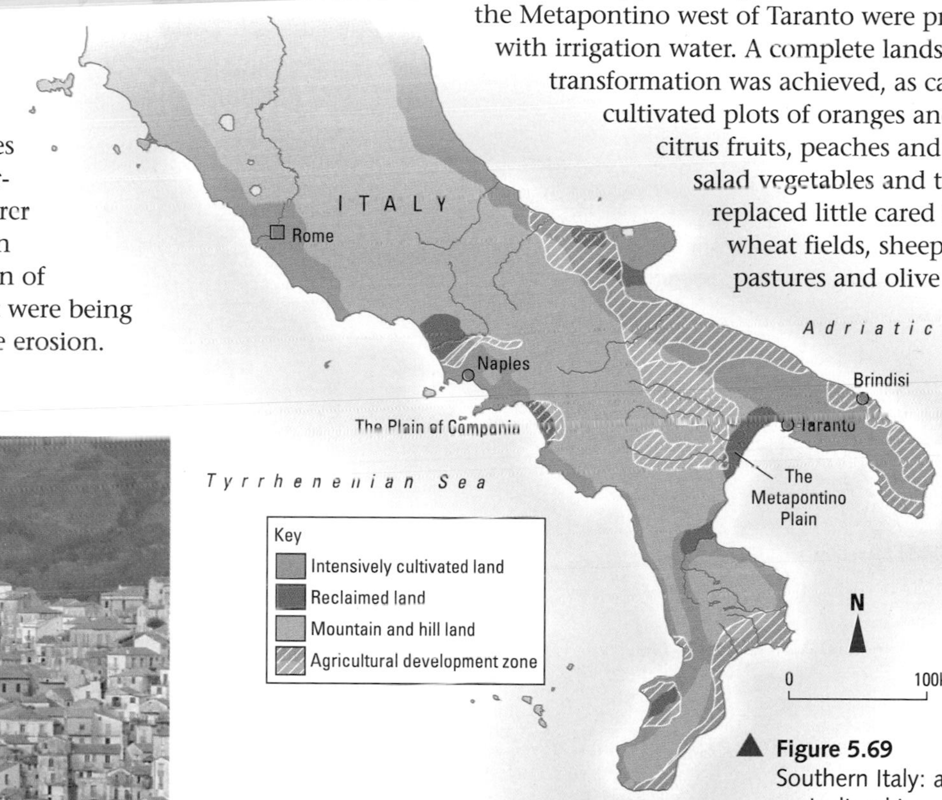

ITALY
Rome
Naples
Brindisi
Taranto
The Plain of Campania
The Metapontino Plain
Adriatic Sea
Tyrrhenenian Sea
Key
Intensively cultivated land
Reclaimed land
Mountain and hill land
Agricultural development zone
N
0 100km

▲ **Figure 5.69** Southern Italy: areas of agricultural improvement

▲ **Figure 5.70** The Metapontino Plain after land reform and investment in infrastructure

Questions

1 Study Figure 5.71.

a i Describe the locations of the glasshouses.
ii Suggest reasons for them.

b i State the location of one other type of intensive farming shown.
ii In what way is its site different?

c Outline the map evidence which suggest that there is competition for land and that any farming present must be intensive.

2 **Investigation**

For the urban area in which you live or the one closest to you,

a identify the main land uses in the rural–urban fringe
b show their locations on a map
c highlight those which are agricultural
d examine the extent to which they have been affected by the presence of the urban area.

3 Examine the reasons for the greater success of government schemes in Europe to increase agricultural ouput than in Brazil and Indonesia.

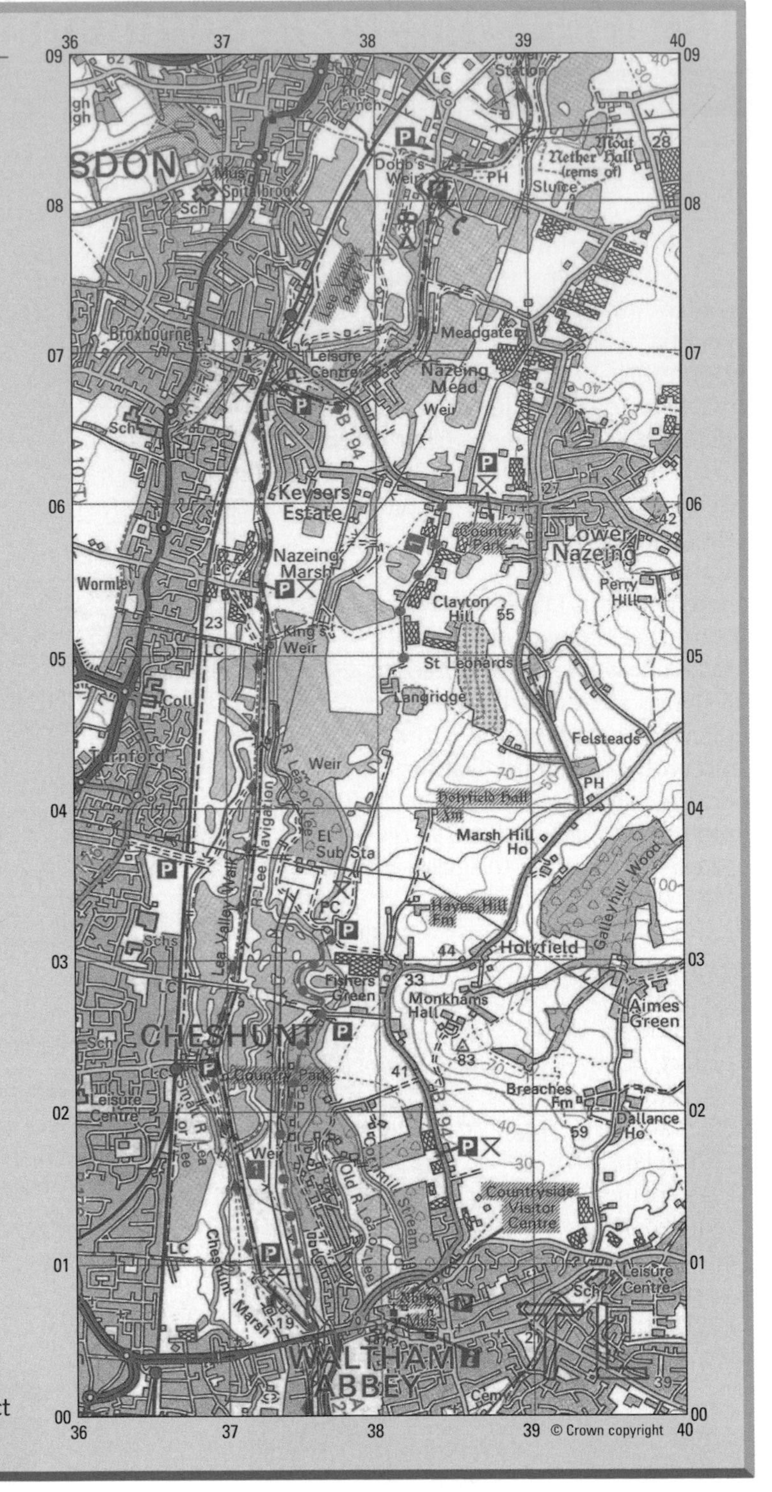

▶ **Figure 5.71** 1:50,000 OS map extract of part of the Lea Valley

Consequences of the intensification of agriculture

EU subsidies promoted environmental damage and destruction. The income to be gained from arable farming in the years of high cereal prices and generous EU support during the 1970s and 1980s in the UK was so tempting that land, previously considered unsuitable for cultivation on grounds of steepness, infertility or shallowness of soil, was ploughed up. Cultivation extended on to the slopes of chalk downlands in southern England, where the long established land use was permanent pasture for sheep. The chalk turf's thick covering and dense roots were replaced by thin lines of young cereal crops, planted in rows in the autumn, leaving bare soil between them. Some were planted on slopes as steep as 20 per cent. This was a recipe for soil erosion; run off from winter rainstorms followed rills and gulleys, which was made worse by the compaction of the soil from the heavy machinery used in the autumn sowing.

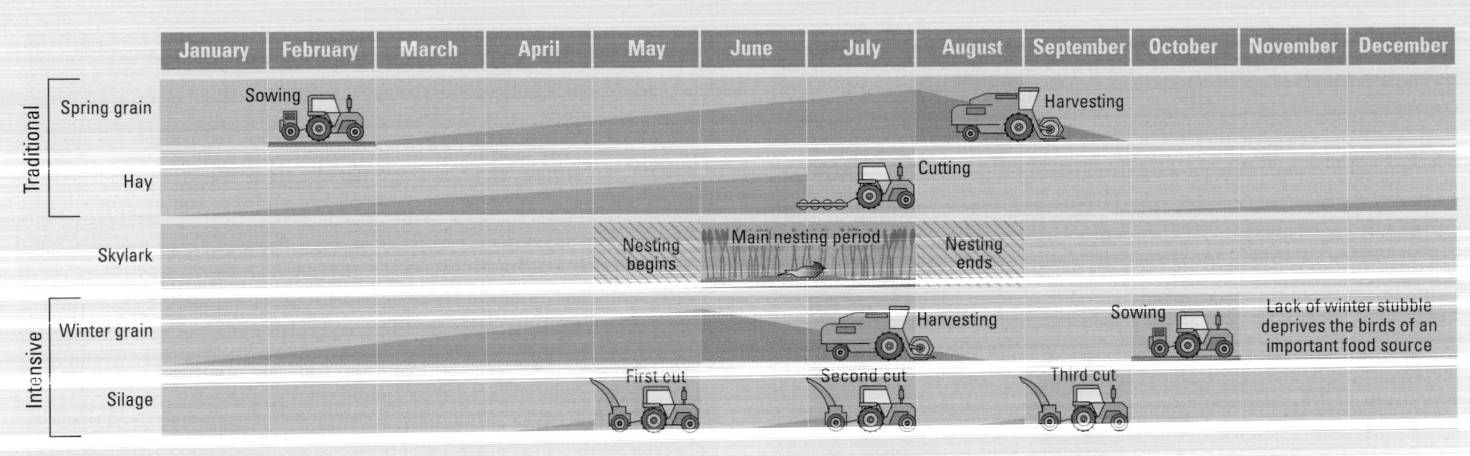

▲ **Figure 5.72** Changes in farming practices. They explain why there have been serious declines in bird populations that depend on grasslands or cropland for their nests. The skylark population in the UK has been reduced by two thirds in 30 years.

Hedges were ripped out in the 1970s and 1980s to make the massive fields that modern agricultural machinery needs to work more efficiently. What has been described as the 'Prairie-ization' of the English landscape allows topsoil to be blown about creating whirling clouds and hazy visibility at those times of the year when nothing is planted and the topsoil dries out. Hedges are 'wildlife reservoirs', providing food and shelter for many small animals and birds. Their numbers have plummeted over the last 30 years (Figure 5.72). There is also eastern England's 'nitrate problem', the main pollution effect from intensive arable farming. The greatly increased use of inorganic fertilizers was encouraged by a combination of their relative cheapness and the need to increase yields of the new varieties of cereals and new crops such as oil seed rape and linseed. Serious increases in nitrate levels in surface streams and groundwater stores from run off and leaching have occurred. Enrichment of nitrogen in rivers, lakes and reservoirs leads to eutrophication, which causes rapid plant and weed growth and surface algae blooms. Light penetration and oxygen levels in the water are reduced, adversely affecting fish stocks and other forms of aquatic life. Farmers are taking more water out of streams in summer for watering crops such as potatoes to increase yield per hectare, thereby increasing nitrate concentrations.

During the 1980s some of the disastrous consequences of CAP were becoming obvious. It had distorted incentives for farmers, raised European food prices to the point where they were the most expensive in the world, encouraged surplus production and caused environmental damage. The operating costs of the CAP were spiralling out of control as it consumed more than 70 per cent of the total EU budget. However, the farming lobby within Europe was incredibly powerful, especially in France where rural traditions remained strongest for longest. Reforms in 1992 did nothing more than cut food mountains to manageable levels. More reforms were agreed in 1999 (reluctantly by some members such as France and the Mediterranean countries), as part of the EU's Agenda 2000. The CAP is changing from costly production-linked subsidies towards direct aid to farmers; increasingly the amount farmers receive will be based upon good countryside management, environmental best practice and use of less intensive forms of production. Agri-environmental schemes (see the Information box) are part of this change.

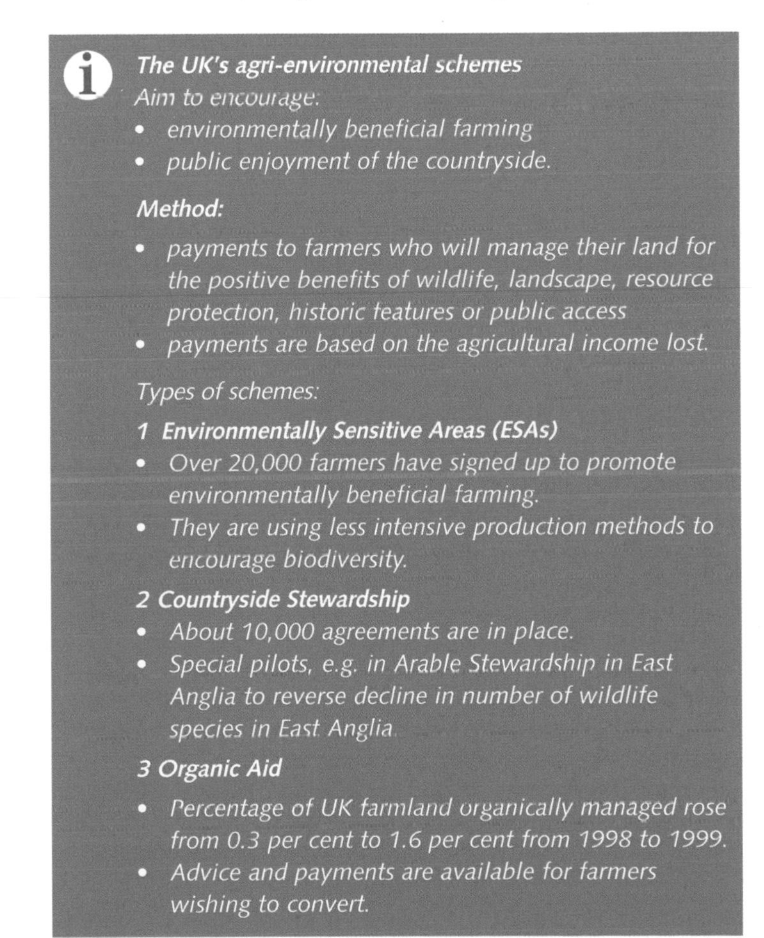
The UK's agri-environmental schemes

Aim to encourage:

- *environmentally beneficial farming*
- *public enjoyment of the countryside.*

Method:

- *payments to farmers who will manage their land for the positive benefits of wildlife, landscape, resource protection, historic features or public access*
- *payments are based on the agricultural income lost.*

Types of schemes:

1 Environmentally Sensitive Areas (ESAs)

- *Over 20,000 farmers have signed up to promote environmentally beneficial farming.*
- *They are using less intensive production methods to encourage biodiversity.*

2 Countryside Stewardship

- *About 10,000 agreements are in place.*
- *Special pilots, e.g. in Arable Stewardship in East Anglia to reverse decline in number of wildlife species in East Anglia.*

3 Organic Aid

- *Percentage of UK farmland organically managed rose from 0.3 per cent to 1.6 per cent from 1998 to 1999.*
- *Advice and payments are available for farmers wishing to convert.*

The earlier Arable Area Payments Scheme, which includes set-aside, is still in force. The set-aside regulations were first drawn up in 1988; farmers are compensated for leaving part of their land fallow. The percentage value has varied but in 1999 all but the smallest arable farmers were forced to set aside 10 per cent of their land. Provided that they agree to certain conditions, farmers can set aside voluntarily 50 per cent or more of their arable land. It is expected that set-aside value will remain at 10 per cent during 2000–06.

▲ **Figure 5.73** Set-aside land in the foreground and field of barley being harvested beyond. Set-aside land must be left fallow, but kept in good agricultural condition.

Cutting of EU and government financial support is forcing a more entrepreneurial attitude on farmers. Not all farmers, however, are doing well. In 2000 the largest quarter of farms in the UK, many of them arable, took two thirds of the subsidies. The incomes of small-scale livestock farmers declined during the 1990s and they have been badly hit by diseases such as swine fever, BSE and foot and mouth. There is EU support for diversification, and for some it is an economic necessity. The growth in farm shops, speciality outlets for ice cream and yoghurt, cafés, restaurants, bed and breakfast places and campsites testifies to the extent to which diversification is a UK-wide phenomenon. Diversification can also be into other rural land uses; the Farm Woodland Premium Scheme encourages farmers to convert agricultural land to woodland by providing annual payments for 10–15 years to replace those lost by not farming the land. Another new rural initiative is the conversion of farm buildings into offices for rent by businesses. Modern communications systems allow the distance separation from urban areas to be overcome.

A debate is raging in European countries over GM (genetically modified) foods. Research scientists in biotechnology (plant breeding) industries have developed insect-resistant GM crops such as soya and maize. The EU requires these 'novel food' sources to undergo field trials to ascertain their effects, if any, upon wildlife and upon animals to which they may be fed. GM foods have been grown and used for many years in North America and other parts of the world without arousing the public reaction seen in the UK and Europe. Every supermarket has already taken note of the public backlash against GM foods. Government policy in 2000 is to continue to explore the potential of biotechnology. One major obstacle is that many people are deeply suspicions of assurances from scientists about the ethics and ill effects of GM foods. There is a widespread public belief that the desire to plant GM foods, like most other recent agricultural changes, is being done primarily for profit without a thought for the environment. The GM debate has many parallels with the nuclear debate where scientific evidence is apparently at odds with many people's perceptions.

Countryside Survey 2000

Changes since 1990 in the UK countryside

Gains

- *Broad-leaved woodland*
- *Wetlands – ponds, marsh and swamp*
- *Biological condition of streams and rivers*

Stabilized *(losses stopped)*

- *hedgerows and dry stone walls*
- *heather moorland*

Continued losses

- *chalk grassland*
- *wild flowers on road verges and sides of streams*

Comments

- *Green policies instituted during the 1990s have checked the previously unstoppable march of intensive farming.*
- *The countryside has now stabilized, though at a lower level than before.*
- *Agricultural support schemes, where farmers are paid to look after wildlife on their land, have helped.*
- *So too have massive investment in environmental improvements by water companies.*

Summary

The main point to note from this section is that government policies and public debate in the new millennium in MEDCs are no longer focused upon growing more food. Observed from a First World perspective there is no shortage of food in the world. Indeed reports from international organizations published in 2000 make it clear that there has never been as much food produced in the world. From 1970 the annual amount of food per person in the world increased by 26 per cent from a crop area that has barely increased in extent. World food production increased by 60 per cent between 1980 and 1997. When adjusted for inflation, world market prices for wheat, maize and rice are the lowest they have been during all of the twentieth century. So why are 800 million people in the world still malnourished?

Questions

1 Explain what Figure 5.72 shows.

2 a Describe some of the ways in which the countryside has changed in the last 50 years.
b Why has it been changed more in some areas of the UK than in others?

3 a State the main ways in which the CAP has changed and is changing.
b Explain why farming policy for European countries is different in 2000 compared with 1957.

Resource response: food shortages in LEDCs

The years between 1970 and 1990 witnessed a substantial reduction in world poverty and hunger, but improvement slowed down during the 1990s. At the UN Millennium Summit as part of Agenda 2000 world leaders made a commitment to halve extreme world poverty by 2015. A person is said to live in extreme poverty if they live on the equivalent of less than one US dollar a day. Worldwide the number has risen to between 1.2 and 1.5 billion in 2000. The pledge to reduce poverty by 2015 looks doomed to fail. The world distribution of extremely poor people is summarized in Figure 5.74. East Asia is the only region where there was a significant improvement in incomes during the 1990s (Figure 5.75). In contrast in sub-Saharan Africa per capita incomes are lower than they were in 1970. Africa has been hurt by a combination of poor infrastructure, inadequate skills, lack of investment capital, wars, political instability, misguided government policies and the ravages of disease, notably the Aids virus and malaria.

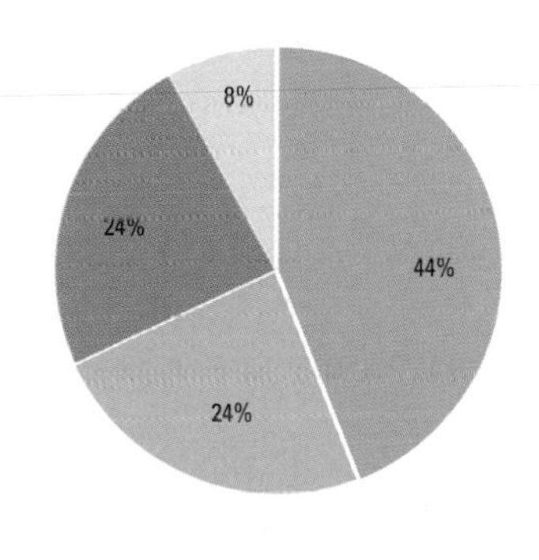

▲ **Figure 5.74** Distribution of people living below $1 per day

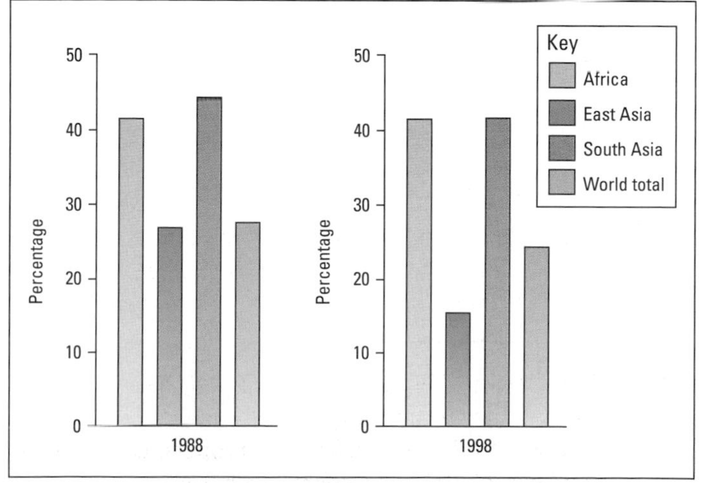

▲ **Figure 5.75** Per cent of total regional populations living below $1 per day

The success in cutting poverty between 1970 and 1990 was put down to the 'green revolution' and increased use of irrigation. The green revolution increased yields of rice, wheat and maize in much of Asia and Central America. The IR8 strain of rice and its descendants are hybrid seeds created in research laboratories to grow faster and give higher yields. It led to long-term doubling of rice yields on irrigated land in much of Asia from three to six tonnes per hectare. Total rice production easily outpaced the substantial increases in population (Figure 5.76). No wonder it was named 'miracle rice'. The 1960s were the beginning of the era of big dam construction in LEDCs. By the 1970s water was available to allow an extension of the cultivated area in water-poor countries such as India, Pakistan and Egypt. Irrigation water helped to guarantee the high yields promised for the new seeds, which require more careful husbandry than the old seeds.

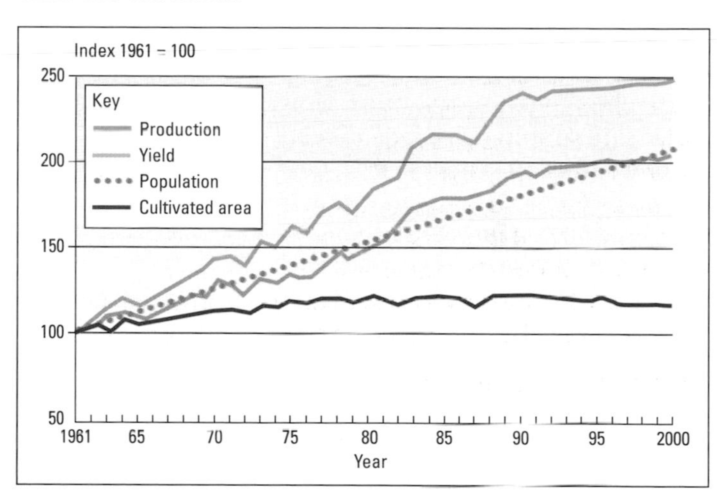

▲ **Figure 5.76** Rice production in Asia

However, some Asian countries have already voiced fears for future rice supplies and some began importing rice again in the mid-1990s after many years of self-sufficiency or surpluses. The challenge facing agricultural scientists is a formidable one (Figure 5.77). Overpopulated Bangladesh has very limited opportunities to expand the area under cultivation. One way to produce more from existing land would be land reform – dividing up the land held by large landowners and redistributing it among landless farmers who make up half the rural households, and who would farm the land more intensively. At the same time separate strips could be consolidated into blocks of land to make farming them more efficient. Land reform is politically unlikely, however, because of the power and influence of the large landowners.

Another way would be to better control water supplies. Flooding is useful for watering the rice crop upon which almost all farmers in Bangladesh depend and leaving a layer of fertile silt, but the uncontrolled flooding, which occurs regularly, leads to severe crop damage. Controlled flooding is one solution; however, river levels in the Ganges are under the control of India, with whom relations are not always cordial. Better canal water distribution and the availability of more diesel pumps to draw up underground supplies would extend the area that could be cultivated in the dry season, but the country is poor and has little money for new agricultural schemes. There is a heavy reliance upon money donated by overseas aid agencies. The government needs to pay back international debts and maintains high levels of military spending because of poor relations with India and Pakistan.

A third way, that of attempting to increase food output by development programmes among the rural communities with a high level of local involvement, has faltered for the same reasons as the other two, namely opposition from local landlords, who wanted to maintain the status quo, and insufficient finance. The Rural Development Policy Initiatives, begun in 1982, recognized that a package of improvements were needed, including health, education, family planning and advice on agricultural improvement. By involving the local people this is potentially an appropriate way forward with a high chance of success. However, as in many LEDCs, rural initiatives fade quickly with increasing distance from the capital city.

▼ **Figure 5.77** Adapted extract from *The Financial Times*, 6 December 1995

Can the scientists beat the Asian rice shortage?

Scarcity of water, the increasing cost of irrigation and growing awareness of the damage which insecticides and other chemicals can do to the environment has, in effect, frozen the scope for increasing the area of land for irrigated rice production in many Asian countries. Meanwhile Asia's population continues to expand by more than 2 per cent a year. 'If you look at the scale of the problem, it is quite frightening,' said a water management expert at Irri (International Rice Research Institute). 'The demand for water is increasing exponentially as urban populations grow. This leaves less water for rice production yet a growing demand for rice.'

According to Irri scientists, who attempt several hundred cross-breeds every year, it takes at least five years to develop a new strain and another five years to spread its cultivation. 'The prototype we are working on will increase irrigated rice yields by 50 per cent to around 10 tonnes a hectare. The most difficult job will be to make the strain disease-resistant. We're genuinely working against the clock.'

To obtain the full benefits of new hybrids, farmers must invest more in irrigation, fertilizers and pesticides. This is one of the reasons why the uptake of new seeds has been lowest in Africa; the typical African farmer is too poor. Nor do most African governments provide either the political atmosphere or the physical infrastructure for new initiatives to be adopted. The graph for food production in Africa reveals a very different picture to the one for Asia in Figure 5.78. The United Nations warns that Africa is facing an escalating food crisis which could make 60 per cent of its population go hungry in 25 years. Yet Africa is a continent with a wealth of mineral resources and is an exporter of a range of tropical crops such as cocoa, tea, coffee and cotton. However, market prices for commodities are set in financial centres such as London and New York, not in Africa; commodity prices are volatile, but have tended to be low in the recent past.

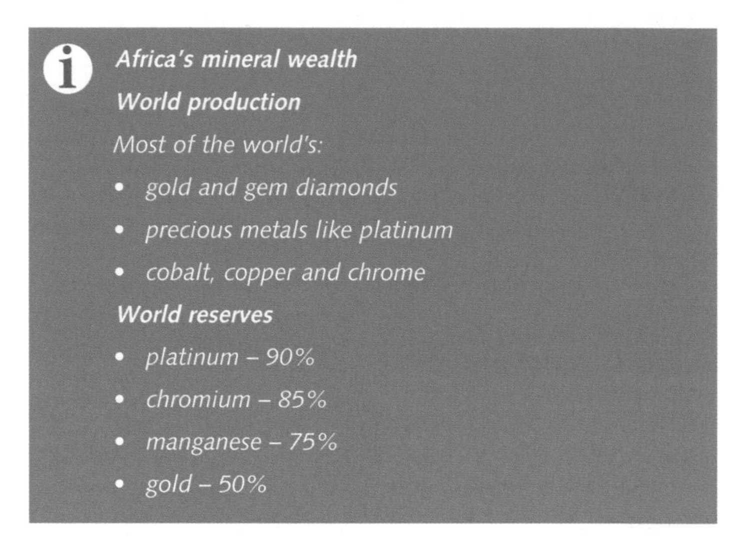

Africa's mineral wealth

World production

Most of the world's:

- *gold and gem diamonds*
- *precious metals like platinum*
- *cobalt, copper and chrome*

World reserves

- *platinum – 90%*
- *chromium – 85%*
- *manganese – 75%*
- *gold – 50%*

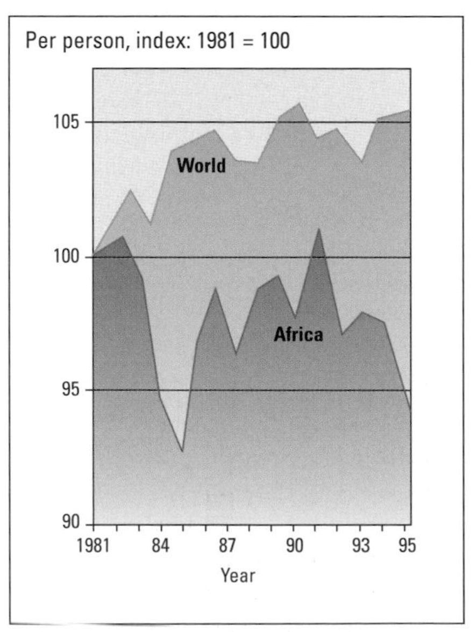

▲ **Figure 5.78** Food production in Africa

Food shortages in Africa

Case Study

Africa is the continent of poverty. The world's poorest region is sub-Saharan Africa. It makes no difference whether economic or social measures of development are studied; the wealth and human welfare gap between most African countries and the industrialized countries is enormous and increasing (Figure 5.79). (Look back also at previous figures on pages 198–201 and question 4 on page 202.)

Africa is a continent of crises (Figure 5.80). Some are natural, some human. Africa is a dry continent. Only on the western side around the Equator is precipitation high and reliable. The Sahara desert is at the continent's widest point; it is the world's largest hot desert. Many of the inhabited parts of west and east Africa have a savanna climate with its two season regime, one wet and one dry. There are also wide variations from year to year in the length and intensity of the dry season. Rainfall is most unreliable around desert margins; protracted droughts in the 1980s brought the Sahel region to the attention of the international media. Perversely, other areas suffer from too much rain and floods. Mozambique was hit by tropical cyclones causing extensive floods in two consecutive years (2000 and 2001). Somalia in the 'Horn of Africa', having been devastated by heavy monsoon rains and floods from the 1997–8 El Niño effect on the world's climates, suffered drought in 2000. Even governments and farmers in rich countries would have problems managing agriculture to deal with climatic extremes such as these, so what chances have the world's poorest people?

The colonial legacy in Africa was worse than that of any other continent. Africa was a populous continent when the European colonial powers carved it up into separate countries. They ignored the natural territories of tribal groups when they drew national boundaries on maps, often as straight lines. As a result, the majority of African countries are multi-tribal which has led to conflict, civil wars and political instability. European farmers and companies setting up plantations selected the most fertile land; tribespeople were forced off the best cropland and migration routes used by the nomadic pastoralists for centuries were disrupted. The best farmland in any African country is most likely to be used for growing export crops and not for growing staple food crops such as maize and millet for African people.

▼ **Figure 5.79** Sub-Saharan Africa compared with the industrialized countries

	Sub-Saharan Africa	Industrialized countries
Life expectancy at birth (years) 1998	48	78
Life expectancy 1970–98	44–48	72–78
Infant mortality rate per 1,000 live births, 1998 (aged under 1 year)	107	6
Total adult literacy rate, 1995	56	98
Population with access to safe water, 1990–98 (%)	77	-
GNP per capita, 1997 ($)	513	27,146
Radio sets per 1000 population, 1996	166	1,319

▼ **Figure 5.80b** Starving child in Sudan

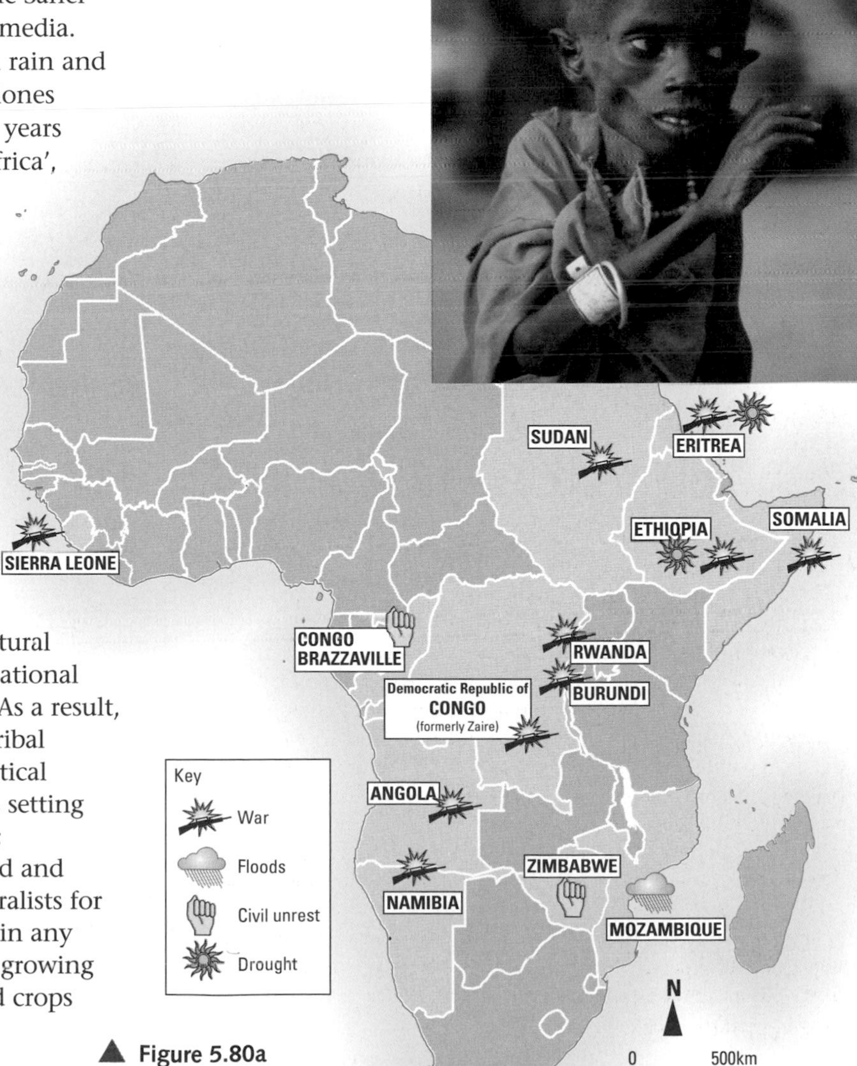

▲ **Figure 5.80a** Africa: continent of crises

Colonial land tenure systems relegated the majority black population to communal lands, many of which were physically marginal for cultivation. In many African countries females are the cultivators of small plots near the village while men wander around communal pastures with a mixed collection of animals. There is no specialization here; it is subsistence farming with the hope of obtaining a small surplus for sale in local markets in a good year. Many traditional farming practices lead to poor land management. Shallow ploughing leaves a loose surface soil structure; delaying planting until the rains arrive leaves surface soil exposed for even longer; cutting down trees and bushes for fuel wood lays the surface bare. All increase the dangers of soil erosion by fluvial erosion and aeolian (wind) action.

However, in pre-colonial days when tribespeople cultivated the good land and human and animal populations were much lower than today, poor management mattered less. Rates of soil erosion, land degradation and desertification have greatly accelerated now that population pressure has led to land and water shortages, livestock numbers in excess of carrying capacity and an unsustainable demand for fuelwood. It is at this point that physical factors make the environmental problems more serious. Periodic drought, especially in Sahelian countries, adversely affects soil structure. When the drought ends the rain typically returns in heavy downpours that encourage sheetwash and gulleying. Many Africans have neither the finance nor the knowledge and awareness to adopt better tillage and growing methods, such as crop rotation, contour terracing and conservation tillage, techniques which are predominantly restricted to commercial farms in African countries.

African people have not been well served by their leaders since independence from their colonial masters. Most countries are run by dictators, even if elections are held; the majority plunder the country's wealth and resources as if they were their own. Money is more likely to be laundered into overseas bank accounts than invested in the rural areas where three quarters of sub-Saharan Africans still live. Leaders in at least ten African countries drew or led their peoples into wars or civil unrest in 2000 (Figure 5.80). On top of all of this is the Aids plague. Of the 36 million people in the world living with HIV or Aids in 2000, 25 million of them lived in Africa and 2.4 million died of HIV-related causes. Life expectancy is being reduced by as much as twenty years and families are losing their strongest workers on the land and their source of money from family members who have moved away to work in the cities and mines.

Bad government and bad weather hit Africa's food

West may be making matters worse, but seems less inclined to help out as position deteriorates.

Severe food shortages will affect 28m people across Africa this year, prompting humanitarian organizations last week to issue an urgent appeal to donors. 'The food outlook is generally unfavourable due to last year's drought in eastern Africa, prolonged mid-season dry spells and subsequent floods in southern Africa.' The weather has always caused difficulties, but there is also evidence that the weather is getting worse and that the West may be to blame. International experts in Nairobi warned last week that global warming was boosting the frequency of the El Niño weather pattern, increasing droughts and floods.

In recent years there has been a proliferation in wars with millions displaced causing production shortfalls, and making it difficult to make outside deliveries of food. The West has proved reluctant to intervene in African wars. Also because the USA, Canada, Europe and Japan subsidize their farmers to the tune of £700m a day, African markets are swamped by artificially cheap produce, discouraging local production.

▲ **Figure 5.82** Adapted extract from *The Financial Times*, 18 April 2001

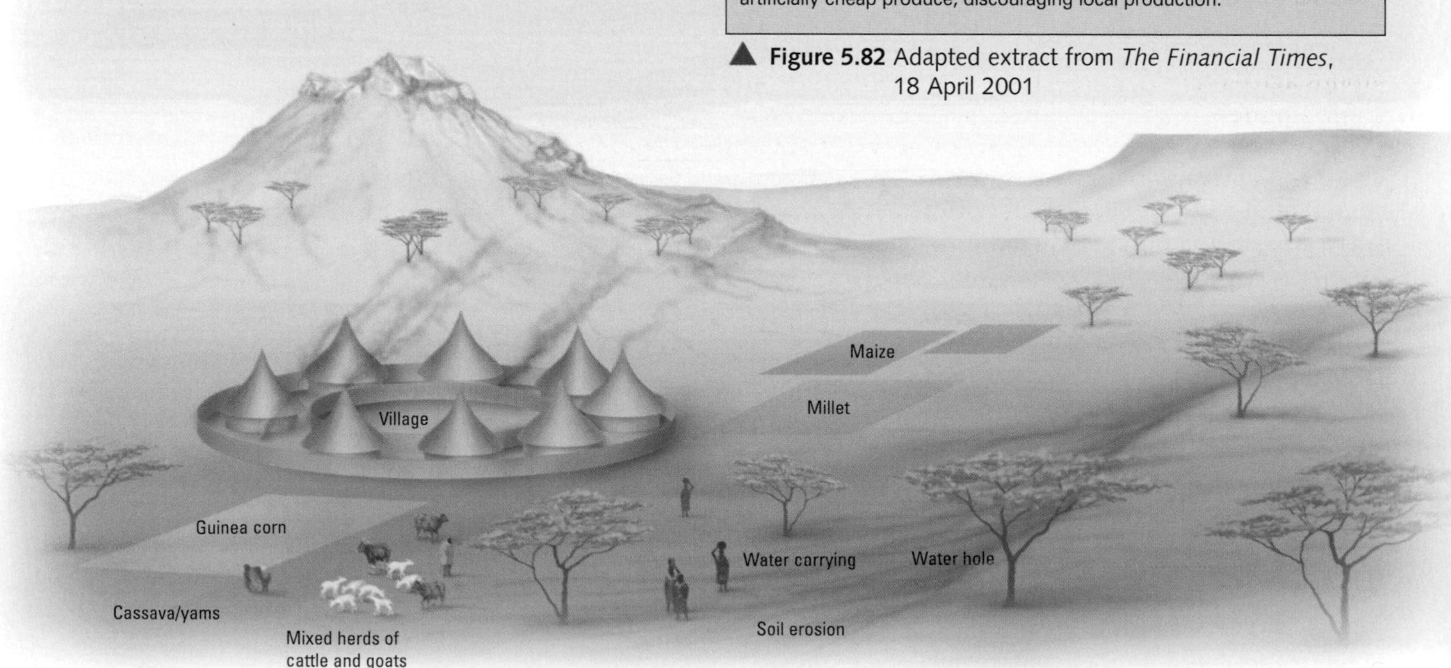

▲ **Figure 5.81** Traditional pattern of farming on communal lands in the savanna lands of West Africa

Summary

Wealth gaps between rich and poor individuals within countries and between the world's richest and poorest countries are widening. The same can be said in the context of world population, resources and food supply, and here there is an increasing gulf between pessimists and optimists.

As soon as there are reports of drought and famine, the pessimists go into full cry. In the best traditions of Malthusians they see the world moving from an era of food surpluses to one dominated by scarcity. Miracle cures such as high yielding seeds will not save the world again because of the scale of population growth and the constraints it is placing on land, water and other resources. Therefore the past cannot be used as a guide to the future. Increasing affluence in Asia is increasing the demand for grain as animal feed and alternative food sources such as fish are no longer plentiful. Intensive farming is eroding the soil quicker than it can be replaced. The ecological limits to growth have been approached or even passed.

The optimists retaliate by pointing out there was almost a three-fold increase in the world grain harvest between 1950 and 1990; they have every confidence in further agricultural innovation. The most optimistic predict that not only will the world's additional numbers be fed in 2030, but that they will also enjoy better diets. Technological improvements in agriculture will mean less soil erosion, better management of fresh water supplies and higher crop yields. As developing countries become wealthier, more attention will be paid to air and water quality, which will lead to significant environmental improvements for many of their inhabitants.

Are you an optimist or a pessimist? Remarkably both groups agree on one thing – that whatever happens the world's hunger problem is not going to be solved over the next 50 years. In 2000 there was plenty of food in the world for all, but 800 million went hungry. Average daily calorie intakes in Europe and North America are one third higher than they need to be. Hunger and the export of food crops exist side by side in many LEDCs. Experience suggests that in global terms ensuring a fairer distribution of food and improved access to it will contribute more to the problem of hunger than increasing food production. However, experience also shows that this is unlikely to happen.

Questions

1 a Describe and give reasons for what Figure 5.76 shows.
  b How well does the information in Figure 5.76 relate to the theories of Malthus and Boserup?
  c Why may future increases in food output in Asia be more difficult to achieve?

2 a Assemble evidence from earlier in the chapter to show that Africa has the greatest population increase of all the continent and give reasons for this.
  b Describe and comment on what Figures 5.75 and 5.78 show in general terms for people living in Africa.
  c With the help of a sketch map (or maps), describe **i** the physical and **ii** the human problems facing farmers in African countries.
  d How and why are environmental problems in Africa more serious now than in the past?
  e Give evidence in support of the following views:
  i Africa's poverty and hunger have global causes. It is globalization and the world dominance of MEDCs that is most responsible.
  ii Africa's poverty and hunger have African causes. It is corrupt dictators and badly managed governments that are most responsible.
  f Assess the extent to which Africa in 2000/1 confirms or negates the theories of Malthus, Club of Rome, Boserup and Julian Simon.

3 **Essay**

Famine and hunger have human not physical causes. Do you agree?

Chapter 5 Questions

1 a Figure 1 shows information about global water supply and sanitation.

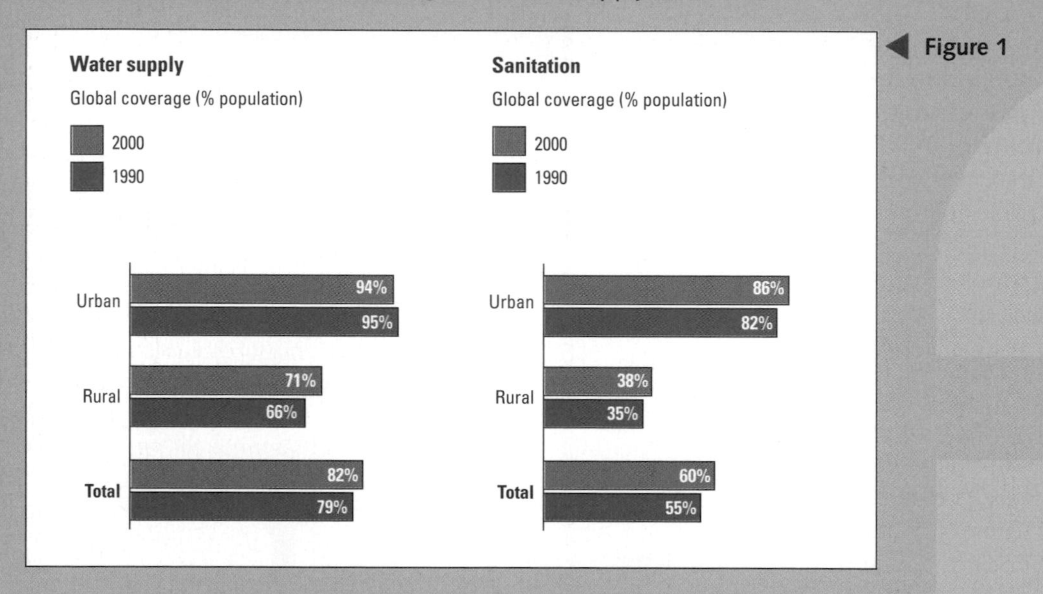

Figure 1

i Describe and outline reasons for what Figure 1 shows. (4 marks)

ii Comment on the usefulness of water supply and sanitation as indicators of development and welfare. (4 marks)

b Choose one renewable natural resource. Explain why its conservation is highly desirable if not essential. (7 marks)

Total: 15 marks

2 Synoptic essay.
Two views about world food production in 2000 for feeding the 6 billion are printed below:
"A great human achievement"
"An environmental disaster".
Examine and consider the relative merits of each view. (30 marks)

Chapter 6 Managing cities – challenges and issues

Figure 6.1
The Millennium bridge known locally as the 'Blinking Eye' is just one of the symbols of regeneration along the banks of the River Tyne in the twenty first century. Notice the relics from the past, such as the Tyne Bridge in the background, the symbols of older phases of regeneration and the high rise tower block and multi-storey car park sited in Gateshead across the river. The car park, a white elephant since it was built, has been earmarked for demolition although there is much opposition from the fans of the film starring Michael Caine, *Get Carter*, in which it featured.

Changes in the central areas of cities

Traditionally most businesses, especially those connected with retailing, were concentrated in the central area or CBD of towns and cities. Without businesses there would be no work and no wages to provide people with their homes and standard of living. Without wages local authorities could not collect council taxes or rates and many services such as healthcare, schools and social services would suffer. Businesses are the economic lifeblood of cities and in particular the central area or CBD.

In the 1960s comprehensive redevelopment affected CBDs as well as the inner city. In many cities parts of the historic core were bulldozed to make way for new shopping centres such as the Bull Ring in Birmingham and Eldon Square in Newcastle. Many of these developments were criticized for their stark appearance of glass and concrete. The shop frontages were depressingly uniform and office developments were often functional but monotonous tower blocks. At the same time every effort was made to accommodate the motor car with inner ring roads, urban motorways and multi-storey car parks. These developments blighted not only the CBD but also parts of the inner cities and caused increased traffic and pollution. Rates and rents were increased to pay for the developments forcing many small independent retailers to close down, which made way for the chain stores to move in. As a result city centres became very alike and they were criticized for not providing the variety of shopping that consumers would like. In addition there were often rigid zoning policies and activities other than commerce were discouraged in town centres. Hence the residential population declined further and the areas became ghost towns at night. These problems were compounded by the growth of out-of-town retailing and the decentralization process that followed.

From the late 1960s growing concerns were expressed and gradually there was a return to using traditional building materials and smaller developments. The 1967 Civic Amenities Act encouraged the conservation of historical areas and listed buildings and there was greater control over the demolition of all buildings and trees. Since then money has been made available to restore the historic parts of the urban environment. Increasingly it is only the interiors of buildings that are changed leaving the historic façades intact. An example of this is the old Baltic Flour Mill on the banks of the River Tyne (Figure 6.3).

▲ **Figure 6.2** 1960s redevelopment – the era of high-rise office blocks and urban motorways

▲ **Figure 6.3**
The Baltic Flour Mill on the banks of the River Tyne, a grade II listed building currently being renovated to preserve the façade and to create an Arts Centre

However, the city centre and inner city redevelopment schemes in the late twentieth century forced large numbers of people out of the central areas of cities. Many of these displaced people moved into the suburbs or New Towns beyond the edges of the urban area. This and the growth in personal mobility triggered the decentralization (Information Box) of businesses including retailing functions.

Up until the 1970s there were generally three types of retailing function in cities:

- the CBD with its department stores, chain stores and specialist shops
- shopping parades with small groups of shops which usually included a small supermarket, post office and newsagent
- corner shops, small general stores scattered mostly in the Victorian inner city.

This threefold classification still exists, but the out-of-town shopping area or retail park where huge superstores are built has now been added to it. This movement was most powerful in the USA although similar movements have taken place in the UK and other MEDCs. Research in Atlanta, USA, in the 1980s showed the CBD as only the sixth most important shopping area in the city; the top five were out-of-town retail parks.

Since then an increasing number of businesses have moved out of city centres in MEDCs. This increases the burden of taxation on the remaining businesses and encourages them to look for alternative locations and even drives some to closure. Hence what begins as a trickle may turn into a 'flight'. Many CBDs in MEDCs have been the focus of considerable investment in order to reverse this decline.

The initial impetus for decentralization was inner city redevelopment. This led to the processes of suburbanization and counter-urbanization (Information Box). Increasingly more and more people left the inner city areas and moved into the suburbs and the rural–urban fringe. This fuelled decentralization of businesses and frequently had a detrimental impact on shops and services in the high streets. Some businesses and high street shops were forced to close down – a process called deindustrialization.

The decline of city centres

Four main processes have contributed to the decline of city centres:

- ***Counter-urbanization*** *is the reverse process of urbanization. This occurs when people move beyond the limits of the urban area into the rural–urban fringe or the countryside areas beyond. Commuting to the suburbs is much easier than venturing into the city centres which made the suburbs attractive locations for businesses and retailing.*
- ***Decentralization*** *is the process of moving away from city centre locations. This includes population and business activities – offices, retailing and industry. They have moved away from city centre locations, usually the CBD, towards the edges of the built-up areas and/or rural–urban fringe. A process that began with the movement of people in response to redevelopment schemes.*
- ***De-industrialization*** *is the continued decline of factories and businesses, which are unable to adapt to the demands of the modern world. Some businesses including shops and offices have simply ceased to trade. Most are known only locally, for example Doggart's department store in Durham City, Wenger's department store in Newcastle-upon-Tyne. The national chain stores have tended to survive.*
- ***Suburbanization*** *is the expansion of cities or urban sprawl into the rural–urban fringe. Increasingly people wish to live in the less polluted, less densely populated suburbs. Once businesses and retailing have set up in the suburbs, people have less distance to travel in these out-of-town locations; communication links may be less crowded and there are motorway links giving rapid access to businesses that are further away.*

The CBD versus the greenfield site?

The causes of the accelerated decline of businesses in city centres include the redistribution of the population through the processes of suburbanization and counter-urbanization. The decline was also encouraged by a combination of both push and pull factors. The push factors are the relative disadvantages of city centre locations while the pull factors represent the relative advantages afforded by alternative locations most often in the periphery of the urban area. The typical features of the CBD that once provided advantages for commercial and business enterprises now present some disadvantages and disincentives for those same functions.

Pull factors

These are the advantages of out-of-centre locations that attracted businesses to the outskirts of cities.

Greenfield sites are areas of land that are usually located in the rural–urban fringe that have never previously been built upon. Before development they are occupied by rural land uses such as fields, woodlands or heath. Such greenfield sites offer good accessibility to motorways and A roads in the rural areas and plenty of space for car parking and later expansion. The greenfield sites offer the developer land at much cheaper costs than in the traditional CBD. This has been helped by the demise of the farming industry where crises caused by animal diseases such as BSE and foot and mouth and collapses in the market price for sheep encouraged farmers to sell up. Greenfield sites also offer a more pleasant working environment with less pollution. These factors have been crucial in some areas in attracting high quality employees and a large customer base.

▲ **Figure 6.4** Greenfield sites offer many attractions for developers not least because they are convenient for the growing population

The greater mobility and the increased use of the private car have further emphasized the advantages of the out-of-town location for businesses along with the building of motorways and intersections. These major lines of communication have improved the accessibility of the suburbs and rural-urban fringe for deliveries and customers. A survey at the Metro Centre in Gateshead located on the A1(M) Western Bypass showed that 41 per cent of those visiting travelled from over 15 kilometres away.

In recent years there have been changes in people's shopping habits. Due to increased mobility people travel further to shop. In response to demand the shops offer a much wider range of goods. Monthly pay packets and the use of deep freezers mean more people buy in bulk and go shopping less frequently making the weekly or monthly visit to the out-of-town superstore more attractive. More women work full time and have less time to shop.

Access to airports, which are mostly located on the fringes of cities, is important for some industries and businesses. Many business parks prefer locations close to airports for the convenience of travel by their own and visiting executives.

Planning policies encouraged the movement of people and businesses to the suburbs and beyond, especially with the establishment of New Towns and the redevelopment of inner city areas, which forced many businesses to relocate. Initially there were few planning restrictions for out-of-town shopping areas and business parks. However, today local authorities and national government control planning applications for out-of-town shopping areas.

As wealth and mobility have increased urban populations have had a desire to improve their quality of life. The suburbs and rural–urban fringe offer larger, more modern homes with gardens; a more rural location with reduced pollution levels and lower density housing. Suburban dwellers also demand easy access to modern conveniences and services located at the edges of the built-up area which has led to new developments in retailing such as shopping under one roof that require large single storey buildings with huge car parks. Location within a CBD would be impossible due to lack of space and the high cost of land. Examples of these vast, modern superstores and retail warehouses include Sainsbury's, Tesco and MFI. They provide self-service shopping and a large range and volume of stock, which is often at reduced prices due to the retailer's ability to purchase in bulk and the high volume of trade. Customers can save time and money through shopping under one roof with free parking in these out-of-town locations rather than travelling into city centres.

▲ **Figure 6.5** Tokyo's CBD with its high land values, lack of space and relatively high pollution levels has increasingly proved unattractive to developers requiring large land areas and a high quality environment

The push factors

These are the disadvantages of the CBD forcing businesses out of city centre locations.

Traditionally the CBD has high land values. These resulted from competition between businesses to locate in the CBD. The lack of space led to high-density construction and the need to build upwards creating a skyline of multipurpose skyscrapers in many CBDs. The modern trend towards shopping under one roof and the modern one-storey factory and business units with landscaped grounds and large car parks require vast areas of land. The CBD location is prohibitive due to lack of space and the high cost of land.

The residential population is small in the traditional CBD which means that most people live further away. This leads to commuting on a massive scale by local populations in order to access work, shopping, entertainment and other services. In London over one million people commute in and out of the city each day presenting huge problems especially during the rush hours. In many cities there are severe problems of traffic congestion, environmental pollution, and car parking problems. There are also the increased costs of petrol, the travelling times and the consequent stresses and strains for commuters that all combine to make city centre locations less attractive for businesses.

In some city centres redevelopment schemes to create new facilities such as shopping arcades have seen the loss of smaller, often independent retailers who are unable to compete or pay the increased business rents and rates being charged by local authorities.

The traditional CBD once had the advantage of being the focus of communications. CBDs have a high concentration of buses and taxis, the bus and rail stations are nearby and many A class roads focus on the city centre with traffic movements assisted by inner and outer ring roads and urban motorways and flyovers. However, the massive increase in car use especially since the 1980s has meant that most town centres cannot cope with the volume of traffic; car park provision is inadequate and levels of pollution reach danger levels.

In many city centres certain types of businesses clustered together, such as in London, the financial institutions in the City, jewellers in Hatton Gardens, the newspapers in Fleet Street. This clustering of similar businesses benefited the consumer in terms of choice and competition but also benefited the businesses by allowing close communication. This need for communication is largely redundant today with the advent of modern telecommunications including fax, modem, video conferencing and the Internet. Most businesses today are footloose and are not tied to specific locations.

Effects of decline in CBDs

The process of decentralization brings both advantages and disadvantages. In general the advantages are mostly to be found in the out-of-town locations where the retail parks have been established. The disadvantages are concentrated in the city centre locations.

Traditional CBDs have always exhibited constant change. Different areas experience growth (zones of assimilation) and decline (zones of discard) at different times. For example, in London, Fleet Street is barely recognizable today as most of the newspaper companies have moved to Kensington, the Isle of Dogs or Battersea. Fleet Street became a zone of discard while areas in the Isle of Dogs became zones of assimilation. However, in some CBDs the trickle of movement of businesses developed into a 'flight to the fringe'. This accelerated movement of population and businesses from the CBD was in danger of creating many dead hearts in city centres. A summary of the consequences is in the information box.

Summary of the consequences of the decline of city centres:

- *The trickle of people and businesses becomes a flight.*
- *A downward spiral of decline occurs in city centres and the inner city increasing areas of discard.*
- *Environmental decay and degradation leads to vacant buildings and derelict land.*
- *Crime and vandalism increases in unoccupied properties.*
- *A dead heart is created in city centres.*
- *Ghettos and slums form in the inner city where the disadvantaged sectors of society become concentrated – the wealthy and more mobile sectors of the population having moved out to the suburbs or rural–urban fringe.*
- *Commuting and traffic congestion increases in out-of-town locations.*
- *Local authorities raise less money in taxation and rates leading to less investment.*
- *There is high unemployment in the inner city as the poorer members of society are unable to afford the increased travel costs to find work in the suburbs and beyond.*
- *Intensity of land-use decreases.*

Taunton Riverside: a retail park

Case Study

1 Taunton Riverside: a retail park

Taunton Riverside (Figure 6.6) is a retail park to the east of Taunton on the southern bank of the River Tone. It illustrates the advantages of an out-of-town location for retailing, leisure, recreation, offices and business. It is adjacent to junction 25 of the M5 motorway and close to the A358 and A38 giving good accessibility for both deliveries and customers. The land was formerly Hankridge Farm, which became available for development. Taunton itself is an expanding regional centre for Somerset with a growing population, who mostly move into the new housing estates in the suburban locations. The development of the Riverside has eased the pressure on the traditional CBD where space for new developments was limited and traffic congestion a major problem.

The announcement of a proposal to build an out-of-town retail or business park is often greeted with dismay by local people, especially local shop owners and traders who fear the worst for their own livelihoods. As the views in Figure 6.7 show the high street traders in Taunton were very worried.

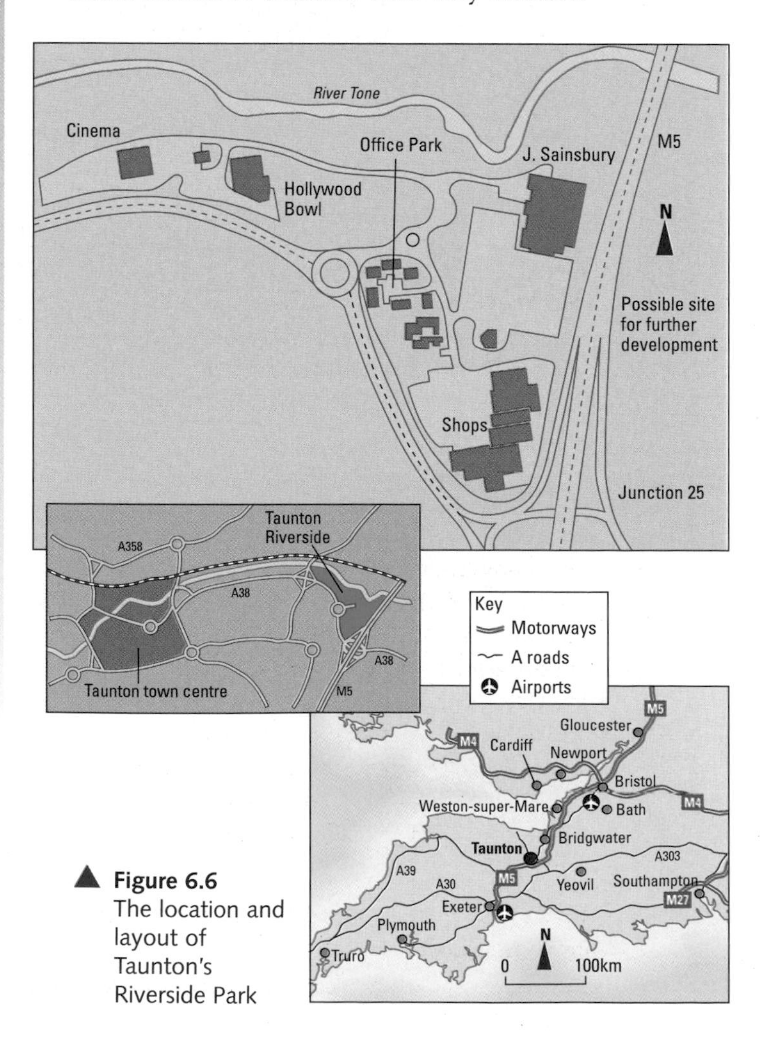

▲ **Figure 6.6** The location and layout of Taunton's Riverside Park

▼ **Figure 6.7** Views for and against Taunton Riverside

Views for:

Mr Latham, local resident
I'm a relative newcomer to the area and I'm astonished by how few shops there are compared with Poole in Dorset where I used to live. Taunton is definitely behind the times. The young people of Taunton must feel quite deprived when they see what is available elsewhere.

Richard Parrish, local councillor
The scheme gives Taunton the opportunity to rightfully take its place alongside Exeter and Bristol. We lose millions of pounds each year to other areas because we do not have the facilities. We have lost jobs, infrastructure and vibrancy in the community.

Howard Morris, property developer
It will be a benefit to the community, surrounding villages and Taunton's economic prosperity. Taunton is not currently equipped to meet the needs of modern-day retail warehouses and the car-borne shopping public.

Views against:

Christina Townsend, local resident
Not everyone has transport to get to an out-of-town site, or wants to shop at the edge of a motorway. If shoppers are lured away from the centre, the town at night will be a sitting target for crime and general vandalism.

R.C. Boobyer, local resident
The development represents a threat to small businesses. This area does not need it, or a county council which consistently complies with the wishes of greedy developers instead of standing up for local people.

Sandy James, local shopowner
I run a small business in the town centre and am fighting to survive as we have more huge supermarkets going up, selling everything from milk to lawnmowers.

What actually happened once the retail park was opened in November 1994 at Taunton Riverside?

- In February 1994 the Gateway supermarket in the High Street closed down.
- In August 1994 the Plaza cinema closed in the town centre – there was a new cinema at the Riverside site.
- A survey in May 1995 showed that 79 per cent of shoppers at the Riverside had previously shopped in Taunton's town centre.
- A survey showed that 19 per cent of shoppers thought the town centre was poor in facilities, there was too much noise, crowds, traffic, as well as parking and the dispersed layout of all of the shops being a problem.
- However, it has not been all bad news. Taunton's CBD and the city centre traders have responded to the challenge of the nearby retail park. Plans were made to pedestrianize the city centre by 1996, to renovate an area of derelict warehousing and to convert the County Hotel into a covered shopping area with six new retail units. The Riverside has acted as something of a catalyst to improve Taunton's CBD. Overall there has been a boost in the economy of the whole area as people now travel from further afield to visit the Riverside and often also visit the town centre and other tourist attractions in the area.

▼ **Figure 6.8** Summary of the advantages and disadvantages of decentralization

	Out-of-town retail parks	City centre locations
Economic advantages	Lower overheads, e.g. rates and rents, make prices cheaper for the consumer. Between 100 and 500 jobs are created in each superstore although most are part time. Cheaper, more convenient shopping for those who live in the suburbs. Developers buying up farmland may help the farmer to retire early.	Encourages investment in the CBD to improve the environment and facilities so it remains a focus for shoppers, workers and those seeking entertainment.
Economic disadvantages	Loss of agricultural land and output. Land costs increase.	Competitors in local shopping parades may go out of business. May lead to job losses in city centre locations. Loss of certain functions from the CBD especially food retailing, DIY. Creation of a 'dead heart' in city centres.
Environmental advantages	Extensive land available to make large superstores and car parks with delivery vehicles kept separate.	Eases traffic congestion in city centres. Opportunities for new developments in the CBD, such as specialized shopping areas and the expansion of leisure facilities.
Environmental disadvantages	Urban sprawl and loss of farmland, some of which may be Green Belt land. Visual pollution. Increased traffic congestion and noise, litter and air pollution. Service roads and new access roads may need to be built in the out-of-town location.	Developments in the suburbs are deflected from using derelict and vacant land or brownfield sites in city centres. Large areas of derelict and empty properties are left by the businesses moving to the suburbs. These areas can go into a spiral of decline and form 'zones of discard'.
Social advantages	Increased choice for shoppers. Longer opening hours stretching to 24 hours at peak times. Easier bulk purchasing. One-stop shopping. Single storey shops encouraging disabled access. Crèches and play areas for families. Easier parking with disabled and family bays.	May create opportunities for new developments in the CBD, improving the environment and increasing facilities.
Social disadvantages	Caters for the younger, more affluent and mobile sectors of the population excluding the poorer and less mobile people, often elderly, and those located in the inner-city areas. Less convenient for the less mobile and those close to the city centre.	The poorer and less mobile people, often elderly, are denied access to out of town services.

Questions

1 Explain the causes of the decline of businesses in the CBDs of cities. Include the disadvantages of the CBD location as well as the advantages of the out-of-town location.

2 With the aid of examples describe the impact of decline in the CBDs of cities.

3 **Investigation**

Select a local CBD to investigate the changes that have occurred. You will need a GOAD map which is about ten years old to compare the current land uses with either an up-to-date GOAD map or primary fieldwork.

a Is there any evidence of:
- the loss of certain functions and/or a decline in their quality, e.g. food retailing, DIY, electrical goods, growth of charity shops
- the creation of a dead heart
- an increase in the number of vacant buildings/development of areas of discard
- development of specialized shopping areas/leisure facilities/zones of assimilation.

b **Essay**

Comment on the changes that have taken place in your chosen CBD.

Reversing the decline in central areas

After the initial approval of many planning applications for out-of-town centres and large superstores some local authorities and town councils in the UK have resisted their development. This has been largely due to the perceived negative impact on the CBD. However, it was also recognized that they would be popular attractions that were likely to increase the prosperity of the local area as well as providing employment. As a result many authorities approved plans for the building of retail parks and at the same time invested in the CBDs to make sure they did not decline. There has been an increase in the appointments of city centre managers in order to co-ordinate this planning and to promote CBDs.

The example of Taunton shows how the presence of out-of-town retail parks and the CBD can be complementary. The out-of-town location caters for the large supermarkets, DIY and self assembly furniture stores that all require large floor space and car parks while the CBD concentrates on the specialist stores and consumer durables.

The main aims of recent planning strategies in town centres have been:

• *The beautification of the CBD*

Most city centres have received something of a face-lift in recent years with schemes to enhance the environment. Such schemes include adding attractive street furniture, floorscaping of pavements and roads, tree planting and pedestrianization. Durham city centre, a historic market town in north-east England, is a good example. Here tarmac and concrete roads and pavements have been removed and replaced with traditional cobbled walkways. Pedestrianization is now extensive in the city centre and the new shopping mall has traditional shop fronts. Covent Garden in London has seen similar changes since the old fruit and vegetable market moved to Vauxhall in 1974. The old central market was renovated to provide accommodation for numerous small shops, bars and restaurants. The residential population has increased from 2800 to 6000 with community facilities provided. A new market was opened in 1980 and five years later Covent Garden became the second most popular tourist attraction in London. However, these traditional schemes based upon renovation and the re-creation of the past are not universally welcomed. Some criticize the developments as "unhealthy nostalgia" claiming they stifle modern architecture while others criticize the high costs involved.

▼ **Figure 6.9** Schemes in Durham City to enhance the environment: traditional street furniture, pedestrianization, cobbled streets and traditional shop fronts

In many cities the rigid land use zoning has disappeared and a variety of land uses has been encouraged largely to attract the residential population back to the city centre. In Edinburgh the old town had a population of 60,000 in the 1860s but this had fallen to about 4000 in the 1980s. Today an Enterprise Trust is carrying out renovation and creating properties around squares in order to attract people back.

• *New retailing developments*

A visit to any CBD of a large town or city in the UK will reveal the modern shopping precinct and new retailing developments. Examples include the Churchill Centre in Brighton, the Westgate Centre in Oxford and the Prince Bishops precinct in Durham City. Many of these precincts have attracted branches of the major chain stores but also specialist shops catering for the niche market not provided for in the large out-of-town superstores. Increasingly the architecture blends in more carefully with the existing buildings and traditional building materials are being used. The opportunity has been taken to diversify the functions offered so that they cater both for the local population and for visitors.

▼ **Figure 6.10** The Prince Bishops shopping precinct in Durham City where the architecture blends in with the existing city centre and niche shops offer complementary shopping to the out-of-town outlets.

• *Gentrification and re-urbanization*

A major aim of many modern development schemes has been to achieve gentrification and re-urbanization. Gentrification is a process of raising the status of an inner-urban area that has become unfashionable and neglected. The aim is to upgrade the area and to encourage wealthier populations to move in. This generates re-urbanization, thus increasing the number of people in the urban areas who have previously lived in the suburbs or outside the urban area.

Gentrification has been a feature in both the CBD and inner-city areas of cities in the UK with many examples including the development of the London Docklands, the Sunderland Riverside, Salford Docks and the Newcastle Quayside (see case study, pages 229–230). A common feature is that these zones of discard have become zones of assimilation demonstrating growth and dynamism.

• *New office developments*

Maintaining the success of the CBD requires the continued attraction of modern business and the provision of offices to compete with those to be found on the modern business parks on greenfield sites. With the increasing globalization of the economy it is particularly important to attract international companies to maintain the status of the city in world markets and trade. Multinationals can afford to be choosy about where they locate. City centres need to be able to offer a high quality environment and the facilities to attract them and their employees.

• *The global and 24 hour city*

The process of globalization or internationalization is affecting urban developments as well as the social and cultural scenes in cities. Improvements in communications are shrinking the world and many of the world's largest cities are now global cities. There continues to be a rise in international travellers and an increase in international trade including banking and the expansion of multinational companies. Production is no longer raw material-based and most industries are free to locate anywhere. Cities in MEDCs in particular must increasingly develop services to compensate for the loss of jobs in manufacturing. Manufacturing is often lost to the LEDCs where labour and production costs are usually much cheaper. Global cities centred upon the provision of knowledge and information as well as services are growing because of these changes. Knowledge-based cities treat knowledge as the basic resource hoping to attract activities connected to science, education, technology, finance, marketing, logistics, cultural and international affairs. Such cities need a good quality of life to attract workers. The world's major cities such as New York, Hong Kong, Paris, London and Tokyo are increasingly global cities with multicultural populations and a range of shops and other services that reflect the cultural variety and varied cuisine of the world. Many smaller cities such as Newcastle-upon-Tyne, Manchester and Birmingham are also developing as global cities.

▲ **Figure 6.11** The taste of Italy and India next door to each other reflecting the increasingly multi-cultural nature of cities

The global city is typically the location of the headquarters of many international companies, a centre for international banking, insurance and finance and a focus of international meetings and conferences. Global cities are also often developing as 24-hour cities. The concept of a 24-hour city is the city that never goes to sleep – a city in which the streets are busy 24 hours a day with shoppers and workers during business hours and the party goers and entertainment seekers during the night.

Newcastle-upon-Tyne: reversing the decline?

Case Study

Newcastle upon Tyne lies on the north bank of the River Tyne in north-east England. During the nineteenth century the city benefited from the great wealth generated by the coal mines, shipyards and trade. Many beautiful buildings were created – the world famous Nicolaus Pevsner, a professor of architecture, described Grey Street as the finest street in England (Figure 6.12). However, from the 1950s there was a decline in the traditional industries leading to decay in parts of the CBD and inner city. There was a need to redevelop areas including the decaying inner city terraces and to adapt the city to modern day living. Figure 6.13 shows the core and frame areas of Newcastle's CBD in the 1980s and the areas where renovation and redevelopment were needed.

Figure 6.12 The stunning architecture of Grey Street in Newcastle-upon-Tyne where the majority of buildings are grade II listed buildings

Zone 2: Grey Street/ Bigg Market/ Market Street/Grainger Town area
This is the heart of the central conservation area, in which fine Regency buildings and traditional street markets are to be preserved. Some areas of Grainger Town are in need of redevelopment.

Zone 3: Civic Centre, Polytechnic and eastern fringe area
This area is primarily used for administration and higher education. There are a number of houses, some of which are partially used as small offices, health practices, or as hotels/guest houses. The former Manors Station area is to be redeveloped, mainly for industry and commerce.

Zone 1: Principal shopping area
This contains the multi-million pound Eldon Square Shopping Centre, many other large shops and chain stores, offices, places of entertainment and car parking. This is the high value core of the CBD.

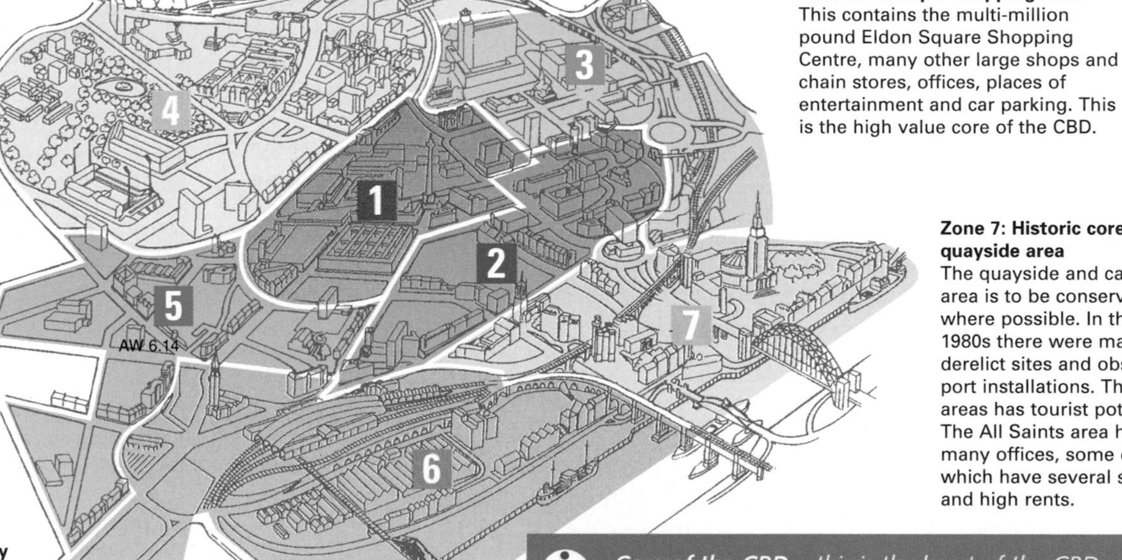

Zone 4: University/Leazes area
The functions of the University, the Royal Victoria Infirmary and the football ground dominate this area. There are many ageing houses, some small shops and some offices. The area will be developed by renovating old property.

Zone 7: Historic core quayside area
The quayside and castle area is to be conserved where possible. In the 1980s there were many derelict sites and obsolete port installations. The areas has tourist potential. The All Saints area has many offices, some of which have several storeys and high rents.

Zone 5: Blackfriars, brewery and Blenheim Street area
This western fringe of the CBD contains many small, specialist shops in a lower rental area. Many of the buildings are in need of repair or replacement.

Zone 6: Central Station area
This part of the CBD has been mainly concerned with rail- and river-based activities. Many of these activities are declining and there is much derelict land south of the station. North of the station there are a number of specialist shops in lower-rental areas.

▲ **Figure 6.13** The core and frame of Newcastle-upon-Tyne's CBD in the 1980s. Where was the greatest need for renovation and redevelopment?

__Core of the CBD__ – this is the heart of the CBD containing the high value properties. It is usually the retailing and commercial core of a city with the headquarters of banks, building societies and insurance companies, the department stores and other businesses with high profit margins that can afford the high rents

__Frame of the CBD__ – this is the periphery of the CBD where rents and rates are lower. Businesses with lower profit margins are often located in the frame along with bus and rail stations, universities and hospitals.

Newcastle is the regional shopping centre for the north east. However, development schemes have been needed in order for the city to maintain its leading position for retailing. Changes were necessary to cope with the changing demands of the local population and businesses, to counter zones of discard within the city and to remain competitive against other retail developments such as the Metro Centre in Gateshead.

The city centre had extensive zones of discard due to outward movements of people and businesses, as well as environmental degradation and deindustrialization associated with the closure of shipyards in the dockland areas.

Newcastle City Council in partnership with various private developers has not been complacent and many developments have taken place in order to maintain and improve the status of the city. Since the late 1970s an impressive range of new developments in all aspects of the economy are creating a vibrant and cosmopolitan society, reversing the process of decentralization of both people and business and attracting visitors from all over the world.

▲ **Figure 6.14** Part of the Metro Centre, Gateshead's out-of-town shopping centre

Eldon Square

In the late 1970s Eldon Square, a covered shopping mall, was created through the demolition of some of the finest Regency buildings in the city. At the time it was one of Europe's largest covered-in shopping centres with over 100 shops, restaurants, pubs and cafés as well as a large modern recreation centre. The centre was developed in conjunction with four main transport plans. A large modern bus station below the four-storey shopping complex was built along with two multi-storey car parks at either end of the development. An inner city urban motorway with associated flyovers eased the pressure of traffic in the city centre and the opening of the Metro rapid transport system, with a nearby station at the Monument in 1981, improved the accessibility of the city centre and encouraged the use of public transport.

In 1989 Eldon Garden opened as an addition to the Eldon Square shopping centre. It houses a range of exclusive shops with designer clothing and household labels. In 2000 Eldon Square had 25.3 million visitors – the eighth busiest shopping area in the UK.

Competition from the Metro Centre

In 1980 the site for the Metro Centre in Gateshead just five kilometres south west of Newcastle city centre was surveyed and final plans were published in 1983. It was planned to be a major out-of-town retailing and leisure facility. The out-of-town centre has free parking for 10,000 cars and new bus and rail stations. There are over 300 shops and 40 eating places, as well as numerous leisure activities.

The development of the out-of-town Metro Centre potentially posed a threat to the success of Newcastle's CBD and is considered by some to have been the impetus to further improvements to Eldon Square in Newcastle and other parts of the CBD. However, in reality while many of the same shops and services established premises in the Metro Centre branches did not close down in Newcastle city centre. Research suggests that many people who use the Metro Centre still visit Newcastle city centre as their main shopping area although there has been a decline in the number of pedestrian visits to both Newcastle and Gateshead city centres. Store managers were surveyed in Newcastle, Sunderland and Gateshead to discover the reasons for changes in sales levels since 1986. Initially 50 per cent stated that the Metro Centre was a major reason for changes but this figure has since declined. The economic growth in the region and increased wealth and mobility of much of the population as well as the growth in demand for retailing facilities would suggest that the area needed the provision of more shops and services to cope with the ever-increasing demand.

Newcastle Quayside and Gateshead Quays

November 2000 saw the £22 million Gateshead Millennium bridge put in place by the largest crane in the world – the Asian Hercules. It has already been nicknamed the 'Blinking Eye Bridge' (Figure 6.1) because it opens and shuts like an eye to allow shipping to pass through. The bridge is for pedestrians and cyclists and links the new arts and cultural developments on the Gateshead Quays and Newcastle Quayside, which are part of the joint Newcastle Gateshead bid for the title of European Capital of Culture in 2008.

The banks of the River Tyne have seen massive changes, redevelopments that are leading to gentrification and re-urbanization. The development costing £300 million in the former Baltic Flour Mills (Figure 6.3) includes five main galleries, a lecture theatre, cinema, artists' workshops, a café and shop. It will be the biggest arts centre outside of London. The flour mill is a listed building so much of the façade is being retained while the interior will be totally transformed. Close by will be a magnificent domed concert hall designed by Sir Norman Foster and capable of seating 1650 people. This will be the permanent home of the Northern Sinfonia Orchestra. Behind these developments the Baltic Business Park and Knowledge Campus are planned.

The Newcastle Quayside has also seen striking changes with thousands of jobs created in new business parks and offices that replace disused warehouses and shipyards, relics of the city's industrial heritage. There is a striking new courthouse, piazzas and offices hosting hi-tech companies. The quayside is now a dynamic area and a focus for the city's nightlife with smart cafes, cosmopolitan restaurants and fashionable bars.

Figure 6.15 'The Pitcher and Piano', a popular focus for evening entertainment on Newcastle's Quayside.

At St Peter's Basin, a former dockyard, has been converted into a small marina surrounded by executive apartments.

A growing number of listed companies are locating in the Tyneside area (from 31 to 40 in the last 10 years). There has also been the success of homegrown companies such as Sage, a software giant and now an international company employing 4000 people worldwide whose profits last year rose by 46 per cent to £108 million. The city is also home to one of the leading stockbroking firms in the country, Wise Speke. The city has also experienced rapid growth in the tourist industry with over 70,000 shoppers each year from Scandinavia alone and a huge demand for conventions leading to a bid to stage the G8 summit in 2006.

Newcastle upon Tyne is rapidly developing a reputation as a party city and a global city. The city attracts people from the local area and from around the world to sample the night-life, theatres and shops as well as to visit tourist attractions both within the city and beyond in Northumberland and Durham.

The Grainger Town project

One of the most acclaimed projects is the Grainger Town project, a 90-acre site stretching from Grey's Monument to the Central Station. Over 60 per cent of the buildings in the area are listed but many of them have physically deteriorated.

Figure 6.16 High quality new office developments to attract international companies

The city council has now put together a joint public–private initiative called the Grainger Town Team with a regeneration package of £120 million. Restaurants, pubs and an art gallery along with leisure facilities are planned. New housing will be built including 415 private sector properties and 265 housing association dwellings. By 2000, 90 housing units had been created by a housing association under the LOTS scheme, the acronym for the living-over-the-shops scheme.

The Grainger Town scheme is gentrifying what had become a rundown zone of discard within the CBD. The scheme is encouraging reurbanization by attracting people back into the city. The local council has a target of increasing the city centre population by 25 per cent or 1000 people by 2003.

Questions

1. With the aid of examples discuss why the growth of out-of-town shopping centres may prove beneficial rather than detrimental to the CBD.
2. Define the following terms: gentrification; re-urbanization; global city; 24 hour city
3. Study Figure 6.13 on page 228. Rewrite the labels for each of the zones to demonstrate the changes that had taken place by 2001.
4. In what ways has Newcastle redeveloped its central areas in order to:
   - **a** develop new retailing and office functions
   - **b** beautify the CBD to conserve the environment, and promote pedestrianization and tourism
   - **c** achieve gentrification and re-urbanization
   - **d** become a 24 hour city.

Urban deprivation in MEDCs

Ghetto *– a poor urban area that is often densely populated by people from deprived social groups. The term has traditionally been applied to inner-city areas in the USA where particular racial groups dominate. In European cities the term was used to describe the part of a city in which Jews were restricted.*

Inner city *– the adjacent zone to the CBD in a city. It is often densely populated and with high levels of urban decay and deprivation including economic, social and environmental problems. In the UK these are areas of mixed land uses – a product of their growth during the Industrial Revolution when factories, warehouses and Victorian terraces developed side by side.*

Urban decay *– the decline in the socio-economic and environmental quality of urban areas.*

Urban deprivation *– the hardship suffered by local communities living in areas of urban decay. It is defined by the Department of the Environment as when 'an individual's well-being falls below a level generally regarded as a minimum for Britain today'.*

Urban decay and deprivation

The inner-city areas of many UK towns and cities have an image of decay and deprivation with problems of poverty, pollution, crime, overcrowding, poor housing conditions, unemployment and racial tension. While this may represent an oversimplification and stereotyped view research shows that such problems are more prevalent in inner-city areas than in other areas of cities.

The UK Labour Government stated in 1997 that a person living in an impoverished inner-city estate was likely to die seven years before someone living in the relatively affluent county of Surrey. Tessa Jowell, the Minister for Public Health at the time, stated, 'We are committed to reducing inequalities in health …we want to attack the underlying causes of ill health and to break the cycle of social and economic deprivation and social exclusion. Poverty, unemployment, bad housing, social isolation, pollution, ethnic minority status and gender have for too long been regarded as peripheral to health policy.'

Decay and deprivation are both relative concepts: they are to do with how deprived an area is in relation to more prosperous areas. In UK cities, as in most MEDCs, there are areas of decay and deprivation, that would be considered to be poverty-stricken. But how do those areas compare with the poorest districts in the shantytowns in cities of the LEDCs? Poverty is a relative concept.

Measuring decay and deprivation is therefore about measuring the relative status of areas. A variety of indicators are used. Figure 6.18 shows deprivation indices for two wards in Newcastle-upon-Tyne using the results from the Inter Censal Survey of 1996. Elswick forms part of the inner city of Newcastle while South Gosforth represents a more affluent suburban location (Figures 6.18 and 6.19)

▼ **Figure 6.17** Indicators of deprivation – data for Elswick and South Gosforth

1996 inter-censal survey Deprivation indicator	Newcastle as a whole	Elswick	South Gosforth
Residents over retirement age (%)	23	19	19
Lone parent families (%)	6	8	2
Households lacking car ownership (%)	50	66	24
Male unemployment (%)	21	34	6
Overall unemployment (%)	16	27	5
Children in households where there are no earners (%)	33	56	2
Residents with a limiting long-term illness (%)	14	15	9
Asian population (%)	4	25	5
Owner-occupied households (%)	53	43	83
Privately rented accommodation (%)	8	20	12
Consumer durables (% with):			
washing machine	87	79	91
video recorder	69	57	76
microwave oven	65	48	72
home computer	20	13	35
Where most do food shopping (%):			
Food superstore	34	13	66
Local shopping centre	31	60	10
Youth unemployment (16–24 years) (%)	28	35	25
Semiskilled and unskilled manual workers (%)	22	36	9
Professional and managerial (%)	19	11	40

Other surveys and census information may well reveal other useful indicators to identify poverty and deprivation such as numbers taking free school meals, levels of literacy, infant mortality, children in care and youth crime figures.

▼ **Figure 6.18**
a Wards in Newcastle-upon-Tyne
b Housing in Elswick

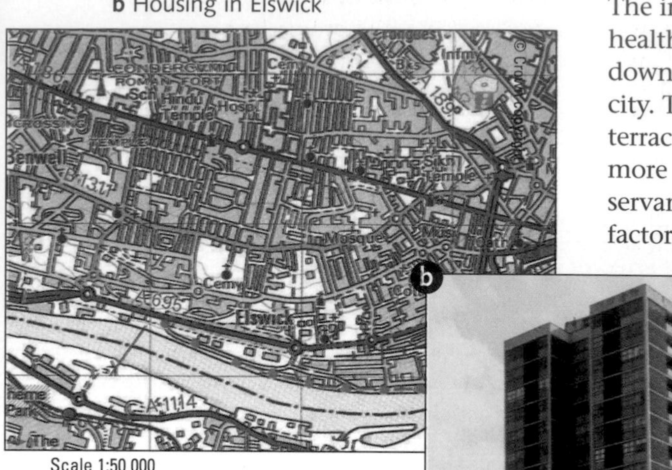

The causes of deprivation

The inner cities were once thriving communities in which there was a healthy social mix. The lower-paid workers lived in the basic two-up two-down Victorian terraces or the characteristic tenements of Glasgow's inner city. The more affluent also lived in the inner city occupying more substantial terraced properties in more salubrious locations. These houses were larger and more decorative. They often included basements and attics to house the servants. There was a real mixture of land uses with terraced housing close to factories, mines and shipyards. In the absence of cars and other forms of transport the local people needed to be able to walk to work. There were shops and public houses, schools and parks. Many elderly residents who remember the 'old days' comment on the strength of the community spirit and the lack of crime. However, even in Victorian times these areas had problems. In the absence of industrial legislation there were high levels of land, air and water pollution; there were high death rates as a consequence of poor sanitation and a lack of medical care and unemployment; and poverty abounded. However, the majority of the residents in inner-city areas all faced similar problems and had a similar way of life.

Since Victorian times, however, the contrasts between rich and poor have increased leading to diverse spatial inequalities within cities. An American geographer, Bunge, describes this as: "The people of the outer 'city of plenty' take benefit from investments in city centres, whilst the profits miss out the 'inner city of death' and only filter into the 'intermediate city of deprivation'." His description of a city with a poor centre and increasing wealth towards the edge of the built-up area mirrors the urban model of Burgess, which is based upon the basic assumption that there was segregation in cities according to social class.

The cycle of deprivation is a theory that attempts to explain the concentration of poverty and deprivation to be found in the inner cities. The theory, summarized in Figure 6.20, is based upon the historical changes that took place in cities in the developed world. During and after the Industrial Revolution sectors of the population became increasingly affluent. The wealth increased the mobility of some people leading to greater social segregation in cities. The wealthy sections of the population were able to afford larger more luxurious homes and those wealthy enough to do so moved out of the inner city. Some invested in older properties for refurbishment in city centres but most moved into the suburbs or beyond leaving behind the poorer, disadvantaged sectors of the population in the inner cities. In general, older residents, single-parent households, students, the poorer families and ethnic minorities were left behind. There was a large influx of ethnic minorities entering the country after the Second World War. They sought cheap accommodation and became concentrated in the inner cities, which led to the formation of ghettos. These communities have been perpetuated and expanded as new arrivals seek areas with similar languages, cultures and services such as churches, mosques and ethnic food stores.

▲ **Figure 6.19**
c Housing in South Gosforth

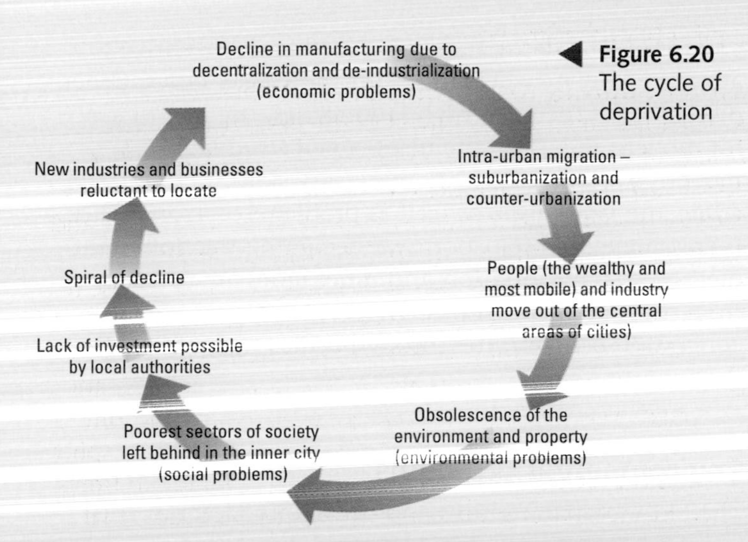

Figure 6.20 The cycle of deprivation

The movement of businesses, including industries and retailing, accompanied the movement of people and worsened the plight of the poorer sectors of the population. The decentralization (and deindustrialization) of industry, especially manufacturing, caused growing unemployment in the inner cities. In some areas the loss of manufacturing was so marked that phrases such as 'flight to the fringe' and 'dead hearts' were commonplace. The poor are less able to pay the transport costs of long journeys to work which has also contributed to the dramatic increases in unemployment in some inner-city locations. The flight of businesses and industry from the inner city fuelled the drainage of money out of these areas. Local authority receipts from taxes, rates and rents plummeted leaving little money to invest in the inner cities.

The movement of retailing to the outskirts disadvantages those in the inner cities. Hence the out-of-town shopping centres tend to be dominated by the wealthier car-owning customers while the less wealthy and less mobile are deprived of access to the better shops and confined to often poorer quality city centre or local shopping facilities. The expansion of the CBD in some cities and the building of urban motorways, flyovers and ring roads added to the blight of the inner cities by increasing noise and pollution.

Inner city problems

The outward movement of the wealthier sections of the community and the processes of deindustrialization and decentralization created inner-city areas with a plethora of social, economic and environmental problems.

Social problems

Inner cities with the characteristic high-density Victorian terraces were mostly built before 1914. While in some areas this housing has been successfully modernized, in others the properties have deteriorated. They were in a poor state of repair and lacked basic amenities. Even by 1981 the census showed that over one million properties still lacked a bathroom, WC or hot water. The small size and high density of the housing also contributed to high percentages of overcrowded households thought to contribute in part to the higher death and infant mortality rates, lower life expectancies and the greater incidence of illnesses.

The social segregation in the cities saw the concentration of unemployed, low income, semi-skilled and manual workers in the inner cities along with a higher incidence of single-parent families, elderly, students and ethnic minorities. Racial discrimination has been a problem and in the 1980s led to rioting in Brixton and other areas (Figure 6.21) and in parts of Leeds, Bradford and Oldham in 2001. The proportion of people claiming welfare benefits is much greater in the inner cities that in other residential neighbourhoods. Increasingly these sectors of the population have become socially excluded. They do not have access to good quality social, educational and recreational facilities available to the majority of the population. Persistent unemployment has generated a culture of poverty associated with low aspirations and achievement and leading to high levels of disaffection especially amongst the younger generations. The plethora of social problems leads to high levels of stress within families and social groups leading to higher than usual incidences of family breakdown and domestic disputes.

Inner-city area	City	Date
Brixton	London	April 1981 November 1985
Southall	London	July 1981
Toxteth	Liverpool	July 1981
Moss Side	Manchester	July 1981
Tottenham	London	October 1985
Handsworth	Birmingham	September 1985

Figure 6.21 The location of riots in inner-city areas in the 1980s

The Brixton riots, April 1981

The three days of rioting in Brixton were probably the worst ever experienced in Britain. Crowds of youths, mostly black, threw bricks, bottles and petrol bombs, looted shops and injured over 50 police and civilians. Petrol bombs caused fires, some buildings collapsed, vehicles were burnt out and people were stabbed.

After the riots the government set up an enquiry headed by Lord Scarman. His main findings were:

- *serious housing problems – a shortage of 20,000 homes, 20 per cent of housing sub-standard and blacks twice as likely to be homeless than whites*
- *a lack of leisure and recreational facilities especially for young people*
- *high unemployment especially among young people and blacks – 55 per cent of blacks under 19 out of work (a lack of qualifications and discrimination were given as two factors)*
- *harassment of young blacks by a small minority of police which had a huge impact in the local community.*

Lord Scarman concluded that the police and community leaders had to bear some of the responsibility for the riots. However, the social conditions helped explain why the riots occurred even though they did not excuse them.

Twenty years ago riots consumed three of Britain's cities. How have they fared since?

Brixton

How crunchy do you think a neighbourhood ought to be? How rough-diamond can it be before it gets unbearable? How would you feel, say about living in a riot zone? Could I tempt you with Toxteth in Liverpool, for instance? Or Brixton in London? Or St Paul's in Bristol? How far do you want to make your friends' jaws sag when you tell them where you're living?

After all, a mere 20 years ago saw the first use of CS gas on the British mainland to control a riot situation (Toxteth), post-riot damages claims totalling £17 million, and the refusal of the BBC to show riot footage on *John Craven's Newsround* for fear of accelerating the breakdown of law and order among the pre-teens.

Brixton is nothing but shops, street life, frantic activity, but with less of the architectural splendour than Toxteth. What you do have in Brixton is the chance to make a statement about yourself and the life you lead. You have the Brixton Academy (where Eminem played), and the Ritzy cinema; you have the legendary Fridge and the Bug Bar. You have the market in Electric Avenue, tilapia fish, yams, shouts from the halal meat butchers, trip-hop pouring out of a hole in the wall; and you have the full panoply of mainstream retailing, with Tesco, Marks & Spencer and Argos.

You also have endless grungy student types shuffling about, some nice properties on Loughborough Park and on the Clapham Park side of Brixton Hill, as well as tucked into the Poets' Corner at the Herne Hill end. There are media professionals willing to pay upwards of £400,000 for a family house off Brixton Hill (had they held their nerve in the aftermath of the riots they could have bagged one for £40,000) and take part in this complete United Nations vibrant multi-culturality. You even, according to a poster hanging from one of Lambeth Council's offices, have the fifth lowest council tax in Britain.

Admittedly, Railton Road, the old front line of the early 1980s, still has that after-the-bomb feeling. Like lower Toxteth, it is long on steel shutters and an odd apprehensive quiet. You have to go a fair way along Railton Road before the properties start to brighten and people pluck up the nerve to paint their walls or put palms out by their front door. But they do eventually; and before long you are in the main drag anyway, enjoying the thunderous vitality of Brixton life, so maybe a little peace and quiet isn't all bad.

▲ **Figure 6.22** An adapted extract from *The Daily Telegraph*, 28 April 2001, commenting on the changes that have taken place in Brixton since the riots in the 1980s

Economic problems

The major problems arise from the loss of industries and businesses and the massive unemployment that was created. Between 1951 and 1981 unemployment in the inner cities rose from 33 per cent to 51 per cent above the national average. Some parts of the inner cities had levels of male unemployment above 70 per cent. The poverty and low incomes meant that relatively few people could afford to own their own homes or to invest any money in repairs and improvements. Some of the larger, once middle-class, Victorian properties were bought up by private landlords and sub-divided into flats. This created multiple occupancy of the building, which added to the problems of overcrowding but helped to overcome the problems of high land values in the inner city.

Local authorities, unable to raise very much from taxes, lacked resources to invest in the area. This led to environmental decay that was a further disincentive to attracting any new businesses into the inner cities. Other disincentives included high land values, the lack of space for modern industrial premises, a perceived lack of a modern workforce with the necessary skills, high rates of crime and vandalism, as well as problems of accessibility. Increasingly road transport was becoming the dominant method of transportation and inner cities are remote from most motorway links. They also suffered traffic congestion being on the through routes from the CBD to the suburbs.

Environmental problems

The old Victorian terraces and the empty factories and warehouses suffered from decay and dereliction. They became seedbeds for crime, vandalism and drug trafficking. The housing stock was often in poor repair with empty properties boarded up. There was a lack of open space and green areas other than areas of derelict land where clearances had taken place. In some areas the dereliction was widespread creating a depressing environment. The industrial past often left behind a polluted environment as well as air pollution from the coal fires, which were still the only form of heating in many terraced homes. The Metro Centre at Gateshead was partly built on a reclaimed tip that was polluted in places with heavy metals from past industries. Local water-courses were also often badly polluted with sewage, metals and other chemicals.

The inner-city environment deteriorated and the social, economic and environmental problems grew worse during the second half of the twentieth century. The term multiple deprivation was coined to summarize the serious catalogue of problems the inner cities faced. The problems were recognized by successive governments and there have been numerous initiatives to try to quell the deterioration and to reverse the fortunes of the inner city.

Questions

1 Study Figures 6.17, 6.18 and 6.19. Compare and contrast the characteristics of Elswick and South Gosforth. Use the following questions as a guide.
   - a Identify the zone of a city to which each area belongs
   - b With reference to the data supplied justify your answer to part a.
   - c Select two statistics that were the most and least useful in coming to your conclusion in part a. Explain your choice.

2 With reference to the cycle of deprivation shown in Figure 6.20 describe the problems and explain the likely causes of deprivation in Elswick in Newcastle and other inner city areas in the UK.

Inner city initiatives

Reversing the decline in the inner cities

Stage 1 (1945–67)

After the Second World War many local authorities were faced with a housing crisis. This was due to:

- population growth due to the post-war baby boom and increasing immigration
- increased life expectancies – people were living longer
- family breakdowns and divorce leading to more single-parent families and smaller family units – more people leaving home earlier and needing accommodation
- army personnel returning after the war
- bomb damage during the war
- inner city redevelopment schemes which meant that displaced people had to be rehoused.

The government actively followed a policy of decentralization, encouraging both people and industry to move out of cities. Additional housing for the growing population and those displaced from the inner cities was provided by encouraging people to move into the New and Expanded Towns (Information Box) and newly constructed local authority housing in the suburbs.

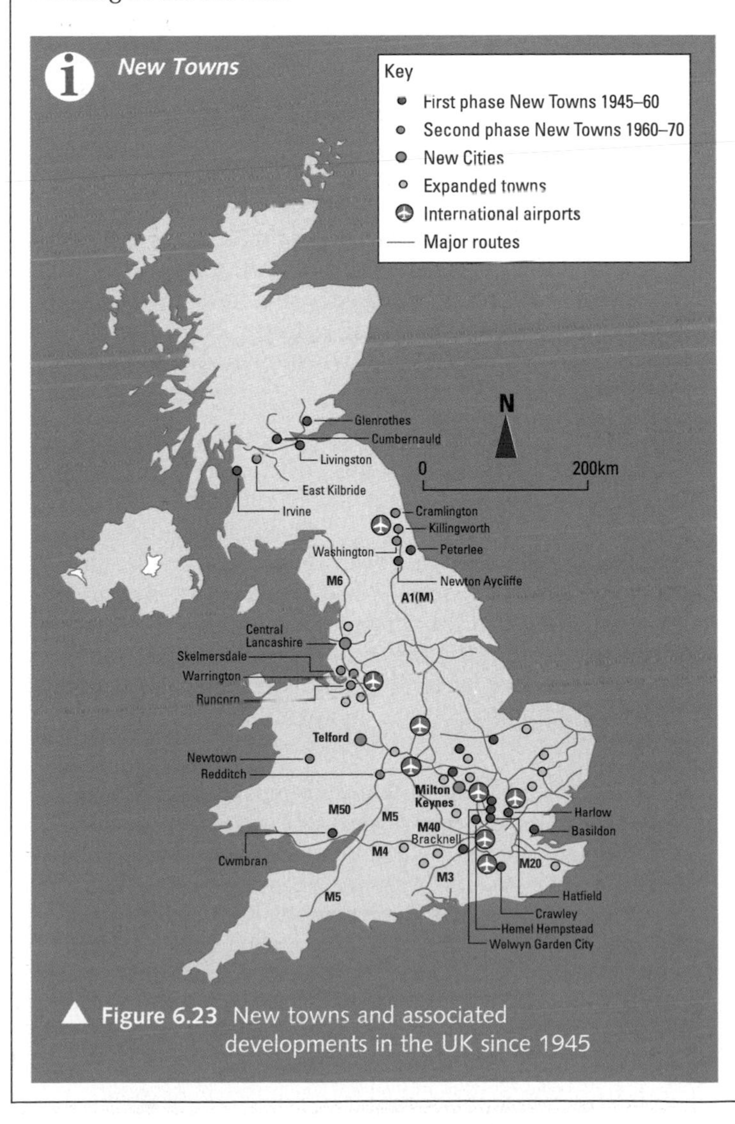

▲ **Figure 6.23** New towns and associated developments in the UK since 1945

Comprehensive redevelopment

A Comprehensive Development Areas programme (CDA) involved 'knock it all down and start again' and began in 1947. The programme involved the large-scale clearance of terraces in order to provide new housing and improve inner-city environments. Over 20 years 1.5 million properties were knocked down in the inner cities. Elswick and Kenton in Newcastle's inner city were two areas earmarked for comprehensive redevelopment. Existing residents were moved either into the New Towns of Cramlington, Washington and Killingworth or to extensive council house estates built in areas such as Byker with its famous Byker Wall (Figure 6.24).

▲ **Figure 6.24**
The Byker Wall – high-density council housing built towards the edge of Newcastle-upon-Tyne to house people displaced from inner-city clearances. The wall has its own incinerator providing heat and hot water to the residents. This is an early example of urban conservation, notice the chimney at the end of the wall.

Most local authorities followed identical planning strategies replacing the former terraces and tenements with high-rise flats. The whole landscape of parts of the inner city was transformed with huge concrete and glass tower blocks separated by flat expanses of grass, the occasional children's play area and blocks of shops and garages. At the time some of these high-rise flats received architectural awards such as those in Hulme in Manchester. However, the CDA policy was not entirely successful. The policy did not keep pace with the rate of housing decay and the redevelopment failed to match the speed of demolition. This added to the acute housing shortage and left vast expanses of derelict land. By 1967 there were still 1.8 million houses unfit for human habitation and 4.5 million in need of repair. The community spirit was lost and problems emerged with many of the tower blocks. The policy also failed to tackle the social and economic problems, in particular unemployment.

▲ **Figure 6.25** The Hulme Crescents in Manchester, award-winning high-rise developments of the 1960s. What was the reality?

The tower blocks fulfilled some of the needs for modern housing in the inner cities. Flats had proper bathrooms and kitchens, central heating and hot and cold running water. However, much of the housing was poorly designed and badly built. Many flats suffered from excessive dampness and the reinforced concrete used to construct the towers often deteriorated. Many of the flats had electric central heating installed, a major improvement on the coal fires of the past but the electricity proved too expensive for many households and there were frequent breakdowns that were expensive to repair. Access to the flats was often along dark dingy corridors, a haven for undesirables and a collecting point for rubbish. The lifts to higher floors broke down making people virtual prisoners in their own homes. Many older residents and parents with young children found the lifts and flights of stairs too much to cope with. Some residents reported the lack of community spirit in the flats, problems with noise from neighbours and the lack of privacy and gardens. Physical and mental health problems continued to be high due to the stress of high rise living.

In the 1980s developers were already beginning to either demolish the tower blocks or to decapitate and refurbish the flats. There was also a growing awareness that solving the housing problems was not enough. Investment in improved services and employment opportunities were equally badly needed to reduce the poverty in the inner cities.

Stage 2 (1968–77)

Research in the inner cities highlighted the complexity of problems including high unemployment, issues about race and immigration and the social dislocation caused by the CDA schemes. The 1968 Urban Aid programme gave grants to local authorities to expand services in deprived areas and to establish community development projects using self help. More emphasis was being placed on improving services and attracting employment opportunities. The schemes were much more localized in scale and involved local communities to a greater extent. It was unfortunate that an economic downturn limited the funds for these schemes.

Stage 3 (1978–90)

The New Towns policy was abandoned in an effort to stop further decentralization of people and business. For the first time, inner cities were officially declared problem areas due to economic collapse caused by decentralization and deindustrialization. New policies have all attempted to tackle whole inner-city areas and they have aimed to regenerate inner city economies as well as to improve the environment and local services.

In 1987 Margaret Thatcher was re-elected and introduced the "Action for cities" policy.

There were four main programmes:

1. The urban programme which gave 75 per cent grants to the most needy local authorities.
2. Derelict land grants for reclamation schemes such as the Garden Festivals held in Liverpool, Glasgow and Gateshead.
3. Enterprise zones (EZs) in which efforts were made to stimulate economic activity by giving businesses tax breaks for ten years, 100 per cent grants for machinery and buildings and access to rapid planning permission.
4. Urban Development Corporations (UDCs) were expanded from London and Liverpool, to includeTrafford Park in Greater Manchester, Teesside, the West Midlands, Tyne and Wear, Bristol, Leeds, Central Manchester and Sheffield. UDCs have been described as the most important attack made on urban decay.

Stage 4 (1991 onwards): City Challenge

Urban areas continue to present a challenge to planners and developers. City Challenge was launched in 1991. Local authorities, where there are severe urban problems, can bid for funds for specific urban projects. For example in Sunderland, City Challenge money has been used to redesign parts of the city centre with a new shopping precinct and bus station and in Leicester derelict inner-city land has been transformed into a show piece area with new shops, services and housing.

In the early 1990s there were many different schemes in operation and urban policy was criticized for being too fragmentary. It was split between six different government departments and not always good value for money. By the end of the 1990s a single government department, the Urban Regeneration Agency, had been created and in 1994 the Single Regeneration Budget (SRB) was launched to draw together funding into a single package. The SRB money is aimed at activities that make a real and sustained difference in deprived areas. Increasingly public and private joint initiatives are being promoted.

In November 2000 the government released its Urban White Paper setting out its vision of urban living where people shape the future, live in attractive well kept towns and cities, live in a more environmentally sustainable way and share property and receive good services. It proposed stamp duty exemptions in disadvantaged communities, tax credits for clearing contaminated land, capital allowances for 'flats over shops' schemes and other tax reforms for property conversions. A new neighbourhood renewal fund of £800 million over three years is also to be introduced.

Greater Manchester: urban redevelopment

Case Study

Phase 1: 1945–60

Bombing during the Second World War destroyed 4.5 hectares of the city and damaged 30,000 homes (Figure 6.26). By the end of the war a further 70,000 homes were deemed unfit for living mostly in the high-density Victorian inner-city area. The City of Manchester Plan was launched in 1945 with the aim of clearing all Victorian housing. Following the repair of wartime damage the Manchester Slum Clearance Programme restarted in 1954. Over five years 7500 properties were demolished mostly in the Miles Platting area.

▲ **Figure 6.26** Bomb damage in Manchester during the Second World War

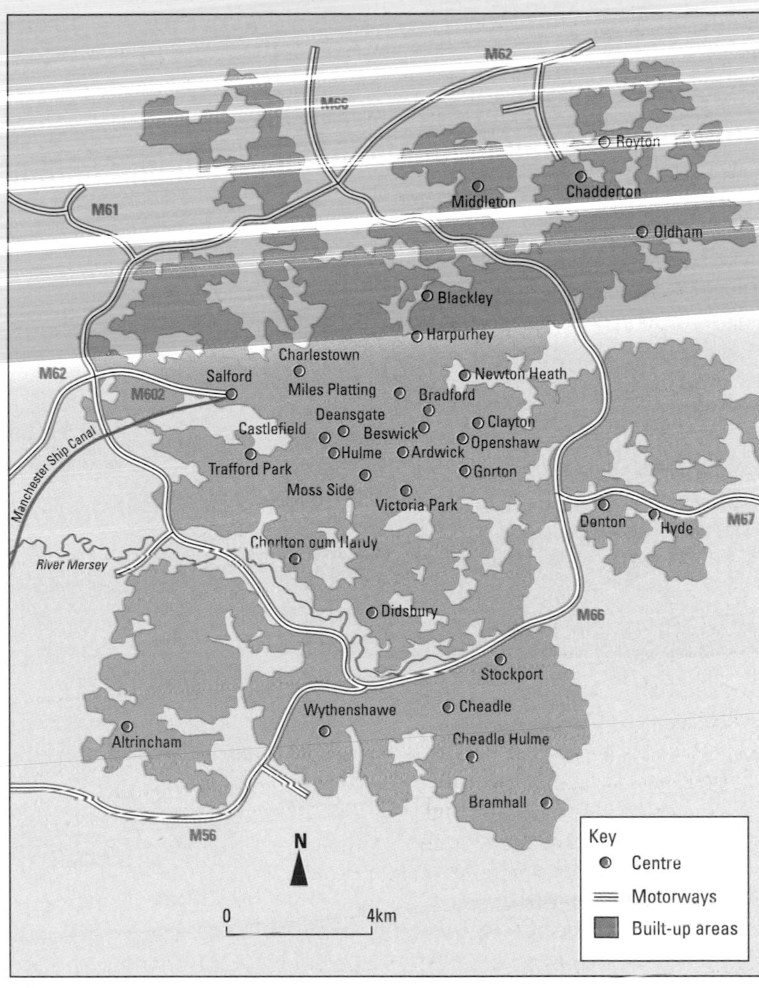

▲ **Figure 6.27** The built-up area of Manchester

Phase 2: 1960–90

A new development plan was introduced in 1961 embracing the policy of comprehensive development. The clearance programme was greatly expanded in four main areas: Hulme, Beswick, Longsight and Harpurhey (Figure 6.27). Prior to demolition the council used compulsory purchase orders. Over 55,000 new houses, a mixture of low and high rise were built to replace the cleared terraces reducing housing density and the population by as much as 50 per cent in some areas. The surplus population was re-housed in areas such as Wythenshawe – suburban locations based upon the Garden City principle with self-contained neighbourhoods of about 10,000 people with associated services.

The Hulme area of Manchester was typical of a Victorian inner-city area of Manchester with its tightly packed terraces. Conditions were overcrowded and unsanitary with few properties having toilets and many houses built without foundations. In the 1960s all of the terraced housing in Hulme was demolished. The central features of the redevelopment plans were the four award-winning crescents of high rise flats and the separation of traffic and people by walkways and bridges. Shopping facilities were concentrated at Moss Side and two smaller locations. By 1972 the redevelopment of Hulme was complete and 5000 new homes had been built. However, within months problems with the new properties began to emerge. There were severe faults in some of the construction and properties leaked. Extensive problems were experienced with condensation and dampness and heating bills were too high for some households. Young families, the elderly and disabled found the accommodation inappropriate. The area fell into a spiral of decline with growing unemployment, problems with drugs and violence and a deteriorating environment.

Phase 3: 1990 to present

Hulme City Challenge was launched in 1992. The plan involved building 3000 new homes, shops, roads, offices and community facilities to replace existing properties in a 60ha area (Figure 6.28). The scheme took five years to complete and cost over £200 million funded by a mixture of government, local authority and private finance.

▲ **Figure 6.28** 1990s redevelopment in Hulme in Manchester

In East Manchester, an area of 16 square kilometres, including the wards of Miles Platting, Beswick and Clayton Heath, became a focus for redevelopment in the 1990s. The nineteenth-century industries, including heavy chemicals and engineering, had declined. The area lost 24,000 jobs between 1974 and 1984. Housing had been redeveloped in the past, for example much of Miles Platting had been redeveloped in the 1950s, but the area still suffered environmental degradation and a lack of employment opportunities. Plans included 2000 new houses and 375,000 square metres of industrial and commercial floor space to provide 10,000 jobs. The area was chosen to be the prime location for sporting facilities to be built associated with the Year 2000 Olympic Games bid. Although the bid to host the Olympic Games failed the area benefited greatly from the additional investment and new facilities have helped the city to a successful bid for the 2002 Commonwealth Games. Seventy hectares of derelict land have been cleared and a new National Cycling Centre at the Velodrome built. An intermediate ring road provides dual carriageway links from East Manchester to the main motorway network. A new National Stadium has been completed and a new metro link.

In 1988 central Manchester (Figure 6.29) was given an UDC to regenerate 200ha of land and buildings in the southern part of the city centre. The area included six conservation areas, over ninety listed buildings, three universities, the Granada Studios Tour and the Museum of Science and Industry. However, there were also areas of contaminated land, derelict warehouses, mills and canals. The UDC ended in 1996 and in the eight years of its operation invested £420 million. The UDC achieved several major improvements:

- the Bridgewater concert hall and office developments
- successful housing in Castlefield
- the attraction of over two million leisure visitors per year
- the redevelopment of the Woodworth's Street area where a thousand homes have been built, many in converted listed buildings.

c

▲ **Figure 6.29** Redevelopment in the central area of Manchester

Since the UDC was wound up Manchester has accessed funds from the Single Regeneration Budget introduced in 1994. Manchester is part of the North West Development Agency (NWDA), which continues to tackle urban deprivation especially in East Manchester where consultation plans were concluded in 2000.

A key feature of urban regeneration projects today is the consultation process that takes place within the local communities. In Eastside a five-year Community Safety project has been launched to deal with issues raised in a crime and safety audit that had involved extensive community consultation questionnaires. This is part of the SRB funded initiative that began in 1996 and will last for six years until 2002.

Similar smaller scale regeneration schemes are now taking place in the central areas of many towns and cities in the UK. To attract funding the schemes need to demonstrate the involvement of the community in their planning and implementation.

However, a major weakness of urban regeneration plans has been a failure to tackle the underlying economic problems. High unemployment has been a permanent feature in many inner-city areas for decades and few authorities have managed to increase employment opportunities to anything like the levels when shipbuilding, textiles, engineering and chemical industries provided thousands of jobs for the people in the inner-city areas. Hence real poverty and all of the other social, economic and environmental problems still remain in some areas.

Other problems arise from the lack of long-term planning in urban regeneration. As shown here, plans rarely last more than the lifetime of a government and funding waxes and wanes according to the general health of the economy. A new government elected into office is often very reluctant to carry on the former initiatives particularly if the political party changes.

Urban redevelopment – a success?

There has been almost 60 years of regeneration in towns and cities, mostly in the CBD and inner-city areas. Successive governments have provided a variety of schemes and financial backing for projects in an effort to improve the living standards of urban communities particularly those in disadvantaged areas. But to what extent have they been successful? What challenges still remain?

In many cities transport improvements such as the Tyne and Wear metro system and the trams in Manchester have improved the accessibility of city centres, reduced the pressure on roads and car parks and helped to reduce levels of pollution. In inner-city areas quality of life has been improved for residents where schemes have successfully targeted the poorer members of the community. However, some schemes such as the High Rise Flats of the 1960s were a disaster and the more recent schemes involving gentrification, for example in several docklands areas, have had debatable success. While docklands schemes may well improve the local environment and encourage re-urbanization by the wealthier and more mobile members of society, they have done little for the poorer sections of communities who remain confined to the worst neighbourhoods in our cities.

Many CBDs have seen successful redevelopment schemes with the addition of new modern shops and indoor precincts with longer opening hours. However, some redevelopment, especially earlier schemes, demolished historic buildings and threatened the traditional character of the city centre. The construction work that has taken place and the new facilities provided do generate much needed employment in the urban areas.

Questions

1 With reference to one or more examples of urban areas evaluate the success of the following inner-city redevelopment schemes:
   - **a** inner-city high-rise developments
   - **b** peripheral council housing built in the 1960s and 1970s
   - **c** gentrification schemes in inner cities
   - **d** more recent smaller scale initiatives, e.g. Grainger Town project in Newcastle, the Eastside Community safety project in Manchester.

2 To what extent should the schemes listed above be an integral part in planning strategies in UK towns and cities in the twenty-first century?

3 'The decline in inner cities is irreversible.'
'You can change the place but you can't change the people.'
To what extent do you agree with these statements? Contribute your ideas to a class discussion.

4 **Investigation**

For an inner-city area in your locality investigate the history of urban planning since 1945. The following headings may be used as a guide:
- the causes and characteristics of problems in the inner city
- inner-city initiatives to solve the problems
- evaluation of the success of the schemes.

Urban deprivation in LEDCs

The majority of people living in cities in LEDCs are unable to afford houses that have been professionally built. Indeed, large numbers are so poor that they are forced to live on the streets or in makeshift, temporary shelters. The fact that about 50 per cent of city dwellers in LEDCs live in sub-standard housing makes the housing crisis probably the most serious problem for the authorities in charge of cities in the LEDW.

Deprivation in cities in the LEDW is concentrated in the shantytowns that have mushroomed since the 1950s. Figure 6.30 shows the percentage of urban populations living in selected cities in the LEDW. The causes of the growth of shanty towns, their location and characteristics were well documented as part of AS Geography and the main focus of this section is to evaluate the initiatives being implemented to alleviate the problems of the shanty towns.

▼ **Figure 6.30** Proportion living in shantytowns, squatter settlements and slums in selected cities in LEDCs

Location	Shantytown proportion (% of city)
Calcutta, India	33
Jakarta, Indonesia	25
Rio de Janeiro, Brazil	27
Santiago, Chile	25
Mexico City, Mexico	46
Lima, Peru	36
Caracas, Venezuela	35
Maraccuto, Venezuela	50

Many governments in the LEDW have attempted to solve the housing crisis in their cities with a variety of approaches. Many early schemes involved the clearance of the shanties and their replacement with high-rise flats such as the super-blocks in Caracas in Venezuela and Rio de Janeiro in Brazil (Figure 6.31). In Rio this was part of a process of gentrification. The city centre slums were cleared and replaced by up-market apartments to extend the high-class zone close to the CBD. The former residents of the shanties either became homeless or were moved to other government housing schemes where they often could not afford to pay the rents. In Manila in the Philippines over 3000 shacks were demolished in a two-week period. Clearing shanty towns was a feature of policies in the 1940s and 50s that has largely ceased today although as the article shows in Figure 6.32 slum clearance is still a feature in some countries such as Bangladesh. It reflected the thinking at the time that shanties represented a failure on the part of the authorities to cope with the housing demand in cities and that all shanties were full of rural immigrants and by knocking them down it would dissuade others from moving to the city.

▼ **Figure 6.31** Gentrification in Rio de Janeiro – high-rise blocks built on areas of land cleared of shanty towns

World Bank criticises slum clearance

The World Bank's senior official in Bangladesh, Fredrick Temple, has criticised a recent slum eviction drive ordered by the government. 'Bulldozing slums was not a solution to the problems of urban life,' Mr Temple said. 'Forcible eviction without relocation simply shifted poor people from one set of slums to another,' he added. The World Bank director called for a national urban strategy to cope with the pressures of urbanization, which he said were a result of economic growth centred around city life. Mr Temple's comments are the most explicit criticism so far from the donor community of the controversial slum demolition drive, which made at least 50,000 people homeless. The World Bank is one of Bangladesh's largest foreign aid donors, providing about $1bn last year. He said that, in general, the clearance programme – carried out because the government said some slum areas in Dhaka and its outskirts were centres of crime – did not constitute a full urban settlement or shelter policy. 'The experience of other countries indicates that it is neither possible, nor affordable, for cities with large areas of slums to relocate the inhabitants,' he added. Quoting the latest Bank study, Mr Temple said that, while four out of five Bangladeshis live in the countryside at present, in two decades every other Bangladeshi would live in cities. The World Bank director said he shared the concerns of the Bangladesh government on urban law and order. But the forcible eviction of slum dwellers undermined the Bank's efforts, in conjunction with the Bangladeshi government, to provide education, health-care, job training and micro-credit to the poor.

▲ **Figure 6.32** Criticism of slum clearance in Bangladesh, BBC News, 29 August 1999

Since the 1960s a more positive view of squatter settlements and shanty towns has been taken in many LEDCs. The terms 'slums of hope' and 'rags to riches' have replaced 'urban cancers' and 'slums of despair'. A British architect, John Turner, who worked in Peru for over eight years did much to change the views of people and governments by arguing that the *barriadas* or shanty towns in Lima should be viewed as building sites rather than slums. He also demonstrated how the slums gradually improve over time and with some help from governments this process can be accelerated. This policy called Aided Self-Help (ASH) has been successful in many cities and involves the government legalizing the land, providing small loans, building materials and technical assistance as well as essential services. The schemes encourage and reinforce the community spirit that is such a feature of squatter communities. The families often work together to build new homes or carry out improvements. In some communities co-operatives have been formed that benefit from a community approach to negotiate with local authorities, building merchants and other suppliers of goods and services. ASH projects involve three approaches (Figure 6.33): upgrading of shanty towns, site and services schemes and core housing schemes.

▼ **Figure 6.33** Types of low-income housing in cities in LEDCs

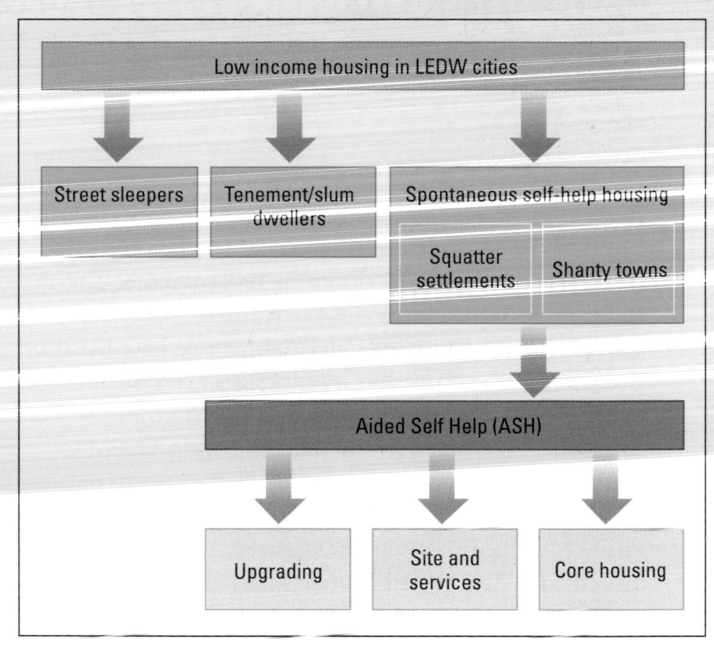

Upgrading existing shanty towns aims to improve the housing and facilities in an area through self-help schemes. The physical layout of the area is planned to reduce the very high density and lots are defined around houses taking care to achieve minimum disruption to existing homes. Families are offered ownership rights or long leases to give them security of tenure and basic services such as water, electricity, toilets, paths and roads are put in place. A good example of an upgrading scheme took place in Manila in the Philippines by the Tondo Foreshore Development Project. The area of reclaimed land close to the port was home to 27,000 squatter families. With the help of a loan from the World Bank, $US 65 million were invested to upgrade 12,000 homes and to re-house 4,000 families. Five years after the programme began over 97 per cent of families had improved their dwellings and 12.5 per cent had built entirely new homes.

Site and services schemes use new land often on the edges of cities. Houses are built on planned plots or sites and provided with services. Sometimes the people are left to build their homes. They often begin with a small home that they can afford and add to it later as circumstances change. The essential services so often absent in shanty towns are provided at the outset. The schemes are mostly successful although some have been abandoned because they moved people away from their work in the city centres and did not provide suitable locations for them to carry out their informal employment activities.

Core housing schemes are similar to site and services schemes but the first stages of the house are also provided. These usually include the bathroom and toilet, to ensure basic levels of sanitation are achieved, as well as the shell of the total dwelling. Often a mixture of starter homes is provided to cater for different incomes; the poorest are only able to afford the minimum toilet and bathroom.

Chennai (formerly Madras) in India

Case Study

Urbanization, a result of rural to urban migration, and high birth rates have caused a rapid increase in the population of Chennai (Figure 6.34), although the rate of increase has slowed down in recent years. The rapid increase in population has been mirrored by a rapid growth in the slums in Chennai. About one third of the Chennai population live in slums, mostly in the shantytowns where the typical building materials are mud and coconut thatch. The shantytowns or squatter settlements are mostly located on river banks adjacent to the Buckingham Canal and on other spare land close to industrial sites and markets. There is also a section of the population known as pavement dwellers. These people live in makeshift temporary accommodation on the streets. The slightly better-off inhabitants may access low-quality rented rooms and tenements. Some of these are relics of the colonial past while others have been newly erected by the government in an effort to ease the housing problems. The problems of this slum housing are summarized in Figure 6.35.

▼ **Figure 6.34** The impact of urbanization in Chennai
a Location of Chennai
b The growth of population in Chennai
c Number of slums in Chennai
d Slums in Chennai

▼ **Figure 6.35** The problems of the slum housing in Chennai

- Vulnerable to physical hazards, e.g. cyclones, fire, floods
- Lack amenities such as water, toilets, electricity, refuse collection. Many have no access to piped water and use street tanks; other water supplies may only be available for three hours a day.
- Low standards of hygiene due to lack of sanitation
- Overcrowding with families sharing rooms as small as 9 square metres
- Poverty – families have low incomes or no permanent income; many employed in the informal sector
- Lack of access to transport especially buses which are in short supply and cannot cope with the demand for three million journeys a day.

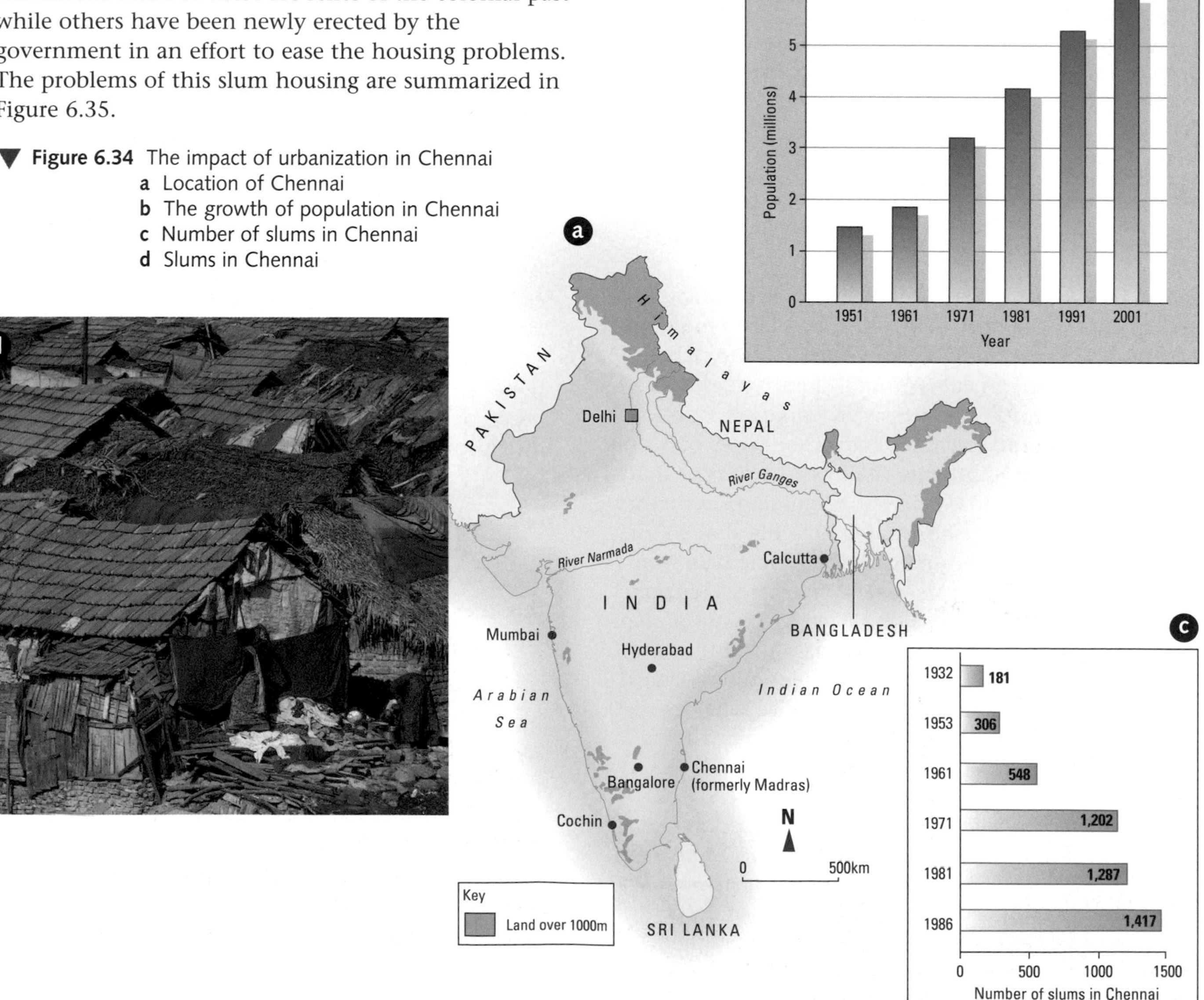

Planning solutions

The Housing Board and the Slum Clearance Board are responsible for housing improvements in Chennai. Initial schemes involved the building of four- to six-storey tenements but these largely failed due to poor maintenance and the lack of uptake as the disadvantaged could not afford high rents. If lower rents were charged the schemes would have proved too costly. The Board was forced to consider other options mostly targeted on the existing shantytowns areas.

Upgrading of some slums took place with the aims of providing 1 bath and 1 toilet per 10 families; 1 public fountain per 20 families, 1 street light per 40m of road and 1 pre-school per 200 families. Other schemes were required to be self-financing initiatives once some initial investment had been made. The city, the state or the World Bank provided the initial investment through offering loans, setting up self-help schemes and through welfare organizations. These schemes also encouraged greater community involvement. Some start-up loans were made available to families to build their own homes. Once the loans were repaid then new loans were made available for further improvements. Site and services schemes (Figure 6.36) were implemented with finance provided for the acquisition of land, purchase of building materials, road building and the provision of basic services such as water, sewage and electricity. The new owners were then responsible for building the property on the plot they had been allocated. The upgrading that took place often led to the sale of the homes to higher income groups. This generated some money for the poor families and allowed the Board to re-invest in new schemes. Providing permanent plots and improving the security of tenure helped the pavement dwellers. In addition to housing schemes youth training schemes were developed especially in nursing, welding, electrical, computing and plumbing skills. Campaigns were targeted at improving health and nutrition and reducing drug addiction.

▲ **Figure 6.36** Site and services schemes in Chennai

Velacheri, an area in the southern outskirts of Chennai, was the location for a site and services scheme (Figure 6.37). The Slum Clearance Board provided fourteen hectares of land to house 2,640 families many of whom were being forced out of the Canal Bank Road in Chennai by a rail building scheme. Others came from Tank Bund Road where there were many street dwellers and from the banks of the River Adayar. Waiting for the new residents to build their homes would have delayed the rail building programme so contractors were used to construct the houses, lay out the roads and provide a water supply, street lights and other services. Earlier site and services schemes had experienced problems with unfinished services and extra floors being added against regulations. Some new residents also quickly sold their properties for a profit and the poorest families were unable to afford to live in the new homes.

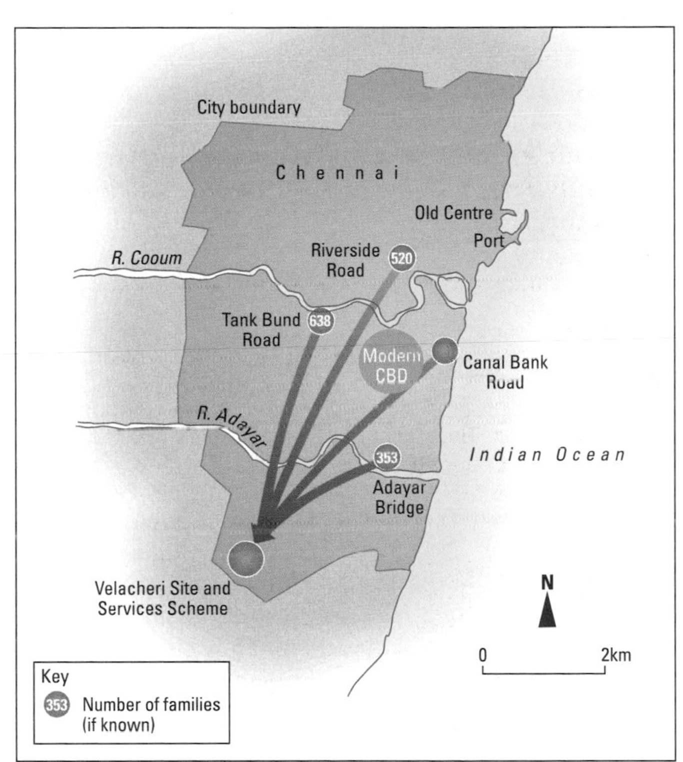

▲ **Figure 6.37** The relocation of squatters and street dwellers to Velacheri in Chennai

In some LEDCs plans to provide housing for the urban poor have involved schemes outside of the main city. Examples include:

- satellite or dormitory settlements such as 10th Ramadan near Cairo in Egypt (page 245)
- building New Towns, e.g. Brazil's new capital city, Brasilia (page 246)
- improving life in the rural areas to prevent the growth of shantytowns
- transmigration policies such as in Indonesia and Brazil where city residents are attracted by government packages back into the rural areas.

Cairo's New Towns

Case Study

Cairo is one of the world's megacities. The city's population has grown rapidly (Figure 6.38) since the 1950s reaching over twelve million at the beginning of the twenty-first century. The rapid rate of growth has outstripped the authority's efforts to increase services and there are increasing demands for piped water, sewers, schools, paved roads and electricity. Traffic congestion, air and water pollution add to the massive problems in the city. Every Cairo citizen, on average, has only 13 square centimetres of space to live in giving a population density of 32,759 people per square kilometre.

> ***New Towns in LEDCs***
>
> *New Towns were a major part of planning policies in countries of the developed world such as the UK. One of the aims was to provide a solution to the overcrowding and poor quality housing in many inner-city areas. Similar planning policies have been followed in some developing countries such as Egypt, Brazil and Nigeria where New Towns have been created in the hope of controlling urban growth and in particular the expansion of the shantytowns.*

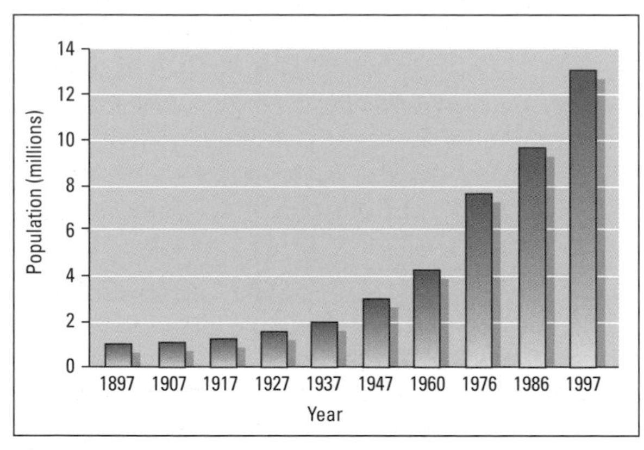

▲ **Figure 6.38** Cairo's population growth

Old Cairo is sited on an area of slightly raised land, the Muquattam Hills to the east of the modern CBD. The old city developed with narrow alleyways. In the mid-nineteenth century Parisian-style boulevards and apartment buildings were constructed near the River Nile in an attempt at modernization and as a result of European influence. However, the city's greatest expansion took place after the 1950s and between 1968 and 1982 alone the area of the city doubled. The fertile irrigated farmland along the banks of the River Nile was sold and illegally built on at an average rate of 600ha a year. Figure 6.39 summarizes Cairo's expansion.

Many cities in LEDCs are characterized by massive shantytowns on the fringes – communities living in home-made shacks and shelters. However, this pattern is not typical of Greater Cairo where brick-built houses and flats, which have often been constructed in stages, are more common. Many of these homes have been built illegally on state-owned or 'green land' (Information Box) and today these 'informal houses' cover an estimated 80 per cent of Cairo's built-up area (450 square kilometres). The areas of housing are very overcrowded and at the height of summer, when temperatures are over 40°C, the stifling heat and pools of polluted water from broken or non-existent sewers generate extremely unpleasant living conditions. In Al-Munira, for example, 600,000 people are crowded into just two square kilometres of land.

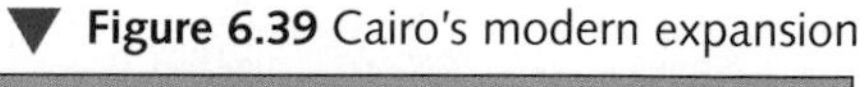

▼ **Figure 6.39** Cairo's modern expansion

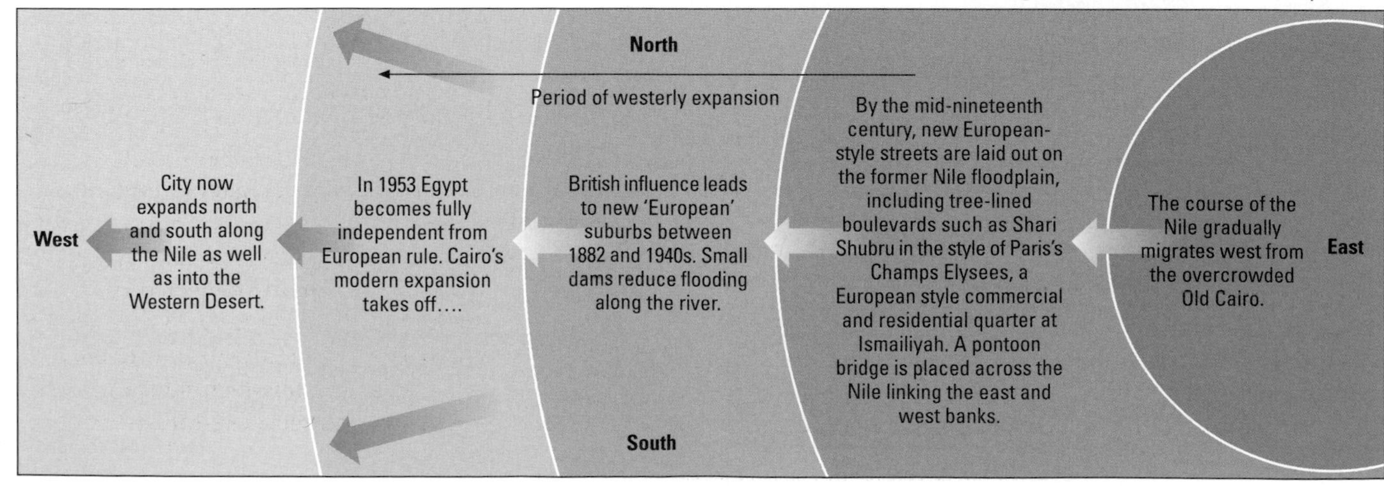

> *Green land – irrigated farmland close to the River Nile, officially protected from development by ancient laws in order to ensure the country's food supply.*

Cairo's poorest citizens have chosen to also live in two other unusual locations. In the Cities of the Dead (Figure 6.41) an estimated two to three million people have taken up residence in the tombs of Old Cairo and about half a million people occupy home-made huts on rooftops or in roof spaces in the city centre. Such is the housing crisis that some landlords have illegally added extra storeys to existing blocks of flats to create more rooms. In Old Cairo particularly, some of the properties are on the point of collapse either through the lack of repairs or due to the reckless addition of extra storeys that destabilize the foundations.

▼ **Figure 6.41** The Cities of the Dead where two to three million inhabitants have made their home

Despite a shortage of finance the Egyptian authorities have implemented a number of projects in an attempt to tackle Cairo's problems. New satellite and dormitory settlements such as 10th Ramadan and 15th May have been built in an effort to disperse some of the city's population. The New Town 10th Ramadan is located 55km ENE of Cairo (Figure 6.42) and eventually aims to house up to 300,000 people in six neighbourhood units. Each neighbourhood unit has high-rise apartment blocks and some open space and gardens, a mosque, junior school and local shopping centre. Industrial zones are an integral part of the scheme as without employment opportunities few people are likely to move in as it is too far to travel to Cairo for work. However, the scheme initially had great difficulty attracting residents and only had 30,000 people after eight years. Many of the apartments were too expensive for the intended residents and the costs of travelling to work in Cairo were prohibitive. Despite government aid, new industries were slow to move into the New Town, which proved a disincentive for people to move out of Cairo.

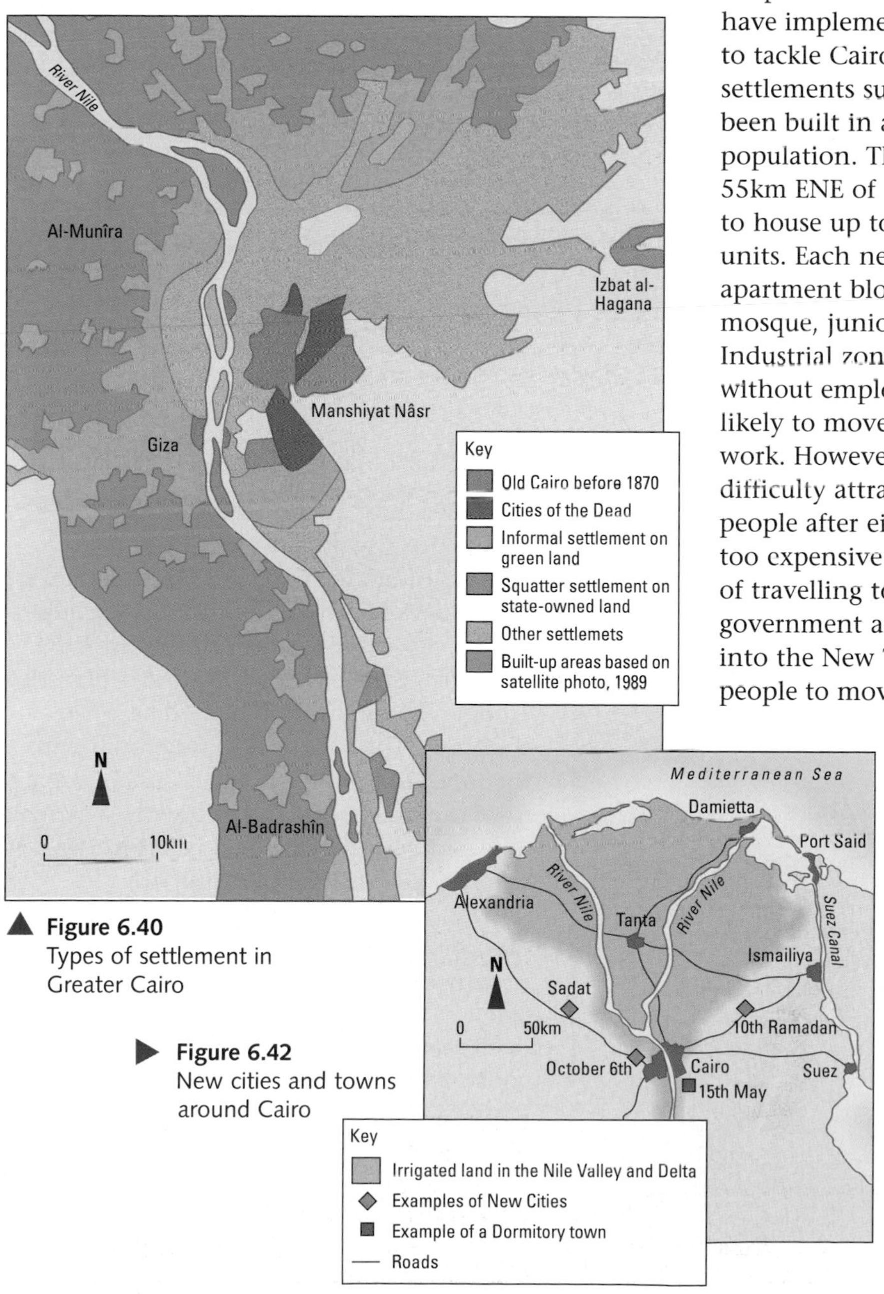

▲ **Figure 6.40** Types of settlement in Greater Cairo

▶ **Figure 6.42** New cities and towns around Cairo

A massive new ring road has been built in an effort to ease traffic congestion and a modern metro system is being constructed and already carries over one million commuters every day. The Greater Cairo Sewage project provides aid to repair and extend the city's crumbling sewage system and to extend it into areas currently without any sewage system. The Zabbaleen people traditionally collected the rubbish in Cairo with their donkey carts. They have now been officially licensed as the low-tech refuse collectors and recyclers for the huge slum areas.

Brasilia, a New Town

Case Study

In 1952 the Brazilian government narrowly voted to move the capital city from Rio de Janeiro to Brasilia (Figure 6.43). The aims were to achieve a more even distribution of wealth and development within the country and to divert growth away from the rapidly growing south east. Dramatic industrialization and urbanization in Rio de Janeiro, São Paulo and Belo Horizonte were creating a rich core with the attendant problems of overcrowding, pollution and squatter settlements. Construction of Brasilia began in 1957 following an aeroplane design and layout. It was planned for the motor car and contained housing superblocks in the 'wings'. The superblocks contain between nine and eleven apartment blocks each ten storeys high and designed for 2,500 people. The blocks provided some low-cost housing, although most was luxurious, executive accommodation targeted at the bankers, politicians and industrialists and well beyond the finances of most Brazilians.

The city's first residents arrived in 1960 and by 1986 the population had reached one million. This reflects some success in redistributing the country's population but many of those who work in Brasilia still commute between Brasilia and Rio where they prefer to live. In addition even the low-cost housing is too expensive for the urban poor and so the *favelas* have continued to grow in São Paulo and Rio de Janeiro and have begun to appear in Brasilia.

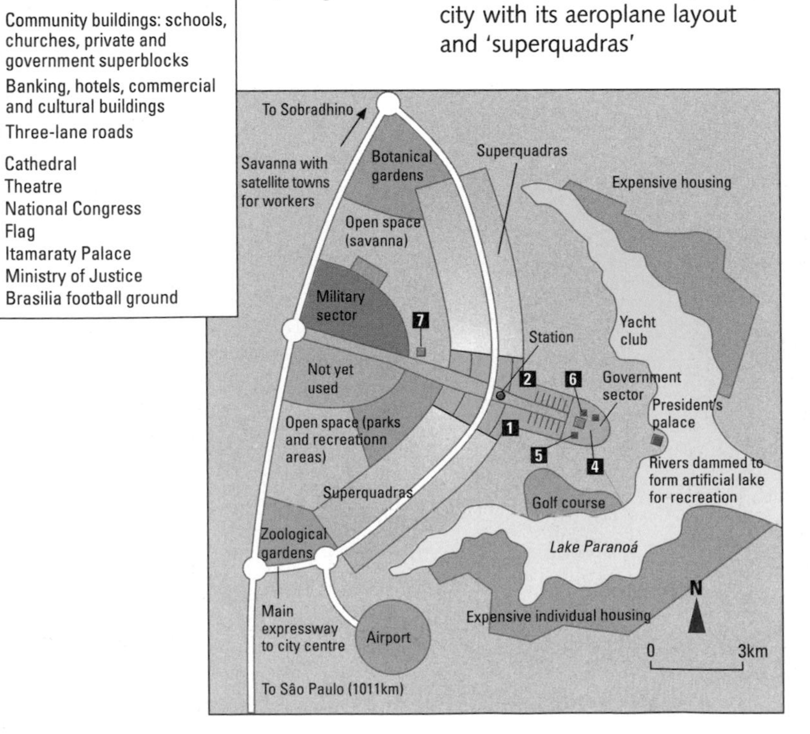

▼ **Figure 6.43a** Brasilia – Brazil's new capital city with its aeroplane layout and 'superquadras'

▲ **Figure 6.43b** Brasilia's superblocks (superquadras)

Caracas, the high rise blocks

Venezuela has fared better than many LEDCs because of its wealth from large reserves of oil. In the 1950s, 97 superblocks, 15 storeys high, were built in Caracas, the capital city using some of this oil wealth. The plans were based upon similar high-rise schemes being built in many developed countries. The superblocks were built with the intention of rehousing 180,000 people from the rancheros (shantytowns). The new flats had basic services and between two and four rooms. However, initially the scheme was not successful. It encouraged even more migrants to flock to the city and rents were too high for the ranchero dwellers leading to sub-letting and overcrowding. The superblocks were poorly constructed and rarely repaired; there were few social facilities and the blocks were built too close together leaving no open space and affecting lighting in the apartments. Despite this rural migrants flocked to the area and several thousand were left squatting illegally.

Rio de Janeiro's shantytowns

Case Study

The extract below summarizes the ways in which the authorities in Rio are attempting to tackle some of the problems in the favelas.

▼ **Figure 6.44** Solving the problems in the favelas

Renovating Rio's shantytowns

For thousands of families Rio has left few options. The most common: invade some hillside and, on an unoccupied corner, build a typical house, slapped together from clapboard, stone, mud or home-made cement. Forget about a home loan. Staying put depends on the blind eye of the authorities. But in Vidigal and a hundred other shantytowns in Rio de Janeiro there is the embryo of a new sort of urban reform. They call it *Favela* Bairro. It was born of the idea of recognizing the shantytown and, then, converting it into a legitimate neighborhood. The program means turning alleys into streets, dead ends into lighted plazas and financing the building of proper homes inside the *favela*.

Favela Bairro has brought many improvements to the people of Vidigal. For one, the *favela* re-conquered a semi-abandoned sports centre that had fallen into the hands of drug traffickers. Now it is the official venue for soccer championships. The shanty dwellers are also awaiting the inauguration of a cable car which could free them from the vagaries of transport by minivans, which are expensive and keep irregular hours. In the *favelas* of Caju, in Rio's decadent port zone, the project has helped spawn workers' cooperatives, offering a wage for those who had all but given up the dream of steady employment.

The fruits of *Favela* Bairro have reached some 450,000 people in 105 *favelas*. Now in its fifth year, the program has won several prizes including one from the Inter-American Development Bank (IDB) as well as the famous Habitat award from the United Nations.

Internet report from Terra, Brazil

▲ **Figure 6.45** Rio de Janeiro's favelas

Summary

Improving conditions for the urban poor in cities of the LEDW remains a key issue for many governments and local authorities. Most LEDCs want to improve life for the urban poor although lack of finance, difficulties over land ownership and the continuing flood of rural migrants into cities make the task extremely difficult. In many LEDCs the supply and high costs of land are major problems. Land reform is needed in many countries to remove the large tracts held, for example, by the Church, wealthy landowners, military governments and politicians and to make it affordable for the poor. Once land ownership is legalized for the shanty town dwellers then self help by the majority of squatters can bring lasting improvements to their way of life. As the case studies have shown past experience would seem to indicate that the most successful projects have revolved around self help schemes that can be made affordable for even the poorest sections of the shanty town communities. They also maintain the community spirit and enable the families to continue to access their places of employment. Less successful schemes include the high rise flats and those involving the re-housing of the squatters on the periphery of cities or beyond. The dislocation of the families and removal from their working environments destroys community spirit and may threaten their ability to earn a living, however small. Schemes must provide continuity of employment, formal or informal or provide alternative employment opportunities.

Questions

1 a Summarize the links between the growth of shanty towns and the process of urbanization in LEDCs.

b For each of the following schemes draw up a table to summarize its main characteristics giving examples of the schemes, main characteristics; advantages and disadvantages to the shanty town dweller and to the local authority/government.

Schemes: site and services; co-operatives; self-help schemes; high-rise blocks; new settlements; satellite settlements.

2 **Essay**

With reference to examples, evaluate the success of the schemes that have been implemented in an attempt to solve the problems of housing in cities in LEDCs.

Environmental issues in urban areas

Modern urban planning takes much greater account of environmental issues than in the past. Concerns about increasing levels of air, water and land pollution and their attendant health risks and threats to urban ecosystems have seen much greater emphasis being placed upon urban conservation projects and strategies to control pollution and the growth of urban areas.

Air pollution

Study at AS level introduced pollution of air, water and land including studies of smog and low level ozone. Air pollution and its links to human health have been well documented for decades. Hazardous atmospheric pollutants include sulphur dioxide, smoke, dust, benzene which is carcinogenic, lead and noise. The links between different forms of atmospheric pollution and health risks are shown in Figure 6.46.

Most cities suffer from air pollution although it varies both spatially and temporally. Cities in LEDCs tend to suffer severe air pollution due to rapid population growth and the increases in motor vehicles and industrialization. This is compounded by a lack of legislative controls on sources of pollution and inadequate policing and enforcement of laws to control emissions.

Mexico City has one of the worst records for air pollution. In some years acceptable limits for atmospheric pollutants have only been achieved on less than 10 days in a year. The site of the city in a basin surrounded by mountains compounds the problem. Smogs are frequent as the pollutants are trapped in the basin under high pressure conditions and temperature inversions frequently form (Figure 6.47). The greatest

▼ **Figure 6.46** The links between air pollution and health

Type of pollution	Pollutant	Associated health risk	Pollution controls
Air pollution	Carbon monoxide – mostly from vehicle emissions	Reduced absorption of oxygen by haemoglobin in the blood, increased heart stress, affects nervous system. Unborn children at risk.	Catalytic converters
	Sulphur dioxide – major component of winter smogs associated with high pressure and temperature inversions	Aggravates asthma, coughs, bronchitis.	Use of sulphur free fuels, e.g. natural gas. Burning less coal.
	Particulate matter, e.g. smoke, dust	Higher levels of illness and death through decreasing lung capacity and increasing heart and lung diseases including asthma.	Clean Air Acts of 1956 and 1968 controlled emissions of particulate matter – chimney heights were controlled and smoke control areas introduced.
	Noise	Stress	Noise abatement measures and noise pollution legislation that covers everything from the noisy neighbour to the large industrial or mining operation.
	Lead – major source in urban areas from leaded petrol	Increased blood pressure, heart attacks, kidney failure, brain damage. Children are most at risk – can cause behavioural problems, reduced concentration levels and poor performance at school.	Levels reduced by 90% in UK and USA since introduction of lead-free petrol – needed also for cars to run with catalytic converters. However, still very high levels in many LEDCs – 70% of children in Mexico City thought to have impaired development as a result of high lead concentrations.
	Nitrogen Oxide – a major cause of vehicle smog	Coughs and sore throats	
	Ozone – a major cause of photochemical smog	Stinging eyes, coughing, headaches, chest pains, nausea, shortness of breath. Severe breathing problems for asthmatics.	Not directly emitted but a product of various chemical reactions involving nitrogen oxides. Background levels have increased.

contributor to the pollution are motor vehicles which generate 97 per cent of the carbon monoxide and 66 per cent of nitrogen dioxide. However, the large number of industries – over 35,000 – make a significant contribution. Many are old, inefficient and largely unregulated and pump out large quantities of pollutants including lead. Smogs have been so severe that schools have been closed for a month and about 3,000 deaths every year are attributed to the poor air quality. A number of schemes have been implemented in Mexico City such as colour-coded permits allowing access into the city on only certain days of the week. This reduced the numbers of vehicles by about 400,000 a day and air quality improved by about 15 per cent. In addition all taxis over ten years old have been replaced and the amount of lead in petrol has been cut by 50 per cent.

▲ **Figure 6.47** Air pollution in Mexico City – notice the temperature inversion trapping the pollutants in the lower atmosphere.

In MEDCs air pollution is variable. Athens, for example, is very polluted due to industries and vehicles. Los Angeles is one of the most polluted cities in the world with unhealthy air quality on more than one-third of days in a year. In the UK air pollution increases from south to north. It is particularly severe in places like Oxford where the physical geography adds to the air quality problem and in the large conurbations such as Greater London, Greater Manchester, Birmingham and Teesside where high pressure conditions trap high concentrations of pollutants.

In December 1991 in London levels of nitrogen dioxide peaked at 423 ppb (parts per billion), more than twice the World Health Organization (WHO) safe limit of 209 ppb. Over 160 deaths were attributed to the smog. Summer (photochemical) smogs have also increased in Britain especially in suburban and rural areas when hot, high pressure conditions occur. The main cause of the increase is the number of motor vehicles.

Despite a fall in the levels of air pollution caused by sulphur dioxide and smoke in London (Figure 6.55), the rise in motor transport and emissions of carbon monoxide and nitrogen oxides led to a return of smog. Various schemes were put in place in the 1980s and 1990s in an effort to further improve London's air quality. These included variable speed limits on the M25 to keep traffic jams to a minimum, red routes where stopping is prohibited to reduce exhaust fume emissions, pedestrianization schemes and the introduction of trams, e.g. between Croydon and Wimbledon.

Despite these schemes and many other initiatives around the world air quality still presents major problems as the news articles show in Figure 6.49.

▼ **Figure 6.48** Trends in sulphur dioxide and smoke levels in London 1960–2000.

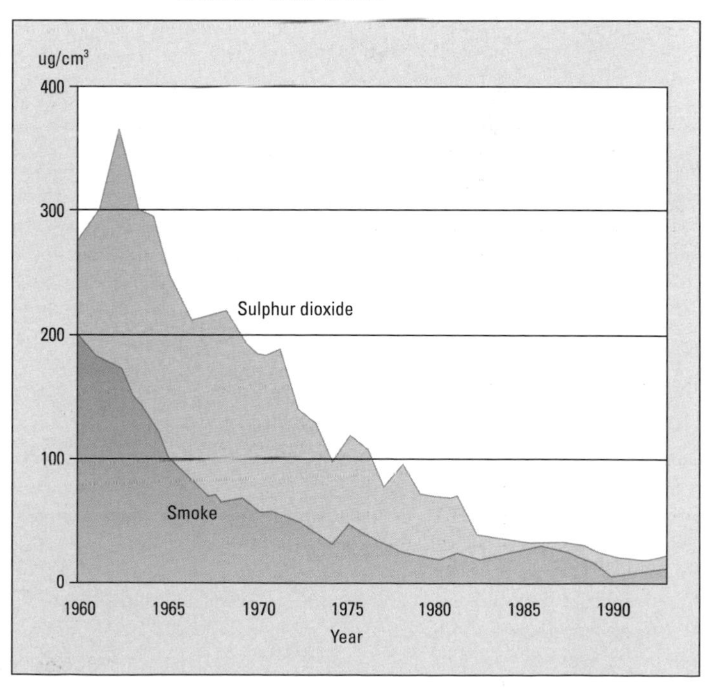

Figure 6.49 Air pollution problems in cities around the world

Supreme Court takes on pollution battle (22 May 2000)

The US Supreme Court is to examine claims that the Environmental Protection Agency (EPA) acted illegally by introducing tougher clean air standards. Industrial and environmental lobby groups are at loggerheads over the clean air issue, which government lawyers say carries 'profound implications for the health of the American public'.

The new standards were successfully challenged by a large alliance of industry groups and three states – Michigan, Ohio and West Virginia. The Supreme Court will now review that federal appeals court ruling which prevented the EPA enforcing its new standards, which are aimed at reducing smog and soot.

The revised air standards limited the allowable level of ozone – an essential part of smog – to 0.08 parts per million, instead of the previous 0.12 parts per million. And for the first time states were required to limit soot emissions from power plants, cars and other sources.

The EPA says that smog and particulate matter like soot accounts for 15,000 premature deaths, one million cases of respiratory disease and 400,000 asthma attacks in the US annually. The EPA says the tougher standards are needed to protect people with respiratory ailments, the elderly and children from air pollution.

Internet report from BBC News

Hong Kong hit by smog (29 March 2000)

Hong Kong has suffered a third day under thick smog with air pollution reaching record highs in some areas. The authorities have warned people with respiratory and heart problems to cut back on outdoor activities and physical exertion. Most areas were registering 'very high' air pollution levels of more than 100 on the air pollution index, the Hong Kong Observatory said. Levels above 100 are potentially hazardous to those with respiratory and heart ailments, while at the 200 mark, all residents would be advised to stay indoors.

Smog on the island is a recurrent problem and is usually attributed to vehicles, particularly diesel-powered taxis, trucks, light buses, as well as from factories and power stations in mainland China. The department assistant director said: "You can imagine, [that it is] just like a box, everything is trapped there and therefore all the pollution builds up.' Friends of the Earth Hong Kong took to the streets wearing masks and urged the government to do more to clean up the air. Six months ago, Chief Executive Tung Chee'hwa made air quality a priority in his policy address and allocated $180m to get taxi drivers to switch to liquefied petroleum gas.

Internet report from BBC News

Questions

1 Describe and explain the trends shown in the graph on Figure 6.48.

2 Sulphur dioxide and smoke were the main causes of the smogs in London in the 1950s. Why do smogs continue to occur in London and what measures could be taken to reduce their incidence?

3 Explain, with the aid of examples from both LEDCs and MEDCs, the links between air quality and health in urban areas.

Water pollution

People use water for a range of purposes including domestic, industrial, power production, agricultural, leisure and waste disposal. The purity or quality of the water may vary for different uses although in MEDCs domestic water needs to have no smell, no colour, no unpleasant taste and no pathogenic bacteria. The need for high quality water for domestic consumption conflicts with the lowering of water quality caused by waste disposal from both domestic and industrial users of water. In many MEDCs including the UK there have been huge improvements in water quality in recent years due to stricter legislation and improvement works by the Environment Agency and Water Authorities.

In urban areas the main sources of water pollution are sewage, manufacturing industry and power stations. In addition agricultural areas upstream of urban areas may contribute excess chemicals in runoff from the application of fertilizers, pesticides and herbicides. Cattle slurry and silage may also leak into rivers and streams.

In MEDCs most sewage is transported via the drainage systems to treatment works where it is cleaned before re-entering watercourses. However, some old treatment works are inefficient and until recently raw sewage was sometimes emptied directly into rivers or the sea. Occasionally there are also leaks of raw sewage especially when drains overflow during a flood. In the UK in Autumn 2000 people cleaning up after serious floods were warned to wear masks to prevent contracting Wiel's disease as a result of being in contact with raw sewage.

Towns and cities in LEDCs are often less well served by sewage systems especially when there are large expanses of squatter settlements (see the case study on Cairo, page 244). Water pollution often reaches dangerous levels making water unfit for human consumption. Sewage entering rivers is broken down into ammonia by the action of bacteria. However, large quantities of oxygen are used up in the process, which reduces the number of organisms that can survive in the water. Bacteria break down the ammonia forming nitrates that lead to the eutrophication of rivers and algal blooms. The growing algae use more of the oxygen and block out the light. In the worst cases watercourses may become deoxygenated killing all river life. The European Union has become concerned about nitrate levels in water and has set a limit of 50mg/litre. This will only be possible with expensive water treatment and by limiting nitrate fertilizer use by farmers.

Manufacturing industries are often located close to water sources and may use copious amounts in manufacturing finished products and for cooling processes. Water used for cooling is often returned to the river at a higher temperature and while this does not create a health risk to people it may alter the ecosystem of the river as some species cannot withstand the warmer conditions. More dangerous to human health are the myriad of other by-products that may be emptied into water courses. In MEDCs such effluent disposal is largely controlled and

▼ **Figure 6.50** 'Water Quality on Teesside' an Environment Agency pamphlet

What is water quality?

Water quality in the Tees is a measure of just how 'healthy' the river environment is. Environmental quality is dependent on a number of factors including the type and level of 'pollutants' going into the river, and their effect on the water and the wildlife that it supports. By measuring water quality, we can work out how healthy the river is and this helps us to pinpoint the sources of problems and keep them in check.

What pollutes the River?

Water quality in Teesside is reduced by low dissolved oxygen in the water, an excess of ammonia, an imbalance of nutrients, the presence of toxic substances and rising water temperature.

Did you know? Over £500 million has been spent by Industry and Northumbrian Water to reduce polluting discharges to the Tees.

POLLUTANTS AND THEIR EFFECTS

Type of pollutant	Description	Effects
Ammonia	Industrial/sewage dicharges containing toxic ammonia.	Poisonous to fish, algae and other creatures.
Dissolved oxygen	Chemicals in industrial/sewage effluent consume oxygen in the water.	Without enough dissolved oxygen, most river life cannot survive.
Nutrients	Industrial/sewage discharges and agricultural run off carry nutrients into the river which can 'over-nourish' it.	Too few nutrients and small aquatic life will starve; too much and seaweed threatens to suffocate the water and its inhabitants.
Toxic substances	Chemicals in industrial effluents which are toxic to river life.	Chemicals can kill or affect the health and reproductive systems of river life.
Temperature	Water used for cooling is pumped back into the river still warm.	A rise in water temperature will reduce dissolved oxygen levels and increase the growth of seaweed.

Who discharges effluent into the River?

Chemical plants, sewage works, the iron and steel industry, power generation, and refineries are the main sources of discharges into the river. All have contributed to the Tees clean up. The Environment Agency works with industry to ensure that improvements are prioritised and the money spent gives environmental benefits.

Did you know? From the 1930's until 1982, there were no recorded catches of salmon.

POLLUTANTS AND PRODUCERS

Average daily load of oxygen reducing chemicals into the Tees Estuary (Tonnes per day; Year: 1970, 1980, 1990, 1996, 1999, 2000 – Projected)

Top four producers of oxygen reducing chemicals: 47%, 26%, 6%, 22% – Northumbrian Water, Du Pont, BASF, Other Industry

Average daily load of ammonia to the Tees Estuary (Tonnes per day; Year: 1994, 1995, 1996, 1997)

Top five producers of ammonia: 27%, 26%, 18%, 14%, 6%, 9% – BASF, Northumbrian Water, Corus, Terra, Ienos Acrylics, Other industry

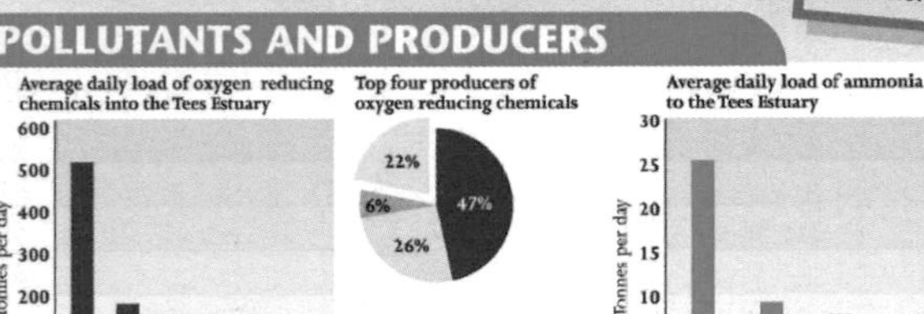

Water quality on Teesside – a vast improvement

From a position in 1970 when the Tees Estuary was virtually dead, significant progress has been made to bring it back to life. Improvements already made to industrial and sewage discharges have dramatically improved dissolved oxygen levels, cut levels of ammonia, and reduced the presence of toxic chemicals in the water.

TEES ESTUARY WATER QUALITY

1970 / 1999 – Pre-barrage Tidal Limit, Horseshoe Bend, Barrage, Billingham Beck, Seal Sands, Teesport – Good, Fair, Poor, Bad

Wildlife returns

A sure sign of improvement, wildlife is now returning to the river and its estuary. A rare sight in the early seventies, common and grey seals are now breeding successfully on Seal Sands as are a wide and varied selection of waterfowl. Salmon and sea trout are also using the river again. The growth of excessive seaweed, however, is a cause for concern which is being investigated.

Did you know? In the early 19th century there were said to be over 1,000 common seals on seal sands. This had declined to just three in 1862, but is now increasing again, a sign of the improving ecological conditions.

TEESSIDE'S CHANGING ECOLOGY

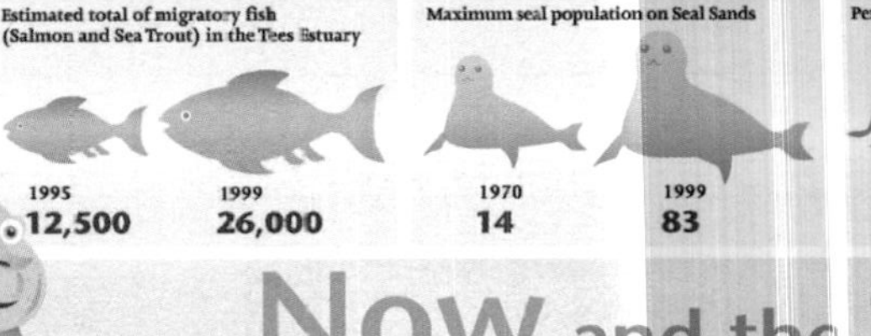

Estimated total of migratory fish (Salmon and Sea Trout) in the Tees Estuary: 1995 12,500; 1999 26,000

Maximum seal population on Seal Sands: 1970 14; 1999 83

Percentage of Seal Sands covered by seaweed: June 1992 11.3%; Sept 1999 55.0%

Now and the future

The main objective for the Tees Estuary is to continue to improve water quality so it can support increased levels of wildlife. The Environment Agency along with Local Authorities is working with industry on a number of projects to encourage this.

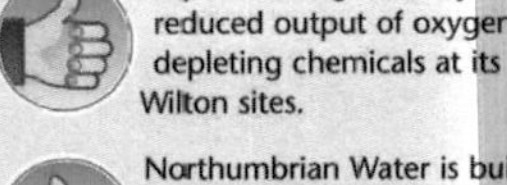

Dupont has significantly reduced output of oxygen depleting chemicals at its Wilton sites.

Northumbrian Water is building a £190 million sewage/industrial effluent and sludge treatment centre on contaminated land at Bran Sands which will be fully commissioned by 2001.

BASF is installing new process equipment, which will reduce their releases of ammonia by 33 per cent.

An acid spill at the Tioxide plant affected marshland at the mouth of the estuary in February 1999. Steps were taken to minimise the impact and the risk of it happening again.

large fines are handed out to companies that accidentally leak unwanted by-products. In the LEDCs legislation is often lacking and there is little enforcement so that dirty, polluting industries often locate in LEDCs sometimes with disastrous consequences. In Colombia children have been born with severe disabilities, some without limbs, others blind, deaf and badly brain damaged. The high incidence of malformation has been traced to nearby industries dumping heavy metals such as lead and mercury into rivers. The pollutants are then concentrated through the food chain eventually affecting people through their consumption of water and fish.

Power stations use large quantities of water for cooling purposes leading to thermal pollution. Those burning fossil fuels, such as gas, oil and coal, also discharge large quantities of gases that contribute to the formation of acid rain, which is responsible for acidification of many lakes and rivers. There have also been some massive pollution incidents caused by oil spills in estuaries.

The River Thames, water pollution

Case Study

There has been concern about the pollution of the River Thames since medieval times when in 1383 people living with latrines over the Wallbrook Stream (a tributary) were to be charged 2 shillings a year towards cleaning up the river. Since then there has been a long list of legislation in an effort to keep the river clean although it mostly failed due to lack of enforcement and rapid population growth. The last salmon to be caught on the Thames was recorded in 1833. By 1841 there were 270,000 houses in central London, most with cesspits that would overflow straight into the river. This was exacerbated by the considerable discharges from the growing numbers of industries and the introduction of water closets by Thomas Crapper that released untreated waste water into the river. Throughout this time water was being abstracted from the river for drinking water and so it is not surprising that cholera was rife. Between 1831 and 1866 there were four cholera epidemics during which over 35,000 people died. During heatwaves there was the most disgusting smell from the river which in 1856 became known as the 'big stink'.

By 1860 several commissions had been set up to find a solution to the problems and in 1864 a network of sewers was completed with outfalls far enough downstream not to affect residential populations. This improved river quality in Central London but transferred the problem downstream. A steamer the 'Princess Alice' sank close to one of the sewage outfalls. An inquiry into the 600 people who died found that some of the deaths had been accelerated by the putrid state of the water. Later improvements in water treatment failed to keep pace with the growth of population and industries. This was compounded by bomb damage during the Second World War, increasing use of non-biodegradable detergents and thermal pollution from power stations. In the 1950s the river was virtually biologically 'dead' with little or no oxygen in some stretches and only a few bacteria and tubifex worms living in the foul waters. Since then there has been a dramatic improvement in water quality due to the decline in manufacturing industry and improvements in waste water treatment. In 1974 salmon returned to the Thames – the first for nearly 150 years along with many other species of fish, invertebrates, birds and plants.

There is still a potential danger in the summer months if heavy rains cause drains to overflow. The river is at low flow and the addition of large quantities of sewage cause oxygen levels to deplete quickly to dangerous levels. This is likely to cause deaths of fish stocks as happened in 1973,1977 and 1986. Since 1989 the Thames Bubbler has been used to inject 30 tonnes of oxygen a day into the river wherever it is needed. A second vessel, the Thames Vitality, has performed a similar role since 1997. Hydrogen peroxide, an additional oxygenation source, can also be discharged into the river from treatment works at Kew and Pimlico.

It is claimed that the Thames is now the cleanest metropolitan estuary in Europe. However, accidental pollution and incidents of vandalism are still a problem (Figure 6.51). In other areas large quantities of litter are deposited each year making it dangerous for people and wildlife. Cans, bottles and even shopping trolleys are dumped into the Thames along with other rubbish which blows in from open skips. The Environment Agency operates a Hotline for people to report polluters in an effort to reduce the problems.

▼ **Figure 6.51** Spillage of sewage in the Thames, fish stocks killed by vandals

Fish killed by vandals

Vandals have caused five million gallons of raw sewage to pour into the Thames estuary, decimating fish stocks in part of the River Cray. The sewer involved carries all the waste from the nearby town of Dartford. The Environment Agency says it is one of the worst spillages of its type and has wiped out vital fish stocks in the surrounding area.

The vandals cut through a chain fence and closed the valves of a sewage pipe leading to a nearby treatment works. This caused a build up of pressure which blew open a manhole cover. Workers had to overcome ammonia fumes to stop the flow of sewage, which is thought to have continued for three hours. The pollution wiped out all life in a 200m stretch in the River Cray, killing fish including pike, roach and rudd.

Internet report from BBC News

The River Ganges, water pollution

Case Study

Today the River Ganges is one of the world's most polluted rivers. A report by scientists and environmental specialists stated that 'everyday 350 human corpses, 1500 tonnes of wood and almost the same weight of animal carcasses are thrown into the River Ganges.' This is despite the river's importance for irrigation, washing and drinking and its role as a sacred place for religious purification.

The Ganga Action Plan (GAP) reports that the main sources of pollution of the river are urban wastes, industrial liquids and sewage. They are thought to be responsible for large-scale ecosystem destruction. GAP has managed to convince the authorities that action is needed and the following proposals have been made:

- building of water treatment works to purify water before being returned to the river
- recycling of gas and fertilizer from wastes
- building of dams to isolate soiled waters
- launching of cheap sanitary programmes
- educating the population about the serious pollution problem.

▲ **Figure 6.52** Bank of the River Ganges

Questions

1 Study Figure 6.50, Water quality on Teesside.
  a What are the main pollutants and sources of the water pollutants on Teesside?
  b What are the likely impacts of the pollutants on the environment and people?
  c To what extent and with what impact has the water quality on Teesside improved?
  d Explain any further changes that may be expected in the future?

2 With reference to examples, compare and contrast the problems associated with water quality between MEDCs and LEDCs.

Land pollution

Waste disposal, landfill sites and incineration

As the consumer society has developed so the amount of solid waste increases (Figure 6.53). In recent years there has been concern expressed about incineration and the use of landfill sites for the disposal of solid wastes. However, there are few alternatives and the selection of a disposal method depends almost entirely on cost – the cheapest option almost always being the preferred method.

Country	Annual domestic waste (tonnes)	Equivalent per person (kg)
United States	177,500,000	721
Australia (1)	12,000,000	690
New Zealand (2)	2,106,000	662
Finland	3,100,000	624
Canada	16,000,000	601
Netherlands	7,430,000	497
Norway	2,000,000	472
Denmark (1)	2,377,000	460
Switzerland	3,000,000	441
Japan	50,441,000	411
Sweden	3,200,000	374
Germany (3)	28,401,000	360
Great Britain	20,000,000	348
Italy	20,033,000	348
Belgium	3,410,000	343
France	18,510,000	328
Spain	12,546,000	322

1 1992 figures (1990 unavailable)
2 1982 figures (latest available)
3 Figures for former East and West Germany combined

▶ **Figure 6.53** Annual domestic waste per person in selected countries, 1990

Solid waste is material resulting from human activities that is useless, unwanted or hazardous. It includes:

- *rubbish that may decompose, e.g. food materials*
- *non-decomposable wastes, e.g. metal and glass*
- *ashes*
- *solids from sewage treatment*
- *large debris from construction work or tree removal*
- *industrial wastes, e.g. paint, chemicals, slag heaps and mining waste*
- *farm wastes, e.g. manure, crop residues.*

Techniques of disposing of solid wastes:

1 Composting

This is the decomposition of organic wastes by micro-organisms. The wastes have to be sorted and ground up to improve the efficiency of the process. The process takes up to three weeks before the material can be finally prepared, bagged and sold to be reused as fertilizer.

2 Recycling

Some local authorities recycle the waste once it has been collected, e.g. by using magnets to remove metals, or by centrifuge to separate lighter and heavier materials. Increasingly local authorities rely upon the householders to separate the wastes at source. This is then either collected separately for recycling or from recycling points that are often adjacent to supermarkets. This reduces the volume of waste at incinerators and landfill sites.

Composting and recycling are used to varying degrees in different parts of the world and within different countries. The overall contribution of these techniques is small, however they are growing as space for landfill sites is dwindling and opposition to incinerators grows.

▲ **Figure 6.54** Overflowing landfill

3 Landfill

Landfill sites (Figure 6.54) are often disused quarries that are used to bury waste. Once full, topsoil is added and the area is often landscaped for recreational use. Landfill sites are often the most economic solution provided there are suitable sites available and they are close to the sources of the waste (75 per cent of the costs involved lie in the transportation of the wastes to the site). At a landfill site the waste is spread in thin layers and bulldozed to compact the waste between each layer. The threat of pollution to local sources of groundwater is reduced by using concrete linings and contouring the site. In addition local soils are used for landscaping and only sites not susceptible to flooding are selected.

4 Incineration

Incineration is the burning of waste materials. It leaves behind ash that is buried. The process of incineration usually leads to 85–90 per cent total combustion. The heat from the incineration process has been harnessed in some areas, such as the Byker Wall in Newcastle-upon-Tyne, as a source of domestic heating. Other products of combustion include carbon dioxide and water as well as oxides of sulphur and nitrogen. Non-gaseous products such as fly ash may also be emitted although modern installations tend to use wet scrubbers, electrostatic precipitators and bag filters to remove any particles likely to become airborne. In recent years, fears of global warming and the release of other harmful substances into the atmosphere, such as dioxins, has made the siting of incinerators difficult because of the local opposition. However, a new generation of energy from waste (EfW) facilities are being developed that meet the UK and EU environmental standards (Figure 6.55).

▲ **Figure 6.55** Artist's impression of proposed Capel EfW plant

Questions

1. On a blank outline map of the world, mark on the countries listed in Figure 6.53.
2. Construct a choropleth map to show the annual domestic waste per person for the countries shown. Describe and explain the pattern shown on the completed map.

Surrey Waste Management and the CAPEL action group

Case Study

Surrey Waste Management Ltd has a contract for the next 25 years to treat and dispose of all of the county's waste. The company has plans for an integrated waste management strategy involving waste minimization, recycling, energy recovery and disposal. As part of these plans two 'energy from waste' facilities are to be built, one at Copyhold near Redhill and one at Capel near Dorking. Local residents at Capel have set up an action group to oppose the plans believing the 'energy from waste' facilities to be merely a new phrase for an incinerator.

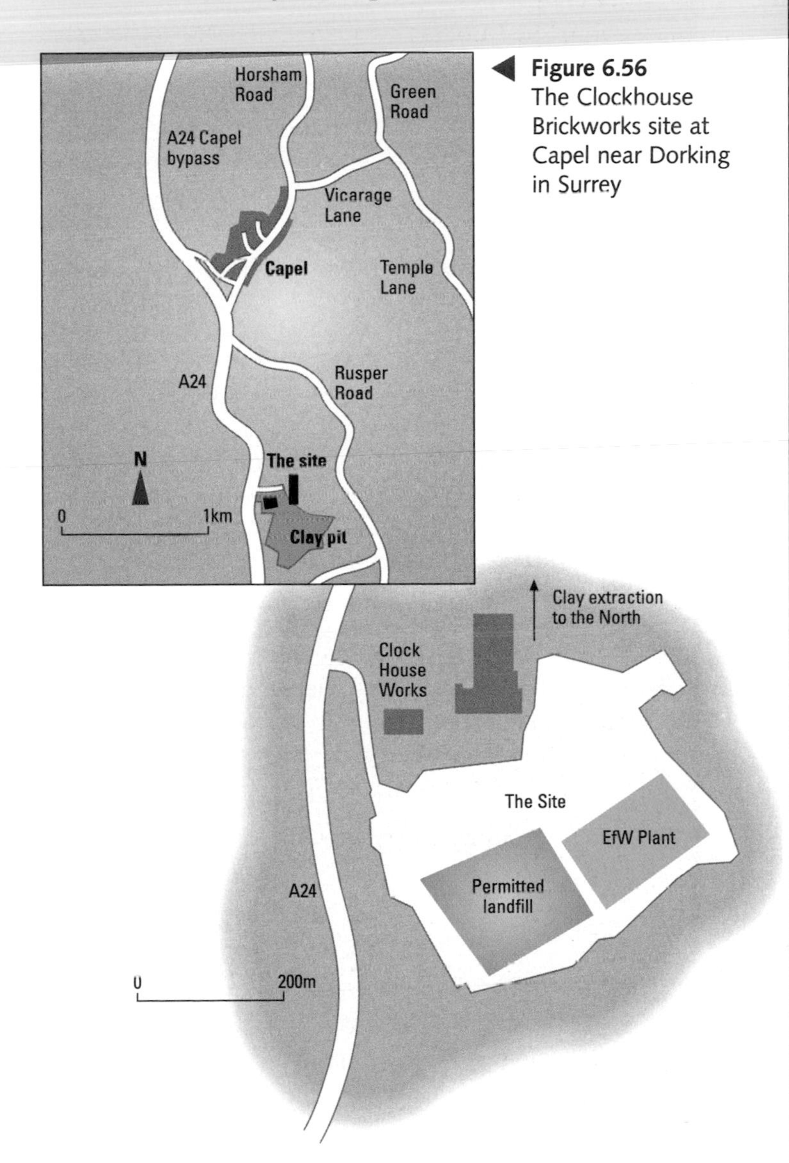

Figure 6.56 The Clockhouse Brickworks site at Capel near Dorking in Surrey

Surrey Waste Management says:

Surrey householders discard 530,000 tonnes of rubbish a year – enough to fill Guildford Cathedral three times over. Ninety per cent of Surrey's waste currently goes into landfill sites, many of which are outside Surrey. Suitable landfill sites in Surrey and the south-east as a whole are dwindling and the practice also attracts a landfill tax that has cost Surrey County Council £3.5 million in 1997, £5 million in 1999 and it is likely to increase further. The EU has also set landfill targets to reduce the amount of rubbish going into landfill sites. The new plans hope to reduce the amount of waste put into landfill sites by 70 per cent. More recycling is planned for the county with a target of 25 per cent of all waste to be recycled by 2005 but there would still be large amounts of waste to dispose of.

Energy from waste (EfW) facilities are cleaner than the old incinerators, which were all closed down several years ago for failing to meet European environmental standards. The new EfW facilities are extremely clean and meet UK and EU environmental standards. Energy from waste facilities are an important source of renewable energy. Electricity will be supplied to the National Grid via underground cables (not overhead pylons) and enough will be generated to supply over 30,000 households. This reduces the burden on burning fossil fuels. The plants will only handle waste from Surrey and not from other counties outside of Surrey.

One of the new EfW plants is planned for 44 acres at Clockhouse Brickworks site at Capel near Dorking. Figure 6.55 shows an artist's impression of the proposed EfW plant. The site lies outside of the Green Belt and will have the capacity to process 110,000 tonnes of waste per year. It will not accept hazardous or special wastes. The plant will be built in the base of a former clay pit to reduce visual impact although the site is already well screened with trees. The plant will generate 8MW of electricity to be fed into the National Grid. The ash by-product from the incineration represents about 26 per cent of the original waste. The majority can be recycled for use in the construction industry and in metal recycling while about 4,400 tonnes will be bagged and placed in landfill sites. This will reduce the landfill capacity needed and reduce the need for mining and quarrying of aggregates and metal ores. An environmental statement has been prepared showing how any environmental issues will be dealt with to ensure UK and EU standards are met, for example on possible pollution to air, land and water; traffic and transport; and noise, odour and visual impact. It is estimated that about 33 lorries of waste will go into the site each day. These lorries are currently using the existing road network. There will be a further 8 lorry movements representing a one per cent increase in traffic movement, below the threshold set by Highway planners.

Planning permission was sought in 2000 and a decision is expected late in 2001. For an update consult the website of Surrey Waste. (See www.heinemann.co.uk/hotlinks and insert code 2822S.)

Government strategy

The government strategy is called A Way with Waste. It was adopted early 2000 and involved:
- An integrated approach to waste management
- The diversion of biodegradable household waste away from landfill – reduced to 35 per cent of 1995 levels by 2016
- A reduction in hazard to water supplies
- Higher levels of recycling and material re-use
- Increased energy recovery
- To recycle or recover energy from 45 per cent of waste by 2010
- For all counties to deal with their waste within their own boundaries

The government envisaged the need for the building of new facilities to meet these targets.

NSCA (National Society for Clean Air) is alone amongst environmental groups in believing that energy from waste can sometimes represent the best bet for the environment. 'We spent the last twenty years campaigning to have old-style incinerators closed down,' said Tim Brown, Deputy Secretary of NSCA. 'But the new breed of plant are designed to be extremely clean. People are right to be concerned about dioxins, but wrong to see incinerators as the major source.'

The CAPEL Action Group

Following the planning application being submitted to Surrey County Council the Capel Action Group (CAG) published a range of information (Figures 6.57 and 6.58), some on its website, using the headline: 'Russian Roulette with 30 million people a year'. The website urges people to write to Surrey County Council Head of Planning saying they will not tolerate the installation of the EfW plant because:
- it is premature
- it breaks proximity principles
- it is dangerous to allow the company whose sole aim is to make a profit at the expense of our health build this proposed plant
- the proposal completely disregards the fact that it will be directly under the Gatwick airport flight path. Anybody flying into or out of Gatwick could have his or her future health jeopardized.

▼ **Figure 6.57** The views of the Capel Action Group

Incinerator

No Way

We **WILL** be heard

At last. The truth starts to seep out
Incinerators cause illness and DEATH.
The Incinerator operators know it.
The Government know it.
...but it seems that they would rather you did not know.

Warning

SITA or Surrey Waste Management's plans have been submitted. We now need to act.

▼ **Figure 6.58** Comments from 'well known and respected sources' chosen by CAG to support their case

'Incinerator plants are the source of serious toxic pollutants: dioxins, furans acid gasses, particulates, heavy metals, and they all need to be treated very seriously...the emissions from the incinerator processes are extremely toxic.'

The Right Honourable Michael Meacher, House of Lords, 14 April 1999.

'Once dioxins have entered the environment or body, they are there to stay due to their uncanny ability to dissolve in fats and to their rock-solid chemical stability. Their half-life in the body, is on average, seven years... In terms of dioxin release into the environment, solid waste incinerators are the worst culprits due to incomplete combustion.'

World Health Organization

'The favoured alternative disposal method to landfilling in the UK is burning waste in incinerators. This is often referred to as 'energy recover', because the electricity produced can be supplied to the national grid. But in fact there is a net energy loss, as more power is used elsewhere to process new material. Smoke and gases given off when waste is burned contain pollutants such as dioxins, which even at very low levels harm the environment and human health. European pollution control law is prompting construction of cleaner incinerators. But incineration always leaves a toxic ash. This has to be disposed of, usually to landfill. There it may be more likely to pollute water than unburnt waste. Landfill and incineration do not solve the waste problem, but just create more hazards for human health and the environment.' Friends of the Earth

Questions

1. Describe and explain how the Surrey Waste management company's plans for Surrey meet the criteria and targets laid down by the Government's 'A Way With Waste' Strategy.
2. Using the Surrey Waste Management Strategy produce two tables showing the advantages and disadvantages of the proposals for the environment and for local residents.
3. What additional objections of the residents have not been answered by the Surrey Water Management group?
4. **Essay**

   Using the case study information discuss the relative merits of the possible strategies for waste management in the twenty-first century.

Urban ecosystems

Up until the latter half of the twentieth century people created towns and cities with little regard to the impact on natural systems. Towns and cities became built-up environments relying upon artificial systems such as concrete drainage channels and sewage systems and using copious amounts of fossil fuels. They relied upon inputs from areas beyond the city for food, water and other raw materials. These were consumed within the city and then returned as waste to the land, air or water outside the city limits (Figure 6.59). Many city dwellers became, and still are, divorced from the countryside living, working and sleeping in the urban environment.

▼ **Figure 6.59** Interdependence between the city and its surrounding environment – a one-way or two-way process?

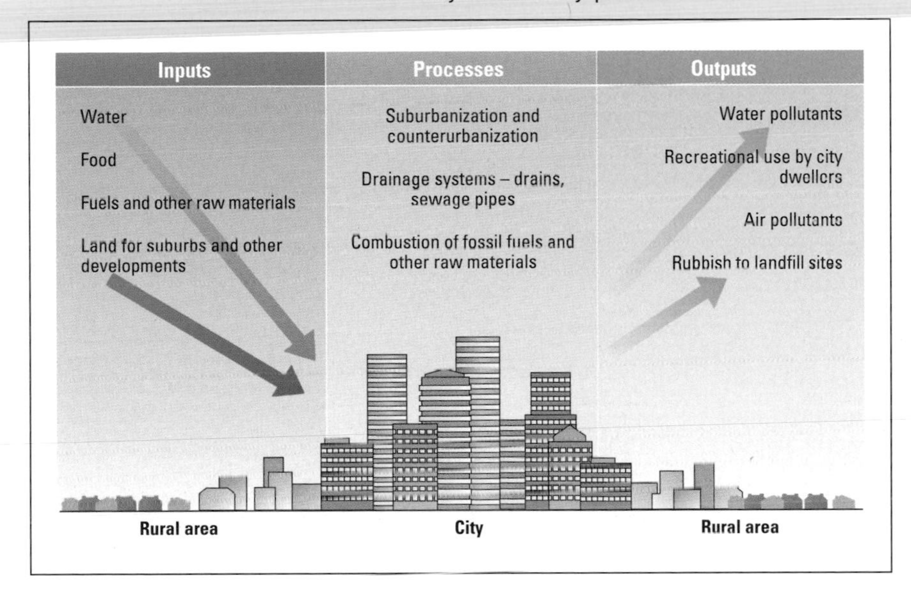

The urban ecosystems have also been threatened by developers who want to use parkland or areas of Green Belt for new buildings. The growing amount of traffic has generated massive problems of congestion and pollution. For many people, cities became unattractive places to live in, which started the suburbanization and counter-urbanization processes of the late twentieth century in many cities in the developed world. The quality of life declined as levels of pollution rose, areas within cities became damaged and were sometimes abandoned and social problems grew worse.

There is a movement today to 'green' the city and create and preserve urban ecosystems; they are sometimes referred to as 'regenerative' cities, eco-cities or sustainable cities. They all have similar aims, to preserve and enhance the natural and built environment in cities so they become more sustainable and self-supporting. Many of the ideas behind the Ecological Cities Project in North America have been adopted in the UK and other European countries (see Figure 6.60). The Grainger Town and quayside projects in Newcastle-upon-Tyne (see pages 229–230) are examples of urban conservation projects that target the built and natural environments. The following examples look at other plans to improve the urban environment.

Transport planning in Groningen, Netherlands

Transport planning in Groningen is aimed at stimulating the use of public transport and cycling and discouraging the use of the motor car in order to improve the quality of life and shopping climate in the city. This was a major change for the city where previously private cars could drive anywhere and the central square within the city was a huge roundabout from which traffic could move in all directions. The new traffic circulation plan divided the city centre into four zones. Private traffic may only move between the zones via a ring road that surrounds the city centre. Pedestrians, cyclists and public transport including taxis have free access to all areas. Pedestrianized areas have been expanded and there are larger areas off limits for motor vehicles. The plan generated enormous political discussion and shopkeepers in particular were opposed to its implementation fearing that their sales would decline as shoppers found their premises more difficult to reach. There was an initial decline for some shops although two years later this had been completely reversed and there has been an overall increase in the number of shoppers using the city centre. In addition, the quality of life and shopping climate has improved. The city centre is now a much more attractive public space and the use of public transport and bicycles has increased mirroring a decrease in the use of the motor car. The plan has proved beneficial for both the environment and the economy.

▼ **Figure 6.60** The North American Ecological Cities Project

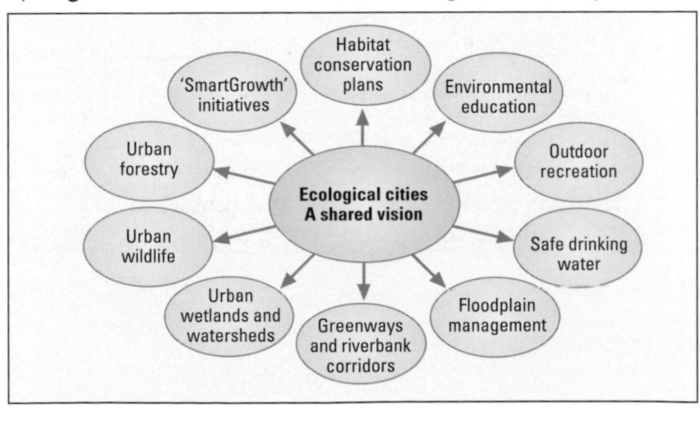

Urban forestry in the UK

In the UK the National Urban Forestry Unit (NUFU) aims to encourage local councils to include extensive planting of trees and woods as part of their planning strategies in towns and cities to improve the local environment. Such a scheme has been suggested for Burton on Trent, the largest town in the National Forest. By 2006 it is hoped that 250,000 trees will have been planted in and around the town as part of the creation of the National Forest. The Forest of Belfast is a second example where central and local government, voluntary groups, businesses and individual residents are working together to green the city. Thousands of new trees have been planted along with a range of projects to highlight the value of urban trees. Large holly trees have been planted at community centres to be decorated each year as living Christmas trees, new sculptures have been developed in parks and there are free garden trees for all new millennium Belfast babies.

Containing the growth of towns and cities

Large urban areas in both MEDCs and LEDCs generate political, social, economic and environmental problems. The purely physical growth of cities both upwards and outwards destroys valuable agricultural land and ultimately may become detrimental to the urban way of life. It may be difficult in particular to make provision for adequate food and water supplies, sewage and rubbish disposal. Urban decay and problems in the inner cities and shantytowns become difficult to overcome along with severe traffic congestion, air, water and land pollution. There is a need to control urban growth. To do this sections of green land, especially in the MEDW, have been designated Green Belts, wedges, buffers or hearts.

Green Belts encircle towns. They are broad rings of countryside often up to 10km wide in which urban development is restricted. The aims of Green Belts were to stop urban sprawl, prevent neighbouring towns from merging and to preserve the special character of towns. Since then other functions have been added including provision for recreation, safeguarding agriculture and assisting in urban regeneration. The first Green Belt surrounded London. It was proposed in 1944 and approved between 1954 and 1958 following legislation by the Government. In the UK there are 21 Green Belts covering nearly 2.5 million hectares of land – about 15 per cent of the land area (Figure 6.61a).

Closely associated with the implementation of Green Belts was the development of new and expanded towns in order to house the overspill population from the cities. In some locations a complete ring or belt of preserved land was not possible or desirable. In these areas wedges or buffers have been used; these are smaller zones of 'green' land protected from development. This was typical of areas beyond London's Green Belt as shown in Figure 6.62. However, the pressures for development have continued for new housing, industry, retailing developments and recreational facilities. As a result there have been calls for Green Belt land to be released for development. This has led to considerable opposition from interested groups as shown in the variety of articles in Figure 6.63.

▼ **Figure 6.61a** Green Belts in England

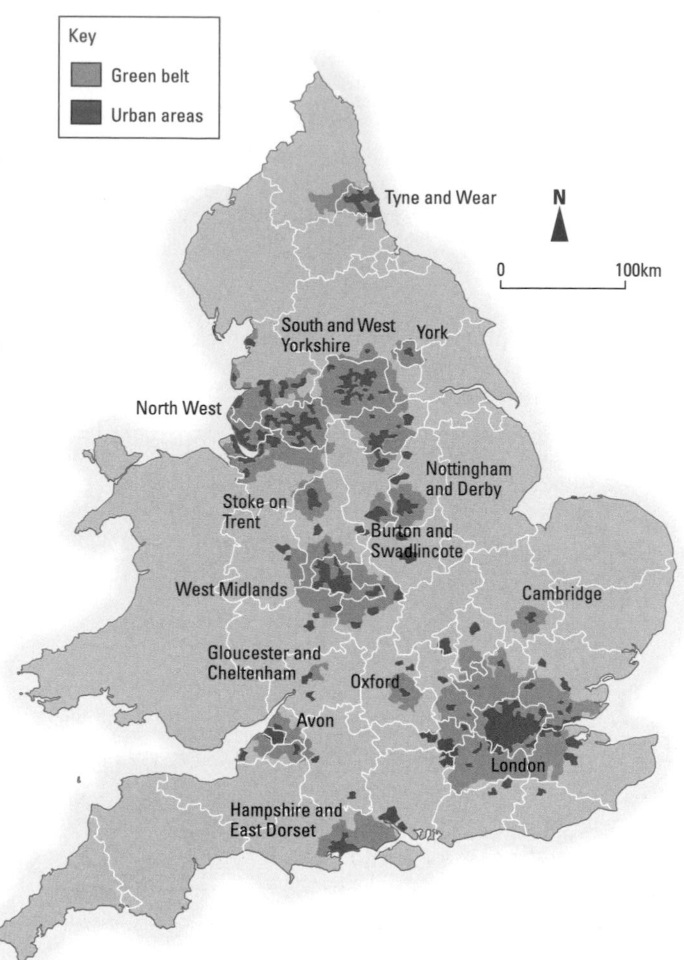

▼ **Figure 6.61b** Areas of Green Belt land in England

Area of designated Green Belt land (1997)	Hectares
England	1,650,000
Tyne and Wear	53,000
York	23,400
South and West Yorkshire	251,300
North West	249,500
Stoke on Trent	44,100
Nottingham and Derby	62,000
Burton and Swadlincote	700
West Midlands	229,800
Cambridge	26,700
Gloucester and Cheltenham	7,000
Oxford	35,000
London	514,300
Avon	68,400

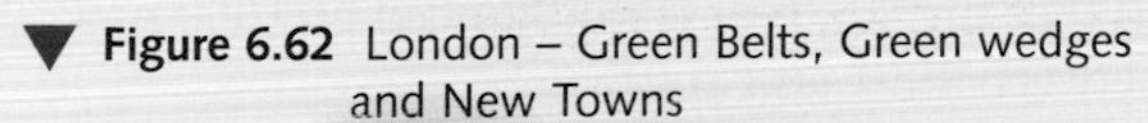

▼ **Figure 6.62** London – Green Belts, Green wedges and New Towns

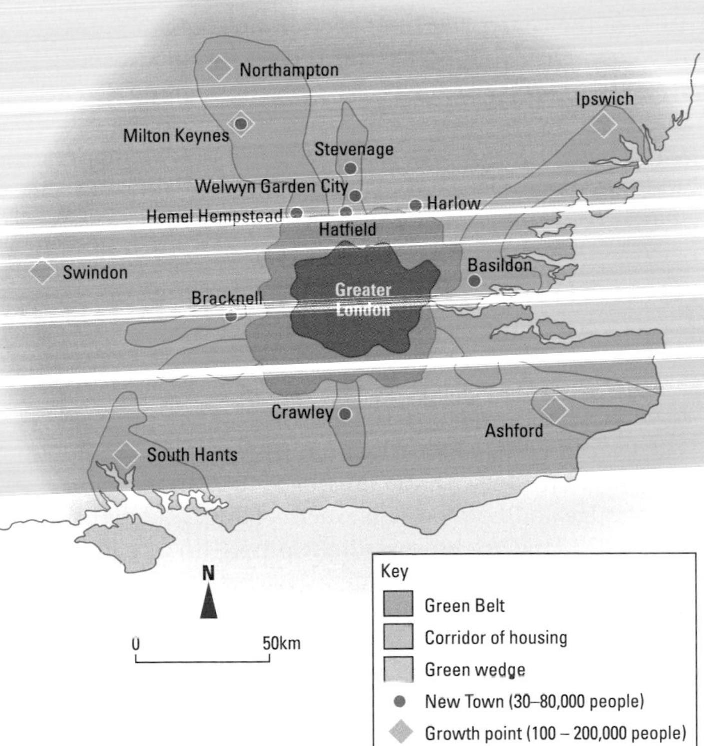

Green Belts have many positive aspects and have played a major role in controlling the growth of many urban areas and in recent years have encouraged the redevelopment of brownfield sites within urban areas. However, there have been some negative side effects. The presence of a Green Belt forced urban developments further out into the countryside and often led to increased road building and commuting. In some cases the density of development within the urban areas increased along with land prices close to the Green Belt.

Since the 1960s some Green Belt areas have come under considerable pressure from planned developments due to continued population growth, a shortage of housing and the high development costs within cities. Between 1960 and 1980 over 600ha a year were lost from London's Green Belt including land for the M25 orbital motorway. Opponents of Green Belts claim that they 'strangle' developments in cities and they instead advocate a policy of green wedges which would allow development along certain corridors. The latest plans to control the growth of London is to allow housing to expand along some routeways leading out of the urban area leaving green wedges in between each corridor.

In the UK controls on Green Belt land have relaxed and strengthened over time but the policy has remained in tact and since the 1990s the policy has gained further support in order to preserve the countryside from out-of-town commercial developments including housing, shopping, industry and offices. However, despite public support for Green Belts most demands for new housing and commercial

▼ **Figure 6.63** Green Belts – conservation or development?

Thousands march against Green Belt 'threat'

(18 April 1998)

Thousands of people have taken part in a demonstration against plans to build 10,000 homes on farmland in Hertfordshire. The controversy encapsulates a national building problem. Experts predict that 4.4 million new homes will be needed countrywide over the next 20 years. But environmentalists and countryside lovers say the government should build homes in run-down areas of cities, and concentrate on urban regeneration.

Internet report from BBC News

BNRR – Death of the Green Belt

Campaigners sent a clear message to banks and construction companies involved in the Birmingham Northern Relief Road, Britain's first toll motorway, that they have not gone away following the decision to go ahead in September. A 'funeral' procession took place in Birmingham City Centre today. During which symbols of the destruction which the BNRR will wreck across the West Midlands were delivered to branches of the Abbey National.'

...Campaigners are warning that not only will the motorway cut a huge swathe through the Green Belt, it will also act as a catalyst for further Green Belt development pressure...

The motorway destroys 27 miles of the West Midland's Green Belt and damages two nationally important nature sites (SSSIs). It is unclear how much traffic it will attract because it runs parallel to three A roads, but it is acknowledged by the Highway Agency and Midland Expressway that congestion on the M6 will be similar whether or not it is built.

Friends of the Earth 28 October 2000

Internet report from Dialspace (see www.heinemann.co.uk/hotlinks)

Problems hamper brownfield development

(23 February 1998)

In the Black Country, just to the west of Birmingham, housing has been built on the site of what used to be an old foundry. But building homes on once smoke-blackened heartland comes at a cost. The outlay for building each house on the Black Country ex-industrial land was between £2,000-£8,000 more than on a greenfield site. Cost is not the only hurdle though...chemicals and contamination can also get in the way of such projects. Seemingly undeterred, ministers are thought to want 60 per cent of new homes to be built in urban areas. One option the government could try is taxing more profitable greenfield sites to give an added financial incentive to develop derelict land. The problem is that in England, most old industrial land is in the Midlands and the North – the biggest demand for new homes is in the South East.

Internet report: http://news1.thdo.bbc.co.uk

Green Belt plan for Wales

(27 February 2001)

Plans to halt further destruction of the countryside have been unveiled by the Welsh Assembly. The assembly has developed proposals for Green Belts in Wales to act as buffers zones and contain the spread of development into the rural areas.

Internet report from BBC News

developments have been on Green Belt land, e.g. Birmingham's National Exhibition Centre, the Nissan car plant at Washington and the Blackbird Leys housing estate in Oxford. In London the building of the M25 attracted further demands from developers to build commercial and industrial premises while other demands for use of Green Belt land have come from Stansted airport, Heathrow's fifth terminal, the Channel Tunnel and from housing developers. Estimates suggested that the South East would need 460,000 new homes between 1991 and 2001.

Parts of the Green Belt have been lost to new developments while others are already rundown as a result of mining and quarrying, landfill sites and derelict buildings. Farms in the rural–urban fringe also often suffer higher rates of vandalism and feel hindered by the additional pollution and planning controls. The land may become underused and eventually derelict.

Oxford's Green Belt

Case Study

Oxford's Green Belt was created in the 1950s and extends for about six miles beyond the edge of the urban area. The Green Belt was implemented to preserve Oxford's green setting and includes river meadows, fields and parts of the surrounding hills. However, parts of the Green Belt have only unofficial status and areas, especially on the inner edges, have been developed for sports facilities and roads. Developments that have already taken place or are proposed in the Green Belt include:

- The Pear Tree park-and-ride scheme (14ha)
- The Blackbird Leys housing estate
- Hinksey Hill golf course
- University business centre
- International centre for Islamic Studies
- An international faith centre at Westminster College
- All-weather athletics track at Horspath
- Oxford United new sports ground with a 15,000 seater stadium at Minchery Farm including a conference centre, fitness centre, 2000 car parking spaces, hotel and leisure facilities
- Oriel College sports ground development
- Oxford Science Park (30 hectares)
- Unipart factory at Horspath

The last brownfield site within Oxford has now been used and the pressures to open up the Green Belt are greater than ever. There are real demands for more housing and shopping developments, park and ride schemes and for job creation but there is considerable conflict as to whether they should be allowed on Green Belt land.

Residents in Horspath claim that 'step by step industrialization' is taking place and destroying the character of their village. Plans for a fifth park-and-ride scheme at Kidlington are opposed due to its closeness to an environmentally sensitive site vulnerable to vehicle pollution and development pressure.

Part of the problem in Oxford is that the land is covered by five different councils and there is no overall management policy for the area. Planned developments tend to be opposed by local councils representing the local residents who do not want the developments to take place while the schemes are part of the larger scale regional plan designed to solve broader urban problems. The Oxford Preservation Trust has proposed the setting up of an Oxford Green Belt Watchdog similar to those in Cambridge and London. Opponents of developments on Green Belt land are however increasingly finding it difficult to justify their arguments against development in the Green Belt. The recent demise in the farming industry has led to very low prices for agricultural land and the dereliction in some areas as a result of dumping encourages local councils to remove that land from the Green Belt and to include it in their plans for future development. The planned park-and-ride scheme was to be constructed on the Green Belt at the Dalton grain silo, a disused derelict site near the A4165 Oxford Road.

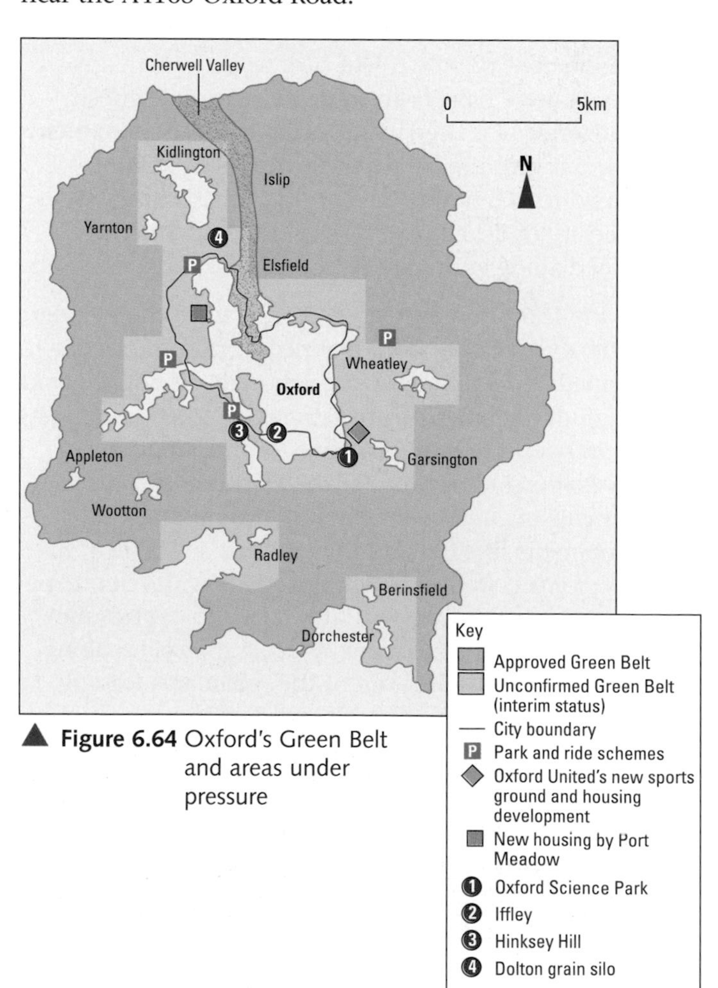

▲ **Figure 6.64** Oxford's Green Belt and areas under pressure

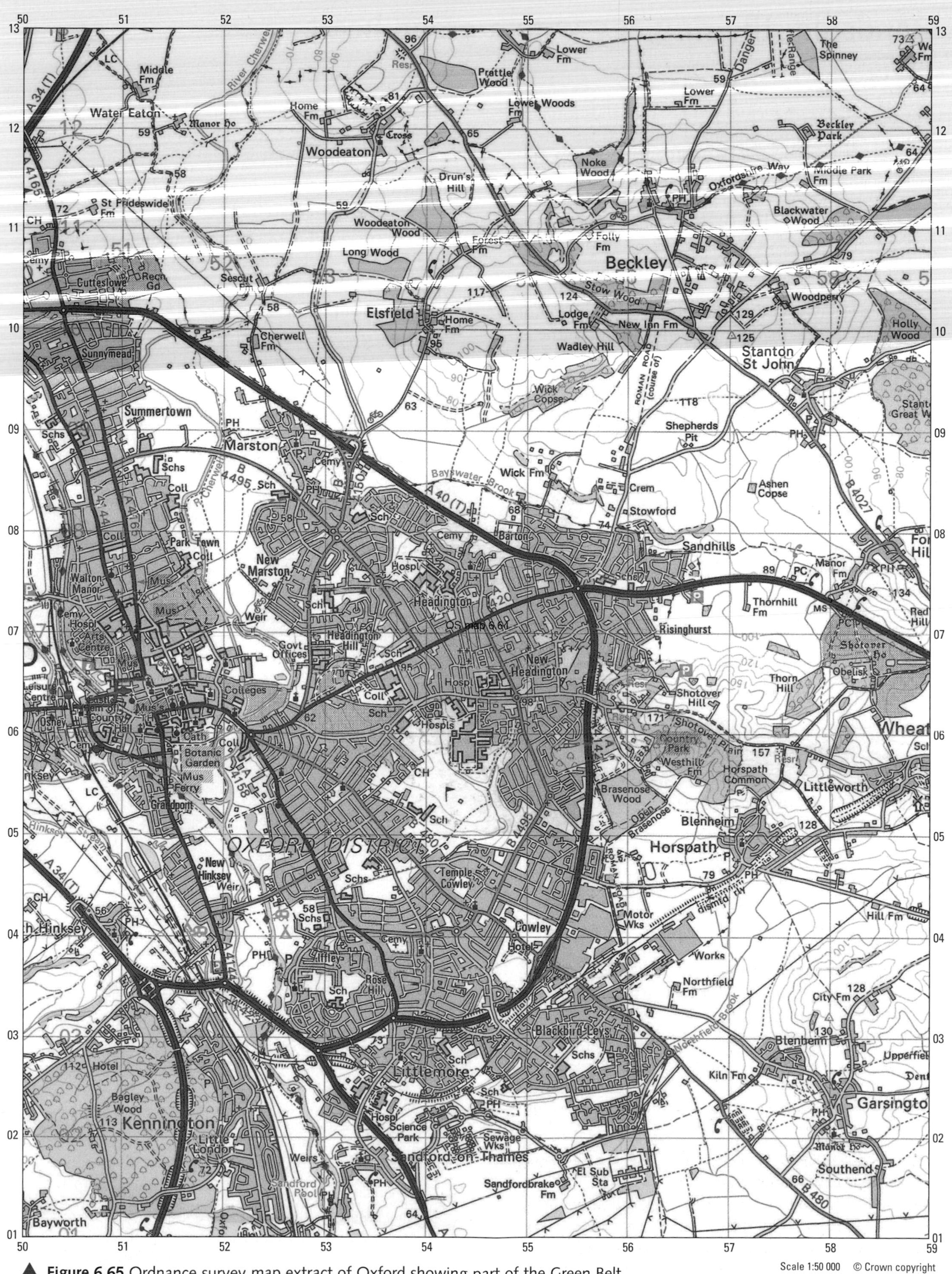

▲ **Figure 6.65** Ordnance survey map extract of Oxford showing part of the Green Belt

Randstad, the ring city with a green heart

Case Study

The Randstad or ring city in the Netherlands forms one of the fastest growing urbanized areas in the EU. It contains two major urban regions with the cities of Amsterdam, Utrecht and Haarlem to the north and Rotterdam, and The Hague in the south (Figure 6.65) creating a horseshoe-shaped urban area. This polycentric city region with a 'green heart' presents major problems for planning and controlling growth. There are particular dangers of pollution at the mouth of the River Rhine and threats to the fertile agricultural land in the centre that produces 40 per cent of the country's total food supply.

Without planning controls the Randstad's growth would undoubtedly lead it to coalesce and expand into the valuable green heart. The preservation of the open centre within the Randstad has been a major concern in recent years. The green heart is polder land, mostly below sea level and used for intensive and varied agriculture, e.g. horticulture, arable and dairy farming. There are some lakes that are popular for recreation, sailing and fishing with picnic areas and camping sites. The agricultural green heart has faced similar pressures as the Green Belts in the UK especially for land for housing and industry. Since the 1980s, the cities of the Randstad have been crowded and short of land.

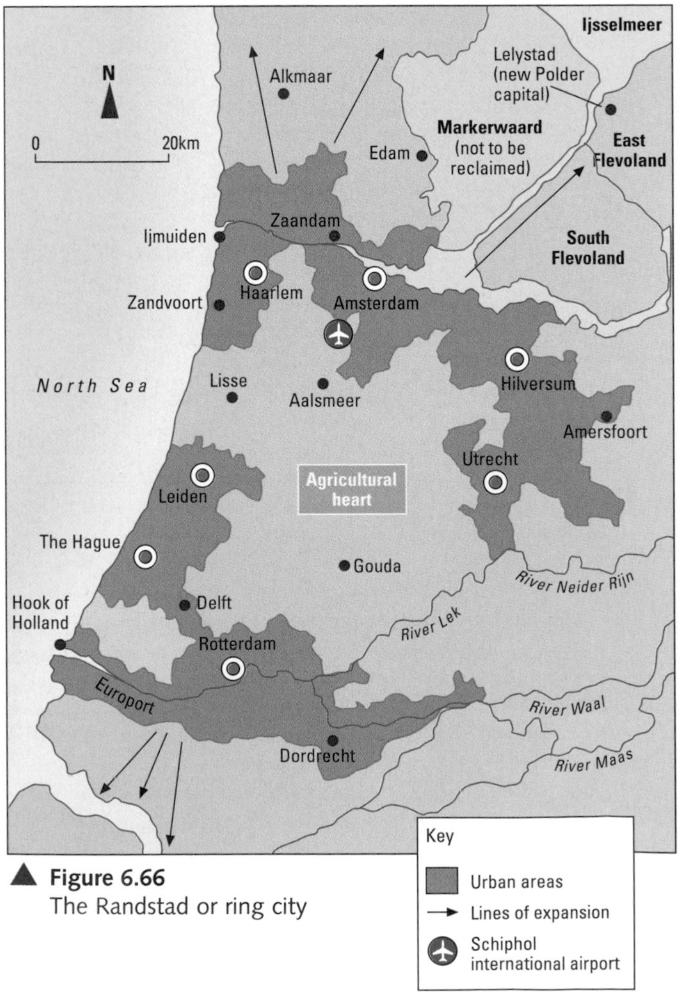

Regional planning in the Randstad has been active since 1945 and the main aims have been to:

- disperse overspill population to the more peripheral areas of the Netherlands in the east and north
- preserve the historic cities of the Randstad by placing wedges or buffers between the cities
- preserve the green heart apart from limited growth within existing historical towns such as Gouda.

This has created the horseshoe of urbanization with effectively a Green Belt within. However, over 50,000ha of land have been lost from the green heart and the pressures for development continue. To control urban growth and to preserve the green heart, new developments have been channelled along four main corridors of growth that follow main lines of communication away from the green heart. These are separated by buffers or wedges that are protected from development. This policy has been further strengthened by plans to reduce the growth in the Randstad region by diverting developments to twelve urban centres outside the region.

Figure 6.66
The Randstad or ring city

Questions

1. Answer these questions using the OS map of Oxford in Figure 6.65.
   a. Draw a sketch map of Oxford to show the extent of the built-up area and the rural–urban fringe.
   b. Annotate the map to show the current land uses in the rural–urban fringe (Green Belt area) and those areas under threat from development.
   c. To what extent is the rural–urban fringe today dominated by land uses linked to the urban settlement of Oxford? How might this change?
   d. Should Oxford's Green Belt be preserved at all costs?
2. How successful has the Green Belt policy been in achieving its aims?
3. Should Green Belts and green hearts be preserved at all costs?
4. With the aid of examples, explain how you would control the growth of urban areas in the future.

Summary

Throughout this unit you have been studying the ways in which urban areas are changing as a result of economic, social and environmental processes. These processes result in great variations in the quality of life both spatially and temporally in cities. Spatially, parts of the inner city in MEDCs and shanty towns in LEDCS have some of the worst living conditions and poorest members of society. However, over time the quality of life may change.

Economic processes are important in determining the affluence and success of urban areas. The cycle of deprivation, so common in many inner-city areas in MEDCs, was in many cases precipitated by the decline and decentralization of manufacturing industry. The social processes of suburbanization and counter-urbanization increased segregation in the developed world's city with those able to move seeking improved quality of life away from the inner city. Similar segregation can be recognized in the shanty towns where those with better jobs and higher incomes gradually move up the housing ladder. The concentration of the poorest members of society into particular zones of urban areas often goes hand in hand with poor environmental conditions.

Managing cities is a complex issue and there have been both failures and successes with the various schemes that have been implemented. Some planning strategies have transformed areas as in the redevelopment schemes in Newcastle-upon-Tyne and Manchester. However it is worth reflecting on who have been the beneficiaries of the schemes especially those that have involved gentrification. The young, wealthy executives moving in to their expensive apartments in marina locations may well have benefited from the improved environment and housing but what of the original residents of these locations. Where are they now? Indeed many people who once resided in the area of London Docklands were extremely upset at being moved out and then when they were unable to afford the redeveloped housing. To what extent have planning strategies helped the poorest members of society in MEDCs? Have they merely improved the environment with little consideration for the economic and social problems of the poorest sectors of the community? The high-rise flats so common in UK towns in the twentieth century were largely unsuccessful whereas it may be argued that the more recent smaller scale schemes that involve the local community in decision-making are proving more successful. In LEDCs many schemes attempting to divert the population back into rural areas or to new towns and cities failed as housing proved too expensive and employment opportunities were limited. It has been the small scale improvements such as site and services schemes that have had greater impact on the quality of life of the shantytown residents.

In parts of the world the spatial variations in the quality of life are dependent upon the attitudes and values of decision makers, the politicians and planners who control the planning mechanisms. They also control the financial resources that would be available for tackling the economic, social and environmental problems that create inequalities in the quality of urban life for sections of the population.

In many countries the disparity between the wealthiest and poorest members of society remains and in some cases continues to grow. The majority of people believe this to be undesirable but often the political will and/or the financial resources to change things are unavailable.

Questions

1 For cities in both LEDCs and MEDCs summarize the spatial variations in the quality of life for urban residents.

2 Explain the political, economic, social and environmental factors that have contributed to the spatial variations in quality of life you have identified in question 1.

3 Select a variety of schemes that have attempted to improve urban areas. What were the aims of the decision makers in each of these schemes? To what extent were the schemes a success? For whom were they a success and to what extent did they improve the quality of life for local residents?

4 Adopt the role of a decision maker with responsibility for reducing spatial variations in the quality of urban life in an urban area. Reveal your aims in a ten point plan and explain your priorities.

Chapter 6 Questions

1 a Figure 1 shows population changes in large urban areas in England 1961 – 1994

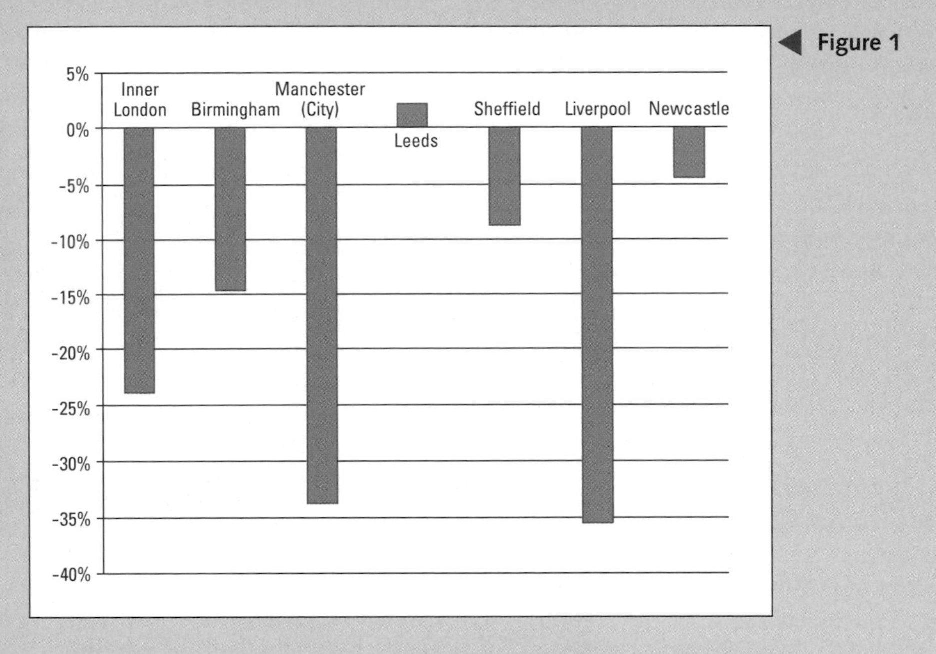

◀ **Figure 1**

i Comment briefly on the causes of these changes (4 marks)

ii Suggest reasons why the size of the changes was greater in some cities than others. (4 marks)

b Outline some of the initiatives to reverse the decline of business in the central area of cities in MEDCs. (7 marks)

Total: 15 marks

2 Urban deprivation is one of the characteristics of large cities in all parts of the world. How similar are the initiatives being undertaken for its reduction between cities in the more and less economically developed worlds? (30marks)

Chapter 7

Recreation and tourism

igure 7.1 Brazilian visitors to the Iguacu Falls. A scenic spot undamaged by tourism?

The resource base

The terms leisure, recreation and tourism are sometimes used interchangeably by people, although officially they do have separate meanings (Information box). Privately most people make a distinction between going on holiday (whether it be the main annual holiday or a short break), and visiting places either as part of their work or to see people they know. However, official bodies such as the world and national tourist organizations do not attempt to make this distinction because it is too difficult to separate out the different types of travellers. Also there is overlap. A business trip, for example, can be solely for business, but sometimes business is combined with pleasure. It can include visiting friends and relatives while in the vicinity. Business travel, which includes attendance at conferences, exhibitions and trade fairs, accounts for a growing share of the tourism market.

Basic definitions

Leisure *– free time (from work), time at one's own disposal. This can be enjoyed at home and includes watching television or surfing the net.*

Recreation *– activities and pastimes in which people indulge outside the home and garden. The most popular participation activities in the UK are walking, swimming, snooker/pool, keep fit/yoga, cycling and football. Non-participation activities include going to the pub or cinema, shopping for non-essential items, eating out and watching a match.*

Tourism *– activities that require travel from home and staying away from home for at least one night. This is the definition used by the World Tourism Organization. It not only includes people going on holiday, but also people taking business trips and/or visiting friends and relatives.*

Leisure time, which is used for recreational activities and tourism, is just one of the signs of the high quality of life experienced by the majority of those living in developed countries. When the employment and income generated by recreation and tourism is added up, it amounts to a substantial business. Government statistics for 2000 estimated that some 1.78 million people were employed in tourism and related activities in the UK; this accounts for about 6 per cent of the GDP. About 160,000 businesses, mainly independent small ones such as hotels and guest houses, restaurants and cafes, holiday homes, caravan and camping parks and so on, are responsible for providing the bulk of the tourism services. Recreation and tourism also make substantial contributions to other larger businesses within the service sector, notably in retailing, transport and entertainment (Figure 7.2). Tourism is regarded as one of the UK's key long-term growth sectors. Expansion in the UK is just a small part of the global growth of international tourism, which increased by more than 40 per cent during the 1990s. In 1950 there were only 25 million international tourists in the world; by the end of the 1990s more than 600 million were criss-crossing the globe. Globally the tourist industry had become a very big business worth more than US$450 billion annually (Figure 7.3).

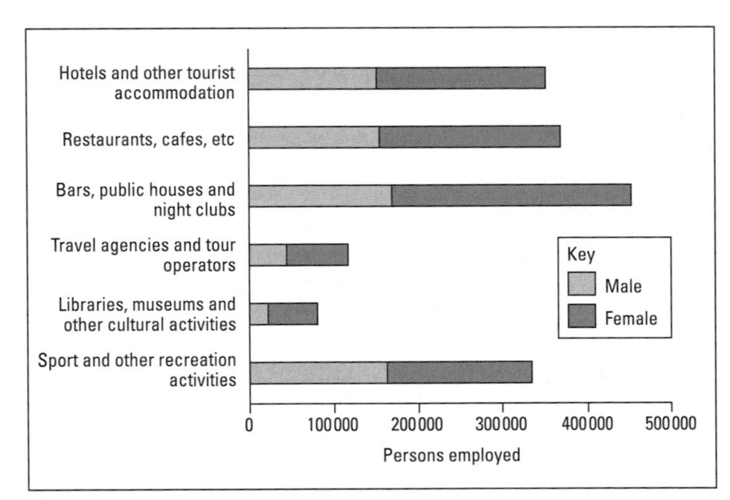

▲ **Figure 7.2** Employment in recreation and tourism-related industries in the UK (June 2000)

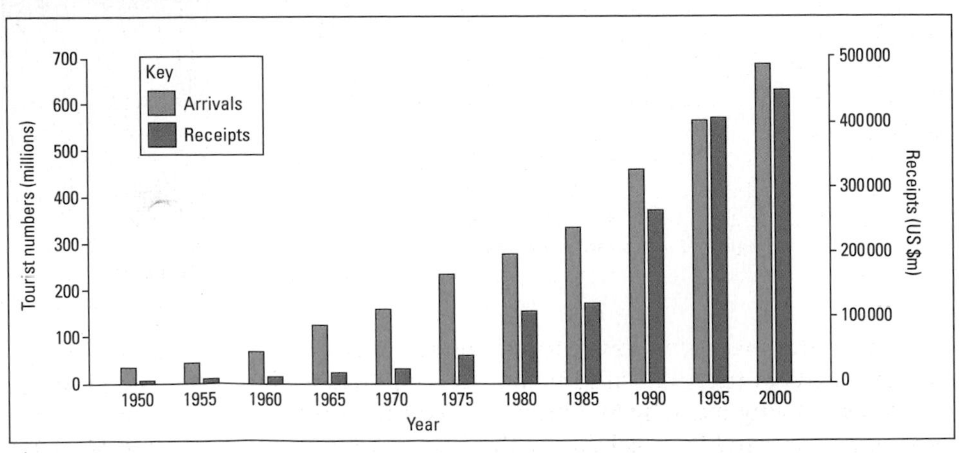

▲ **Figure 7.3** The world: international tourists and tourist receipts (1950–99)

Geographers are primarily interested in two aspects of recreation and tourism. One is its spatial effects and the other is the contribution it makes to employment and economies. Both are studied at the full range of scales from local, through regional and national, to global.

Many recreational activities were traditionally concentrated in town or city centres in the UK; some remain, but as part of the process of suburbanization, others have moved out and into the rural–urban fringe. However, tourism has played a part (and sometimes a key role) in the renovation of some old inner-city industrial and port areas (Figure 7.4), and not just within the UK (Figure 1.1d). Improvements in mobility, enabled by higher levels of car ownership, have helped to restore economic viability to declining rural areas and have led to an aesthetic and economic re-appraisal of the value of many of the UK's upland areas. Certain tourist-dominated locations exist such as Blackpool and Torbay in the UK. However, examples on a much grander scale are plentiful around the shores of the Mediterranean Sea, where tourist developments dominate whole regions such as along the Spanish 'costas' (Figure 7.5). Spatial impacts are both positive and negative, both for people and the environment. This will be explored later in the chapter.

▲ **Figure 7.4**
Brindley Place in the CBD of Birmingham. Around the restored canal basins and towpaths recreational facilities such as pubs, cafes and restaurants have been built. In the same area there are facilities of national importance, notably the ICC (International Convention Centre) and NIA (National Indoor Arena).

Tourism contributed enormously to the tremendous improvements in the levels of economic development and standards of living made by Mediterranean countries such as Spain, Greece and Portugal during the final quarter of the twentieth century. A number of developing countries see tourism as a ladder to growth and for many small countries it is the only possible alternative to the more traditional manufacturing route to higher economic development. Island nations in the tropics are examples. The greatest concentration is in the Caribbean, but Indian Ocean islands such as the Seychelles and Mauritius (Figure 7.6) are also included. Their plentiful natural resources of 'sun, sand and sea' have always contributed to their scenic beauty but, until recent times, not their wealth. A total re-appraisal of natural resources has been made in relation to the current demand for sun and sea holidays among wealthy inhabitants of MEDCs located in cool temperate latitudes in the northern hemisphere.

▼ **Figure 7.5** Benidorm is one of the symbols of Spain's tourist boom and accompanying economic growth since 1960.

▲ **Figure 7.6**
Daybreak on the tropical island of Mauritius. The island nation has primary resources that are in scarce supply in northern and western Europe. Distance from the source areas for visitors means that mass tourism on the scale of that in Spain and its Mediterranean islands is out of the question. Tourism, therefore, as on some of the Caribbean islands, is directed more towards the middle and upper end of the market (page 292).

When examining the spatial and occupational patterns of leisure-related activities it is difficult to isolate what proportion of the leisure facilities serves local people and how much is provided for tourists. Both use the same facilities, albeit to varying degrees, apart from hotel accommodation which is most clearly targeted at visitors. Recreation and tourism has become too important an industry to be left in the hands of amateurs. Most countries have an administrative hierarchy consisting of National Tourist Board or Authority at the top, regional or state tourist boards below and a network of tourist information centres and local tourist offices at the base providing points of contact with customers.

Questions

1. **a** Distinguish between recreation and tourism.
   b Why are the distinctions between **i** recreation and tourism and **ii** between business and tourism often blurred?
2. **a** Draw a labelled sketch of Figure 7.4 as an example of an area of urban recreation and tourism in the UK.
   b Suggest reasons why a recreation and tourism element is often incorporated into inner urban schemes of redevelopment.
3. Suggest reasons for each of the following observations about leisure and tourism.
   a The greatest concentration and variety remains in the CBD.
   b The growth zone is in the urban–rural fringe.
   c Provision is lowest of all in the outer suburbs.
4. **Investigation**

   For one town or city in the region where you live,
   a research the types of recreation and tourist attractions and facilities
   b show their locations either on a sketch map or on a spatial diagram similar to the one used in Figure 7.7
   c give an explanation for the main features of the spatial distribution you have shown.

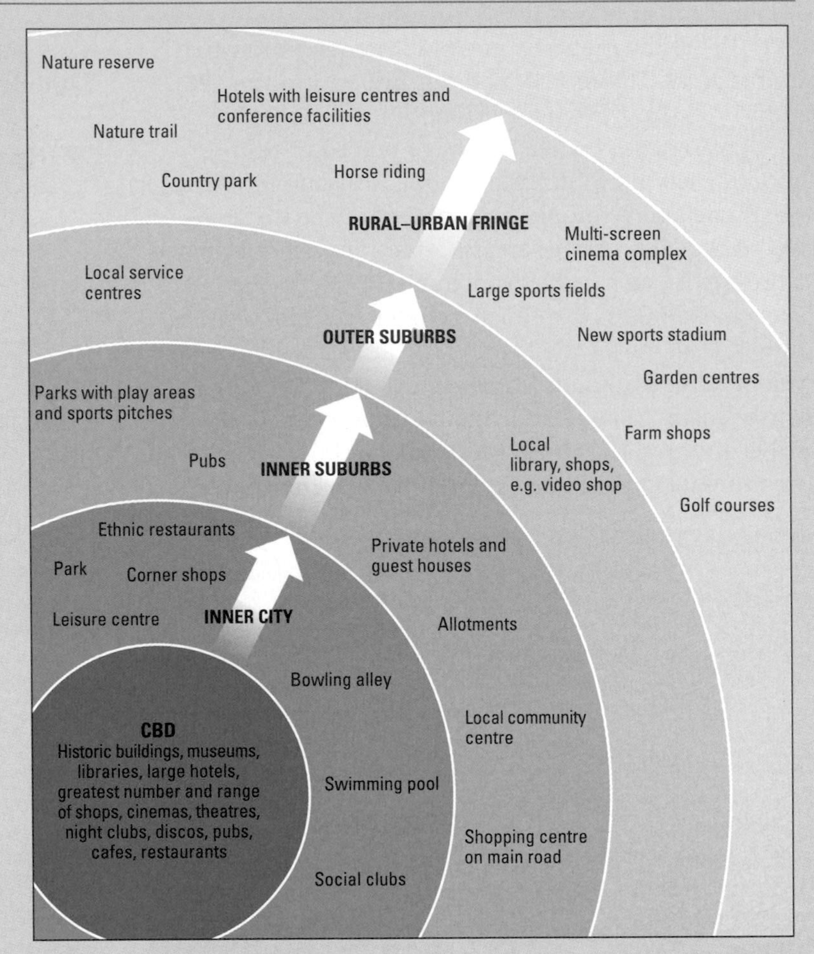

▲ **Figure 7.7** Summary of the location and type of typical recreation and tourist provision in towns and cities in the UK

Primary and secondary resources

It is customary to classify resources for tourism into primary and secondary. To a degree primary is synonymous with natural resources and includes physical attractions such as scenery, climate and ecosystems. However, it is broader than this and also includes historical buildings and structures, as well as various other records of earlier human settlement. Egypt boasts a rich heritage of pyramids, temples, palaces and statues from advanced civilizations who began living in the Nile valley 5,000 years ago (Figure 7.8). Therefore, primary resources are what people go to see and form the basis for a place's tourist potential; secondary resources determine the extent to which this potential is realized.

The seven wonders of the ancient world

These were the pre-eminent sights in the ancient world listed in the second century BC. The oldest, and the only one of the seven substantially in existence today, are the Pyramids at Giza, now on the edge of the built-up area of Cairo. The other wonders were

- *Hanging Gardens of Babylon*
- *Statue of Zeus at Olympia*
- *Temple of Artemis at Ephesus*
- *Mausoleum of Halicarnassus*
- *Colossus of Rhodes*
- *Pharos (lighthouse) of Alexandria*

▼ **Figure 7.8a** The Sphinx and Great Pyramids, which have stood for 46 centuries, make an impressive sight.

▲ **Figure 7.8b** Part of today's local service sector next to the site, which makes a less impressive sight.

Secondary resources are the facilities provided by governments and people, without which mass tourism cannot take place. The list is long and includes accommodation (everything from hotels and guest houses to camping and caravan sites), eating places (from restaurants and cafes to fast food outlets and street stalls), entertainment (from films and exhibitions to local events such as folklore shows and carnivals) and infrastructure (including transport and the provision of reliable public services such as electricity, clean water and sanitation). This is the human side of the tourist resource base. A few people, usually young and travelling on a budget, are prepared to trek to a region or travel on a local bus for 24–48 hours over roads that are no better than dusty tracks. They are willing to tolerate an absence of secondary tourist resources when visiting unspoilt places off the beaten tourist track in a spirit of adventure. At some point even these people rely upon a modern secondary resource such as an international airport. Expectations of tourist visitors are increasing: more of the people staying in B&Bs in the UK expect en-suite facilities, as also do young people on tours that are otherwise described as 'adventure journeys'.

▼ **Figure 7.9a**
Part of the road to the Monteverde Rainforest in Costa Rica. Many conservationists prefer that it remains in this condition. Having to travel at an average of 20kph while breathing in dust and being bumped from side to side reduces the number of visitors and makes conservation of the unique rainforest easier.

▲ **Figure 7.9b** The Monteverde Rainforest is dense and diverse and rich in wildlife, including howler monkeys, toucans and rare birds such as the quetzal.

Primary resources

Of all the natural resources for tourism the one with the most pervasive influence is climate. Two branches of mass tourism depend upon it almost entirely, namely beach holidays and skiing.

Seaside holidays still account for almost half the main holidays taken by households within the UK. The mass summer exodus to Mediterranean beaches became fashionable and widespread in the late 1960s and 70s, helped by the organization of charter flights and package holidays. Most UK seaside resort towns came to recognize, albeit belatedly in some cases, that to remain in business they needed to increase the number of cold and wet weather alternative attractions. British beaches are still packed when the occasional summer heatwave arrives, but these are mainly day visitors. Those seeking a guaranteed annual dose of sun book packages to Mediterranean resorts. Summer drought is perhaps the most characteristic feature of a Mediterranean climate. As a result of the global shift of world pressure belts, ridges of high pressure sit over the Mediterranean basin for most of the summer. Sun and warmth can be relied upon in a way that they cannot in the UK and adjacent continental countries, which are located in the climatic zone dominated by low pressure and the passage of frontal depressions.

Heat and sun cannot be guaranteed in any European destination in winter. Low pressure and fronts extend their mean position southwards to the zone from Portugal to Greece, which increase the chances of cloudy, wet, windy and cool weather from time to time. Any resident of Europe looking for guaranteed winter sun and heat must travel further afield. The Canary Islands, off the coast of Africa, lie towards the southern edge of the winter rain belt and, being further south, the sun remains at a higher angle in the sky. Their peak season is winter, as it also is in the Caribbean from late November onwards after the hurricane risk has receded. Visitors on many Caribbean islands are largely Americans and Canadians from the interior and north, where winters are much colder than in equivalent latitudes in Europe. The latitude of Winnipeg in the Canadian Prairies is slightly lower than that of Birmingham, but because of greater continental effect and an absence of moderating sea influences upon temperatures, daily winter maximums are colder by 10°C or more (Figure 7.11).

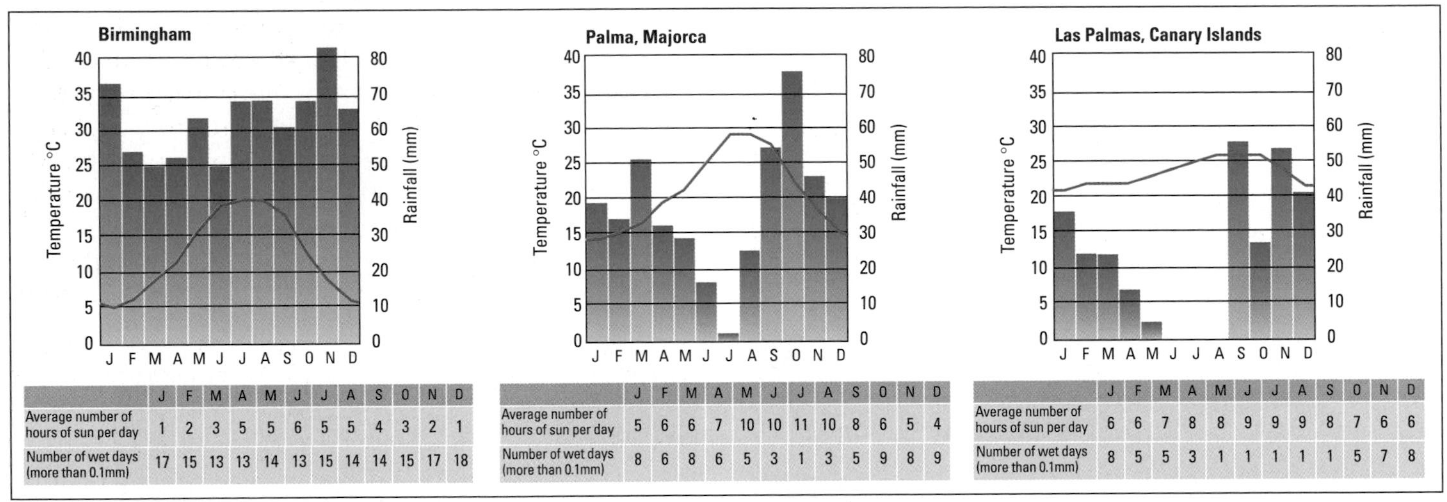

Birmingham

	J	F	M	A	M	J	J	A	S	O	N	D
Average number of hours of sun per day	1	2	3	5	5	6	5	5	4	3	2	1
Number of wet days (more than 0.1mm)	17	15	13	13	14	13	15	14	14	15	17	18

Palma, Majorca

	J	F	M	A	M	J	J	A	S	O	N	D
Average number of hours of sun per day	5	6	6	7	10	10	11	10	8	6	5	4
Number of wet days (more than 0.1mm)	8	6	8	6	5	3	1	3	5	9	8	9

Las Palmas, Canary Islands

	J	F	M	A	M	J	J	A	S	O	N	D
Average number of hours of sun per day	6	6	7	8	8	9	9	9	8	7	6	6
Number of wet days (more than 0.1mm)	8	5	5	3	1	1	1	1	1	5	7	8

▲ **Figure 7.10** Climatic data for Birmingham, Palma (Majorca) and Las Palmas (Canary Islands)

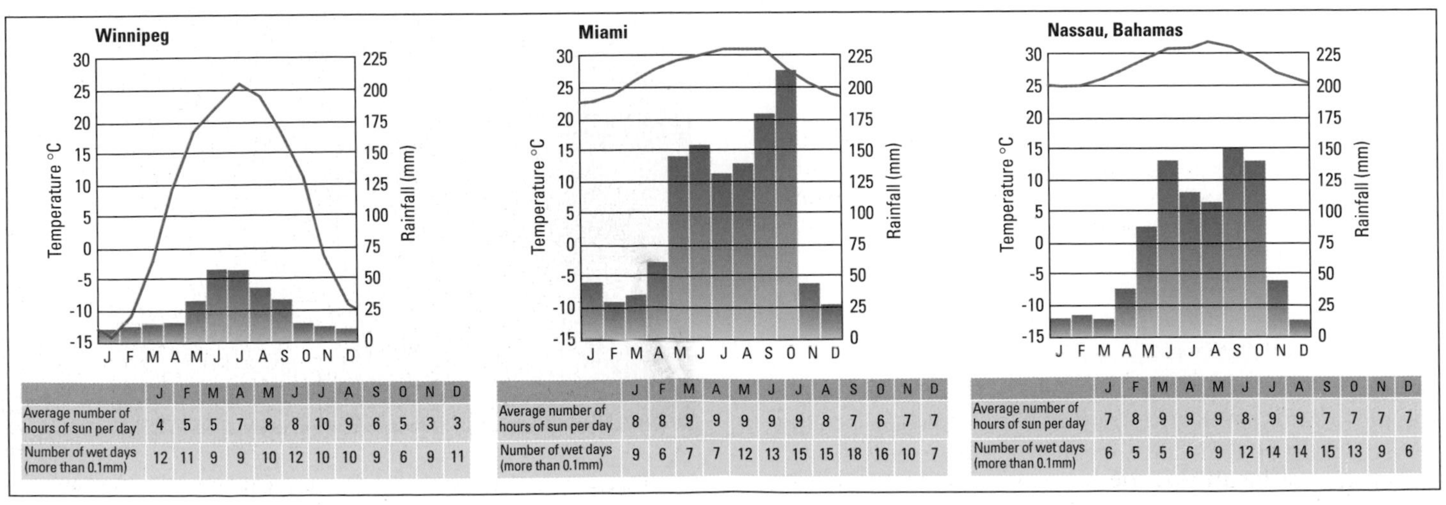

Winnipeg

	J	F	M	A	M	J	J	A	S	O	N	D
Average number of hours of sun per day	4	5	5	7	8	8	10	9	6	5	3	3
Number of wet days (more than 0.1mm)	12	11	9	9	10	12	10	10	9	6	9	11

Miami

	J	F	M	A	M	J	J	A	S	O	N	D
Average number of hours of sun per day	8	8	9	9	9	9	9	8	7	6	7	7
Number of wet days (more than 0.1mm)	9	6	7	7	12	13	15	15	18	16	10	7

Nassau, Bahamas

	J	F	M	A	M	J	J	A	S	O	N	D
Average number of hours of sun per day	7	8	9	9	9	8	9	9	7	7	7	7
Number of wet days (more than 0.1mm)	6	5	5	6	9	12	14	14	15	13	9	6

▲ **Figure 7.11** Climatic data for Winnipeg (Canada), Nassau (Bahamas) and Miami (Florida)

Snow can be made artificially but it is an inferior substitute for natural snowfall, which liberally covers mountain slopes over a wide area. In the winter of 2001 ski runs in the Scottish Cairngorms were the best that they had been for a decade; at times snow conditions for skiing were better than in more famous Alpine resorts, where mid-winter shortages of fresh snow existed from time to time. As with summer sun in the UK, winter snow in Scotland cannot be guaranteed, whereas it can be more relied upon in Alpine countries and guaranteed at the higher levels. Although to beach lovers and skiers climate is the factor of overriding importance, a good infrastructure also matters, particularly to skiers. If the ski runs cannot be reached speedily and easily, inadequate secondary resource facilities act as a limiting factor upon the number of visitors. European skiers are increasingly looking elsewhere as well. Popular skiing destinations in the Rockies in the USA and Canada, such as Aspen in Colorado and Banff in Alberta, are attracting more skiers from the Old World. Snow in the Rockies arrives earlier, falls in larger amounts and stays for longer than in the majority of Alpine resorts.

▲ **Figure 7.12**
Valle Nevado, one of several Chilean ski resorts in the Andes that are within two hours' driving time from metropolitan Santiago. The resorts are busy between June and September due to good snow conditions, well-maintained ski runs and lifts, as well as proximity to the capital.

Climate affects recreation and tourism in less precise ways. When the weather is dry, there are fewer restrictions on holiday activities and movement. Even if viewing the scenery is not the prime intention of a visit, more can be seen when the weather is dry. Even in non-beach tourist locations, the wet season tends to be the low season. People who visit the countryside and mountains with the prime aim of enjoying the scenery while walking, hiking or trekking, are likely to accept the vagaries of the weather, but their holiday experience is far more enjoyable when the weather is dry. The higher a mountain range and the more dramatic its scenery, the more frequently its views are likely to be interrupted by bad weather. The north–south trend of the Andes includes a central section in southern Peru, Bolivia and northern Chile that passes through the high pressure horse latitudes. This gives a zone of desert climate in which there is a high chance of clear mountain top views at any time of year (Figure 3.1 page 69). Whereas trekking holidays to the Himalayas, which trend west–east, are subject to particularly poor weather at certain times of the year.

In certain destinations the prime focus of interest for tourists is ecological through the observation of plants and animals in their natural surroundings. The Monteverde rainforest in Costa Rica, shown in Figure 7.9, is one example. For many people in the UK small-scale habitats exist at no great distance from home, such as a pond, woodland, wetland, nature reserve or wildfowl park. Sites are often owned and managed by an organization such as the Natural Trust or Forestry Commission, which marks out trails, provides information sheets and installs notice boards. The RSPB facilitates viewing of birds from hides at distances that do not cause interference with nesting and feeding. The nests of hundreds of thousands of sea birds cling to coastal cliffs around the UK in late spring and early summer. Particular concentrations are found on the Farne Islands off the coast of Northumberland, where a variety of species (puffins, eider ducks, terns, cormorants, gulls) compete for nesting space, and on the Bass Rock in the Forth estuary, which is taken over by gannets each summer.

Figure 7.13 Giant tortoises on the Galapagos Islands, from which the islands take their name

By their very nature, most ecological destinations are not part of the mass market, either as a result of remote location, or because invasions of visitors in great numbers are likely to destroy the wildlife attraction that is the focus for the visit. The wildlife destination that comes closest to having the mass tourist label attached to it is the big game zone on the plateau lands in east and southern Africa. Enormous numbers of grazing animals (zebra, wildebeest, antelope, giraffe and elephant) feed on the savanna grasslands, and they attract predators (lions and cheetahs) and scavengers (hyenas and vultures). In areas where numbers of big game animals are high, game reserves and national parks have been set up, principally in Kenya, Tanzania and South Africa. Coral reefs teem with colourful species of tropical fish. They are much visited (and sometimes over-visited) when they are located close to well-developed beach resorts, such as around some Caribbean islands and in the Red Sea and Indian Ocean. Australia's Great Barrier Reef is another example of a much visited tourist attraction on a larger scale (Figure 2.69 page 59). More specialized ecological destinations with limited capacity for tourists include the Galapagos Islands (giant tortoises, iguanas and different types of boobies), and the islands and peninsulas of the South Atlantic and Antarctic Oceans. The latter provide summer nesting sites for the millions of seabirds and other marine animals that feed on krill and fish in the plankton-rich cold waters (Figure 4.1 page 119).

▲ **Figure 7.14** African elephants grazing the scrub savanna in Kenya

Heritage sites from previous advanced civilizations have an uneven spatial distribution. They are most concentrated in the eastern Mediterranean where the impressive remains from Ancient Egyptians, Greeks and Romans abound. There are occasional pockets in the New World from later civilizations such as those of the Mayas and Aztecs in Mexico and Incas in Peru. Another example is Venice, which is a unique example from the Middle Ages in Europe. Venice is an extremely important cultural heritage centre with 2,000 plus sculptures and stone carvings adding to the magnificent historical legacy of religious buildings and palaces. Venetian merchants prospered and their mercantile wealth was converted into splendid buildings and monuments. Many of these continue to line the sides of the city's central transportation axis, the Grand Canal, despite the problems posed by rising sea levels.

▲ **Figure 7.15** The Grand Canal in Venice

Questions

1 Temperature data is continuous. Rainfall data is discrete.
- **a** Explain what this means.
- **b** Why are different techniques of representation used for temperature and rainfall?

2 Outline the climatic data which supports each of the following statements.
- **a** Many Britons seeking a beach holiday in summer prefer Mediterranean resorts to coastal resorts in the UK.
- **b** Winter is the high season in the Canary Islands but the low season in Majorca.
- **c** The cost per night of a room in a beach resort hotel in the Bahamas varies from £134 in the low season between 13 July and 18 December to £178 in the high season between 2 January and 22 April.

3 Explain what is meant by 'ecological primary resources for tourism' and give examples from Britain and around the world.

4 **Investigation**

For one world tourist destination in which ecological resources are its dominant attraction,
- **a** locate it on a sketch map
- **b** provide further details about the nature and range of its ecological attractions
- **c** outline the secondary resources and infrastructure for tourism.

Secondary resources

On occasions no primary resource for tourism exists. A human attraction is deliberately created to draw visitors. A museum that is separate from a historical site is one example; another is factory visits to whisky distilleries, creameries, chocolate makers, wood carvers, glass makers and many more. The theme park is a third. The theme park is largely an American creation and had much to do with Disney. Disneyland in Los Angeles was an incredible success and still attracts some 15 million visitors a year. A direct copy, Walt Disney World in Orlando, was later built in the midst of otherwise useless swamplands in Florida. Visitor numbers were boosted when the same organization built Epcot next door; despite a stronger focus on science and knowledge, amusement and pleasure were not forgotten. A third theme park was added in the 1990s, Disney-MGM Studios at Walt Disney World, and there are plans for a fourth. Along with Universal Studios and Sea World of Florida, Orlando has become the amusement and theme park capital of the USA and the world (Figure 7.16).

Artificially created secondary resources that are indoors have the advantage of eliminating or reducing the effects of the weather. The Centre Parcs concept in the UK includes water activities that are all indoors. This is essential for year-round operation in a cool temperate climate. The desert climate of Los Angeles makes it an ideal location for Disneyland, which is essentially an open-air theme park. Florida has sun for most of the year and winter warmth, although it has a more marked wet season (in late summer and autumn) than has California (Figure 7.11). When the same style of theme park was built at Disneyland Paris, it did not achieve the immediate success that had been anticipated; climate was one of the contributory factors. In an attempt to counteract the effects of bad weather the number of indoor attractions and rides were boosted. Despite its location in the middle of the EU's wealth belt, it is still not a huge financial success, with its share price in 2001 languishing at well under ten per cent of the original price.

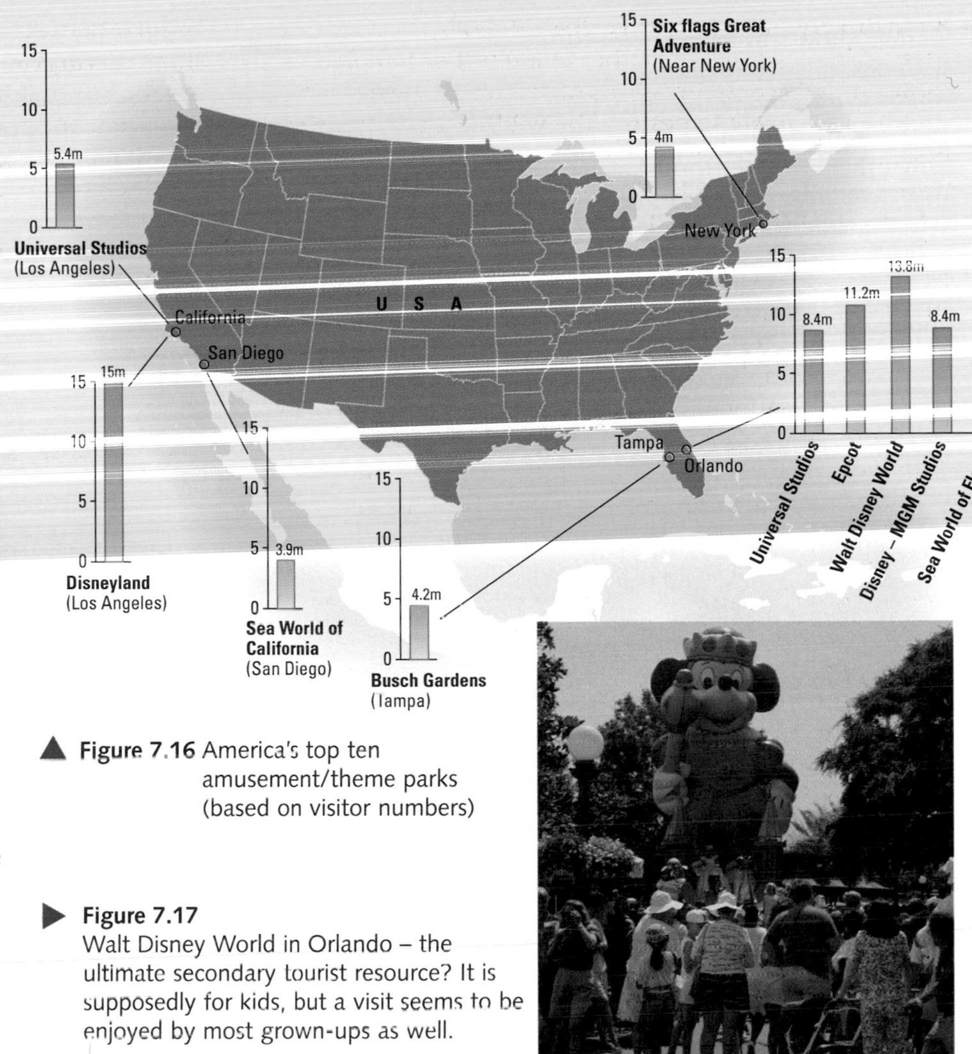

▲ **Figure 7.16** America's top ten amusement/theme parks (based on visitor numbers)

▶ **Figure 7.17**
Walt Disney World in Orlando – the ultimate secondary tourist resource? It is supposedly for kids, but a visit seems to be enjoyed by most grown-ups as well.

The UK

Human-created attractions are expensive to build, maintain and operate. Success is not automatically guaranteed, as the Millennium Experience at the London Dome showed. Yet the London Eye, another millennium project and only a short distance higher up the Thames, was an immediate success. Judging by initial public reaction before and at its opening in March 2001, the Eden Centre, a giant collection of spherical glasshouses set in a disused china clay pit near St Austell in Cornwall, is also going to be a runaway success.

Why did the Millennium Experience fail as a visitor attraction? Lack of a clear purpose? Insufficient amusement ideas inside it? Not good value for money? Negative press publicity? Imposition by politicians? Bad location? Or was there simply a lack of realism about how much could be earned from a tourist attraction with high fixed costs in just one year of operation? Despite leisure, recreation and tourism being major growth areas, it is a reminder that success is not automatic. Attractions are vulnerable to changes in fashion and the fickleness of consumer tastes.

Theme and amusement parks in the UK are a major growth area and attract over 37 million visitors a year. The five most visited ones are included in Figure 7.18a. Every year Blackpool Pleasure Beach tops the list of visitor attractions in the UK. Free entry is only one reason. Blackpool has maintained its long established position as the country's leading seaside resort by enhancing its secondary resources. Larger and more spectacular 'white knuckle' rides draw visitors back again. Out-of-season events such as the Blackpool illuminations create a second visitor peak in autumn at a time when most other seaside resorts are beginning to close down for winter. Alton Towers in Staffordshire has consolidated its position as number one among the entry fee theme and amusement parks. The only other entry fee tourist attraction that drew in more visitors is Westminster Abbey, helped by its position in the heart of London. The dominant number of attractions in and around London reflects population concentrations and a nodal transport network. The UK's main motorways and the fastest railway lines converge on London to provide the highest level of national accessibility, while internationally it is served by the country's two largest airports at Heathrow and Gatwick. Surveys reveal that about half of overseas visitors spend all or most of their visit in London.

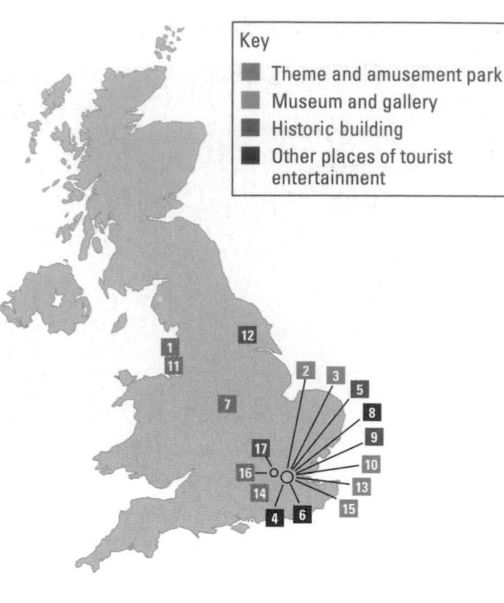

1 Blackpool Pleasure Beach	7.1m		Free
2 British Museum, London	5.6m		Free
3 National Gallery, London	4.8m		Free
4 Palace Pier, Brighton	3.5m		Free
5 Westminster Abbey, London	3.0m		Pay
6 Eastbourne Pier	2.8m		Free
7 Alton Towers, Staffordshire	2.8m		Pay
8 Madame Tussaud's, London	2.8m		Pay
9 Tower of London	2.6m		Pay
10 Tate Gallery, London	2.2m		Free
11 Pleasureland, Southport	2.1m		Free
12 York Minster	2.0m		Free
13 Natural History Museum, London	1.9m		Pay
14 Chessington World of Adventure, Surrey	1.7m		Pay
15 Science Museum, London	1.6m		Pay
16 Legoland, Windsor	1.5		Pay
17 Windsor Castle	1.5		Pay

▲ **Figure 7.18a** Attendance at the UK's top tourist attractions in 1998

▶ **Figure 7.18b** Entrance to Blackpool Pleasure Beach

Examples of resource bases

The UK

Resources that are the basis for recreation and tourism are widely distributed throughout the UK. The signs of the long history of settlement – churches, cathedrals, abbeys, castles and old buildings – are everywhere. Non-historical towns and villages, bereft of something from the past, which are worthy of at least a short visit are unusual. Although the greatest concentration of historical and heritage sites are in London (as a consequence of its long established function of capital city), York Minster did reach number 10 in the UK attractions list for 1998. The Minster is the symbol of York, but the city was a centre of some importance in Viking, Roman, Norman and medieval times and the plan of narrow streets within the city walls has been largely preserved. Secondary resources include a variety of museums from the Jorvik Centre to the National Rail Museum, special events such as the mystery plays and race week, and a wide range of accommodation. Large numbers of foreign tourists visit the university cities of Oxford and Cambridge, partly because they are within easy reach for day visits from London. Other places are on the visitor trail simply because of an association with one person; examples include Stratford-upon-Avon for Shakespeare and Grasmere in the Lake District for Wordsworth.

The least densely populated rural areas are upland areas in the UK, where natural scenic resources take over from human resources as the primary attraction for visitors. The distribution of protected areas, which matches those of greatest natural interest, is shown in Figure 7.19. The UK may not have the dramatic scenery associated with the world's major young fold mountain ranges, such as the Alps, Himalayas, Rockies and Andes, but this is partly offset by scenic variety. In both the Lake District and Snowdonia National Parks glaciation and related processes sharpened and steepened the mountain peaks, deepened the pre-existing river valleys and formed lakes to carve landscapes of great natural beauty. In the Lake District, the lakes are larger and more numerous than elsewhere in the UK, as the name suggests, and they are the focal point for many tourist-related activities. In Snowdonia the mountain scenery is the centre of attraction. Landscape differences between the Yorkshire Dales and Dartmoor are in the main a reflection of differences in weathering and erosion between Carboniferous limestone and granite. However, upland landscapes are more than just physical creations. The pattern of dry stone walls, barns and farms found in the Yorkshire Dales has no equivalent on the generally higher and wetter moorlands in Devon.

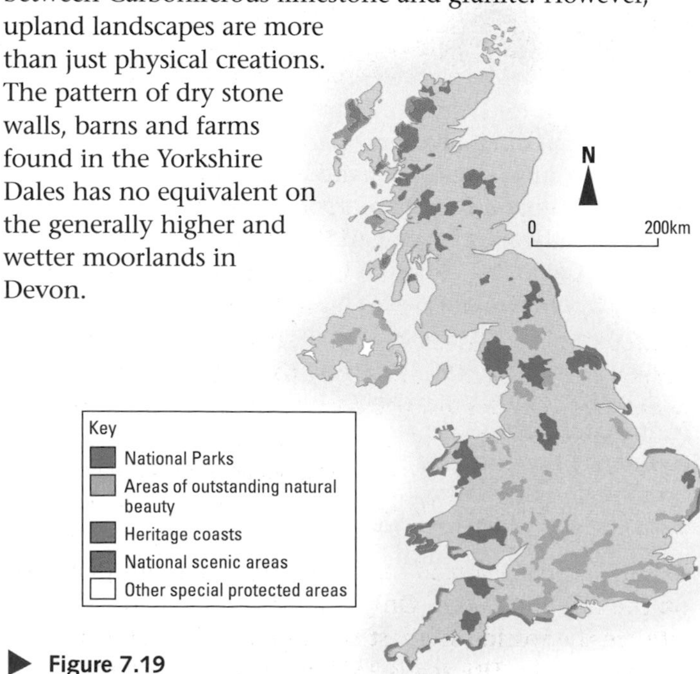

▶ **Figure 7.19** Protected areas in the UK

▼ **Figure 7.20** Some of the natural primary resources for tourism in South America

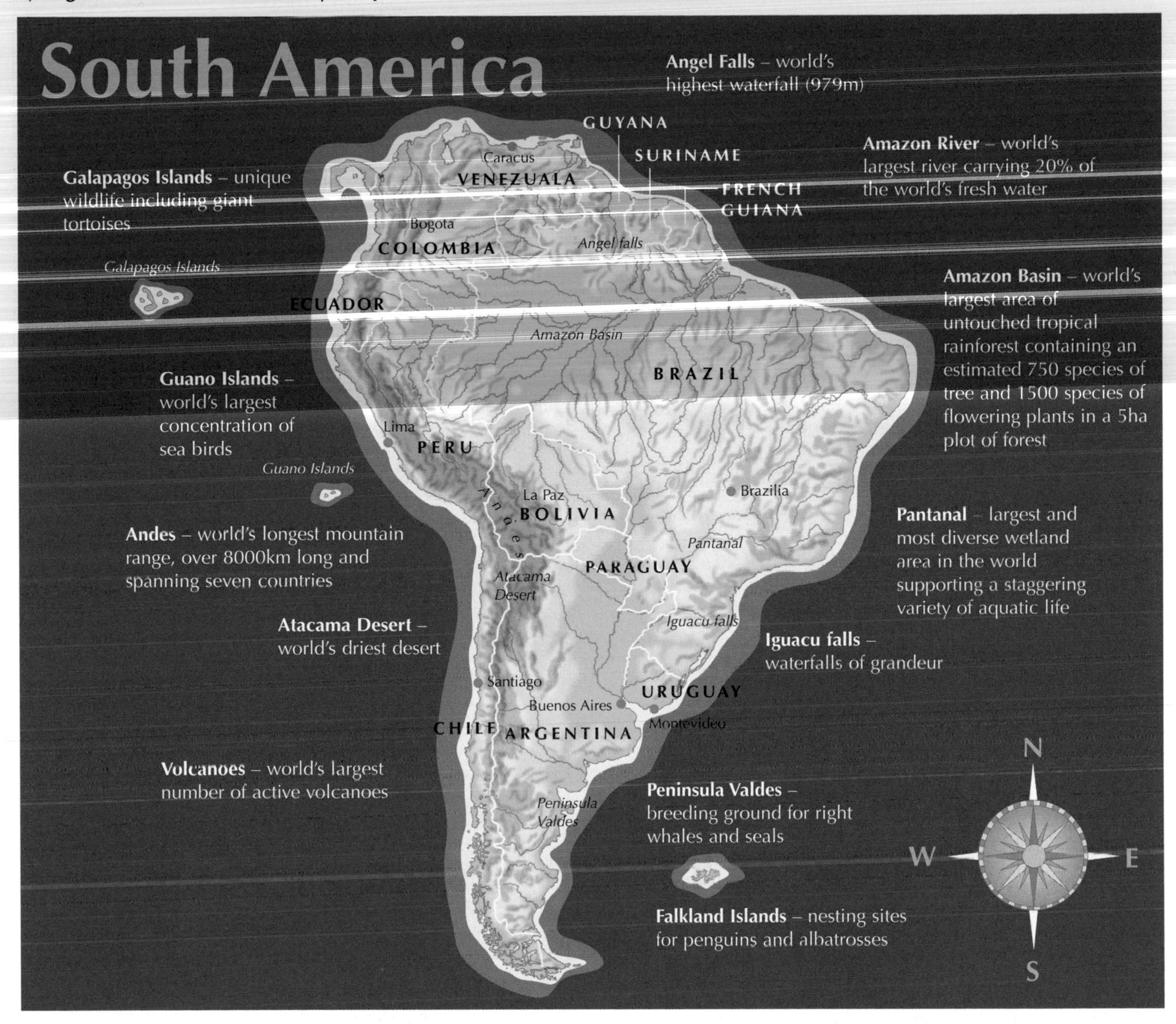

South America

In contrast to the UK in particular and to Europe in general, the continent of South America contains examples of some of the world's record-breaking natural features (Figure 7.20). These include the world's highest waterfall, its largest river, its largest area of natural rainforest, its longest mountain range and its driest desert. Unlike the Alps, many of the high mountain peaks in the Andes are volcanic cones and the continent contains more active volcanoes than any other. Humans have contributed to the superlatives as well. La Paz in Bolivia is the world's highest capital city; its city centre is located in a natural basin 3,600m above sea level, while its suburbs have spread onto the *Altiplano* (high plateau) on the rim at 4,000m. Only a short distance from the city are the world's highest ski slopes at Chacaltaya (5,600m). Lake Titicaca is 150km away. At 3,800m it is the world's highest navigable lake. For comparison, the top of Mt Blanc, the highest point in the Alps, is 4,807m.

Ecological variations are on a scale not witnessed in Europe. The Andes mountain range separates tropical rainforest from barren desert (in Peru). The Amazon Basin, which contains the highest bio-diversity on Earth, is usually considered to only belong to Brazil, but its edges do in fact extend into another eight neighbouring countries. To the north and south of the Amazon Basin there are wet landscapes, the Orinoco lowlands in Venezuela and the Pantanal in Brazil, both noted for the immense wealth of their bird and aquatic wildlife. Plankton-rich cold ocean currents, supplied from Antarctic waters, support a wealth of sea bird life in and around the Falklands, in coastal Chile, on the guano islands off the coast of Peru and on the Galapagos Islands (owned by Ecuador). Plant and animal life is so diverse mainly because of the continent's latitudinal range from 12°N to 55°S. It is also due to variations in height – many Andean peaks are above 6,000m whereas substantial areas of *altiplano* are between 3,500 and 4,500m. Another element contributing to this theme of diversity is the northward projection of the Antarctic peninsula, which brings the Antarctic continent closer to South America than to any other land mass.

There are over forty UNESCO (United Nations Educational, Scientific and Cultural Organization) world heritage sites in South America. These sites include some of the most visited natural features such as the Igacu Falls (Figures 1.1C and 7.1) and Perito Moreno glacier. They also include wildlife locations such as the Galapagos Islands (Figure 7.13), and cultural heritage sites, notably the old Inca city of Machu-Picchu in Peru and Easter Island in the Pacific which belongs to Chile (Chapter 5 pages 182–3). The section of the Andes from Ecuador southwards into central Chile was the most populated part of the continent before the Spaniards arrived. It belonged to the Inca Empire, whose rulers developed an elaborate centrally planned civilization between the twelfth and sixteenth centuries. The mass of people were part of an organized scheme of work. Some were farmers growing the staple crops of potatoes and maize, depending on altitude; others extended the available area for cultivation by building terraces on hillsides. Traditional skills such as metal working were used to fashion gold and silver objects. Spinning and weaving wool from the flocks of llamas and alpacas into ponchos was another specialized activity. The centrally organized food stores released others for building work. Perfect stonework is one of the hallmarks of the Inca period. Fortresses, buildings, walls, arches and doorways are built of blocks of stone fashioned to fit together perfectly without mortar; they have remained undisturbed despite centuries of earthquake shocks. The distant parts of the empire were held together by a system of roads, built as steps on the steepest land, along which couriers sped. The streets of Cuzco, the old Inca capital, are lined by examples of the skill of stonemasons in Inca times. About 100km away is the Inca city of Machu-Picchu, which was 'lost' for centuries buried by jungle until it was rediscovered in 1911. As a result it is in a comparatively good state of preservation; the ruins include staircases, terraces, temples, palaces and sun-dial (Figure 7.21). The Spanish colonists laid out new cities. These were always built to a grid iron plan around a central square (plaza). The cathedral and public administration buildings were built on the sides of the square. Otherwise the main contributions of the Spaniards to the historical heritage are colonial churches, monasteries and convents.

▲ **Figure 7.21** Machu-Picchu and cultivation terraces leading down from the main site

Questions

1 Distinguish between primary and secondary resources for tourism.

2 **a** What is a theme park?
  b Justify and explain Orlando's label as the 'theme park capital of the USA and the world'.
  c Outline and comment on the types, distribution and relative importance of the UK's tourist attractions in Figure 7.18.

3 **a** Describe the primary resources for tourism in South America using the following headings: **i** scenic, **ii** ecological and **iii** historical and heritage.
  b Draw a summary sketch map to show where the three types of primary resources are most concentrated.
  c **Investigation**

  From web sites or brochures of tour companies specializing in South America, identify and give further details about the areas of South America that are most visited by tourists.

4 Discuss the reasons why the importance of climate as a primary resource for recreation and tourism varies in significance from high to low.

The Lea Valley, East London: recreation in a small area

Case Study

▼ **Figure 7.22** The location of the Lea Valley Regional Park

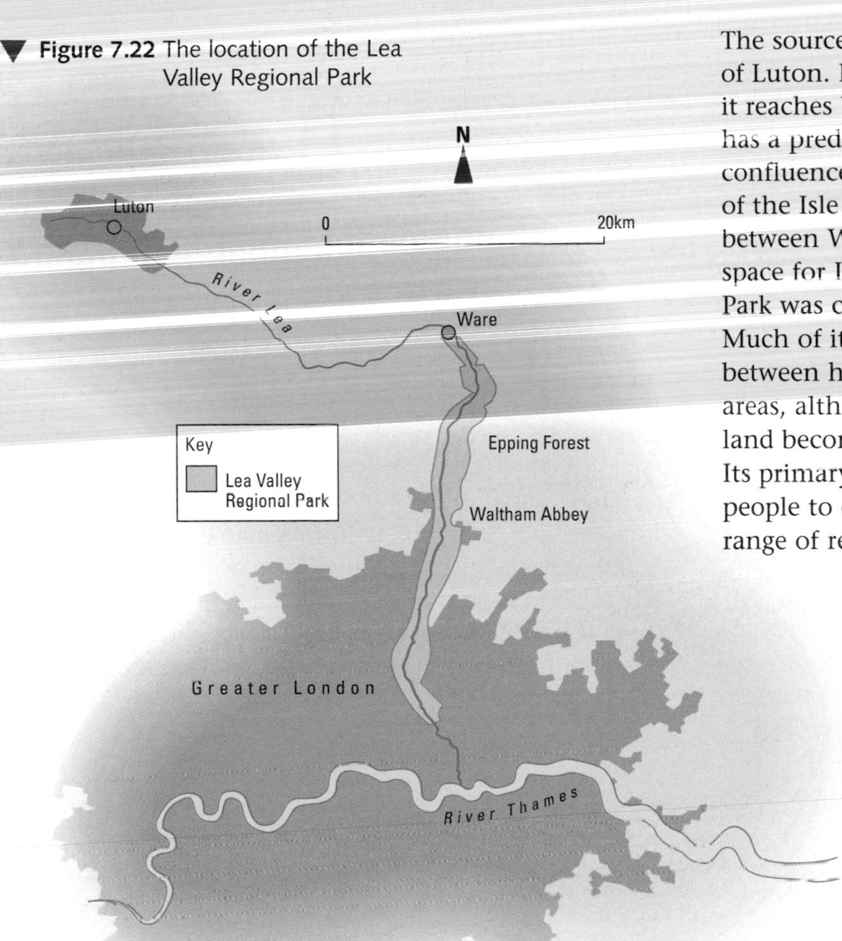

The source of the River Lea is within the built-up area of Luton. Its main direction of flow is eastwards until it reaches Ware in Hertfordshire, from which point it has a predominantly southerly course until its confluence with the River Thames on the eastern side of the Isle of Dogs (Figure 7.22). The 40km section between Ware and Stratford was designated as leisure space for Londoners when the Lea Valley Regional Park was created by an Act of Parliament in 1966. Much of it is a narrow corridor of more open space between heavily built-up residential and industrial areas, although to the east of Waltham Abbey the land becomes more rural as Epping Forest is reached. Its primary function is to reserve open space for local people to enjoy their leisure time and engage in a range of recreational activities.

Two of the problems for the fully effective management of the park and for users are

- the haphazard distribution of recreational opportunities
- the difficulty of continuous movement through the different sections of the park (the only link through the parks's entire length is the Lea Valley Walk, which follows the canal towpath).

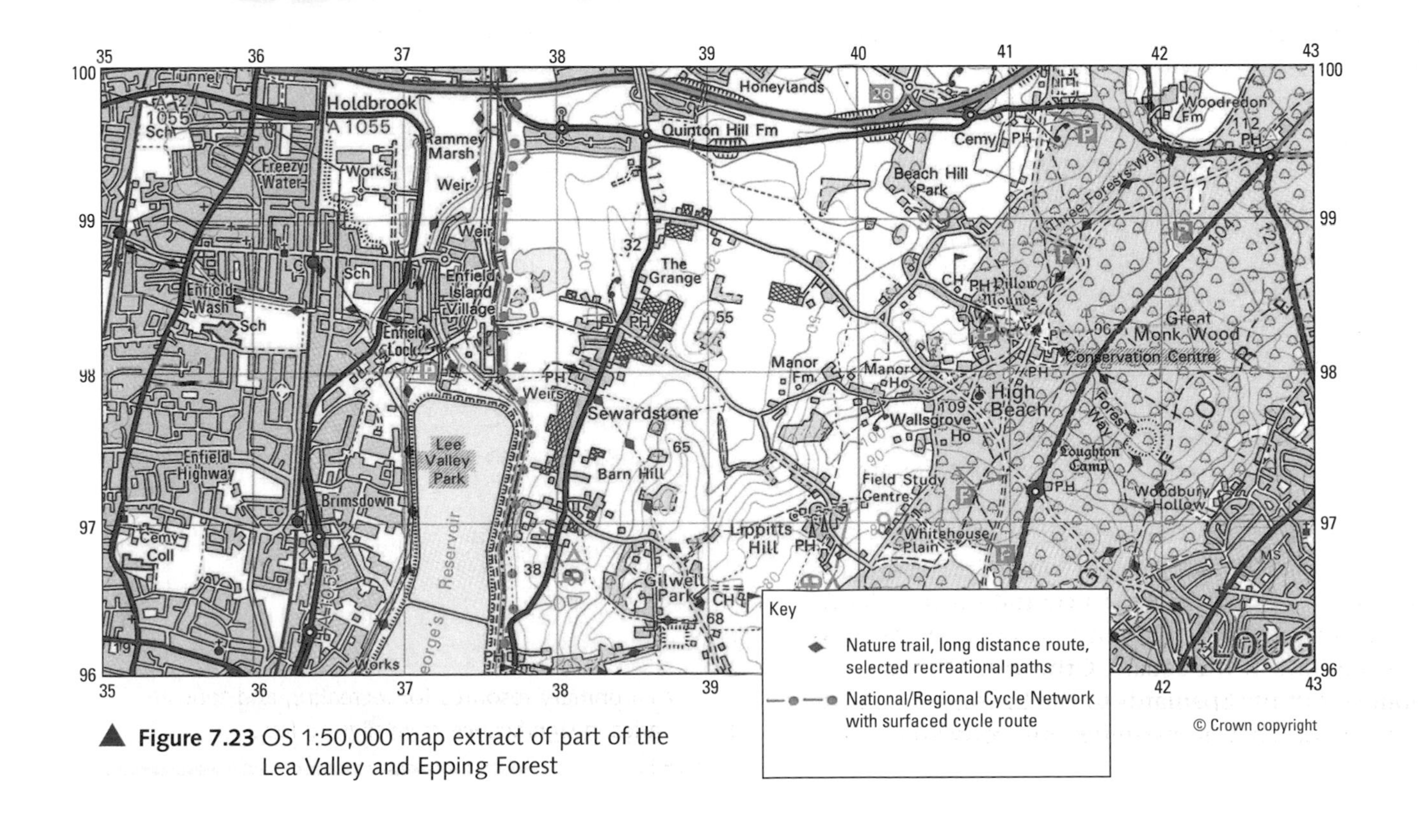

▲ **Figure 7.23** OS 1:50,000 map extract of part of the Lea Valley and Epping Forest

Questions

Use Figure 5.71 as well as this case study.

1 Describe the location and extent of the Lea Valley Regional Park.

2 People can engage in a wide variety of recreational activities in the park.

Elaborate upon this statement by quoting and using map evidence for the following: walking; cycling; other outdoor leisure activities; indoor leisure activities.

3 a As far as the OS maps allow, make lists for the primary and secondary resources of areas in and adjacent to the Lea Valley.

b Attempt an evaluation of their relative importance.

4 a What evidence is there on the two OS map extracts for the problems of:

i haphazard distribution of recreational opportunities,

ii difficulty of continuous movement through the park.

b Suggest reasons why solving these problems is difficult.

Capacity of tourist resources

Recreational activities and tourism compete for space with other activities. In urban areas land values are high; decisions about location are influenced by economic considerations. Large-scale commercial operations, such as hotels, casinos and night clubs, can charge prices that take account of the high business rents and rates associated with city centre locations. Whereas activities that are exhaustive of space, such as sports stadia, tend to relocate away from urban cores when they are modernized or have their capacity increased, for example at Milton Keynes. Many of the leisure facilities provided by local authorities are non-profit making and subsidized. Using public money for expensive town centre sites cannot always be justified, which explains why a more likely location is in the inner city or inner suburbs where competition for land is less great. Not only is the level of financial support from the public purse lower, there is also the additional advantage of locations closer to where people live. Most urban facilities have a known capacity, which, once reached, results in further potential users being turned away. Capacity can sometimes be increased provided that the forecasted extra demand is sufficiently great to give a return on new money invested. Otherwise, as with a heritage site or a sports event that is too popular, numbers visiting have to be rationed by one means or another to the capacity available.

In rural areas ever-growing leisure demands have created serious concerns about the capacity of some natural environments to meet these needs. At one level there is the destruction of wildlife habitats that inevitably accompanies the construction work needed to supply the secondary resources for tourism (these include roads, accommodation and essential services such as water supply, sanitation and electricity). The severity of the effects varies greatly from area to area. Many rocky coastal stretches around the Mediterranean were species poor so that ecological losses to tourist developments were not too great, although the scenic beauty of natural coastlines was taken away. Along many sections of the Spanish coast further growth of tourist cpacity was limited by the physical shortage of unused land rather than ecological considerations. Suitable building sites along undeveloped coastlines for new tourist ventures are in short supply throughout the Mediterranean zone in Europe, which is one of the reasons why developers are casting glances ever further eastwards and into Turkey (Figure 7.24).

All set for a boom on back of devaluation

Turkey's tourism is looking forward to a renewed tourism boom. The Ministry of Tourism is forecasting a record 12 million arrivals in Turkey after the Turkish lira was devalued. A year can make a big difference. In 1999, Turkey's visitor numbers fell to 6.8 from 8.9 million the previous year, after the Kurdistan Workers party guerrilla group threatened to attack tourism centres. The problems were compounded by the August 1999 earthquake.

However, a lack of capacity is the industry's Achilles heel. 'If Turkey had accommodation which reflected market demand, it would attract 16m visitors annually,' said the president of the International Federation of Tour Operators. 'Spain and other European holiday destinations are full and therefore Turkey has a real opportunity for growth.' By way of example he added that 'the focus had been on hotel development although half the German visitors and more than 80 per cent of Swedes want to stay in apartments'. International tour operators blame the lack of investment and the daunting red tape and bureaucracy before any development can take place.

The Turkish Minister of Tourism is keen to encourage the modernization of the hotel sector, seeking smaller, more personalized developments, which take into account both the individual characteristics of the locations as well as market demands. Releasing the tourist industry's potential will help increase both growth and employment.

▲ **Figure 7.24** Adapted extract about tourism in Turkey from *The Financial Times*, 18 April 2001

Clearing a few patches of rainforest on the sides of the Amazon river in Brazil for tourist lodges is of no big ecological significance given the extent of the forest that remains. However, it can be different on tropical islands and in more densely populated countries where further clearance greatly endangers the local bio-diversity. Clearance has gone beyond the danger point and has reached the point of no return when too little forest is left to sustain the plants and animals that remain. Penang in Malaysia is a densely populated island. Recent tourist developments have been concentrated in the hitherto less developed north. Areas of climatic climax rainforest exist, but are shrinking fast as hotels and associated tourist facilities continue to expand the island's visitor capacity (Figure 7.25).

▲ **Figure 7.25** Penang, Malaysia. Two views photographed from the same place but pointing in opposite directions. One shows almost untouched rainforest, the other new infrastructure works to support further tourism growth. What factors will determine for how long the untouched forest will be safe?

Reaching agreement about the tourist capacity of an area is difficult, especially in rural areas. If all the car parks are full and other potential visitors trying to reach there are stuck in traffic jams, it could be taken as a clear indication that the capacity of the area for visitors has been exceeded. However, it could also be interpreted as a sign that a greater provision of secondary resources is needed. Some villages and small towns in the main tourist season are teeming with people and people spill over from the pubs and cafes on to the streets. To some this would be a clear sign that the settlement's visitor capacity had been reached and exceeded; to others it would be a sign of a lively and vibrant place, a good place to visit. Therefore in many ways the idea of capacity is one of human perception. Visiting busy honeypot sites is not a problem for some, yet it is for others. Some people seek out beaches already packed with bodies, probably because these are located close to stalls, shops and amusements, whereas others prefer empty stretches of beach devoid of facilities. Near and between many rural honeypot sites are seriously eroded footpaths. If a site's carrying capacity is defined as the threshold level of tourist numbers or activities beyond which damage will occur, footpath erosion is a sign of visitor pressure leading to over-capacity. However, others would look at it from the viewpoint that it shows visitor concentration, which leaves most of the area undamaged. Footpaths away from the car parks and picnic sites may be little used and unaffected by excessive numbers of tourists.

Questions

1 What is meant by the capacity of a tourist resource?

2 The capacity of tourist resources can be examined in terms of **a** physical, **b** ecological, **c** economic and **d** perceived. For each of the four headings, explain how the capacity of a tourist resource may be reached or exceeded.

3 **a** In what ways and why is there a lack of tourist capacity in Turkey?

b How does the article on Turkey illustrate the difficulty of planning for tourism?

Recreation and tourism in the MEDW

In the non-human animal world it is survival and sleep which occupies the time, with a little time taken out for breeding, often at the same time each year. It used to be the same for humans. The concept of leisure time is quite recent. So too is the idea of paid holidays. The term holiday literally means 'holy day' and for centuries in the UK holy days (i.e. Sundays and special church festivals such as Easter and Christmas) were the only days off work that most people were allowed in a year. Today most people in the developed world take holidays for granted. Indeed within the EU holidays are a right. An annual minimum of four weeks, paid holiday (including Bank Holidays) is guaranteed for all full-time workers. In addition the standard working week of five days and up to 40 hours gives people more leisure time than ever before, some of which is used for recreation and tourism. Yet before the 1960s half the working population of the UK had a holiday entitlement of one week or less.

The growth of tourism in the MEDW has been nothing short of startling. The principal factors determining recreational and tourist activities are income and available leisure time. As the length of the working week has been progressively shortened and paid holiday entitlement has increased, wages and salaries have been maintained. Personal incomes and living standards have improved over time. A lower proportion of family incomes in MEDCs is used for the essentials of life (food, shelter and clothing) than at any previous time, which gives higher disposable incomes (Figure 7.26). Another vital factor has been technological advance in means of transport allowing greater mobility. At one level there has been the tremendous increase in car ownership. The reliability and comfort of modern cars and the building of motorways (congested though they may be) have allowed distances to be covered within a day that were previously inconceivable. Particularly relevant to the upsurge in overseas and longer distance travel has been jet aircraft. The increased range and the speed of getting there has been accompanied by a dramatic relative reduction in airfares, especially on charter flights and low cost airlines. Most places in the world can be reached by wide-bodied jets within 24 hours. Another significant factor has been the change in social attitude. It is considered normal for a family to disappear on holiday for a fortnight each year and families budget for this. It is part of the rising expectations from increased income. What began as a fashion for the rich in Victorian times has now become the fashion for all. It has never been easier to book or organize a holiday. A package can be taken off the shelf, individually assembled for the client by one of the smaller more specialized tour operators or self arranged by making rail, ferry, air and hotel bookings over the phone or via the Internet. Modern computer technology streamlines the reservations process.

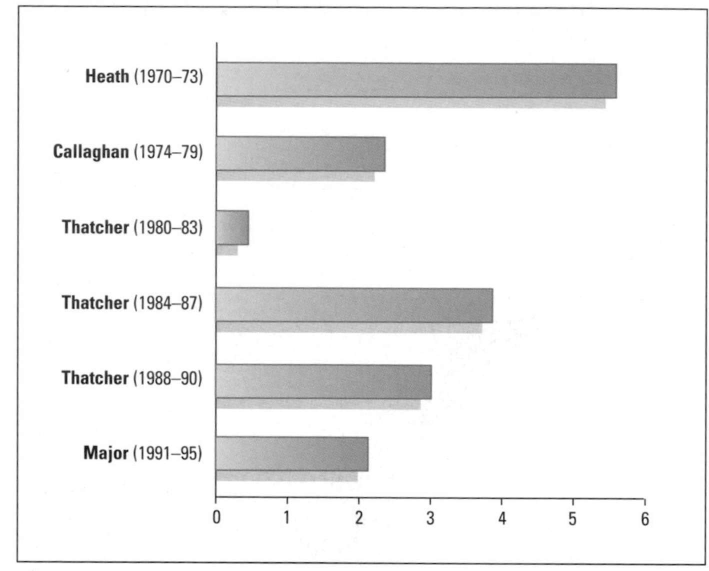

▲ **Figure 7.26** Income: percentage changes in real personal disposable income in the UK

News flash

From 1 April 2001 United Airlines is launching the world's longest non-stop passenger service.
It is to fly daily between JFK in New York and Hong Kong. The planned journey time is 15hrs 40mins.

Package holidays and holiday airlines

It was Thomas Cook who pioneered in 1869 the inclusive tour with his organized trips to the Nile for wealthy Victorians. He put together the individual components that make up today's typical package holiday that included visits to the Pyramids (Figure 7.8). The big three tour companies that dominate today's holiday market in the UK (Thomsons, Airtours and First Choice) are directly involved in every stage of package tour operations. Each one produces its own brochures, owns high street travel agencies and runs its own airline. Some also own and manage certain resort hotels that their clients use.

Holidays are heavily advertised and promoted, supported by the use of slick and sophisticated marketing techniques. Most television channels screen holiday programmes so that public awareness of holiday possibilities is constantly high.

Larger holiday companies produce a suite of brochures for both mass and niche markets. British Airways Holidays offered eight brochures in 2001 (Figure 7.27). As a scheduled airline operator, based mainly at Heathrow, British Airways does not attempt to compete in the market place for the standard 14-night summer holiday to Mediterranean resorts based upon charter flights from as many as a dozen provincial airports. The titles for five of the eight brochures show that they are more interested in the long-haul market. Figures 7.16 and 7.17 provide the explanation why Florida has a brochure of its own for this as well as those from other holiday operators. The rising popularity of Australia and New Zealand, helped partly by family ties and a common language and culture, has not just encouraged separate brochures from large companies, but has supported the growth of companies specializing in selling round-the-world air tickets via Australasia. The fact that there are brochures devoted entirely to golf holidays and weddings illustrates two developing features of the holiday scene – the market for activity and speciality holidays is growing, and holiday companies are increasingly targeting particular groups of people. There are holidays specifically designed for the 18–30s, usually Mediterranean-based in summer. The destinations that are considered to be 'cool' keep changing, but Ibiza was the most popular destination for this age group during the 1990s.

Activity weekends in the UK in May 2001

A sample of what is on offer.

Fishing
- *Devon from £160*
- *Scotland from £64 per night*

Painting
- *Gower, Wales £350 all inclusive*
- *Cumbria from £50*

Sculpture
- *West Sussex from £170*
- *Cornwall £160 all inclusive*

Flying
- *Manchester from £55*
- *Maidenhead £110*

Cooking
- *Wales from £150*

Creative writing
- *Cornwall from £50*
- *Somerset from £27*

Diving
- *London Try dives £20*
- *Wales from £150 all inclusive*

4WD
- *Durham from £25 per hour*
- *Wiltshire from £35*

Sailing
- *Hampshire from £145 for two days*
- *Isle of Wight Lessons from £55*

Golf
- *Scottish Highlands Lessons from £40*
- *Lincolnshire from £95 per night*

▲ **Figure 7.27** British Airways Holidays brochures for 2001

At the over-50s end of the age range, Saga has grown into a company of substantial size by specializing in the holiday needs of the retired. Whilst some people in MEDCs retire into poverty, those who have supplementary private or employment pensions, which is an increasing proportion, have higher disposable incomes than ever before. Outgoings are reduced after children have left home and the mortgage has been paid off, leaving a greater percentage of savings and income available for recreational activities and for holidays. The big attraction of this age-group to businesses engaged in any aspect of recreation and tourism is that many are free to travel and to use facilities at off-peak times, namely during the day mid-week, outside school holidays and away from bank holidays. The demographic structure in Europe is one of progressively ageing populations. Numbers of people over 50 years old will continue to grow and will be targeted by holiday companies.

Of the brochures from British Airways Holidays, only the short breaks one for Cities is dominated by European destinations. It is in the area of short breaks that many tour operators see the greatest growth potential in the UK and other MEDCs. Now that the main holiday is a fixture in the annual calendar of events in many households, increasing affluence and more leisure time are allowing a shorter second, or even a third, holiday to be taken at other times of the year. Many of these are city breaks. Within the UK, popular destinations are London, York and Edinburgh; within Europe, Paris and Amsterdam are the cities that are easily accessible and most visited. For most people taking short breaks time is a limiting factor. Therefore proximity and good supporting transport infrastructure increase in importance with short break holidays. Bruges and Brussels have moved up the table of popular short break destinations from the UK since the start of Eurostar services in 1994. Being able to reach a European destination by sea or tunnel is more significant than for long holidays.

Questions

1 Describe and explain the factors responsible for the growth of recreation and tourist activities in the UK and other MEDCs under the following headings:
a physical, **b** economic, **c** social, **d** technological.

2 To what extent are these factors of limited application to people living in countries of the less economically developed world?

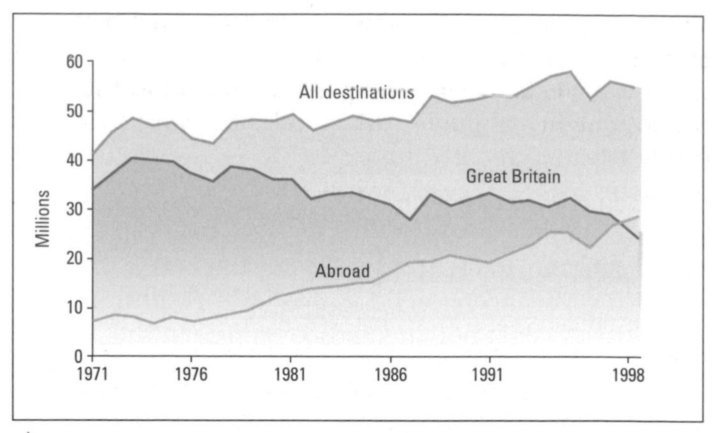

▲ **Figure 7.28** Holidays taken by UK residents (1971–98)

UK tourism

The trends in number of holidays taken by UK residents is shown in Figure 7.28. (In this graph a holiday is defined as a stay lasting four or more nights away from home.) For a combination of factors referred to above, the upward trend in number of holidays taken has been persistent, despite the occasional blip. However, a significant change occurred in 1998 when for the first time the number of holidays abroad (29 million) exceeded the number taken in Britain (27 million). What the line for holidays taken in Great Britain cannot show is the declining percentage of people who still choose a traditional seaside holiday. As late as 1972, over 80 per cent of domestic holidays of four nights or more were taken in seaside towns such as Blackpool, Bournemouth, Great Yarmouth and resorts in Devon and Cornwall. By 1998 it had fallen to 47 per cent. To some people it may come as quite a surprise that almost half the people taking holidays in the UK still go to coastal resorts, especially as many resorts give the appearance of having fallen on hard times with crumbling piers, boarded-up shops and toilets, abandoned theatres and peeling paint on facades of guest houses and other sea-front properties.

A study of the regions in Great Britain in which the 4+ day holidays were taken reveals the continued popularity of the West Country (Figure 7.29). In fact this region accounted for over one quarter of these holidays. It is the part of the country with the greatest number of coastal resorts and its relatively warm climate (by UK standards) extends the season compared with resorts further north and east. There are also rural inland attractions, notably the Dartmoor and Exmoor National Parks. The lowest proportions were to Greater London and Northumbria; each accounted for only two per cent of domestic holidays. Northumbria has some fine sandy beaches and great coastal scenery, but the weather is unpredictable. The combination of proximity to a cold North Sea and peripheral location make a formidable negative force for coastal tourism. Holidays in the countryside are becoming more popular, with an increasing interest shown in farm holidays and rented accommodation in villages and small market towns. This type is more evenly distributed throughout Britain. Rural tourism does not require the same specialized infrastructure and concentration of secondary resources as needed in coastal resorts. Take up is higher among people in higher socio-economic groups, who have private transport, higher disposable incomes and more individual interests.

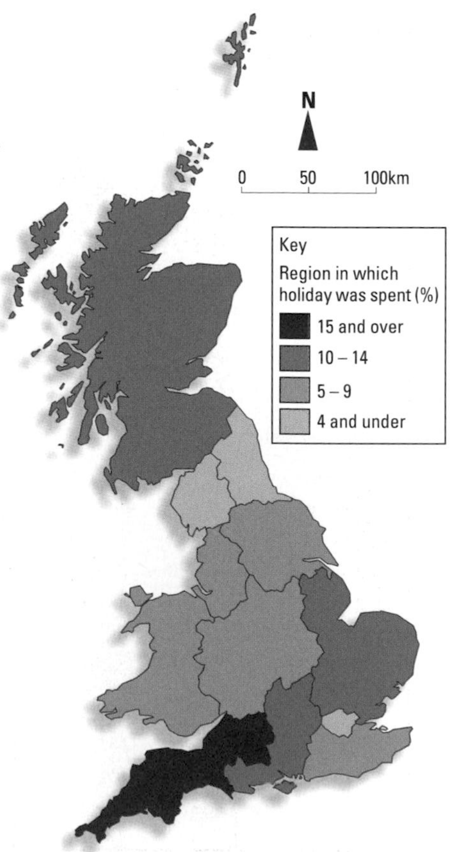

▲ **Figure 7.29** Domestic holidays by destination 1998

As for British people going abroad, the rise in numbers has been phenomenal over the last 30 years (Figure 7.30). (All visits made for holiday purposes are included; there is no four night minimum, although business trips and visits to friends and relatives are excluded.) Elements of the pattern have not changed much over the years, notably the dominance of France and Spain as the top two destinations. These two countries are responsible for around half of the market. Also unchanged is the predominance of countries in the top five that have coastlines on the Mediterranean Sea. Austria as a mountain destination has not been able to maintain its position in the face of people 'soaring off to the sun' and by 1998 its percentage had fallen by over four points to 1.3. Moving up is Turkey from a tiny 0.1 per cent in 1981 to 3.0 per cent in 1998. Long haul holidays are on the increase; for these the mass market destination is the USA, which rose by six percentage points between 1971 (1 per cent) and 1998 (7 per cent). Holidays included city breaks to Los Angeles, San Francisco and Las Vegas in the west and to New York and Washington in the east, as well as touring holidays taking in National Parks in the Rockies such as Yellowstone, Yosemite and the Grand Canyon. However, the bulk of the growth is accounted for by visits to Florida and its theme parks, which are becoming a very popular family holiday destination.

▼ **Figure 7.30** Holidays abroad (1998)

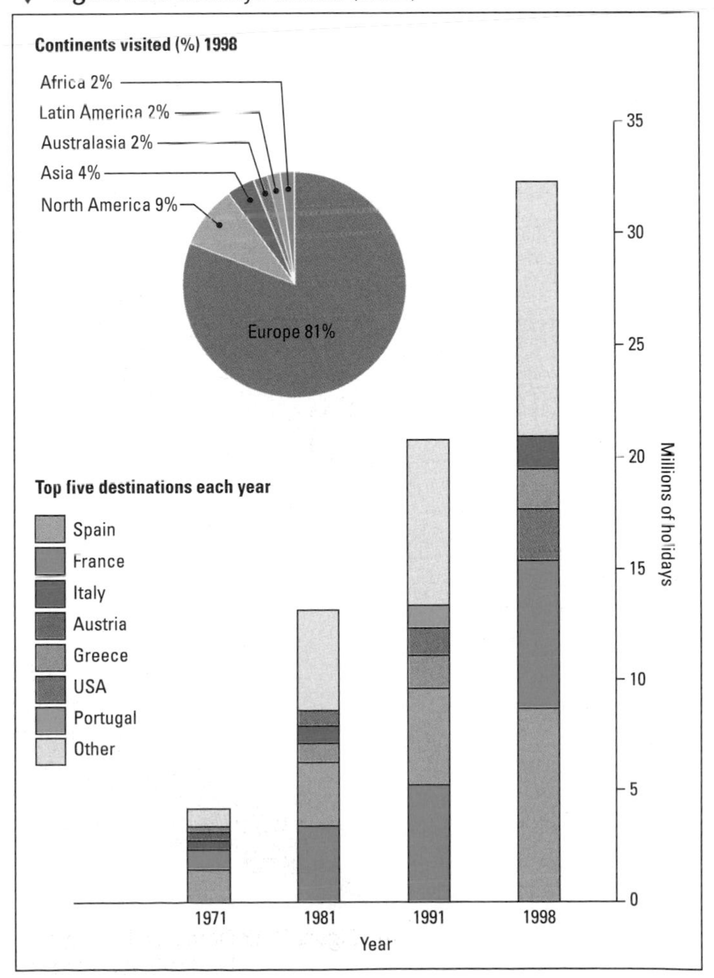

Questions

1 Some details about tourism in London are given below.

- Only 2 per cent of domestic holidays of 4 nights or more are taken in London.
- Some 48 per cent of overseas visitors spend all or most of their visit in London.
- Nearly 12 times as many staying visits by people from overseas were made in London than at the next most visited city or town (Edinburgh).
- Eight out of the fifteen most popular visitor attractions in the UK are in London (Figure 7.18).

Suggest explanations for each of these facts.

2

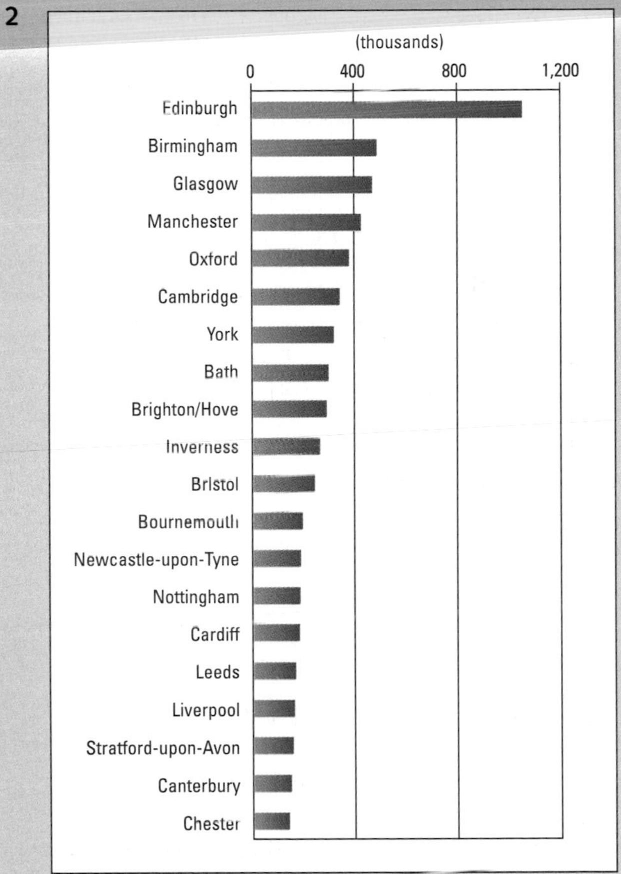

▲ **Figure 7.31**
The top 20 UK cities and towns (excluding London) for number of visits by overseas tourists in 1998

a Attempt a classification of the cities and towns named in Figure 7.31 on the basis of their visitor attractions.

b Examine the factors which affect the relative order in Figure 7.31.

c Choose two of those named in Figure 7.31 taken from different groups in your classification. For each one, investigate and give details of its resources for tourism.

3

Tourist numbers from the UK		
	to Central and South America	to North America (USA and Canada)
1989	94000	2218000
1990	119000	2325000
1991	95000	2370000
1992	102000	2813000
1993	140000	3052000
1994	154000	2927000
1995	212000	3120000
1996	314000	3584000
1997	439000	3594000
1998	557000	4158000
1999	542000	4733000

Percentage change in tourist numbers from the UK		
		Percentage share of total
	1989–99	1999
Central and South America	+ 477	1
New Zealand	+ 203	*
The Far East	+ 156	3
South Africa	+ 119	*
Australia	+ 116	1
North America	+ 113	9
Middle East	+ 108	1

* = less than 0.5 per cent

▲ **Figure 7.32** Data tables for tourists from the UK

a **i** Present the data in both tables in appropriate graphs and diagrams.
ii Describe what the graphs and diagrams show about the similarities and differences between Central/South America and North America as tourist destinations from the UK.

b Suggest reasons for **i** the relatively low total numbers and **ii** the high percentage increase in numbers of visitors to South America from the UK.

The French Riviera: growth of Mediterranean resort

Case Study

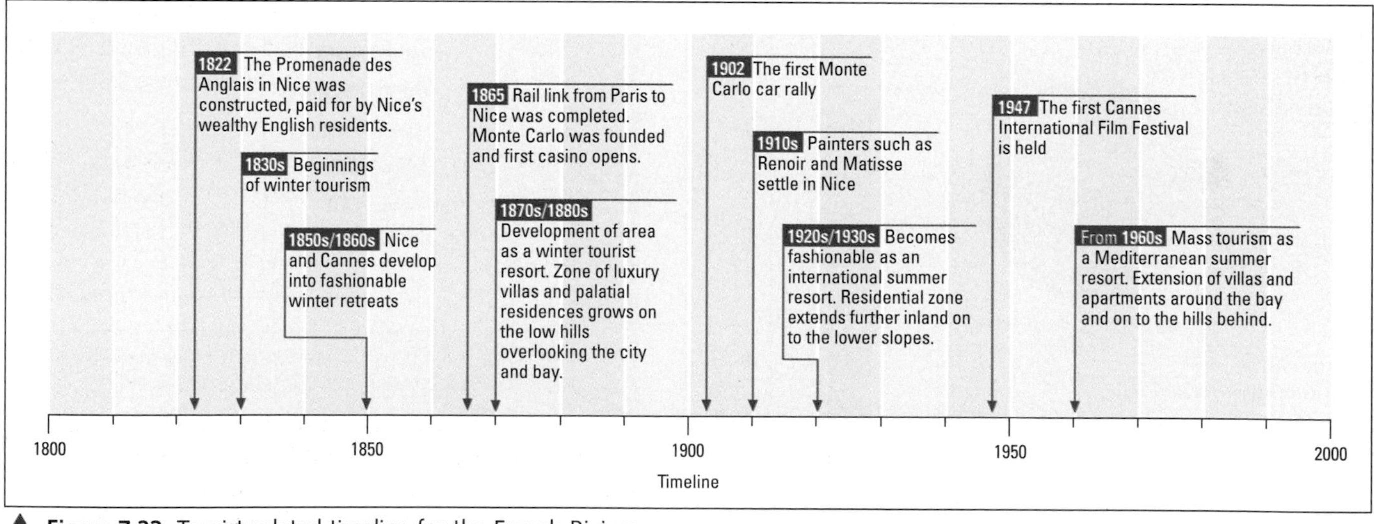

▲ **Figure 7.33** Tourist-related timeline for the French Riviera

Mediterranean tourism began in the south of France on the French Riviera. In the beginning it was a retreat for wealthy English people in winter, who were impressed by the mild temperatures, the brilliance of the sunlight and the stunning coastal scenery of rugged headlands and sheltered bays. After the Paris to Lyons railway line was extended to Nice in 1865, thousands of extra visitors began to arrive and facilities were greatly expanded. During the twentieth century the Riviera was transformed from a winter resort for the wealthy to a summer resort, at first for the rich and fashionable, and then increasingly since 1960 for the ordinary visitor as well. Where space allowed, camping and caravan sites were snuggled in behind the beaches. Although high speed TGV rail services reach Nice, the majority of arrivals now come by car and air.

The original Riviera coast was the stretch between Nice and Menton, which includes Monaco and Monte Carlo, but now it is taken to include the fashionable yacht-havens of Antibes and classy Cannes, as well as a string of popular family resorts as far west as the trend-setting and chic St Tropez. Despite joining Europe's mass market for tourism, it is still patronized by the wealthy and famous and attracts a rich assortment of actors, artists, writers, pop stars and royalty. The annual Cannes film festival in early May draws in a clutch of Hollywood stars. Luxury hotels, designer shops, terrace cafes, casinos and sandy beaches below palm-fringed promenades cater for their needs. There are approximately 300 days of sunshine a year in the region's typical Mediterranean climate. Its long period of development and continuing popularity among people of all socio-economic groups means that little further building space remains in the narrow coastal strip squeezed between the lower slopes of the Alps and the Mediterranean Sea.

The spatial effects of nearly two hundred years of tourist-related growth can be seen in Figure 7.35. Careful study shows the old town, which lies below the castle headland at the eastern end of the Baie des Anges (Bay of Angels), from which the photograph was taken. In front of it is the Promenade des Anglais, which separates the shingle beaches from the hotels and residential apartment blocks that line much of its six kilometre length. On the slopes behind is the residential zone of villas, great residences

▲ **Figure 7.34**
The Negresco in Nice, on the tree-lined Promenade des Anglais. Built in 1912 its guests have since included the likes of Sir Winston Churchill, Charlie Chaplin, Edith Piaf, Picasso, Richard Burton and Elizabeth Taylor, and the Beatles. It is designated as a National Historic Monument and remains a major Riviera landmark.

▲ **Figure 7.35** Panorama of part of Nice

and apartments, which over time were extended higher up the slopes. They have replaced vineyards, olive groves and citrus fruit orchards on the lower slopes and the region's scrub vegetation known as *maquis* (a mixture of heather, gorse, wild flowers and fragrant herbs for which Provence is famous such as rosemary, thyme and basil) on the steeper land.

The spatial pattern displayed in the Riviera is a model for what has happened and is happening elsewhere along the Mediterranean coasts. Development takes place first in the littoral zone behind the beach, which forms the focus for new growth; it soon fills the low-lying land behind the shoreline, which, unlike in Languedoc, tends to be of limited width in many Mediterranean regions. Building then extends on to the slopes behind, leading to the abandonment of farming as orchards, vineyards and olive groves are ripped out by the developers. Some farmers make great profits from selling land. There is usually a mixture of private villas, apartments for the retired, timeshare accommodation and holiday lets. In what is considered to be the most favoured area, a zone of big villas, with private swimming pools and grounds bordered by cypress or eucalyptus trees, grows up for wealthy businessmen or the rich retired from any and all of the colder European countries to the north.

Life cycle of a tourist area

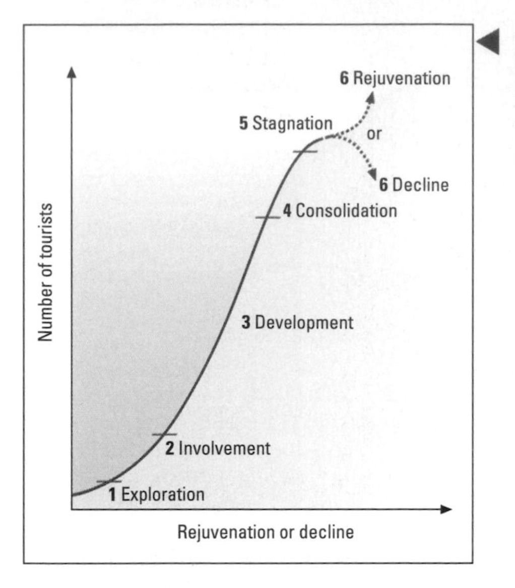

Figure 7.36 Butler's model for the life cycle of a tourist area or resort

Butler's model for the life cycle of a resort is shown in Figure 7.36.

- In Stage 1, something of tourist interest, such as scenic beauty or a heritage site, attracts a few visitors who explore the area, even though few or no facilities for tourists exist. By definition visitor numbers are small.
- In Stage 2 some facilities for tourists are provided; local inhabitants or the council, or a small organization, sometimes commercial and sometimes a trust, takes the initiative and becomes involved. It creates, sometimes unwittingly, the pre-conditions for the considerable increase (or 'take-off') in visitor numbers in Stage 3.
- In Stage 3 large numbers of visitors arrive and tourist facilities are greatly expanded in line with increased numbers. More of the investment and control of the commercial activities passes to organizations and companies from outside the area.
- By Stage 4 tourism has developed into a major part of the local economy, although new growth has slowed down. Some declining facilities are in need of renovation or replacement.
- In Stage 5 the peak is reached. Growth could be waning because the area is no longer at the height of fashion, or else its physical capacity might have been reached. Adjustments are likely to be needed to meet current recreational demands and how successful these are will determine what happens in the future.
- Through Stage 6 there are different possible routes. One is that sufficient, although similar, numbers continue to be attracted; it remains in touch with market needs and adapts, when necessary, to changing fashions. Another is that it is successful in targeting new or niche markets and grows with them, assuming that space exists for capacity to be increased. A third route is 'downhill', either because holiday trends over which it has no control change, or because it lacks the human and physical resources with which to convert and compete.

The British seaside resort

Based upon the model in Figure 7.36, a summary line for the rise and fall of British seaside resorts is given in Figure 7.37. The origins of most date back to Victorian times due to a combination of economic growth, social change and the transport revolution wrought by the railways. Outside periods of war, rising living standards encouraged the great expansion of coastal resorts such as Blackpool, Brighton, Southport, Bournemouth, Skegness, Great Yarmouth, Scarborough, plus Torquay and many other smaller resorts in Devon and a line of resorts along the coast of North Wales between Rhyl and Llandudno. The grand hotels, promenades and piers, and special features such as Blackpool Tower, date from the 100-year growth period between 1860 and 1960 (Figure 7.38).

However, from 1960 onwards economic and social changes increasingly switched the balance of advantage for coastal holidays away from British and towards Mediterranean resorts. Another transport revolution, this time the jet aircraft, allowed it to happen. Whilst it could be argued that British resorts were slow to spot the trend and to organize a response, they were competing against the geographical fact that summer weather in the Mediterranean region is warmer, sunnier and more reliable. As incomes from visitors declined, local authorities in coastal resorts struggled to maintain, never mind upgrade, the inherited infrastructure for tourism. Since then some resorts have been more successful than others at re-designing and re-packaging themselves.

Bournemouth invested heavily in facilities to enable it to become one of the country's leading conference centres. Its location on the south coast on the fringes of the South East region allowed it to expand established functions for retirement and commuting to London. It also helped its expansion in the higher education sector, partly supported by the growth of English language schools.

Opportunities for diversification in coastal towns in the north of England are limited by their location within the UK. While Blackpool is large enough to invest and to market itself quite openly as the traditional British seaside experience, smaller resorts have accepted that all they can do is to adapt as much as possible to the needs of day visitors principally drawn from the local area. Many have restored and refurbished sea fronts with the help of government and EU aid, so that at least the resorts are 'better looking' than they have been for many years.

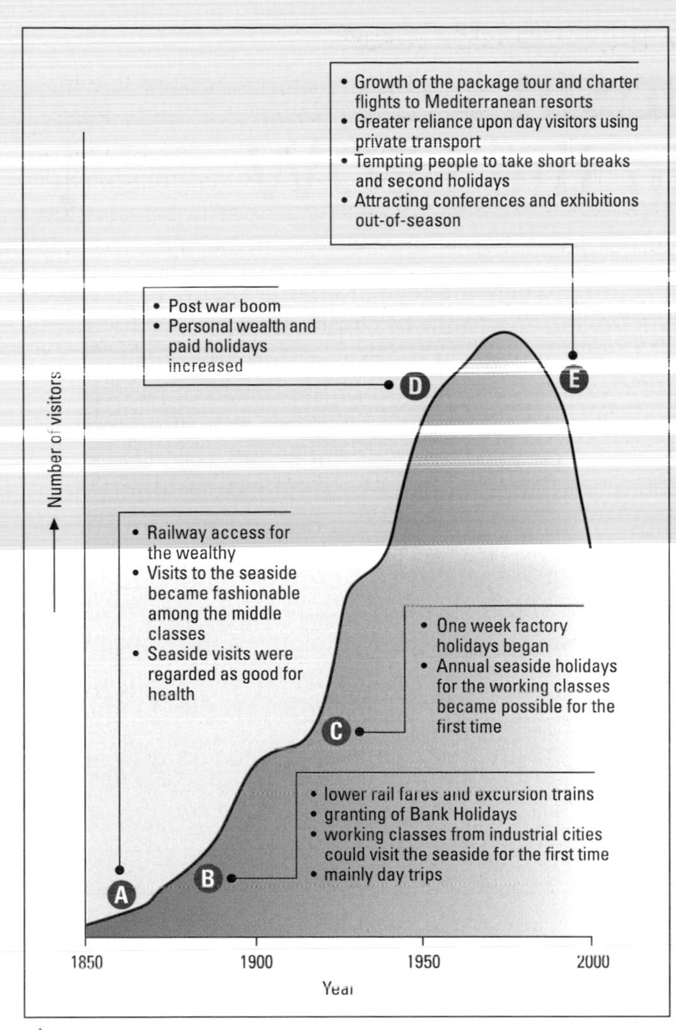

▲ **Figure 7.37** Summary of the life cycle of British seaside resorts

◀ **Figure 7.38** Postcard view of the sea front at Blackpool in 2000

▲ **Figure 7.39** The beach at Scheveningen, the main Dutch coastal resort, on a sunny Sunday in summer. In what sense is the busy scene misleading?

Questions

1 **a** Explain the meaning and usefulness of each of the labels for Stages 1–6 in a tourist area used in Figure 7.36.

b Outline how **i** British seaside holiday resorts and **ii** the French Riviera fit the life cycle model.

2 **a** Describe and give reasons for the sequence of changes, both temporal and spatial, in the French Riviera.

b Draw a labelled sketch based on Figure 7.35 to describe the spatial pattern of land uses in Nice.

c Why is the popularity of the French Riviera as a tourist destination undiminished, despite having a history of tourism extending back about 200 years?

d Study the photograph below (Figure 7.42) taken at Eze, east of Nice, which has experienced tourist related growth.

▲ **Figure 7.40** Eze, east of Nice

Make a careful analysis of what the photo shows.

3 **a** Outline what is likely to be included in 'urban tourism'.

b Account for the increase in 'city break' holidays taken by UK residents. Illustrate your answer by examples.

Recreation and tourism in the LEDW

Fashions are passed down from people in the MEDW to those in the LEDW. Increased incomes, especially in those Asian countries, which have enjoyed considerable economic growth in the last quarter of the twentieth century, have meant that tourist traffic has become a two-way movement. Visitors from Singapore, Taiwan and South Korea have boosted the incomes of neighbouring countries in Asia, while an increasing proportion of middle-class residents can afford visits to Europe and North America. Between the better developed South American countries there is considerable movement. Middle class and wealthy Argentines go on shopping holidays to Brazil when prices are lower there than they are at home as a result of currency fluctuations. Uruguay is a favourite destination for the annual holiday because the beaches at Punta del Este are better than most of those in Argentina. There are regular charter flights from Rio de Janeiro and São Paulo to Florida for visits to the theme parks. The growth of tourism within and outside LEDCs can be seen as part of the spread of western attitudes and values across cultures. It is often referred to as the 'westernization of the world' as societies adopt consumption patterns and lifestyles similar to those of people in North America and Western Europe.

More commonly the tourist flows are one way, from MEDCs to LEDCs, because leisure time for recreation and tourism remains predominantly a developed world phenomenon. Resources for international tourism are different from those needed for farming and industry and are quite widely available. One example of a country that has found a use for nature's gifts of sun, sand and sea is Mauritius. It has built a number of planned coastal resorts.

Mauritius: growth of tourism in a LEDC

Case Study

Figure 7.41 Mauritius

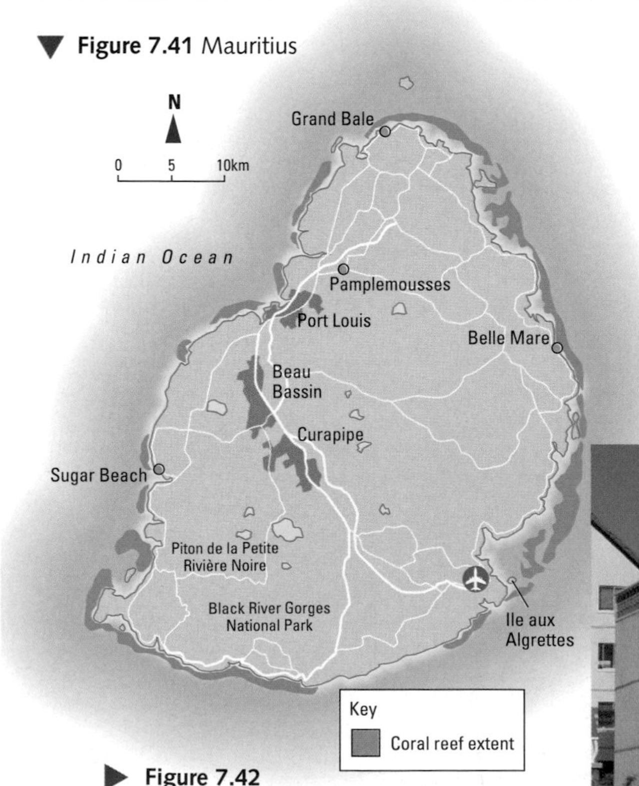

Figure 7.42
Beach side hotel in the north of Port Louis, one of the three locations in which most beach resorts are concentrated

Physical and human background

Mauritius is a volcanic island in the Indian Ocean lying about 800km from the east coast of Madagascar at latitude 20° south. Its population has climbed to 1.2 million to give it a density of over 600 per square kilometre, one of the highest in the world. Its cultural mix is dominated by people of Indian (about 70 per cent of the total), African and Chinese ancestries as well as French and British colonial elements. There is little inter-marriage or social mixing between the communities. There is unresolved tension between the Hindu majority and those of African origin and the previous good record of racial harmony was broken by riots, demonstrations and violence in 1999. The government recognizes that the political stability prior to the violence, in a country without an army, was the basis for economic growth. An arrangement was put in place after the elections in 2000 for a rotation of prime ministers so that for the first time the office can be occupied for a time by a non-Hindu.

For a long time the economy of Mauritius was heavily dependent upon the export of a single crop, sugar cane, which is still the dominant agricultural land use. There has since been diversification into clothing manufacture. Both, however, are heavily dependent upon continued access to EU markets, which is why a further broadening of the country's economic base is considered desirable. Expanding the service sector is seen as the best option. Growth of tourism is one aspect of this. For the future, new service industries such as offshore finance and information technology are being considered.

The national carrier Air Mauritius has weekly flights to many European destinations including London, Paris, Frankfurt, Rome, Vienna, Geneva and Brussels. Many European airlines, such as British Airways, Air France and Lufthansa, have at least one weekly flight and normally two or more. There are also direct connections to Asia (India, Malaysia, Singapore, Hong Kong and Indonesia), Australia and Africa (South Africa, Kenya and Zimbabwe). Main roads, which are paved, link all the settlement centres on the island.

Its attractiveness as a tourist destination is based upon a combination of fine beaches and tropical temperatures. The mainly sandy beaches are bordered by aquamarine lagoons and benefit from the shelter of coral reefs, which dissipate the force of the trade wind driven breakers before they reach the shoreline. Maximum temperatures remain in the hot but comfortable zone between 24 and 30°C all year; the daytime heat and humidity are tempered by sea breezes.

The most scenic part of the island is in the south west. It is possible to hike in the Black River Gorges National Park along forest tracks. The Rivière Noire lookout affords spectacular views of the Black River Gorge, the Rivière Noire Falls and the Piton de la Petite Rivière Noire. At 828m this is the highest point.

▼ **Figure 7.43** Adapted extract about Mauritius from *The Financial Times*, 18 December 2000

Development creating extra tensions

During the past 10 years tourism numbers to Mauritius have more than doubled, and almost 20,000 people are directly employed by the industry.

Unlike other African countries, the industry has seen considerable indigenous investment. 'Tourism here has generated an entrepreneurial spirit,' commented a tourism consultant.

As development continues that is described as 'slow and controlled' by the tourism minister, there are tensions. New luxury hotels have to be crammed in between existing hotels along the beach front. Plans to extend hotel facilities by building golf courses have encountered resistance. Hoteliers complain about the activities of beach hawkers. The traffic in the capital Port Louis is abominable. Comparatively high prices can only be justified by good facilities, high service standards and the peaceful ambience. Questions over the sustainability of the growth in tourism will not go away. However, there has to be a balance between development and the environment.

▼ **Figure 7.44** Tourist arrivals in Mauritius

	1996	1997	1998	1999
Europe	281,817	326,379	352,530	378,761
Africa	165,435	164,198	163,135	156,314
Asia	28,818	30,094	27,279	28,442
Oceania	8,144	9,896	9,349	8,503
America	4,265	5,509	5,842	5,831
Others	388	49	60	234
All countries	486,867	536,125	558,195	578,085

Questions

1 Draw a labelled sketch map which fits the title 'Tourist resources and facilities in Mauritius'.

2 Study Figure 7.45 below.

▼ **Figure 7.45** Climatic data for Port Louis

	J	F	M	A	M	J	J	A	S	O	N	D
Mean daily max. (°C)	30	29	29	28	26	24	24	24	25	27	28	29
Mean monthly rainfall (mm)	216	198	221	127	97	66	58	64	36	41	46	117
Average number of wet days (over 2.5mm)	12	11	11	9	7	6	6	6	4	4	4	7
Average hours of sun per day	8	8	7	8	8	7	7	7	8	9	9	9

a State the main features of the climate of Mauritius.
b Comment on its advantages and disadvantages for tourists visiting the country.

3 Outline the other (non-climatic) resources in Mauritius for tourism.

4 a Show, using a suitable technique of representation, the data for tourist arrivals in Mauritius for 1996 and 1999 from Figure 7.44.
b Describe what Figure 7.44 shows about tourist arrivals with respect to i numbers and ii origins.
c Explain why the government of Mauritius is keen to promote a growth in tourist numbers.
d Suggest reasons for the order of the different regions from which visitors arrived, as shown in Figure 7.44.

Factors affecting tourism

A country's potential to earn income from international tourism depends upon the combined operation of several factors.

Political stability

One of the basic requirements for tourism to flourish is political stability. Tourism does not sit comfortably with wars, civil unrest, frequent changes in government and a strong military presence. If a country has a primary resource with tremendous pulling power, tourists may continue to go even though the political situation is far from ideal. All that happens is numbers slow down or stop completely during periods of flare up, and then pick up again once the trouble subsides. Of all the African countries, Kenya has the longest tradition and best developed infrastructure for welcoming visitors to see big game in its natural setting on the East African savanna lands. It is fortunate in having sandy beaches as well on the shores of the Indian Ocean. Therefore it can offer two distinctly different types of holiday, which widens its appeal. Kenya suffered a sharp fall in tourist numbers in the mid-1990s (Figure 7.49). Since then the numbers have recovered as the main issues have faded.

When the Shining Path guerrillas in Peru were at their peak in the late 1980s and early 1990s, some of the Inca remains became off limits and visitor numbers collapsed, only to pick up again once the leader of the organization was arrested and most of the movement was crushed. However, some countries remain 'no-go' areas for tourists. The British Foreign and Commonwealth Office maintains a list of countries under three headings. There is one list for those countries where British nationals are advised not to travel to under any circumstances. On another list are countries to which travel is considered ill-advised unless for essential business. The third list names countries in which travel is not advised to named areas only within each country (Figure 7.50).

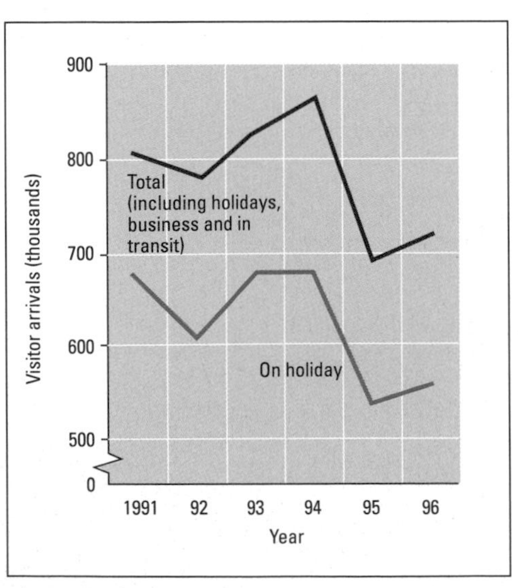

▲ **Figure 7.47** Visitor arrivals in Kenya

▼ **Figure 7.46** Adapted extract from *The Financial Times* 13/14 September 1997

Tourism hit as violence in Kenya flares

Kenya, voted 'top African destination' by world travel agents last year, is heading for a disastrous tourism year following months of pre-election unrest in the interior and the recent brutal killings on the coast. Industry experts said the sector, which should currently be enjoying its high season, has been hit by 'massive cancellations' since violence exploded in the area around Mombasa last month, and new bookings for winter holidays were coming in at a snail's pace. The Mombasa and Coast Tourist Association yesterday estimated arrivals for beach holidays had dropped by more than 50 per cent on last year.

The country's highest single foreign exchange earner, tourism, brings in about $400m a year and employs 150,000 people. After a promising start, 1997 was expected to be a good year for the industry, recovering from a two year slump caused by a flood of negative reports about Kenya and growing competition from South Africa. Instead, television images of riot police beating protesters in Kenyan cities began scaring visitors away in May, June and July. As these impressions faded, the murder of more than 50 'upcountry' settlers by gangs north and south of Mombasa cast a blight over Malindi and other coastal resorts, which normally draw 65 per cent of total tourist arrivals. This reinforced the growing impression abroad that Kenya is no longer safe.

Tour operators said that Italian and Spanish visitors appeared most worried, partly as a result of sensational reports by their local media, with cancellations running at between 80 and 90 per cent. Charter flights from Italy have declined from five to one a week and two hotels catering solely to the Italian market have closed. Figures for German and British visitors, the two biggest foreign groups coming to Kenya, are both 20 per cent down. The collapse in tourist receipts comes at a sensitive time. Because of concerns about top-level corruption, the IMF and World Bank suspended loans in July. A poor coffee harvest is threatening to cut tax revenue.

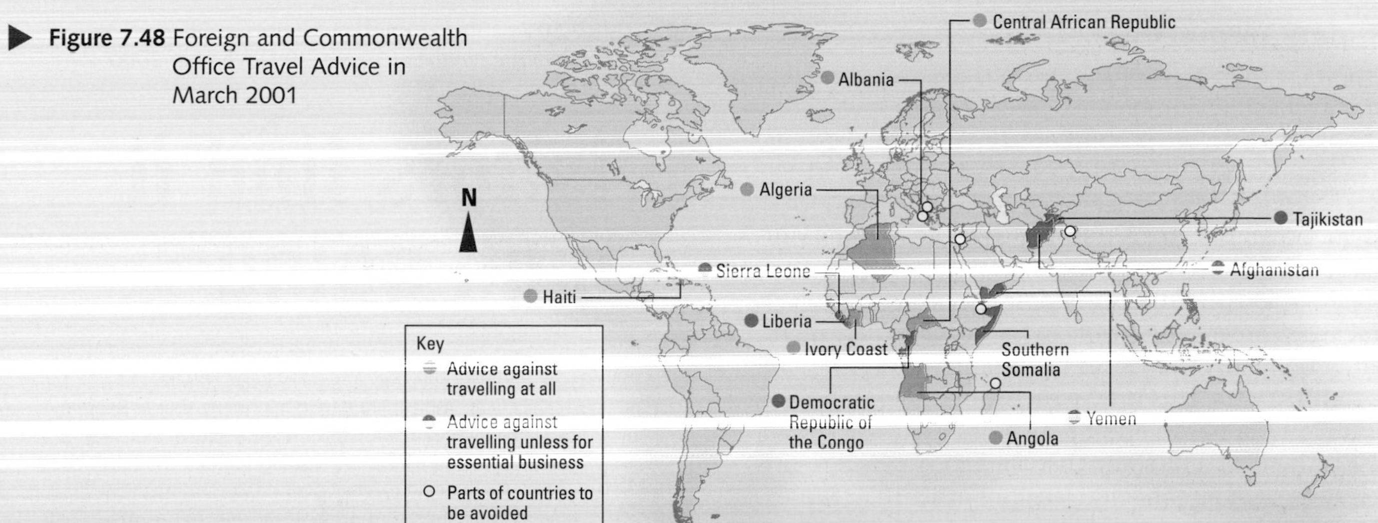

▶ **Figure 7.48** Foreign and Commonwealth Office Travel Advice in March 2001

Location

Location is another factor affecting tourist potential in LEDCs. Proximity to the source regions of tourists in MEDCs remains a great advantage, despite jet aircraft having the effect of 'shrinking the world'. Outside the USA the top two destinations for American tourists are the Caribbean and Mexico. For those living in the heavily urbanized north east of the USA from Washington northwards, where winters are cold, Caribbean islands offer winter sun and warmth, in a similar way that the Canary Islands do for dwellers in northern and central Europe (Figures 7.10 and 7.11). The main holiday choice in the Caribbean is between destination beach holidays and island-hopping cruises. For those living in the south-centre and west of the USA, Mexico offers a destination that is close, but very different culturally, as a result of significant pre-Columbian levels of settlement and colonization by the Spaniards. Many goods and services are cheaper in Mexico and the land border allows easy access.

▲ **Figure 7.49**
Remains of the city of the Mayas at Chitzen Itza, where their advanced civilization thrived between 300 and 900AD. They built huge monuments for religious observances. Although Mexico has many heritage sites, mass tourism is concentrated in beach resorts such as Acapulco and Cancun.

In contrast, most difficult of all to reach are some of the landlocked countries in Africa. Primary attractions need to be strong to attract tourists in any numbers. Burundi is a small country with beautiful mountain scenery, but its only unique tourist attraction is the source of the Nile. Since this is no more than a trickle and 'not exactly a riveting site' according to one guide book, few bothered to make the journey even before the massacres of 1994–96, especially as only two European and no American airlines flew there. Subsequent instability leaves it on the list of places British people were advised not to visit (Figure 7.48). Neighbouring Rwanda is one of the last remaining sanctuaries of mountain gorillas, which live on the bamboo and rainforest-covered slopes of the volcanic mountains that run along the border with the Democratic Republic of the Congo and Uganda. After years of poaching, the gorillas that remain are protected in the Parc National des Volcans. Reservations to see the gorillas have to be made in advance; the fee per visit is $126 for the compulsory guides and guards, on top of the transport costs for reaching the place where the gorillas can be found. Visits to see the gorillas are restricted to one hour. This is an example of a destination visited by interested travellers and not by tourists en masse. Many of the possible dangers and annoyances faced by visitors to Rwanda apply with equal force to a lot of other African countries (information box).

Dangers and annoyances for visitors to Rwanda

- *Night time curfews exist in many places and local soldiers have orders to shoot on sight.*
- *It is unsafe to walk off well-used tracks for danger of landmines after the upheavals of 1994.*
- *Frequent roadblocks and accompanying baggage searches take place along all main roads.*
- *Health treatment that could require a blood transfusion must be avoided as Aids is widespread.*
- *Precautions against malaria are essential.*

Secondary resources

An important third factor for tourism is secondary resource availability and quality. Only genuine travellers and those on a budget are content to endure standards of comfort significantly below those taken for granted in MEDCs. Even youthful budget travellers do not tend to like to go too long without running water and sanitation in their overnight accommodation, both of which are far from being standard fittings in houses in LEDCs, especially in rural areas. American tourists in particular expect high, bordering on luxury, standards of accommodation wherever they visit. This is why such a high proportion of the hotels on Caribbean islands are four or five star premises. These include some that are luxury beach resorts in their own right and include facilities other than those for water sports, such as tennis courts and golf courses. American hotel chains at the luxury end of the market, such as Sheraton, Marriott and Hilton, have invested heavily in Caribbean and Latin American destinations frequented by tourists. Whilst American multinationals are the dominant players in the international tourist market, those from other nations have their own spheres of influence. The Oberoi chain with its headquarters in India has recently added to the ranks of top of the market hotels in Mauritius by building what is described as an 'almost Disneyland creation' in Grand Baie. A visitor's first impression is of a jungle-temple with thatched roofs rather than of a hotel.

Without the supporting infrastructure of paved roads, reliable supplies of electricity, safe water and airports capable of handling modern jets large-scale tourism cannot flourish. Reasons for the lack or absence in their provision vary from place to place. Some places do not have primary resources of interest to tourists. Hot desert environments may be fascinating places geographically, but torrid heat by day and occasional sandstorms are real deterrents to the majority of tourists. Egypt beats most other desert countries in Africa and the Middle East in the tourist stakes because of the remains of 5,000 years of continuous human settlement in the Nile valley. Heritage sites abound for the full length of the valley and a Nile cruise makes an interesting way of seeing them, whereas desert nomads in Arabia left few traces of their occupation. Saudi Arabia has only recently relaxed its strict immigration rules to allow non-Muslim tourists to enter for the first time, provided that they are part of an organized group. With massive oil revenues, the Saudi government does not need the foreign exchange earnings that are highly prized by many LEDCs. Some governments are hostile to tourists due to concerns that damage to their society and culture will outweigh any economic gain. Others would love to increase the numbers, but are finding it a struggle to do so; Ghana is an example (Figure 7.50) A significant number of countries are simply too poor to invest in secondary resources for tourism.

▼ **Figure 7.50** Adapted extract on tourism in Ghana from *The Financial Times*, 29 November 2000

Visitors find it tough going

After a decline during the grim years [of political instability] of the 1970s, visitor numbers and receipts have been climbing slowly for more than a decade. In 2000 according to the Ghana Tourist Board the country will welcome about 400,000 foreign visitors, and they will provide $386m in foreign exchange, making tourism the third most important source of foreign currency after cocoa and gold. By 2010, the GTB expects more than 1m visitors and income of more than $1.5bn.

The figures do not tell the whole story. Many visitors are overseas Ghanaians returning home to see friends and relatives. However, the number of tourists from the USA and Europe is also rising steadily, boosted by Ghana's reputation for friendliness and political stability in an otherwise turbulent region. To encourage the growth of tourism visa regulations have been eased. The main tourist sites are west of Accra, the capital, and include the forested Kakum National Park and the coastal castles from which thousands of slaves were shipped across the Atlantic in the eighteenth and nineteenth centuries.

The obstacles to further growth are nevertheless daunting. One head of a big Accra travel agency, asked what was the main priority for increasing the tourist trade, sighed 'Roads'. Some roads are poorly maintained and travel to remote areas is a laborious exercise. Roads are frequently potholed and badly marked and driving standards are poor. Another travel agent wrote to the main daily newspaper to complain of police roadblocks that cause long tailbacks on the country's main arteries.

The obvious answer, especially for such destinations as the Mole National Park in the Northern Region, is internal flights, but there are none at present. 'We had one that crashed a few months ago and that kind of ended it,' said a GTB official. Perhaps the worst bottleneck is the shortage of adequate accommodation, although this issue is now being tackled with several hotel building and expansion projects in Accra and elsewhere. The high prices for flights from the USA and Europe is another disincentive to travellers, although prices are edging down. 'I'm convinced that in ten years' time Ghana will have huge numbers of tourists – assuming the place is stable,' said the head of Travel Ghana in the UK.

Questions

1 Draw up charts showing positive and negative factors for tourists visiting Ghana, Mauritius and Kenya.

2 **Investigation**

Either – Identify and discuss the factors which explain why Ghana receives more tourists than many other African countries, but fewer than Kenya and Mauritius.

Or – Identify and discuss the factors which explain why some LEDCs receive more tourist arrivals than others.

Tourism and the environment

Meeting increased leisure needs has implications for environments. Since the 1960s, periods of frenzied tourist developments have occurred. Some are still occurring along the coasts of Spain and other Mediterranean countries, as well as in certain locations with favourable conditions for growth in the LEDW. These include Thailand, Penang, Bali and Goa in Asia, Cancun in Mexico, and in coastal Kenya and the Gambia in Africa, to name but a few. What they have in common is that environmental impact studies preceding development were rarely conducted, and that much of the early development was uncontrolled and badly planned. Development was driven by the momentum for growth and by developers' desires for fast profits, without any thought being given for the future. Modern tourism does no more than scratch the edges of the world's surviving great areas of wilderness (Figure 4.71). However, many 'areas of undeveloped land still primarily shaped by the forces of nature', which cover smaller areas, are under threat, if not in the process of being physically damaged or destroyed. For instance, coastal mass tourism tends to be drawn towards areas where environments are fragile and habitats vulnerable.

▼ **Figure 7.51** Paradise lost

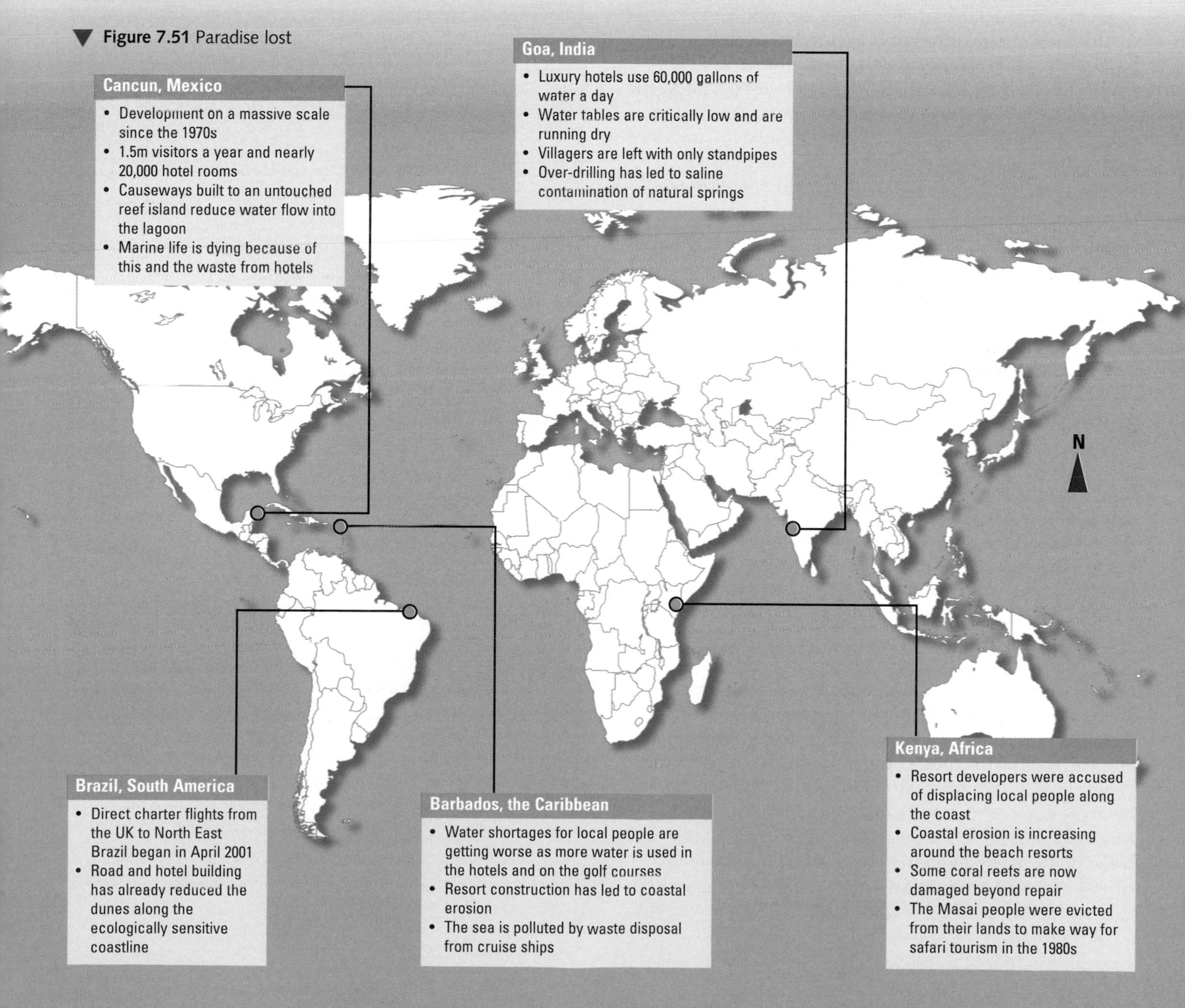

Developers like to place hotels as close to the shore as possible for sea views and easy access to the beach. However, this often ignores the geographical fact that the beach is a constantly changing landform (Chapter 2, page 20). Natural sand movements are altered by buildings and other tourist-related features, such as piers, jetties and harbours. Consequently erosion is encouraged along part or all of the shoreline due to the interruption of the natural movements of sea currents and tidal drift of sediment along the shore. Sand may even be taken from dunes for use during the construction phase. Tropical mangroves are often cleared and dredged to make way for marinas. Coral reefs are not touched by developers because they are known to be a great primary resource for tourism; however, few tourists appreciate that the surfaces of coral reefs are composed of living communities. Coral is easily damaged by snorkellers and divers when they stand on it, bump into it, or cling on to it. Cruise ships, yachts and glass-bottom boats send down anchors that dig into it. Whilst the impact of an individual novice diver or snorkeller is minimal, the cumulative impact of hundreds and thousands of divers over time has been immense, as the poor state of coral reefs off Mombasa in Kenya testifies. The Cayman Islands in the Caribbean are a popular stopping off point for cruise ships. As a result of regular and repeated anchoring in Georgetown harbour the coral reefs had already been reduced to rubble more than ten years ago.

Ever-increasing leisure demands are creating serious concerns about the future environmental capacity of some well-known, as well as new, destinations (Figure 7.56). Adequate water supplies is a world issue of increasing importance (Chapter 5, pages 192–195). Sufficient water may not exist for much longer in those resorts that are using up underground supplies quicker than they are being replaced. Spain's Balearic islands are a very popular destination with both Britons and Germans, but five of the seven underground springs in Ibiza have been so over-used that sea water has seeped in, making their water unsuitable for drinking any longer. On the mainland accelerated demand for water along the Mediterranean coast is creating the need for longer and longer pipelines from the wetter north. Now that the water table below Benidorm has fallen so low, some of the water comes from nearly 500km away.

Eco-tourism

Not all the environmental news is gloomy. Environments are being saved by a combination of tourism income, which generates the money needed for their protection and the motive for their conservation among governments and inhabitants in LEDCs. This is illustrated by extensions of the case studies for Mauritius and Costa Rica (pages 295–299), which include an examination of some of the environmental issues. It is impossible to reverse decades of environmental damage overnight and new issues arise that need to be addressed. However, the growing importance of leisure and tourism as an economic activity has made the governments of Mauritius and Costa Rica consider the environmental implications of their policies and actions in a manner not previously witnessed. Both nations are aware of the rising importance of 'eco-tourism', particularly for destinations that are not primarily orientated at the mass market.

Eco-tourism

Tourism that is environmentally sound, so that:

- *natural environments and wildlife are safeguarded*
- *natural resources are protected in a manner that is sustainable.*

Tourism that is socially sound, so that:

- *local communities are not damaged*
- *local people can participate and share in the financial benefits, in a manner which sustains community and culture.*

Eco-tourism should lead to sustainable tourism.

This is the concept that the needs of the present generation for leisure should be met without prejudicing the ability of future generations to meet their own leisure needs.

Questions

1 a Define the term 'wilderness'.

b Study the photographs of Antarctica and surrounding islands in Chapter 4 (Figures 4.1, 4.68, 4.77)

i State the photographic evidence that shows that Antarctica is a wilderness.

ii Is it correct to regard tourism to Antarctica as an example of eco-tourism? Explain your answer.

iii What risk assessment from tourism would you make for Antarctica compared with other activities that have taken, or are taking, place there?

2 a With the aid of Figure 7.56, describe the ways in which tourist growth and related developments cause environmental damage.

b Is the environmental damage likely to worsen with time? Explain your own views.

Mauritius: tourism and the environment

Case Study

Over the centuries humans have caused the destruction of many species of flora and fauna, the best known of which was the dodo, a large flightless pigeon already extinct by the end of the seventeenth century. Seafarers and colonists who reached this uninhabited island killed dodos and giant tortoises for food and cut down native trees to build ships and make furniture and to establish sugar cane plantations. Today less than two per cent of Mauritius is covered even partially by native forest.

▲ **Figure 7.52** A typical scene in the cultivated interior where the island's country roads are lined by fields of sugar cane.

However, in the last twenty years there has been a great change in attitude, helped by the knowledge that its tourism industry depends heavily on the island's international image as an Indian Ocean paradise. Species of birds that were almost extinct, such as the Mauritius Kestrel, pink pigeon and Echo Parakeet, have been saved at the eleventh hour. The coral island, Ile aux Aigrettes, is now managed by the MWF (Mauritian Wildlife Foundation) as an eco-tourism destination. A nursery financed by the World Bank, grows 45,000 native plants a year for replanting, while MWF workers are trapping and killing the remaining animals that are not indigenous to the island and uprooting invasive foreign plants such as the acacia. All of this is part of an attempt to return Ile aux Aigrettes as near as possible to its original state. If successful over the next fifteen to twenty years, this model will be extended to parts of the main island. Areas of forest would be cordoned off with rat-proof fences and overhanging branches would be cut to keep out monkeys; both species were introduced to Mauritius in the nineteenth century. Animals native to Mauritius could then live and breed in peace, free from the human-introduced predators.

There has also been damage to the marine environment, which is of even greater importance to tourist visitors. Some of the causes include disturbance from motorboats, fishermen and divers, as well as rising pollution from piping untreated sewage straight into the sea. Divers and snorkellers disturb delicate coral reefs, but most detrimental has been the collection of turtle shells and corals mainly for sale to tourists. Now tourists are being exhorted not to buy or take any of these. Big resort hotels are forced to incorporate their own treatment works into their construction plans. Under pressure from environmentalists, laws which have existed for many years are being enforced with greater vigour. One big hotel project on a small island in the Blue Bay Marine Park in the south of Mauritius was put on hold pending the publication of an environmental impact assessment. It had become clear that a boat landing site on the main island was actually going to be a marina. Sun International's plans to build a golf course on the Ile aux Cerfs also encountered resistance.

The changes in attitude reflect not only the growing awareness of the environmental consequences of uncontrolled tourist growth, but also the recognition that sustainable tourist growth and the maintenance of environmental quality go together.

Questions

1 a Outline the main environmental problems.
  b To what extent is tourism responsible?
  c Why is the government interested in tackling these problems?
  d Outline what is being done now and intended to be done in the future.

Costa Rica:

Case Study

growth of tourism in a LEDC and its effects

This tiny republic, about the size of Scotland, is sandwiched between Panama and Nicaragua across one of the narrowest parts of Central America. It is built around a central backbone of mountains, rising to almost 4,000m, and has lowlands on both sides, one bordering the Pacific Ocean and the other the Caribbean Sea. Tourist revenues, from over three-quarters of a million overseas visitors each year, are now Costa Rica's main source of foreign exchange. Some of the country's attractions for visitors are outlined in the booklet produced by the Costa Rica Tourist Board, an extract from which is reproduced in Figure 7.53.

▼ **Figure 7.53** Adapted extract from pamphlet produced by the Tourist Board of Costa Rica

No artificial ingredients

Thinking about taking a holiday? In Costa Rica we've got what you're looking for. Tree-lined tropical beaches whose warmth is exceeded only by the friendly people who live here, spectacular birds and flowers whose intense colours rival those of an erupting volcano, activities ranging from whitewater rafting and surfing to sport fishing and golf, and more than a thousand lodging options to choose from, everything from cosy bed-and-breakfasts to luxury five-star hotels. With so much variety there is guaranteed to be something to suit everyone's taste!

Costa Rica's stunning scenic heritage unfolds in an ever-changing panorama of steaming volcanoes, forested mountains, dramatic skies and bucolic countryside. Dark lowland jungles give way to rolling savannas; Pacific surf crashes against rocky headlands, in sharp contrast to the tranquility of the palm-fringed Caribbean beaches.

The climate is idyllic. In the lowlands, which are dry in the Pacific north west and humid elsewhere, day time temperatures range in the high twenties to mid-thirties °C. Usually at low to mid-twenties at middle elevations; the mercury can fall as low as five to the mid-teens at the top of the mountains. Within each elevational range, temperatures remain relatively constant year-round. Rainfall is subject to annual and regional patterns.

In Costa Rica, tropical nature has reached its greatest expression. Located in tropical latitudes, between the different biological influences of North and South America and bordered by two oceans, mountainous Costa Rica enjoys an immense diversity of climates and environmental regions. Twelve major life zones harbour an astounding amount of plant and animal life. While Costa Rica covers a mere 0.03 per cent of the planet's surface, the nation is endowed with over 5 per cent of all life forms on earth. Costa Ricans have preserved this invaluable biodiversity in protected areas covering fully one quarter of the land and organized into major units called Conservation Areas. No other country in the world has so much actively protected area per capita.

An impressive 36,447km of roads, plus well developed nature trail systems give easy access to every habitat and all but the most remote areas. You can drive to the very edge of a volcanic crater, through the heart of a mountain jungle, take an aerial tram ride in the rainforest canopy and soak up the sun on a deserted beach, all on the same day in all but the most remote areas.

Tortuguero National Park

- 11 distinct and diverse habitats
- 2000 species of plants
- 400 species of trees
- 57 species of amphibians, including smoky frogs, transparent glass frogs, poison dart frogs
- 111 species of reptiles, including four kinds of sea turtles
- 300 species of birds, including great green macaws, great curassows
- 60 species of mammals, including tapirs, jaguars, manatees
- 55 species of freshwater fish

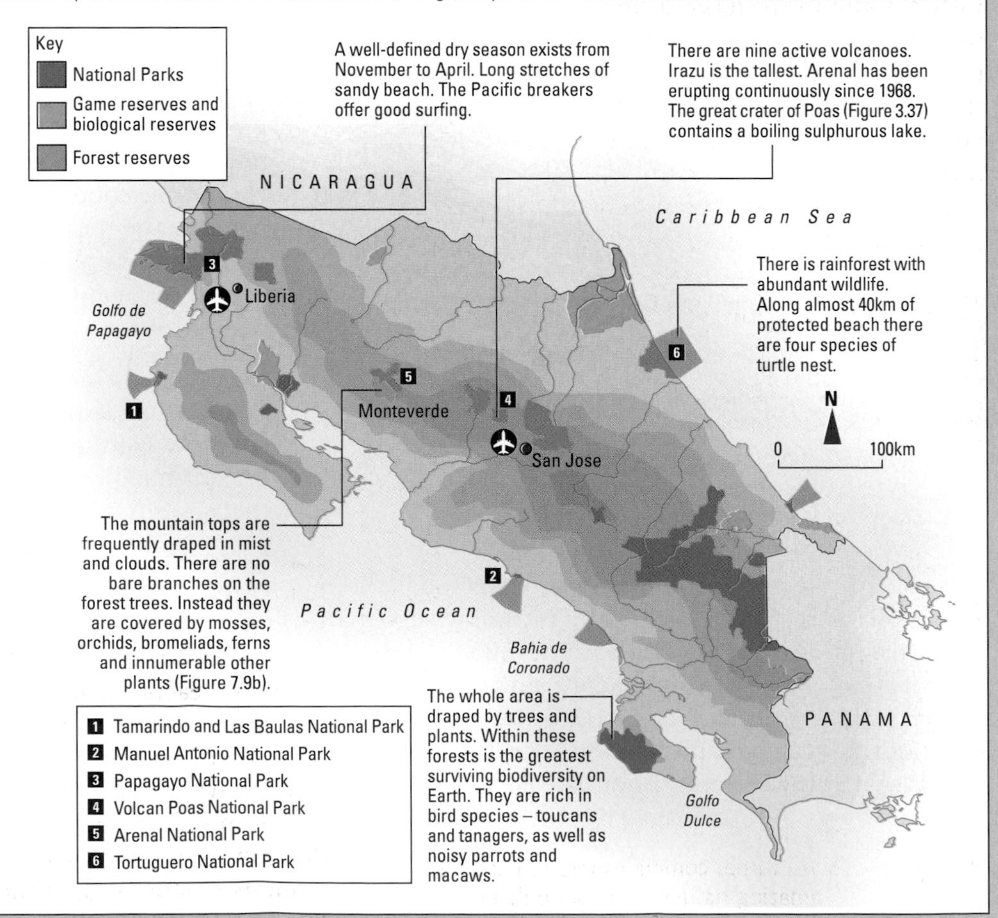

Conservation policy

Costa Rica has the best conservation system of all the countries in Central and South America. One quarter of the country is protected in some way as a result of the government engaging in an active policy of environmental protection since 1988. Full official protection is restricted to the 29 national parks which cover about 12 per cent of the country (Figure 7.53). An area of similar size consists of many buffer zones and forests in which no new development is allowed, as well as game and biological reservations, which are used for reafforestation, environmental projects and eco-tourism. However, there is considerable population pressure and a high demand for logs, so that despite all the environmental legislation and controls, deforestation continues, even though at a much reduced rate due to the controls now in place. Figure 7.54 shows how quickly the forests have been destroyed as a result of logging and clearance for agricultural land uses, such as in the area shown in the third map. Cattle ranching was just the latest agricultural activity established primarily to boost exports. Previously coffee growing was responsible for the disappearance of large areas of forest in the central and higher regions and banana plantations pushed back the jungle especially on the Caribbean lowlands. Tourism now provides an alternative and additional source of foreign exchange and the country has a growing international reputation for eco-tourism. Therefore the government is able to make a strong justification for conservation on economic as well as environmental grounds, which makes conservation easier to implement.

Before national parks were created and controls were strengthened there were many tourist abuses. In the 1970s thousands of leather-backed sea turtles, some weighing over one tonne, came ashore on the beach in the La Baula National Park. Groups of up to 100 tourists or more gathered around females as they laid their eggs; some even attempted to ride on their backs as they heaved themselves up and down the beach in an ungainly manner. By the mid-1990s only a few hundred turtles were using the beach. National Park rangers have been increased to deter both tourists and poachers; on egg-laying nights tourists are now confined to designated viewing platforms.

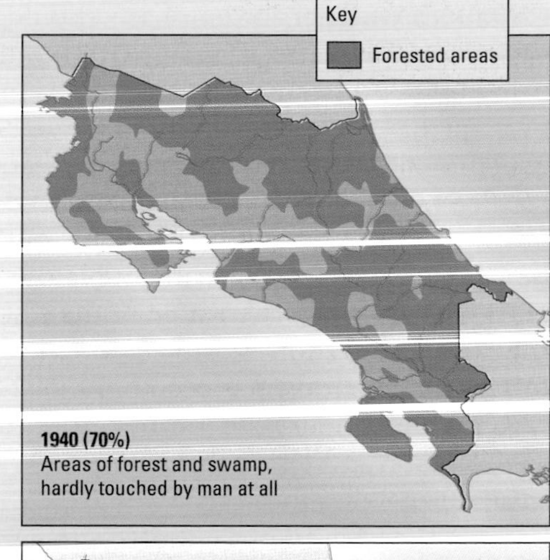

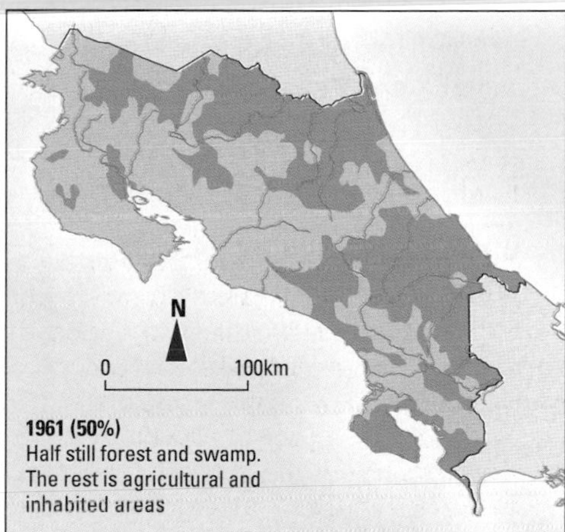

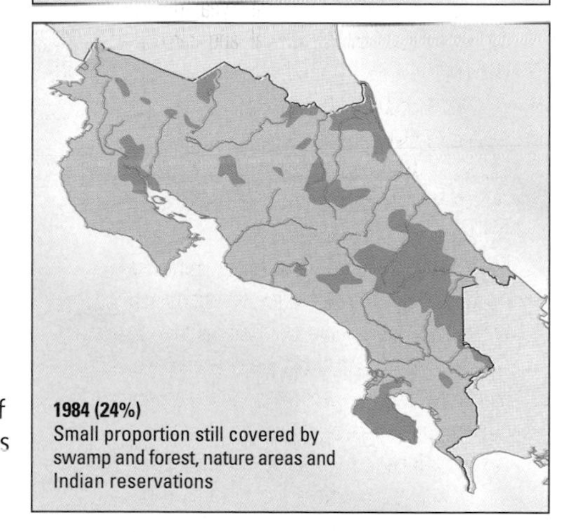

▶ **Figure 7.54** The extent of forested areas in Costa Rica 1940–84

▲ **Figure 7.55** Sea turtles coming ashore to nest; this amazing natural sight can only be witnessed on a few beaches in Costa Rica, Mexico and India.

Further south along the Pacific coast, visitor pressure was felt particularly strongly in the Manuel Antonio National Park. It teems with wildlife and is one of the last refuges of the rare squirrel monkey. The park's other attractions are splendid beaches, coral reefs and unusual coastal rock formations. It lies within easy reach for day visits from San Jose. By the middle of the 1990s the point had been reached where the survival of plant and animal life was at risk from visitor numbers. Birds and animals became more difficult to view and many people took no notice of requests to stop feeding the monkeys. In 1994 entrance fees to the park were raised and visitor numbers were restricted to a maximum of 800 per day.

Nevertheless there is still considerable political debate within Costa Rica whether the emphasis should be upon mass tourism or eco-tourism. Coastal hotels with hundreds of rooms are still being built. The major development is in the Pacific north west near the Bay of Papagayo. About 25 years ago the Costa Rican government began the Papagayo project; the government is leasing 4,000ha of state-owned land to developers along a 50km stretch of coastline. Phase one of the plan is for 15,000 new hotel rooms, which will double the number of bedrooms already available in the whole of the rest of the country. This is the largest single tourist project in Central America. A new international airport has been built near the city of Liberia to save the three-hour road journey from the main airport in San Jose. Supporters believe that this part of Costa Rica can become the 'Hawaii of Central America'. The plan has attracted a great deal of criticism. The developers have been accused of irregularities such as felling trees without permission, clearing mangroves and dredging the shoreline. The government defends their support of the project by arguing that large projects offer the greater prospects of attracting more inward foreign investment and larger numbers of overseas visitors, thereby generating more domestic employment.

▲ **Figure 7.56** Views of Tamarindo, a newly developing resort, in the Pacific north west
a The main (and only) road into the resort
b New tourist developments
c The beach at Tamarindo
d Bar on the beach

Equally there is considerable discussion as to whether the road to Monteverde and its cloud forest should be paved. The final link from the Pan-American highway, which runs north to south down the centre of the country from the capital city, takes a bone-shaking two hours along a potholed track (Figure 7.9a). Paving the road would allow day trippers from San Jose and therefore a considerable increase in visitor numbers. Some argue that the forested area is too small to cope with many more before the biodiversity is put at risk. Hoteliers in Monteverde are not keen on the idea of improvement as the number of visitors staying one or more nights would fall.

As tourism has gone up market to attract overseas visitors, the majority of whom come from the USA and Canada, fewer and fewer Costa Ricans are able to afford to take holidays themselves. Hotel and national park entry prices are prohibitive in relation to local wage levels. Figure 7.57 shows what happened to the number of national visitors to Tortuguero National Park after the canal link to the village of Tortuguero was damaged by an earthquake in 1991 making access more difficult. When the National Park was created in 1975 the two main livelihoods of the villagers, hunting turtles and working in the timber industry, came to an end. The village was only stopped from dying by the growth of national tourism; some of the local people offered simple accommodation, others supplied food and a small souvenir shop was opened. Since 1991 the situation has changed; tour operators have taken over, opening comfortable hotels aimed at overseas visitors. They are placed on the opposite side of the canal to the village and are self-contained, which limits commercial opportunities for the villagers. The hotels employ some villagers, but many of the staff are brought in from San Jose and elsewhere.

▲ **Figure 7.59**
Confluence of streams on the Caribbean lowlands in Costa Rica. One stream looks heavily polluted. A likely first reaction would be to blame people for it. However, the pollution is due to natural causes. The stream on the left drains from one of the country's nine active volcanoes and is discoloured by its high sulphur levels.

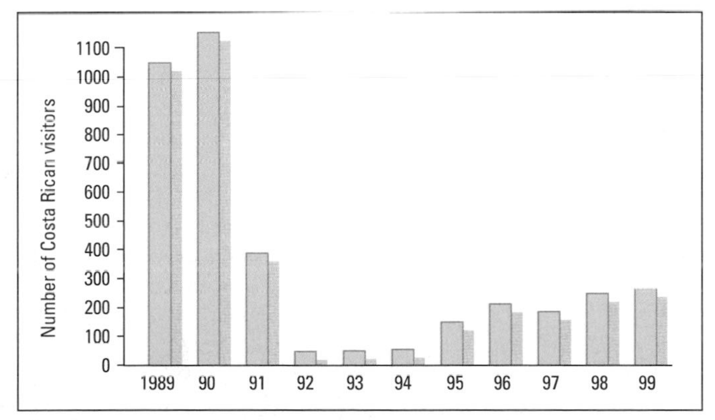

▲ **Figure 7.57** Number of Costa Ricans visiting Tortuguero

▲ **Figure 7.58** The village shop in Tortuguero targets passing tourist trade.

Questions

1 **a** Describe the attractions of Costa Rica for tourists using the following headings:
i scenic, **ii** ecological, **iii** climatic, **iv** provision of secondary resources.
b Draw a labelled sketch map with the title 'Costa Rica – natural resources of great variety'

2 Figure 7.53 – Costa Rica 'No artificial ingredients' – is an abridged version of a pamphlet produced by the Tourist Board of Costa Rica. Comment on the choice and suitability of this title by the Tourist Board.

3 **a** Assemble the evidence which supports each of the following opinions.
'Costa Rica is an eco-friendly country destination for tourists.'
'The environmentally friendly international image of Costa Rica is misleading.'
b What problems in implementing eco-friendly ideas and management are highlighted by a study of Costa Rica?
c Make a study of Tamarindo (Figure 7.56).
i Describe the changes taking place there.
ii Suggest reasons for them.
iii State and justify the likely position of Tamarindo in the model for the life cycle of a resort (Figure 7.36).

The growth of national parks

Even before the modern concepts of sustainable, green and eco-tourism were formulated, some tourist locations were already being managed to preserve the rural environment from visitor pressure, whilst at the same time allowing people to enjoy the countryside. In the UK the creation of the English national parks (Figure 7.19) dates back to the National Parks and Access to the Countryside Act of 1949, but it was not a new idea. The Yellowstone Park in the USA, established in 1872, was the world's first national park. The land in this and other national parks in the Rockies was at first regarded as a national playground within which almost unrestricted access for visitors was allowed. However, improved personal mobility meant that Yellowstone and its geysers (including Old Faithful), hot springs (Figure 3.38), and famous wild life inhabitants, notably bears and buffalo (Figure 7.60), also became one of the world's first tourist honeypots. Visitor growth in the parks forced their re-classification as areas of natural wildernesses in the 1960s. To maintain the wilderness areas in the face of the relentless rising tide of visitors, more and more restrictions were placed on visitor movements, which were enforced by park rangers. At peak times when the Yellowstone Park is full the rangers close the gates. Fees charged for entry to the parks offset the costs of management. Management is not as easy in the UK where people live within the National Parks and they lie within easy reach of many densely populated urban areas. It is impossible to prevent some conflicts of interest from arising, either between local people and visitors or between different groups of visitors, because uses and users cannot easily be restricted to certain areas by zoning. Footpath erosion is a widespread environmental problem and a clear sign of visitor pressure; however, maintenance strategies are in place to deal with it in all the parks (page 305).

Figure 7.60
Dawn grazing by a buffalo in one of the strictly limited number of accommodation sites allowed within the Yellowstone Park.

The Lake District: a UK National Park

Case Study

Basic details

- *Area – 230,000ha (the largest National Park)*
- *Population – 42,000 (the largest number of inhabitants)*
- *Visitors – 12–16 million per year (2nd after the Peak District)*
- *Visitor beds – about 10,000 (hotels, guest houses, farms and time share)*
- *Transport – 90% come by car*
- *Tourist employment – about 20,000 directly employed (full and part time) plus a similar number in indirect employment; an estimated 50 per cent of farms have some visitor income.*
- *Relief – contains England's highest mountains (Scafell Pike, Helvellyn and Skiddaw)*
- *Drainage – 16 large glacial lakes and many smaller ones*
- *Main towns – Keswick, Windermere and Ambleside*

Figure 7.61 The Lake District

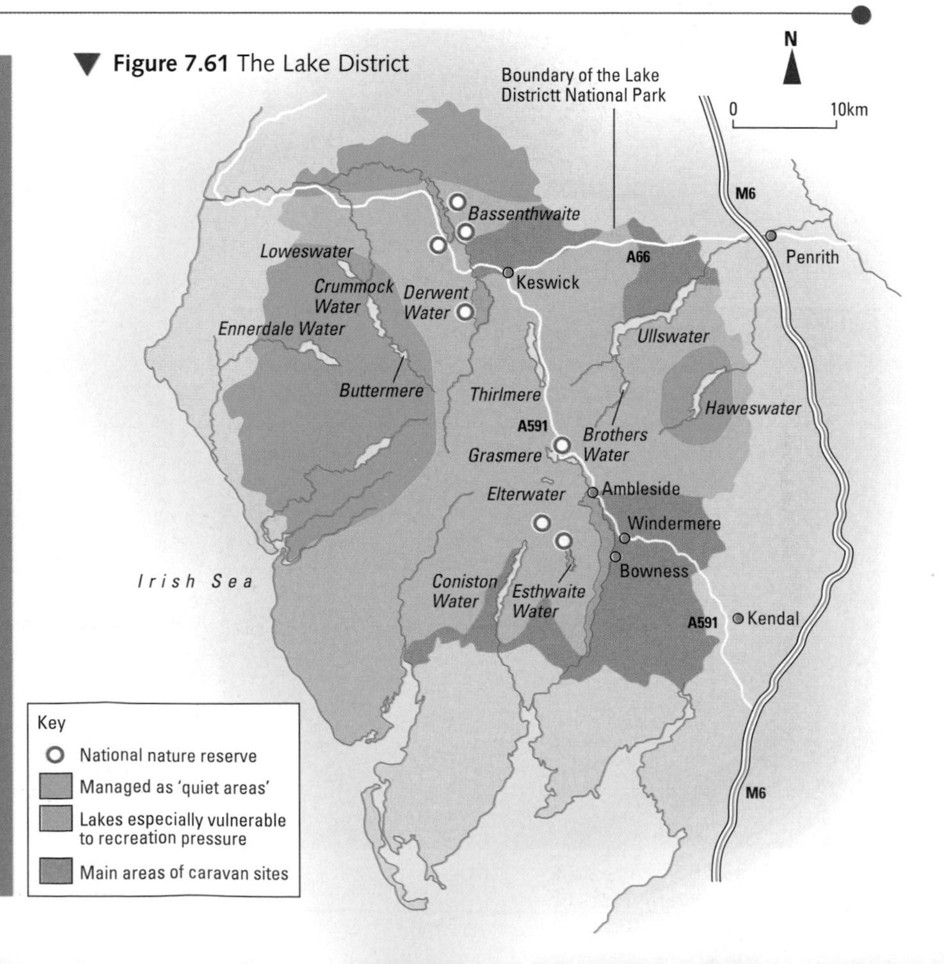

Figure 7.63 Causal factors of footpath erosion. This adverse environmental effect is highly concentrated in certain locations, particularly along lake shores. It is most noticeable on the landscape up the mountain sides and along the ridge tops in the central lakes region, such as in the areas covered by the OS map (Figure 4.78)

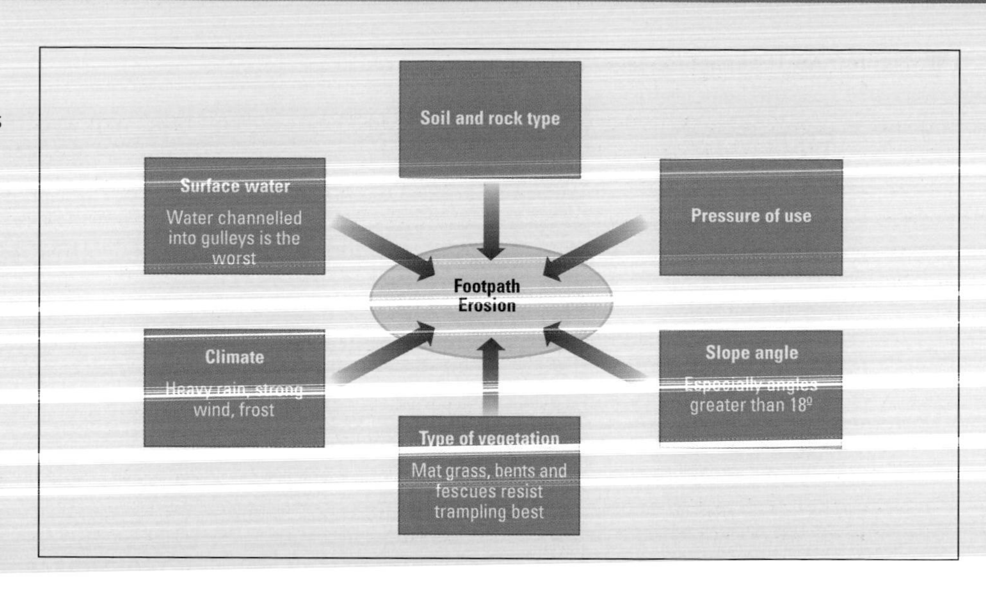

Figure 7.62 Lake Windermere

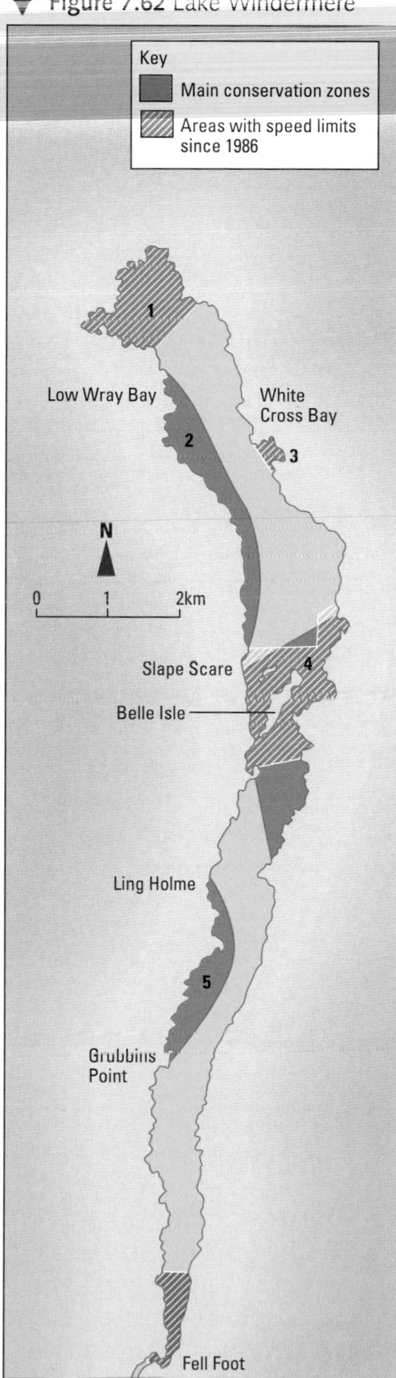

Figure 7.64 Stages in footpath erosion

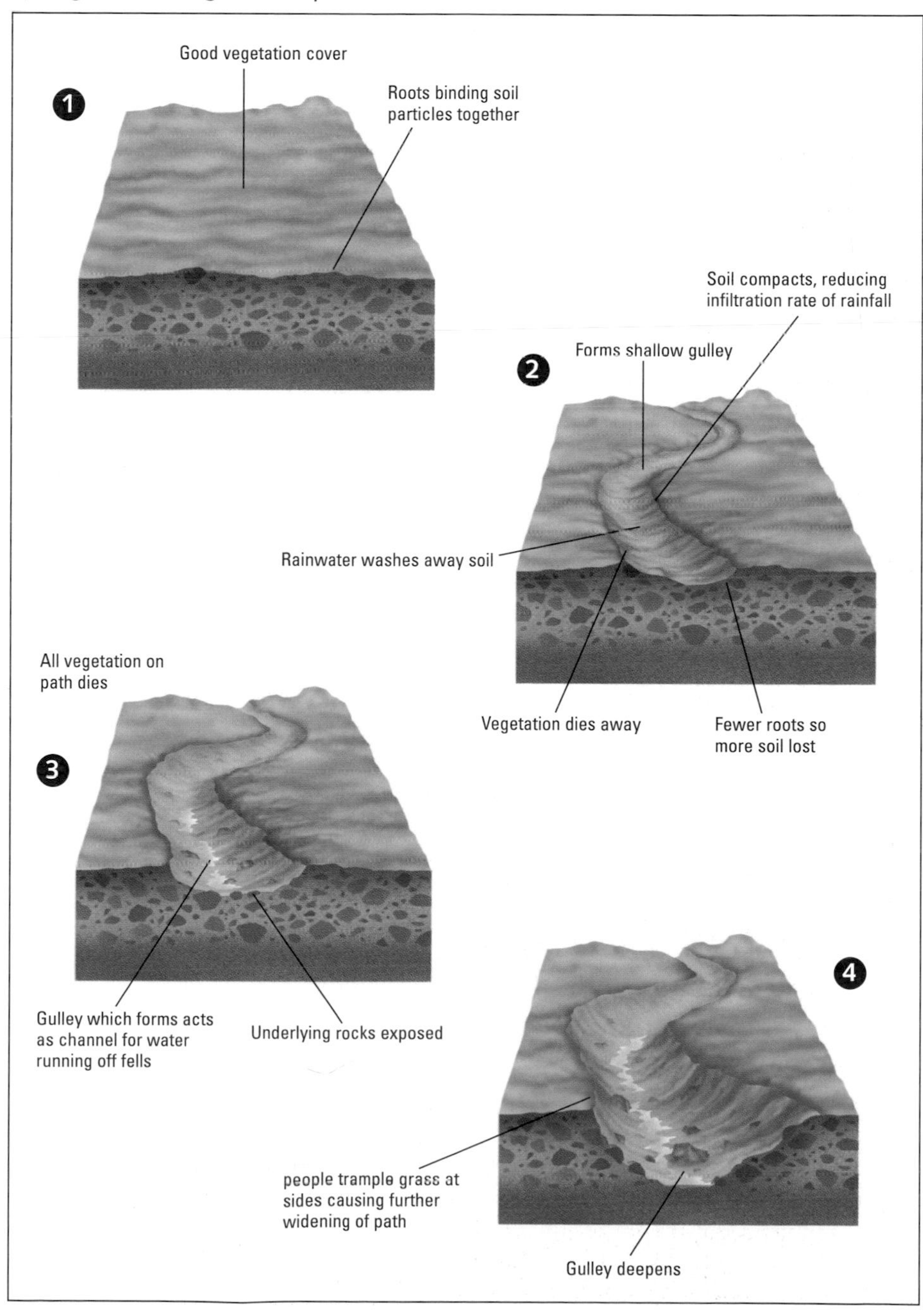

▼ **Figure 7.65** The main management policies employed in the Lake District National Park

1 Zone the park

The purpose is to reduce conflicts of use by:

- setting aside some parts as 'quiet areas' for those wishing to undertake peaceful pursuits such as walking. Increasing access by foot at the expense of the car in the northern and western parts.
- concentrating caravan sites in the southern and north-eastern parts of the park, closest to the access routes.
- allowing motorized boats only on the larger lakes. Big lakes such as Windermere have a management plan, under which certain areas are protected as nature conservation zones; zones with restricted speed limits were established to stop power boats and water skiing.

2 Reduce visitor pressures in honeypot locations in the centre of the park*, such as Windermere and Ambleside, by:*

- promoting the scenic and visitor attractions of the west coast, which lies outside the park.
- advertising out-of-season breaks.

3 Direct visitors along alternative routes; repair and maintain the footpaths through:

- drainage – place small drainage channels along the path side so that rainwater is channelled away more quickly
- path construction, using techniques such as:
  - pitching – sinking stones into the path so that only the tops show to give a hard surface
  - matting – stabilizing the path over boggy ground.
- path repairs, using methods such as:
  - levelling off the scar and the banks on its sides
  - re-seeding with a grass mixture of mat grasses and fescues, which better resist the effects of trampling
  - closing the path with a temporary diversion to allow time for vegetation recovery.

Questions

1 a Using the Discovery Tourist map in Figure 4.79, describe the main tourist resources of the Lake District under the headings **i** primary and **ii** secondary resources.

  b On a labelled sketch map, outline the main features of their distribution.

  c Identify the corridors of greatest visitor movements and the areas of greatest tourist pressure.

  d Suggest reasons for the uneven spatial distribution of visitors.

2 Refer to the OS map in Figure 4.78.

  a Identify and describe the type and location of attractions for tourists shown.

  b Comment on the likely differences between valley floor and mountain tourism for the area shown in the extract.

  c The footpath on the top of Helvellyn is subject to erosion. With the help of map evidence, discuss the physical factors likely to be responsible for causing this erosion.

3 a Give reasons why management and stewardship are essential in the Lake District National Park.

  b Evaluate the likely success of the main management policies employed.

Protected areas within the LEDW

Some countries in the LEDW employ the same strategies to ensure that some of the world's most scenic or ecologically significant places within their stewardship gain the protection they need. Ecuador, although one of the smallest and least wealthy of the South American republics, has maintained an effective management regime over the Galapagos Islands (Figures 7.13 and 7.20), restricting the number of residents allowed, controlling visitor numbers and walking routes, within a regulatory framework that is enforced. The continued healthy level of income receipts from tourism shows the benefit of long-term sustainable stewardship. Smaller protected areas around individual scenic features, such as the Iguacu Falls, Brazil (Figures 1.1a and 7.1), can be National Parks, or else one of the smaller scale designations that include reserves, national monuments or merely protected areas.

Tourism and development

Cost-benefit analyses of tourism can be made using a variety of scales from local, regional, national to global. Many elements in the equation are difficult to quantify, which makes reaching a meaningful overall assessment difficult. The outline for what might be included in a cost-benefit analysis of a local or regional area of countryside in the UK is given in Figure 7.66. Countryside tourism is a significant growth sector within internal tourism in the UK.

Cost-benefit analysis in UK rural locations

Rural communities remain bastions of tradition for longer than those in urban areas; they are also small in scale so that a small number of new arrivals makes a higher proportional difference. In some rural locations, which have become honeypots for urban visitors, tourism is like a monster with the potential to crush whole local communities. Farmers and villagers were often slow to realize the potential for income from visitors; outsiders may jump in before they do and cream off the most lucrative elements of the visitor business. A high percentage of tourism-related businesses are owned and managed by outsiders to a rural area. In turn this means that more of the profits and gains are withdrawn from the local area. Some in the rural community are in a better position than others to make money out of tourism, which results in the traditional earnings structure being broken down. Greater disparities in rural incomes emerge and, as a rule, money divides rather than unites.

Congestion, from traffic and from parking within the settlements and on the often narrow roads leading in and out from them, is frequently a major issue, as is housing. Tourism greatly increases the demand for accommodation within an area. Although rural depopulation and accompanying rural to urban migration initially liberated some old housing stock, planning restrictions on new building in rural and greenfield locations have sharpened up the competition. Demands on housing come from a mixture of needs – holiday accommodation, second homes and houses for retirement. The purchasers are typically from urban areas, more accustomed to metropolitan than country prices, and they push property prices upwards, out of the reach of those in lower-paid rural, primary and service occupations. Houses in some of the most popular destinations are occupied for only a tiny fraction of the year and the in-comers contribute little economically or socially to the village communities in which they lie.

▼ **Figure 7.66** Cost-benefit analysis of tourism in rural areas of the UK

Tourism effect	*Cost*	*Benefit*
Environment	• Physical damage, e.g. footpath erosion • Disturbance and loss of wildlife habitats for flora and fauna • Air and ground pollution from traffic • Pressure for development of tourist facilities • Resulting noise and visual pollution	• Protection for and conservation of landscapes and wildlife • Greater awareness of the value of landscapes and heritage • Redundant buildings that are landscape eyesores, such as barns and farms, are renovated and returned to use
Economic	• Provision of the new infrastructure • Repair of damage from visitors, e.g. to footpaths, fences and dry stone walls • Outside investors withdraw profits • Increases in house prices and council taxes	• Diversification of the rural economy away from farming as the sole activity • More jobs and higher rural incomes • Some of the new infrastructure is useful to local people • Threshold numbers needed for the economic survival of rural services such as shop, post office and pub are reached
Social	• Change and decline in local traditions and way of life • Loss of the local community as outsiders arrive • Shortage of housing at affordable prices • Conflicts between residents and visitors • Influx of outsiders (temporary and permanent)	• Influx of newcomers stimulates activities and brings new ideas • Local customs and traditions can be enhanced by responding to visitor needs, e.g. for crafts and produce • Young people are no longer forced to leave in search of work

Tourism often brings the incentive and generates the cash needed for protecting the landscape, for which money would not normally be available from elsewhere. The entry fees to parks and historic buildings, and profits from museums and associated gift shops, provides the income to fund the maintenance of footpaths and the fabric of buildings, as well as grounds and surrounding parks. A significant proportion of the UK is protected in some way (Figure 7.19) either as National Parks or by some other designations that are used to cover many different types of landscape. Infrastructural improvements, undertaken specifically for tourists such as paving roads or improving the sewage services, are often of long-term benefit to local residents. Some small settlements in remote rural areas, previously almost threatened by extinction, have been given a lifeline to survival by the increase in tourism. Even though tourism is a highly seasonal activity, it returns life to the countryside for at least part of the year, and some areas are no longer automatically drained of all their young people once they reach working age.

For local people judging whether benefits outweigh costs in their area it is often a highly charged personal judgement, controlled by the individual's circumstances and interests. In some locations the large numbers of tourists fuel local antagonism towards visitors; in others it may be more to do with the type of visitor, especially if their presence causes frequent bouts of rowdy behaviour. However, elsewhere the local economy has become so dependent on visitors, with almost everyone involved directly or indirectly in the industry, that large numbers of visitors are seen as healthy and a requirement for continued prosperity. Certainly in this era of declining farm incomes, and as UK farming suffers from one crisis after another, the economic importance of tourism to rural areas is becoming more generally understood. Surveys have shown that up to one quarter of UK farms gain some income from leisure activities. However, this proportion is still lower than in the Alpine areas of Switzerland and Austria, which has been a concentrated tourism zone for even longer and where there are high tourist seasons in both summer and winter. Mountainous and upland areas that are marginal for farming are usually the areas that are most attractive to tourists. As the CAP is gradually reformed, greater emphasis is being placed upon the stewardship of rural areas at the expense of food output; subsidies already exist for good management of land and countryside (Chapter 5 page 211).

Cost benefit analysis in the LEDW

A cost-benefit analysis of rural areas undertaken in the LEDW would include many issues that are similar, though social costs from the loss or dilution of local cultures and traditions would be more prominent. The basic reason for this is clear enough. There is a much wider gulf in cultural values, attitudes and socio-economic status between visitors from a developed world background and those living in rural areas of LEDCs, where existence is typically dominated by survival. Tourism forces 'aliens' upon people living in some of the world's most remote places. Some are less affected, for example Islamic cultures are very strong and are able to resist the onslaught from direct contact with western culture. International visitors to China and India, which together have more than one third of the people in the world, are too few in proportional terms to pose a threat to local cultures and ways of life. Elsewhere local cultures are less resilient. In most places the ordered structure of tribal societies and indigenous cultures relies upon the maintenance of a closed community; they are fragile and easily damaged by outside contacts to the point where they are never the same again. Tourists are fascinated by observing and photographing unfamiliar cultural scenes, but they speed up, albeit often inadvertently, the rate at which the cultural change and loss is already occurring. It must be stressed, however, that tourism is not uniquely responsible for doing this. The same has been happening to indigenous peoples for decades (Chapter 4 page 166).

Figure 7.67a Street market in La Paz for local people, but there is already a separate tourist-orientated part higher up the street.

Figure 7.67b Indian ladies daily bring llamas into the central square in Cuzco and tourists pay for taking photographs. A good source of income or a sign of cultural decline?

At the national level, a cost-benefit analysis for large-scale (or mass) tourism in LEDCs brings in a broader range of effects (Figure 7.68). While there is considerable overlap with the environmental and social effects already mentioned, economic effects carry more weight at country level. The success of Spain and its Mediterranean neighbours in Europe in the 1960s spurred many developing countries to contemplate tourism as a path to economic development. Some of the world's small island countries, like many in the Caribbean, have almost a mono-economic dependence upon tourism. If conditions in a country are conducive to tourist growth, mass tourism offers an alternative route to manufacturing that can lead to the 'take off' stage in Rostow's model of economic development (**AS Level Geography** page 230). For small countries with a home market of limited size, and for those countries without significant quantities of natural mineral resources, tourism may be the only possible route to development. Although there are inevitable fluctuations in numbers of international tourists crossing the globe, the general trend is that numbers are increasing. Healthy returns from investment are much more likely to be achieved on the back of a rising market.

If all goes well, tourism can contribute to increased government revenue, foreign exchange earnings, gross domestic product and employment, accompanied by accelerated investment in services and infrastructure leading to modernization, as the 'tourist tree' in Figure 7.69 shows. These results arise if a multiplier effect sets in, by which the growth of one activity (in this case tourism) directly or indirectly triggers off additional economic activities, which in turn generate new employment opportunities. Further likely consequences are social benefits leading to significant improvements in the quality of life for the majority.

▼ **Figure 7.68** Cost-benefit analysis of large-scale tourism in a LEDC

Tourism effect	*Cost*	*Benefit*
Environment	• Building work destroys natural environments and wildlife habitats, especially in marine locations. • Infrastructure work, like obtaining water supplies, may have wider spatial effects on other areas. • Areas of concentrated development lead to air, land and water pollution. • Modern 'concrete jungles' make a poor match with local traditional architecture.	• Undeveloped areas of mountain, forest, wildlife and marine life are re-appraised and begin to be viewed as valuable natural resources. • National Parks and other categories of protected areas are established because growing tourist interest has stimulated conservation (sometimes for the first time). • Environmental legislation is tightened up and enforced more vigorously. • The value of heritage survivals, such as historic buildings and monuments, is increased and they are more likely to be retained and maintained.
Economic	• Heavy investment in infrastructure, such as airports and roads, is essential, which increases the debt burden and reliance on other countries or multinationals. • Investment is diverted away from other sectors of the economy other areas of the country, some of which would benefit everyone such as health and education. • Benefits from the investment and tourist growth may not spread to other parts of the country, leaving one area advancing and others lagging behind. • There is leakage (see page 000): when controlled by multinationals, profits are withdrawn from the country and foreign personnel dominate higher paid managerial positions. • Labour demands are seasonal and many of the jobs created are unskilled and low paid. • Visitor numbers fluctuate greatly, sometimes for reasons over which the receiving country has no control, such as recession and changes in fashion in the country of origin or wars and political instability in neighbouring countries.	• Direct government income is earned from taxing tourists through visa fees, tourist taxes in hotels and restaurants, entry fees and airport departure taxes, etc. • The GDP is increased by the addition of another productive sector and by the employment that stems from it (both direct and indirect, formal and informal). • Economic activity in other sectors is stimulated, e.g. primary with demand for food and raw materials, secondary with a boost for making craft goods and tertiary with shops, markets and stalls. • Visitors from other countries are a source of foreign exchange for the national economy (hard currency which can be used to purchase goods and services from overseas), which provides an invisible source of income. • New infrastructure and facilities funded for tourism may also be useful to and stimulate the growth of other economic activities (as part of a multiplier effect).
Social	• Most (if not all) signs of indigenous culture and traditional ways of life soon disappear in areas of large-scale tourism. • The breakdown of the family unit becomes more likely as younger age groups adopt the imported culture more readily than the older age groups. • Noticeable differences in wealth develop between members of the local community, which causes tensions and speeds up loss of community. • The risk of local people suffering exploitation from prostitution and an organized sex industry considerably increases. • Ill-effects from the presence of outsiders such as crime, drugs and the risk of HIV infection increase in line with the size of the new development.	• Local people can gain direct benefits from some infrastructure improvements funded for tourism, such as clean water supply, sewage works and clinics, which improves their quality of life. • The government is more likely to invest in social projects such as schools and people can more readily appreciate the usefulness of an education. • The role and status of women in the local community can be improved, which has other knock-on benefits (such as reducing the birth rate – see page 000). • A flow of ideas is set up by contacts with people from other places, which may lead to elements of their life and culture being enriched. • It may encourage retention of the indigenous culture if that is what tourists visiting wish to see, e.g. folklore shows and festivals.

▼ **Figure 7.69** The tourist tree leading to increased economic growth and development

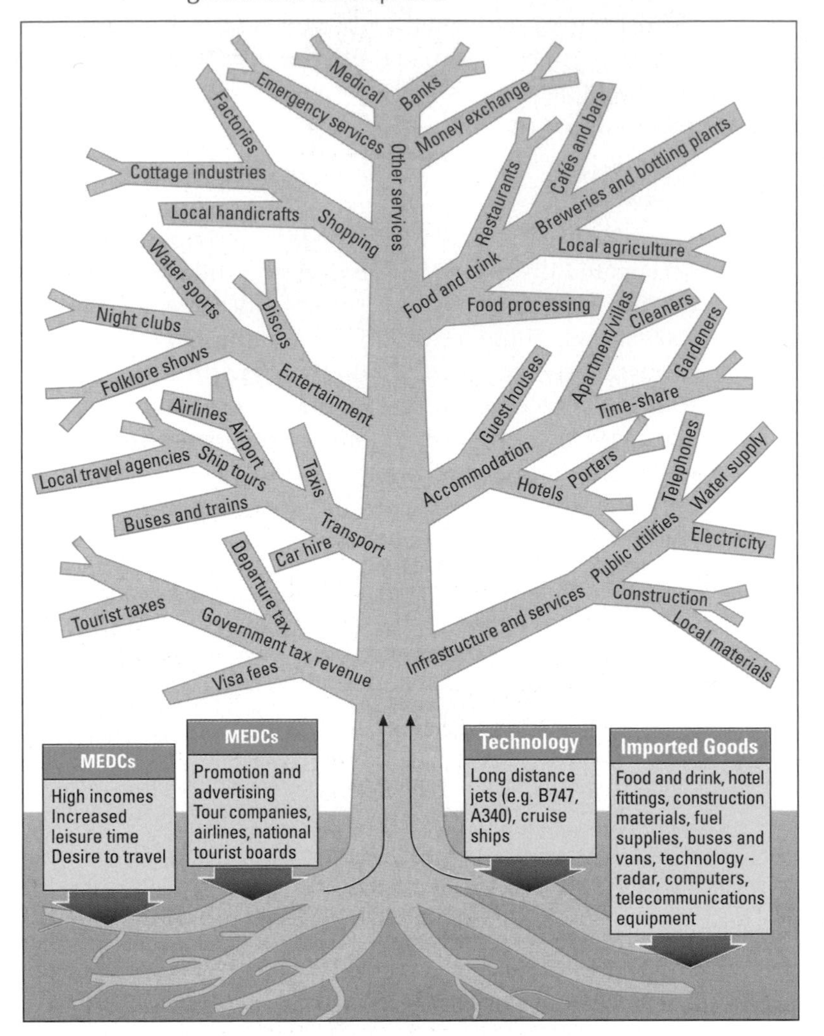

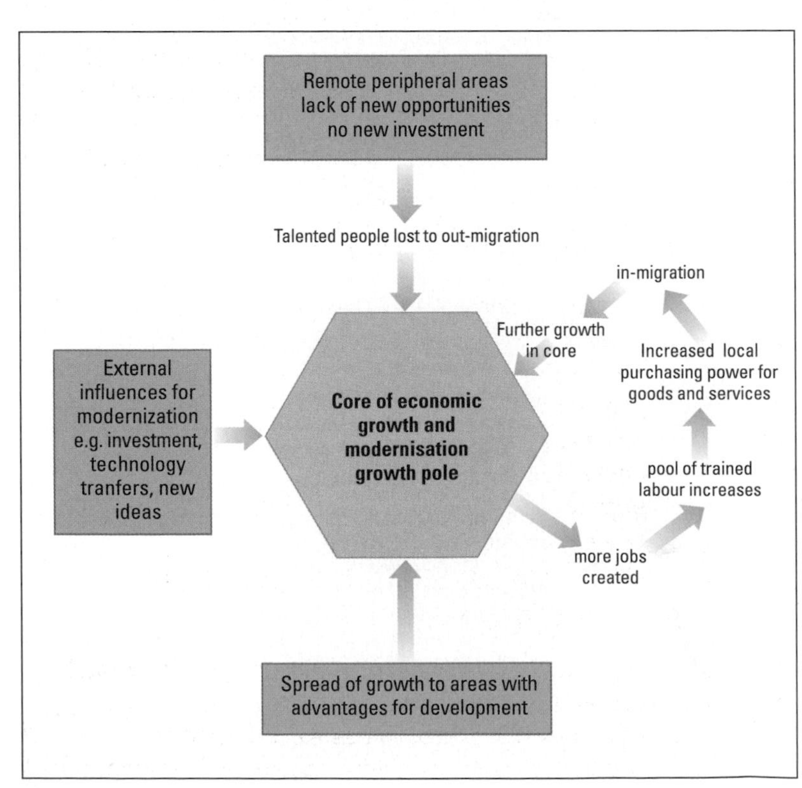

▲ **Figure 7.70** Myrdal's model of cumulative causation

Factors leading to national economic development

Whether or not local growth in income and employment from mass tourism can be harnessed so that it leads to national economic development depends upon a variety of factors. One great problem is that tourist developments usually have very uneven spatial distributions within a country. They are often heavily confined to one area, or at best a limited number of areas. Unbalanced growth such as this can be examined in relation to Myrdal's model of cumulative causation (Figure 7.70). This model gives a spatial dimension to Rostow's model of national economic development. Myrdal's model is based upon core regions modernizing and advancing economically, which widens the gap between them and the remote peripheral regions that are left lagging behind. The forces for mass tourist growth are concentrated only in a limited number of locations, usually coastal, for example in bays where the finest natural beaches are found. Governments may designate certain sites for growth, on terms that are sufficiently attractive for companies and developers to invest in the secondary resources that form the pre-conditions necessary for tourism growth and 'take-off' in any area. Some are in sparsely populated areas so that any beneficial spatial effects from the multiplier effect are limited; the Papagayo project in Costa Rica is an example (page 298). As for spreading growth more widely, this is least likely to happen where all-inclusive resorts are built, such as in the Caribbean. These are so self contained that little of the tourist income reaches the local economy, apart from employment in low-paid service jobs.

This leads into the second problem of 'leakage'. Leakage is the amount of tourist income gained that is subsequently lost. It is money that leaves the country again to pay for the import of goods and services consumed by tourists and the profits on investments that are withdrawn by hotel chains, airlines and travel agencies. These are the profits from tourism that are exported instead of going to local people or increasing the amount available for new government investment. The largest leakages are in small countries such as the island nations of the Caribbean and Pacific Oceans. They are also common in countries that are the least economically developed such as the Gambia, where it is estimated that leakages account for 80 per cent of tourist income.

The underlying cause of leakages is that in many developing countries multinational operators, with their headquarters in North America and Europe, are the dominant players in local tourist operations. Poorer governments in the LEDW welcome investment, and in their hurry to jump on to the tourist bandwagon, they often offer tax-free incentives. These companies are familiar with the standards of facilities and of service that international visitors expect. Most tourists expect these to be similar to those found in short haul destinations closer to home. The big companies, such as Sheraton Hotels, also have the organizational expertise to achieve these standards, even in remote locations. However, they are not philanthropists; they are run by hard-headed business people, who expect profits, some of which are achieved by creating a low wage economy. Therefore the way in which tourism is organized in a country is a crucial factor to determining how much a country benefits from tourism. Annual tourist revenues in Thailand are estimated at about £4 billion per year, but 60 per cent leaves the country because large companies dominate in the beach resorts and at the top end of the market in Bangkok. International tourism income in Sri Lanka is much less, but because more is in the hands of domestic companies, its estimated loss through leakage is only 30 per cent.

In theory, international tourism is one of the ideal ways of transferring wealth between more and less economically developed worlds. Lying in lower latitudes, developing countries have the higher temperatures and more sun, both considered to be essential holiday requirements by many living in the cool temperate lands of Europe and North America. Global interdependence should exist. In practice, the majority of tourists travel to LEDCs on package tours. Without the organization and co-operation of the international tour companies, most LEDCs would have no access to the pool of potential customers in MEDCs. Globalization in tourist terms is favouring the rich world where wealthy countries are increasing their already high GNPs by financial returns from their holiday and transport companies. These are making more money out of the resources for tourism in the developing world than are many of the LEDCs being visited. The way world tourism is organized gives the explanation (Figure 7.71). The end result is that the 'middle men' responsible for the secondary resources for tourism are bigger gainers than the providers with the primary resources.

The significant growth in long-haul holidays to LEDCs is due only in a small part to people wishing to visit heritage sites and participate in tours that can genuinely be described as eco-friendly. The mass market based upon 'sun and surf' holidays is likely to remain. Without a radical restructuring in the way tourism is organized, receiving countries will fail to gain full benefits from the world's fastest growing global industry. Only varied and relatively sophisticated economies can supply all the goods and services needed by the majority of tourists from western countries. Countries in the LEDW, such as India, Brazil and Mexico, are more favourably placed to benefit than many others. Only a handful of countries have been successful in taking control away from the MEDW by insisting on their own terms for tourism. One is Bhutan, a Himalayan republic with a rich culture, whose hereditary ruler some years ago placed a maximum of 4,000 visitors per year to the country, accompanied by a hefty entry fee to the country. Another is Bermuda, which has in place firm controls limiting the number of Caribbean cruise ships allowed to call and number of hotel rooms that can be provided. These are the exceptions.

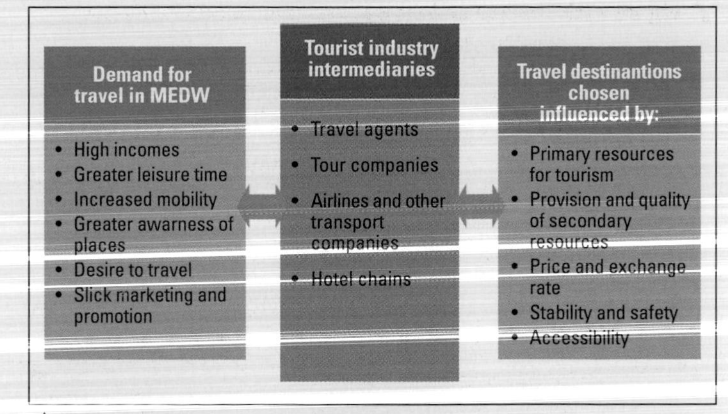

▲ **Figure 7.71** The organization of world tourism

Questions

1 a Outline the main characteristics of rural tourism in the UK.

b **i** Draw an adapted version of the tourist tree in Figure 7.69 for tourism in a UK National Park.
ii Discuss the extent to which the benefits of growing tourism in UK National Parks is outweighing the costs.

2 a Define each of the following terms as used in the geography of tourism:
i eco-tourism; **ii** multiplier effect; **iii** cumulative causation; **iv** global interdependence.

b Why are they still of restricted application in tourist areas or countries in the LEDW?

3 a What is meant by 'economic leakage' in relation to a country's income from tourism?

b Explain how it is shown in Figure 7.71.

c In Kenya the estimated economic leakage for beach holidays is 70 per cent compared with 40 per cent for safari holidays. Suggest reasons for the difference.

d Why is it difficult for LEDCs to reduce leakage to less than 30 per cent?

4 One person's views on mass tourism are summarized below.
Holiday makers have to be squeezed into as small a space as possible for the package tour operation to be profitable.
They do little damage to the local people or the environment because they are confined in a small area.
Package holiday makers do no lasting damage, except possibly to themselves by over-indulging in beer, sex and ultra-violet rays.
Do you agree? Comment on this person's views.

5 **Essay**

Like any other activity, tourism causes environmental damage; but unlike the others, it can lead to environmental protection as well. Discuss this statement, illustrating your answer with examples.

Chapter 7 Questions

1 **a** Study Figure 1 which shows foreign holidays taken from Great Britain.

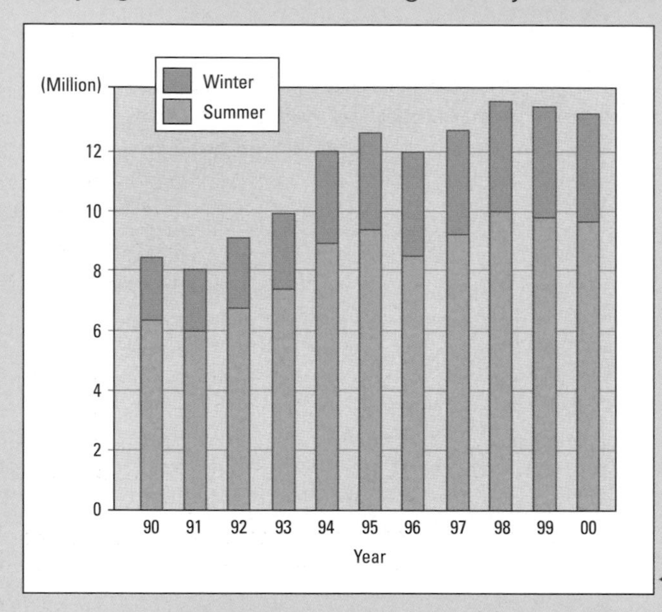

Figure 1

i Identify and describe the main trends shown. (4 marks)

ii Comment on the effects of these trends upon foreign destinations visited. (4 marks)

b How and why are spatial patterns of recreation and tourism changing within the UK? (7 marks)

Total: 15 marks

2 Synoptic essay

The growth in international tourism is providing many LEDCs with new opportunities for economic development, but few derive full benefits from their primary resources for tourism. Discuss this statement. (30 marks)

Mark schemes

Coast Processes and Problems (page 68)

1(a)
- Description focused on the profile - 1 or 2 marks according to precision and completeness.
- Relationship with structure - 1 or 2 marks for comment about the direction of dip of the rock beds. *(3 marks)*

(b)
Best choice is cliff B. As destructive waves continue to attack the bottom of the cliff (by processes such as abrasion etc.) and increase the size of the wave cut notch, there is a tendency for the rock to slip downwards along the bedding planes because of the overhang. Landslips are more likely. Up to 3 marks if well understood and expressed.
If cliff A is chosen, credit can be given for reference to the undercutting at the base, which will lead to fall of the overhanging rock above, but one mark is the likely limit without any references to cliff B. *(3 marks)*

(c)
- Ideal conditions for the creation of destructive waves are long fetch and strong winds.
- Length of fetch controls the height of breaking waves. This is greatest along the west coast of Britain, coinciding also with the direction from which the prevailing winds blow.
- Strong winds are associated with the incidence of gales and storms during which destructive waves are powerful forces.

Importance of fetch = up to 3 marks.
Importance of strong winds = up to 3 marks.
Both used and well understood leads to a four mark answer. *(4 marks)*

(d)
- Outline what is meant by sub-aerial processes
- References to the operation of types of weathering and mass movement
- Understanding how they lead to movement on the cliff top and speed up cliff retreat
- Reference to an example where they operate (e.g. along the boulder clay cliffs of east Yorkshire)

Mark according to level of response

Level 1 (1-2 marks)
References to sub-aerial processes, but they may not be used in the question context of speeding up rates of erosion.

Level 2 (3-5 marks)
A more precise and wider ranging answer in which sub-aerial processes are related to rates of cliff retreat. A brief reference to an example is likely to speed up an award towards the top of the level. *(5 marks)*

Total: 15 marks

2 Synoptic essay
Explain why, for both human and physical reasons, some coastlines attract more human management than others.

The basic answer can be expected to go along the following lines.
- Human management contrives to control or alter the operation of natural coastal processes in order to benefit people. However, the coast is a dynamic environment, a zone undergoing great and continuous changes. Management is often difficult and can be very expensive. Therefore decisions about management (type, amount and extent) have to be made taking into account both human and physical factors.
- Some stretches of coastline are uninhabited or of little interest to people so that natural processes are allowed to operate unhindered and without modification. Factors such as relief and climate are most likely to be the limiting factors for human settlement and interest. High energy coastlines on the western and northern coasts of Britain are examples.
- Other stretches of coastline are continuously settled and densely peopled, especially where there are great opportunities for the growth of coastal economic activities such as ports, fishing and tourism. These need to be heavily managed against natural marine processes and forces in order to preserve them for human needs and use.
- Examples of highly managed coastlines are in urban areas, especially large cities and coastal resorts, and along low lying coasts, such as in the Netherlands. The dominant physical reason is to stop marine erosion; the most important human reason is usually economic gain. Agricultural rural areas are economically less valuable and less likely to be able to bear the costs of management.

The synoptic nature of the question means that references to other subject strands and the inter-relationships between them can be expected at relevant points in the answer. For Example:
- Climatic or tectonic events creating storm surges and tidal waves (physical)
- The continuing growth and development of tourism and recreation in coastal zones and the increasing popularity of coastal resorts for residential purposes (human).
- Both increase the need and pressures for management.

Mark according to levels of response

Level 1 (1-6 marks)
A weak answer with low levels of content and understanding. Only occasionally is information and comment relevant to the answer included. It is likely to be weakly stated in a haphazard manner.

Level 2 (7-12 marks)
A generally weak answer, but from time to time information and comment relevant to the question are included. One element in the question, either management or physical reasons or human reasons may be considered, but in isolation without it being developed properly towards the theme of the question.

Level 3 (13-18 marks)
More structure to the answer, accompanied by greater content, allows an essay style of answering to develop. One or more of the elements in the question are developed; however, the answer remains unbalanced overall because certain aspects of the question are ignored or inadequately covered. For example, the relative element of this question (why some coastlines attract more management) is likely to be weakly explained or avoided. There may be nothing better than passing references to examples of coastlines to illustrate the points being made.

Level 4 (19-24 marks)
This is a good answer because the theme of the question is developed in an organized manner. Knowledge and understanding are displayed in a more prominent and confident way so that comments are supported by content. Physical and human factors may be discussed together so that their combined effects are recognized. One (or more) of the features associated with the top level of answering, such as awareness of values in human decision making, detailed reference to one or more sections of coast or relevant incorporation of a synoptic element, is present.

Level 5 (25-30 marks)
This is a very good answer because the theme of the question is both developed and evaluated. The support comes from the use of appropriate geographical terminology, explanation in terms of both physical and human reasons including the inter-connections between them, and references to places. Relevant synoptic information is incorporated into the answer. Valid comment is made towards the relative importance of different factors that are referred to in a balanced manner. The question theme is addressed throughout the essay in an organized and logical manner. *(30 marks)*

Geomorphological processes and hazards (page 118)

1(a)
- Recognition of immediate decline followed by a gradual resumption towards previous or normal temperatures.
- The main reason is the amount of dust erupted into high levels of the atmosphere and circulated by the world's wind systems, which reduced levels of incoming solar radiation.

Full answer and precisely expressed = 3 marks.
Some understanding = 1 or 2 marks. *(3 marks)*

(b)
- In a large eruption, there can be total destruction of flora and fauna in the immediate area. Sometimes pockets survive in areas missed or lightly touched.
- On the bare or new surfaces created, a plant succession will begin as soon as the volcanic activity finishes. Through a number of seral communities the pre-existing climatic climax vegetation will be re-established over time.

One aspect covered = 1 or 2 marks.
Both aspects examined in a meaningful way = 3 marks.
(3 marks)

(c)
- Where - along convergent plate boundaries. Some idea of, or examples from, their world distribution may be given.
- Why - related to what happens in the subduction zone and to the nature of the materials erupted which contributes to their destructiveness.

Each aspect up to 3 marks, remembering that explanation is needed.
Both aspects covered in a precise manner = 4 marks.
(4 marks)

(d)
- Outline of what is meant by a hot spot.
- Identification of their unique features e.g. points of volcanic activity located away from pate margins.
- Concentration upon differences with other forms of volcanic activity e.g. above a plume of very hot magma.
- Mention any similarity e.g. lava and cone features similar to those along constructive margins.

Mark according to level of response

Level 1 (1-2 marks)
Reference to hot spots, but there may be little attempt to examine differences from other forms of volcanic activity.

Level 2 (3-5 marks)
A more precise and wide ranging answer in which differences are examined is required. Some attempt is made to answer the 'analyze the extent' part of the question by recognizing a similarity as well as differences at the top of this level. *(5 marks)*
Total: 15 marks

2 Synoptic essay
Discuss the view that the later secondary effects of geomorphological hazards have greater impacts on landscapes and people than the immediate primary effects.

The basic answer can be expected to go along the following lines.
- Geomorphological hazards include volcanic activity, earthquakes and mass movements, which have both primary (immediate) and secondary (short and long term) impacts upon landscapes and people.
- Primary effects are the direct results of the hazard event such as land covered by lava, buildings destroyed by earthquakes and surfaces removed or covered over by mass movements. There are varied effects of each event depending upon a combination of the nature, scale and extent of the hazard and the location of area affected (e.g. densely or sparsely populated, in a MEDC or a LEDC). They can cause great landscape changes. Immediate results for people include death and destruction. People may be forced to abandon some locations.

- Secondary effects are those in the aftermath of the event, during the following days and months. For people it involves recovery, repairs, replacing what has been lost and protecting against future occurrence of the hazard, but may also involve further loss of life and suffering. The impact on landscape is much reduced at this stage.

Discussion is likely to be strongest and most credit worthy in answers with specific references to hazards and places.

The synoptic nature of the question means that references to other subject strands and the inter-relationships between them can be expected at relevant points in the answer. For example:
- coastal locations where the effects of mass movement and wave erosion combine to increase the effects upon landforms and people
- the effects on landscapes of changes in vegetation cover both immediate and longer term

Both can be used to illustrate primary and secondary effects.

Mark according to levels of response

Level 1 (1-6 marks)
A weak answer with low levels of content and understanding. The difference between primary and secondary effects may not be appreciated.

Level 2 (7-12 marks)
A generally weak answer, but from time to time information and comment relevant to the question are included. One element in the question, either primary or secondary, or effects on landscapes or people, may be considered, but in isolation without it being properly developed towards the theme of the question.

Level 3 (13-18 marks)
More structure to the answer, accompanied by greater relevant content, allows an essay style of answering to develop. One or more of the parts of the question are developed; however, overall the answer remains unbalanced, for example, between primary and secondary effects, or alternatively there is little reference to one of the aspects of the question, such as impacts on landscape. References to examples may be of a passing nature. Therefore the candidate is not in a strong position to express a meaningful view about relative importance.

Level 4 (19-24 marks)
This is a good answer because the question theme is developed in an organized manner. Knowledge and understanding of primary and secondary effects are displayed in a more prominent and confident way so that views expressed are supported by the content. The effects upon landscapes and people are discussed together so that their combined impacts are recognized. One (or more) of the features associated with the top level of answering is present; such as awareness of the importance of the values and attitudes of people affected, or detailed references to the primary and secondary effects for two or more different hazards, or relevant incorporation of a synoptic element.

Level 5 (25-30 marks)
This is a very good answer because the theme of the question is both developed and discussed. The support comes from the use of appropriate geographical terminology, an exploration of both primary and secondary effects and references to places. Relevant synoptic information is incorporated into the answer. Valid comment is made towards the relative effects of primary and secondary with identifiably separate comment directed at landscapes and at people. The question theme is addressed throughout the essay in an organized and logical manner.

(30 marks)

Cold Environments and Human Activity (page 172)

1(a)i
- Study locations comparing behind with in front of the terminal moraine.
- Examination of deposits looking for signs of rounding and sorting with the fluvio-glacial compared with angular and mixed for the glacial.

Some understanding = 1 or 2 marks.
Understood and well expressed = 3 marks. *(3 marks)*

ii
- Examination of the glacial deposits, especially those well upstream from the terminal moraine, in which boulders are more likely to be aligned according to the direction of ice movement.
- Study of individual landforms, such as the drumlins, which have a blunt upstream end and are tapered downstream.

Some understanding = 1 or 2 marks.
Understood and well expressed = 3 marks. *(3 marks)*

(b) Drumlins are made of boulder clay / glacial drift, which is the most widespread of glacial deposits. In most areas of deposition the hummocky landscape is without organization as the glacial load was dumped in response to melting. Drumlins form where the boulder clay was moulded into shape, which occurs where deposition is accompanied by forward and fast ice movement. Areas around the edges of uplands, such as the Lake District and in southern Scotland, offered ideal conditions for their formation.
Some understanding of drumlin formation / glacial deposition = 1 or 2 marks.
Valid comment about both drumlin presence and absence = 3 or 4 marks. *(4 marks)*

(c)
- Identification of landforms caused by meltwater streams that are widespread in extent and occurrence such as the outwash plain.
- Identification of other landforms, some of erosion such as overflow channels, some of deposition such as flat former lake beds and deltas.
- Examination of the general effects on landscape such as making it smoother and flatter than neighbouring areas of glacial deposition

Mark according to level of response

Level 1 (1-2 marks)
Reference to one aspect of the effects, such as the outwash plain.

Level 2 (3-5 marks)
An answer which examines a wider range of effects. For the top of this level the answer must include precise reference to a named example (e.g. Vale of York). *(5 marks)*

Total: 15 marks

2 Synoptic essay
Choose two different polar environments. Discuss the extent to which the problems and issues associated with human activities between different difficult physical environments, such as these, are similar.

The basic answer can be expected to go along the following lines.

- Two environments are chosen and clearly identified; suitable choices include tundra / Arctic, Antarctic and Alpine / high mountain. Separate statements may be included about the characteristics of the environments that make them difficult for people.
- The problems and issues associated with human activities in each environment are explored with an emphasis upon the physical difficulties for settlement and activities.
- Having identified and explained these problems and issues, similarities and differences are separately identified and commented upon. One similarity is the fragility of these polar environments; the differences are related more to location, access and history of use, which will vary according to environment chosen.
- This leads into an overall conclusion in which the extent to which the chosen environments offer similar opportunities is discussed.

The synoptic nature of the question means that references to other subject strands and to the inter-relationships between them can be expected at relevant points in the answer. For example:

- The world distribution and density of population and why most of these regions are among the least densely populated parts of the world
- World population growth and continued and increasing pressures upon the earth's resources for food and energy supplies.

Mark according to levels of response

Level 1 (1-6 marks)
A weak answer with low levels of content and understanding. Two polar environments may not be clearly identified, which leaves the answer highly generalised in nature.

Level 2 (7-12 marks)
A generally weak answer, but from time to time information and comment relevant to the question are included. Only one polar environment may be referred to in a meaningful manner, which precludes the inclusion of comment towards the main theme of the question.

Level 3 (13-18 marks)
More structure to the answer, accompanied by clear identification of two suitably different polar environments. Greater content allows an essay style of answering to develop. While references to the issues and problems of both environments are included, the answer remains unbalanced overall, because one is covered more thoroughly and knowledgeably than the other. This limits the extent and validity of comparisons between the two environments.

Level 4 (19-24 marks)
This is a good answer because the theme of the question is developed in an organized manner. Knowledge and understanding of both environments are displayed in a more prominent and confident way so that comments are supported by content. Similarities and differences between the chosen environments are highlighted. One (or more) of the features associated with the top level of answering is present, such as differing attitudes and views of the human occupation of the world's fragile environments, or detailed spatial references to the chosen polar environments, or relevant incorporation of the synoptic element.

Level 5 (25-30 marks)
This is a very good answer because the theme of the question is both developed and discussed. The support comes from the use of appropriate geographical terminology, in a wide ranging discussion in which both physical and human factors are considered, and in which plentiful references to places are made. Relevant synoptic information is incorporated into the answer. Valid comment is made towards the question's comparative theme, and a judgement about extent is included. The question theme is addressed throughout in an organized and logical manner.
(30 marks)

Population pressure and resource management (page 218)

1(a)i

- Description of general improvement in provision of water supply and sanitation, but explaining that significant differences remain between urban and rural areas, especially for sanitation. Values may be used (not merely quoted) to support this. Up to 3 marks.
- Outline reasons can be either for urban compared with urban, or for water supply compared with sanitation (or both if time / space permits). Up to 3 marks. *(4 marks)*

ii Clean water and its separation from waste are essential for the prevention of the spread of disease and for human welfare; domestic provision for both is taken for granted (100%) in MEDCs. Therefore a high percentage in LEDCs is a good indicator of development / welfare. This is confirmed by the higher percentages shown for urban areas, which are at a higher level of development than rural areas everywhere.
These two indicators affect the size of other indicators of development such as infant mortality rates and life expectancy.
Some understanding = 1 or 2 marks.
Understood and well expressed = 3 or 4 marks. *(4 marks)*

(b)
This question is best answered if the chosen renewable resource is one of the following, fresh water, forests, animals, fish stocks, or soil, which are essentially renewable, but which can be over-

consumed by people.
- Outline of why it is considered a renewable resource.
- References to why there is much demand for its use.
- Why conservation is needed if future supplies are to be maintained.

Mark according to level of response

Level 1 (1-3 marks)
Reference to the resource and its renewable nature, or to its distribution, but without the answer being well adapted to the theme of the question.

Level 2 (4-5 marks)
Further references which include an examination of why the resource is useful or is needed.

Level 3 (6-7 marks)
Good information about the chosen resource which is placed within the question context of desirable or essential conservation.
(7 marks)
Total: 15 marks

2 Synoptic essay
Two views about world food production in 2000 for feeding the 6 billion are printed below:
"A great human achievement"
"An environmental disaster".
Examine and consider the relative merits of each view.

The basic answer can be expected to go along the following lines.
- Realization that more people are being fed in the world, that there is more food in the world than at any previous time. Reasons for these increases in amount of food can be explored and explained.
- Some of the environmental consequences resulting from the intensification of farming can be examined.
- Either or both of these can be placed within the context of the theories examining the relationship between population and resources (from Malthus onwards).
- Overall comment made about the relative strengths and merits of the two views, from which a judgement is made.

The synoptic nature of the question means that references to other subject strands and the inter-relationships between them can be expected at relevant points in the answer. For example:
- River basin management schemes for irrigation and flood control
- Exploitation of resources in fragile environments
- Extension and intensification of settlement into areas at risk from natural hazards.

Mark according to levels of response

Level 1 (1-6 marks)
A weak answer with low levels of content and understanding. Only occasionally is information and comment relevant to the answer included. These comments are likely to be weakly stated and it may just be chance whether they apply to one or other of the stated views.

Level 2 (7-12 marks)
A generally weak answer, but from time to time information and comment relevant to the question is included. There may be a better attempt to examine one of the two stated views, but even this is likely to remain undeveloped towards the overall theme of the question.

Level 3 (13-18 marks)
More structure to the answer, accompanied by greater content for both views, allows an essay style of answering to develop. One of the views is likely to be better developed so that the overall answer remains unbalanced. The two views may be well examined, but without any attempt to consider their relative merits. It may appear that two separate answers are being given, one for each viewpoint.

Level 4 (19-24 marks)
This is a good answer because the theme of the question is developed in an organized manner. Knowledge and understanding are displayed in a more prominent and confident way so that comments are supported by content. Human achievements and environmental disasters may be discussed together, from which a worthwhile overall consideration may be made. One (or more) of the features associated with the top level of answering is present, such as an awareness of the views of different people and groups in the formulation of theories and models, or detailed references to examples of places, or relevant incorporation of a synoptic element.

Level 5 (25-30 marks)
This is a very good answer because the two views stated in the question are examined thoroughly before an evaluation of their relative merits is attempted. The support comes from the use of appropriate geographical terminology, explanations in terms of both physical and human factors including the inter-connections between them, and references to places. Relevant synoptic information is incorporated into the answer. Valid comment is made towards the relative importance of different factors. The question theme is addressed throughout the essay in an organized and logical manner. *(30 marks)*

Managing cities – challenges and issues (page 264)

1(a)i Reasons for the substantial loss of people in large UK cities include decline in the central areas, and rise in the out-of-town rural-urban fringe, of economic activities, decay and deprivation in the ageing inner city housing areas, and the unpopularity of previously attempted solutions such as high rise flats, and new housing (whether local authority or private) placed in suburban locations.
Some knowledge and understanding shown = 1 or 2 marks.
Known, understood and well expressed = 3 or 4 marks.
(4 marks)

ii

- Because of the scale of the problem of decay / deprivation, which is greater in some of the old northern industrial / port cities than others (e.g. Liverpool and Manchester).
- The amount of urban redevelopment that may have taken place in central areas; this could either be a lot or little depending on the percentage of population change.
- Availability of land and space around the city.
- Effects of planning decisions upon this availability (e.g. Green Belts and New Towns)

Some understanding, expressed in a general manner = 1 or 2 marks.
Good understanding, perhaps with passing reference to places = 3 or 4 marks. *(4 marks)*

(b)

- Retailing - precincts, covered shopping areas within the centre.
- Offices - conversion of warehouses, derelict buildings, old residential areas.
- Recreation and tourism - around old docks, 'landscaping' streets and open spaces.
- Multi-purpose redevelopment of run down central areas some with outside finance and support such as from UDCs.

Note that the focus of the question is upon businesses and not residential.

Mark according to level of response

Level 1 (1-3 marks)
Reference to only one area of business or one type of initiative; perhaps the answer is extended too broadly to include residential. Or it is a very generalized answer.

Level 2 (4-5 marks)
A more precise and better focused answer. More than one initiative is outlined.

Level 3 (6-7 marks)
Several initiatives outlined in a relevant way. Valid reference to a specific place (or places) will aid an award of marks at the top of the level. *(7 marks)*

Total: 15 marks

2 Synoptic essay
Urban deprivation is one of the characteristics of large cities in all parts of the world. How similar are the initiatives being undertaken for its reduction between cities in the more and less economically developed worlds?

The basic answer can be expected to go along the following lines.

- Elaboration upon the characteristics of urban deprivation in cities in both MEDCs and LEDCs in order to establish the context for the rest of the answer, with an emphasis upon similarities and differences between them.
- Inner city initiatives for the main areas of deprivation in cities in MEDCs such as wholescale redevelopment, solutions to high rise flats and gentrification in the private sector, supported by examples. References to any initiatives on the non-private housing estates in the suburbs would also be relevant.
- Shanty town initiatives as the main areas of deprivation in cities in LEDCs such as on-site improvements, new and satellite settlements, supported by examples.
- Comment about the similarities and differences in the approaches to reducing deprivation between MEDCs and LEDCs, which may include wider comment relating to comparisons between the characteristics and causes of urban deprivation.

The synoptic nature of the question means that references to other subject strands and the inter-relationships between them can be expected at relevant points in the answer. For example:

- The different operation of urban processes (urbanization, suburbanization, counter urbanization and re-urbanization) between MEDCs and LEDCs
- Different rates of population growth and internal migration (especially rural-urban in LEDCs as a consequence of limited resource provision in rural areas).

Mark according to levels of response

Level 1 (1-6 marks)
A weak answer with low levels of content and understanding. Only occasionally is information and comment relevant to an answer on urban deprivation included. What is included is weakly stated in relation to question needs.

Level 2 (7-12 marks)
A generally weak answer, but from time to time information and comment relevant to the question are included. One part of the question upon urban deprivation in either MEDCs or LEDCs is included, but in isolation so that it is incapable of being developed towards the similarity focus in the question.

Level 3 (13-18 marks)
More structure to the answer, accompanied by greater content, allows an essay style of answering to develop. The initiatives theme is developed for both LEDCs and MEDCs, but it is better done for one of them, which means that the overall answer remains unbalanced with one part of the question left with inadequate coverage. There may be nothing better than passing references to examples; cities may be named, but information precise to any of them in the context of the question may not be quoted.

Level 4 (19-24 marks)
This is a good answer because the theme of the question is developed in an organized manner. Knowledge and understanding of urban initiatives in both MEDCs and LEDCs are displayed in a more prominent and confident way so that comments about similarities are derived from, and supported by, content. One (or more) of the features associated with the top level of answering is present, such as an awareness of the values and attitudes of inhabitants and of the authorities, or detailed reference to examples of initiatives being undertaken, or the incorporation of a synoptic element.

Level 5 (25-30 marks)
This is a very good answer because the theme of the question is both developed and evaluated. The support comes from the use of appropriate geographical terminology, knowledge and

understanding of the initiatives to reduce urban deprivation and references to places. Relevant synoptic information is incorporated into the answer. Valid comment is made towards the ways in which the initiatives are both similar and different between MEDCs and LEDCs as part of the process of evaluation. The question theme is addressed throughout the essay in an organized and logical manner. *(30 marks)*

Recreation and tourism (page 308)

1(a)i

- Persistent increase in the total number of holidays abroad, as well as in the individual numbers of both winter and summer holidays, with only the occasional blips (e.g. 1996 especially for summer holidays).
- Involves the quoting of values to illustrate this (e.g. from about 8.5 in 1990 to about 13.5 holidays in 2000), and using the values to describe the downturns, or to make other general overall comments, such as the greater proportional rise in winter holidays (from about a quarter in 1990 to over a third in 2000).

Some identification / description = 1 or 2 marks.
Fuller identification supported by values = 3 or 4 marks.
(4 marks)

ii

- Much of the growth in summer holidays is accounted for by travelling to long haul destinations, especially the USA, but old favourites have slightly increased their numbers, such as Spain and France. Of the Mediterranean destinations, growth has been greatest in Turkey.
- Growth in winter destinations has been to cities for short breaks, especially to those within easy reach by road, rail or plane for a two or three night holiday. The arrival of Eurostar has promoted short breaks to Paris, northern France, Brussels and Belgium.

References to other destinations may also be appropriate, such as the growth in long distance winter sun holidays.
Some knowledge and understanding demonstrated = 1 or 2 marks.
Good knowledge and understanding, well expressed = 3 or 4 marks. *(4 marks)*

(b)

- References to the nature of the changing spatial patterns of recreation in the UK.
- Use of examples to illustrate changes e.g. from coastal resorts towards rural and inland destinations and towards theme parks
- Explanation for these in terms of greater personal mobility, changing interests, provision of new attractions etc.

Mark according to level of response

Level 1 (1-3 marks)
Reference to, and attempted explanation for, only one element in the pattern. The theme of change may be under-represented.

Level 2 (4-5 marks)
Broader recognition of the spatial pattern, but only one change may be fully explained and exemplified.

Level 3 (6-7 marks)
Two or more spatial changes are recognized and explained by references to named examples of places. Good organization and use of precise information can be expected to be two of the characteristics of answers at the top of this level.
(7 marks)
Total: 15 marks

2 Synoptic essay
The growth in international tourism is providing many LEDCs with new opportunities for economic development, but few derive full benefits from their primary resources for tourism. Discuss this statement.

The basic answer can be expected to go along the following lines.

- Tourism provides an alternative to the more traditional route of manufacturing industry for LEDCs wishing to develop; it is especially useful to countries with small total populations and without raw materials.
- Natural resources that are important for tourism are different from those needed by other types of economic activity. The main primary resources for tourism include climate, natural landscapes (scenery) and wildlife, which are more fairly distributed between less developed and more developed worlds and some are not available in MEDCs mainly located in temperate latitudes. These natural resources for tourism can be combined with human attractions, such as historical remains and distinctive cultures, in some countries.
- As people in MEDCs become wealthier they are seeking out new, longer distance and more exotic locations, so that there is a natural willingness to transfer resources from the MEDW to the LEDW.
- However, there is financial leakage in the process; for example a high proportion of the money spent on a holiday in LEDCs stays in MEDCs. The size of the leakage can be reduced by the rise of eco-tourism, but this is still very limited in its scale and extent.

The synoptic nature of the question means that references to other subject strands and to the inter-relationships between them can be expected at relevant points in the answer. For example:

- References to the benefits and opportunities of certain types of climate and of tropical ecosystems for tourism;
- The development stage model for economic growth and the rise in tertiary occupations which accompanies economic development.

Mark according to levels of response

Level 1 (1-6 marks)
A weak answer with low levels of content and understanding. Only occasionally is information and comment relevant to the answer included. There may be no more than haphazard mention of a limited number of tourist attractions.

Level 2 (7-12 marks)
A generally weak answer, but from time to time information and comment relevant to the question are included. One element in the question, such as the growth in tourism or the benefits of tourism, may be considered, but in isolation without it being developed properly towards the theme of the question.

Level 3 (13-18 marks)
More structure to the answer, accompanied by greater content about opportunities for economic development and the possible benefits of tourism to LEDCs, allows an essay style of answering to develop. One or more of the different strands in the question are developed; however, the overall answer remains inadequate because an element of it, such as the lack of full benefits to countries receiving tourists, is left uncovered. A key term like primary resources may not be fully understood. There may be nothing more than passing references to examples. Alternatively the answer may be based upon one tourist region or country, without any attempt to make broader references and to provide comment of a more general nature towards the theme of the question.

Level 4 (19-24 marks)
This is a good answer because the theme of the question is developed in an organized manner. Knowledge and understanding are displayed in a more prominent and confident way so that comments are supported by content. Physical opportunities are discussed in terms of promoting economic development and yielding benefits, at the same time as reasons why few LEDCs are able to gain full benefits are also given. One (or more) of the features associated with the top level of answering is present, such as awareness of the variations in opportunities between LEDCs, detailed references to one or more LEDCs and tourist areas, or relevant incorporation of a synoptic element.

Level 5 (25-30 marks)
This is a very good answer because the theme of the question is both developed and discussed. The support comes from the use of appropriate geographical terminology, comment in terms of both the primary resources available for tourism and the limited benefits that many LEDCs receive from having them, and references to countries and tourist regions. Relevant synoptic information is incorporated into the answer. Valid discursive comment is made towards the lack of full benefits in relation to the scale and importance of the natural resources. The question theme is addressed throughout the essay in an organized and logical manner. *(30 marks)*

Key terms

Check list of key terms and themes in the specification

For each topic area, key terms and themes contained in the specification are identified and listed under chapter headings. A2 examination questions will be set on the assumption that these are known and understood. These include the terms most likely to be used in examination questions and also the ones that you are most likely to be asked to define.

After completing the study of each topic, or as part of the process of revision, the best advice is to refer to the list of terms and themes for each chapter. These can be used as the basis for a revision 'crib sheet' for each topic. For some you can give a definition; for others you need to write down what should be included in answers when the terms or themes make an appearance in examination questions. They are listed in order of coverage within each chapter.

Chapter 2 Coast Processes and Problems

Coastal zone: definition and statement of its extent
Coastal system: inputs, processes and outputs
Coastal energy: inputs of energy and difference between high and low energy coasts
Types of waves: destructive and constructive
Coastal (marine) erosion: processes of erosion resulting from wave action and leading to coastal retreat
Coastal processes of erosion: abrasion, hydraulic action, attrition, compressed air, corrosion
Sub-aerial erosion: processes of weathering and mass movement which contributes towards coastal erosion and retreat
Sea level changes: causes (eustatic and isostatic)
Landforms resulting from changes in sea level: rias, fiords, relict cliff lines, raised beaches
Landforms of coastal erosion: cliffs, stacks, wave cut platforms, caves and bays
Landforms of coastal deposition: beaches, spits, bars, sand dunes and salt marshes
Coastal flooding: causes and consequences
Coastal management strategies: flood protection, coastal protection, sand dune management, barrages
Flood protection schemes: dams, barriers, walls, dykes
Coastal protection schemes: groynes, revetments, gabions, walls, beach nourishment
Soft and hard engineering responses: difference between the two, working with or at variance with nature

Chapter 3 Geomorphological processes and hazards

Continental drift: definition and evidence for it
Plate tectonics theory: convection currents, sea floor spreading, magnetic striping, subduction zones
Plate margins: constructive, destructive and conservative
Hot spots: lava plumes away from plate margins
Tectonic landforms:
(a) **constructive margins:** ocean ridge, shield volcano, lava plateau, fissures and faults, rift valley
(b) **destructive margins:** composite volcano, fold mountain, deep sea trench and island arc
Natural hazards: volcanic activity, earthquakes and mass movements
Volcanic activity: variations in type of eruption, in the types of lava, in the form of volcanic cones, in relation to different types of plate margin
Extrusive volcanic landforms: major (volcanic cones, lava plateaux) and minor (geysers, hot springs and boiling mud pools)
Intrusive landforms: batholiths, laccoliths, dykes and sills and the landscape features they produce once exposed on the surface
Earthquake characteristics: focus, epicentre and main types of waves
Earthquake measurement: the Richter scale
Earthquake distribution: world distribution in relation to plate margins and fault lines
Secondary effects of earthquakes: after shocks, tsunamis (tidal waves)
Weathering: definition and how it differs from erosion
Types of weathering: mechanical (physical), chemical and biological
Results of weathering: in relation to rock type, climate and human influences
Types of mass movements: flows, slides and heaves
Examples of mass movements: soil creep, solifluction, earth / mud flows, landslides, rock fall / avalanche, rotational slips
Impacts of natural hazards:
(a) on ecosystems and ecological (plant) succession
(b) on human activity both negative (death and destruction) and positive (fertile volcanic soils, geothermal energy, tourism and mineralisation)
Human responses to natural hazards: prediction, preparation, adaptation, recovery, and adjustment including variations between MEDCs and LEDCs

Chapter 4 Cold environments and human activity

Cold environments: ice caps in the Arctic, Greenland and Antarctica, surrounding seas such as the Arctic and Southern Oceans, tundra biome, and high Alpine areas above the tree line
Climatic hazards: intense cold (leading to permafrost), wind chill and low precipitation totals
Landscape processes in areas of glaciation: glacial erosion, transport and deposition; in addition weathering and mass movement (Chapter 3), and fluvio-glacial processes
Glacial budgets: accumulation and ablation, and the differences between warm and cold glaciers
Glacial system: inputs, processes and outputs
Processes of glacial erosion: abrasion, plucking
Landforms associated with valley glaciation:
(a) **from erosion**: cirque, U shaped valley, truncated spur, hanging valley, rock basin lake
(b) **from deposition:** ground, lateral, medial and terminal moraines, drumlins
Landforms associated with ice sheet glaciation:
(a) **from erosion:** 'knock and lochan' bare rock surfaces
(b) **from deposition**: terminal moraine, boulder clay (till) lowlands, drumlins
Fluvio-glacial landforms associated with meltwater streams:
(a) **from erosion**: overflow channels
(b) **from deposition:** kames, kame terraces, eskers, outwash plain, lacustrine deltas and lake bed sediments
Periglacial processes: solifluction, frost (freeze-thaw and frozen ground), water, wind
Periglacial landforms: solifluction lobes, pingos, patterned ground, V shaped valleys, loess covered lowlands
Polar ecosystems: tundra biome (land based), the Southern Ocean (sea based)
Human activity in cold environments:
(a) **indigenous people:** traditional economy, changes and outside pressures
(b) **resource exploitation by outsiders:** mining, fishing, sealing, fur trapping
(c) **increased geo-political significance:** military and strategic
(d) **impact:** on indigenous people and local cultures, on fragile natural environments
(e) **future issues:** conservation, sustainable development

Chapter 5 Population pressure and resource management

World population growth: birth rates at higher levels than death rates leading to high rates of natural increase
Population concepts:
(a) **under-population:** fewer people than available resources
(b) **over-population:** more people than resources available
(c) **optimum population:** number of people and resources in (reasonable) balance
Models and theories for the relationship between population and resources: Malthus, Boserup and the Club of Rome
Resources: definition, classification (e.g. between renewable and non-renewable), life cycle, exploitation, conservation and re-cycling / re-using, sustainable management
Measures / indicators of development and welfare:
(a) **economic:** GNP, GDP, energy consumption per head
(b) **demographic:** birth and death rates, life expectancy
(c) **social:** health and education indicators
(d) **combinations in an index:** PQLI, HDI
Population policies: anti-natalist (to reduce birth rates) and pro-natalist
Migration controls: - immigration controls between countries
Migration schemes: transmigration in Indonesia and government promotion in Brazil for settlement to open up the interior
Food surpluses in the MEDW:
(a) **causes:** intensification of farming, government support, the EU's CAP
(b) **examples:** from the small scale (e.g. around a city) to the regional

(c) **consequences:** economic, social, environmental and farming crises
(d) **towards sustainable development:** stewardship of the countryside, expansion of organic farming
Food shortages in the LEDW:
(a) **Problems:** physical (e.g. natural disasters) and human (e.g. political instability and poverty)
(b) **improvements:** the Green Revolution, extending agricultural frontiers, modernization
(c) **future development:** greater sustainability, greater use of appropriate technology, fair trade

Chapter 6 Managing cities - challenges and issues

Central area business decline:
(a) **causes:** due to both disadvantages of a CBD location and advantages of an out-of-town / suburban location, part of the process of suburbanization
(b) **effects:** dead heart, vacant buildings, lower quality land uses, loss of certain sectors of retailing (e.g. food, electrical and DIY)
(c) **attempts to reverse the decline:** new retailing, office and tourist developments accompanied by improvements in the quality of the urban environment, part of the process of re-urbanization
Urban deprivation in MEDCs:
(a) **causes and characteristics:** in inner city areas of the UK
(b) **initiatives for improvement:** early schemes of redevelopment, targeted inner city funding, comprehensive redevelopment schemes often around old docks such as in London, Manchester and Cardiff
(c) **evaluation:** degree of success, gentrification, continued plight of the urban poor
Urban deprivation in LEDCs:
(a) **causes and characteristics:** in shanty towns in all large cities
(b) **initiatives for improvement:** on site such as self help and community based, new settlements and satellite settlements
(c) **evaluation:** degree of success, comparisons with cities in MEDCs
Urban environmental issues: examples of air, water and land pollution, threats to urban ecosystems, disposing of waste
Containing the urban area: green belts, wedges and buffers to growth

Chapter 7 Recreation and tourism

Resources for tourism:
(a) **primary:** scenery, climate, ecology, historic and heritage
(b) **secondary:** facilities provided such as accommodation, catering, infrastructure, entertainment and theme parks
Capacity of a tourist resource: physical, ecological, economic, perceived
Model for tourist growth: stages in the development of a tourist area
Growth of a tourist area in the MEDW:
(a) **causes:** physical and human factors (including economic, social and technological)
(b) sequence and pattern of growth
(c) changes with time and their consequences
(d) references to tourist resorts and regions as examples
Growth of tourism in the LEDW:
(a) **causes:** physical and human factors (including economic, social and technological)
(b) **patterns of growth:** coastal planned resorts and developments inland
(c) **nature of the industry:** the role of multi-nationals, airline companies and the influences of globalization
(d) constraints on further development
Impact on the environment: damage and associated conflicts and issues, environmental costs and benefits
Management strategies: for honeypots, footpath maintenance, conservation, access and zoning, including the study of a National Park in the UK
Sustainable future strategies: examples such as eco-tourism, more emphasis upon environment / heritage based holidays
Cost-benefit analysis of tourism in LEDCs:
(a) **economic:**
- benefits such as from tourist taxes and creation of more and more varied employment opportunities
- costs from leakage of earnings abroad and from the creation of a low wage economy

(b) **social and cultural**:
- benefits such as modernisation and releasing money for schools and health services
- costs from diluting culture and community life, health risks and exploitation in the sex industry

(c) **national development:**
- benefits from stimulating growth in new and expanding tourist areas and by investment trickling down to other sectors of the economy
- costs from over-dependence upon tourists from other countries and from risks of increasing unequal spatial development within a country

Index